Elizabeth A. Stephan • David R. Bowman • William J. Park
Benjamin L. Sill • Matthew W. Ohland

Thinking Like an Engineer
An Active Learning Approach

Custom Edition for Michigan State University
EGR 102
Introduction to Engineering Modeling

Taken from:
*Thinking Like an Engineer:
An Active Learning Approach,* Third Edition
by Elizabeth A. Stephan, David R. Bowman,
William J. Park, Benjamin L. Sill, and Matthew W. Ohland

Cover Art: Courtesy of LushPix Illustration/Unlisted Images.

Taken from:

Thinking Like an Engineer: An Active Learning Approach, Third Edition
by Elizabeth A. Stephan, David R. Bowman, William J. Park, Benjamin L. Sill, and Matthew W. Ohland
Copyright © 2015, 2013, 2011 by Pearson Education, Inc.
New York, New York 10013

This special edition published in cooperation with Pearson Learning Solutions.

All trademarks, service marks, registered trademarks, and registered service marks are the property of their respective owners and are used herein for identification purposes only.

Pearson Learning Solutions, 330 Hudson Street, New York, New York 10013
A Pearson Education Company
www.pearsoned.com

Printed in the United States of America

3 16

000200010272037790

GM

ISBN 10: 1-323-40116-4
ISBN 13: 978-1-323-40116-3

CONTENTS

PREFACE

At our university, all students who wish to major in engineering begin in the General Engineering Program, and after completing a core set of classes, they can declare a specific engineering major. Within this core set of classes, students are required to take math, physics, chemistry, and a two-semester engineering sequence. Our courses have evolved to address not only the changing qualities of our students, but also the changing needs of our customers. The material taught in our courses is the foundation upon which the upper level courses depend for the skills necessary to master more advanced material. It was for these freshman courses that this text was created.

We didn't set out to write a textbook: we simply set out to find a better way to teach our students. Our philosophy was to help students move from a mode of learning, where everything was neatly presented as lecture and handouts where the instructor was looking for the "right" answer, to a mode of learning driven by self-guided inquiry. We wanted students to advance beyond "plug-and-chug" and memorization of problem-solving methods—to ask themselves if their approaches and answers make sense in the physical world. We couldn't settle on any textbooks we liked without patching materials together—one chapter from this text, four chapters from another—so we wrote our own notes. Through them, we tried to convey that engineering isn't always about having the answer—sometimes it's about asking the right questions, and we want students to learn how to ask those sorts of questions. Real-world problems rarely come with all of the information required for their solutions. Problems presented to engineers typically can't be solved by looking at how someone else solved the exact same problem. Part of the fun of engineering is that every problem presents a unique challenge and requires a unique solution. Engineering is also about arriving at an answer and being able to justify the "why" behind your choice, and equally important, the "why not" of the other choices.

We realized quickly, however, that some students are not able to learn without sufficient scaffolding. Structure and flexibility must be managed carefully. Too much structure results in rigidity and unnecessary uniformity of solutions. On the other hand, too much flexibility provides insufficient guidance, and students flounder down many blind alleys, thus making it more difficult to acquire new knowledge. The tension between these two must be managed constantly. We are a large public institution, and our student body is very diverse. Our hope is to provide each student with the amount of scaffolding they need to be successful. Some students will require more background work than others. Some students will need to work five problems, and others may need to work 50. We talk a great deal to our students about how each learner is unique. Some students need to listen to a lecture; some need to read the text over three times, and others just need to try a skill and make mistakes to discover what they still don't understand. We have tried to provide enough variety for each type of learner throughout.

Over the years, we have made difficult decisions on exactly what topics, and how much of each topic, to teach. We have refined our current text to focus on mastering four areas, each of which is introduced below.

PART 1: ENGINEERING ESSENTIALS

There are three threads that bind the first six chapters in Engineering Essentials together. The first is expressed in the part title: all are essential for a successful career in engineering. The second is communications. Part 1 concludes with an introduction to a problem-solving methodology.

First, as an aspiring engineer, it is important that students attempt to verify that engineering is not only a career that suits their abilities but also one in which they will find personal reward and satisfaction.

Second, practicing engineers often make decisions that will affect not only the lives of people but also the viability of the planetary ecosystem that affects all life on Earth. Without a firm grounding in making decisions based on ethical principles, there is an increased probability that undesirable or even disastrous consequences may occur.

Third, most engineering projects are too large for one individual to accomplish alone; thus, practicing engineers must learn to function effectively as a team, putting aside their personal differences and combining their unique talents, perspectives, and ideas to achieve the goal.

Finally, communications bind it all together. Communication, whether written, graphical, or spoken, is essential to success in engineering.

This part ends off where all good problem solving should begin—with estimation and a methodology. It's always best to have a good guess at any problem before trying to solve it more precisely. SOLVEM provides a framework for solving problems that encourages creative observation as well as methodological rigor.

PART 2: UBIQUITOUS UNITS

The world can be described using relatively few dimensions. We need to know what these are and how to use them to analyze engineering situations. Dimensions, however, are worthless in allowing engineers to find the numeric solution to a problem. Understanding units is essential to determine the correct numeric answers to problems. Different disciplines use different units to describe phenomena (particularly with respect to the properties of materials such as viscosity, thermal conductivity, density and so on). Engineers must know how to convert from one unit system to another. Knowledge of dimensions allows engineers to improve their problem-solving abilities by revealing the interplay of various parameters.

PART 3: SCRUPULOUS WORKSHEETS

When choosing an analysis tool to teach students, our first pick is Excel™. Students enter college with varying levels of experience with Excel. To allow students who are novice users to learn the basics without hindering more advanced users, we have placed the basics of Excel in the Appendix material, which is available online. To help students determine if they need to review the Appendix material, an activity has been included in the introductions to Chapter 10 (Worksheets), Chapter 11 (Graphing), and Chapter 12 (Trendlines) to direct students to Appendices B, C, and D, respectively.

Once students have mastered the basics, each chapter in this part provides a deeper usage of Excel in each category. Some of this material extends beyond a simple introduction to Excel, and often, we teach the material in this unit by jumping around, covering half of each chapter in the first semester, and the rest of the material in the second semester course.

Chapter 12 introduces students to the idea of similarities among the disciplines, and how understanding a theory in one application can often aid in understanding a similar theory in a different application. We also emphasize the understanding of models (trendlines) as possessing physical meaning. Chapter 13 discusses a process for determining a mathematical model when presented with experimental data and some advanced material on dealing with limitations of Excel.

Univariate statistics and statistical process control wrap up this part of the book by providing a way for engineering students to describe both distributions and trends.

PART 4: PUNCTILIOUS PROGRAMMING

Part 4 (Punctilious Programming) covers a variety of topics common to any introductory programming textbook. In contrast to a traditional programming textbook, this part approaches each topic from the perspective of how each can be used in unison with the others as a powerful engineering problem-solving tool. The topics presented in Part 4 are introduced as if the student has no prior programming ability and are continually reiterated throughout the remaining chapters.

For this textbook we chose MATLAB™ as the programming language because it is commonly used in many engineering curricula. The topics covered provide a solid foundation of how computers can be used as a tool for problem solving and provide enough scaffolding for transfer of programming knowledge into other languages commonly used by engineers (such as C/C++/Java).

THE "OTHER" STUFF WE'VE INCLUDED...

Throughout the book, we have included sections on surviving engineering, time management, goal setting, and study skills. We did not group them into a single chapter, but have scattered them throughout the part introductions to assist students on a topic when they are most likely to need it. For example, we find students are much more open to discuss time management in the middle of the semester rather than the beginning.

In addition, we have called upon many practicing and aspiring engineers to help us explain the "why" and "what" behind engineering. They offer their "Wise Words" throughout this text. We have included our own set of "Wise Words" as the introduction to each topic here as a glimpse of what inspired us to include certain topics.

NEW TO THIS EDITION

The third edition of *Thinking Like an Engineer: An Active Learning Approach* (TLAE) contains new material and revisions based off of the comments from faculty teaching with our textbook, the recommendations of the reviewers of our textbook, and most importantly, the feedback from our students. We continue to strive to include the latest software releases; in this edition, we have upgraded to Microsoft Office (Excel) 2013 and MATLAB 2013. We have added approximately 30% new questions. In addition, we have added new material that reflects the constant changing face of engineering education because many of our upperclassman teaching assistants frequently comment to us "I wish I had ___ when I took this class."

New to this edition, by chapter:

- Chapter 1: Everyday Engineering

  - New section on the field of Engineering Technology.

- Chapter 3: Design and Teamwork

  - New sequence of topics, to allow expanded discussion on defining the problem, determining criteria, brainstorming, making decisions and testing solutions.

- Chapter 8: Universal Units

  - New section on Electrical Concepts.

- Chapter 14: Statistics

  - Combined material from Chapters 14 (Excel) and 18 (MATLAB) in TLAE 2e to make a single unified chapter on Statistics.

- Chapter 16: Variables and Data Types

  - New material on the various ways MATLAB stores and processes data.
  - Selected material from TLAE 2e has been moved to this chapter, including cell arrays.

- Chapter 18: Input/Output in MATLAB

  - Combined material from Chapter 20 in TLAE 2e on using Microsoft Excel to input data to and output data from MATLAB.

- Chapter 19: Logic and Conditionals

  - New sections on Switch Statements and using Errors and Warnings.

- Online Appendix Materials

  - Umbrella Projects have all been moved online to allow for easier customizing of the project for each class.

HOW TO USE

As we have alluded to previously, this text contains many different types of instruction to address different types of learners. There are two main components to this text: hard copy and online.

In the hardcopy, the text is presented topically rather than sequentially, but hopefully with enough autonomy for each piece to stand alone. For example, we routinely discuss only part of the Excel material in our first semester course, and leave the rest to the second semester. We hope this will give you the flexibility to choose how deeply into any given topic you wish to dive, depending on the time you have, the starting abilities of your students, and the outcomes of your course. More information about topic sequence options can be found in the instructor's manual.

Within the text, there are several checkpoints for students to see if they understand the material. Within the reading are **Comprehension Checks**, with the answers provided in the back of the book. Our motivation for including Comprehension Checks within the text rather than include them as end of part questions is to maintain the active spirit of the classroom within the reading, allowing the students to self-evaluate their understanding of the material in preparation for class—to enable students to be self-directed learners, we must encourage them to self-evaluate regularly. At the end of each chapter, **In-Class Activities** are given to reinforce the material in each chapter. In-Class Activities exist to stimulate active conversation within pairs and groups of students working through the material. We generally keep the focus on student effort, and ask them to keep working the problem until they arrive at the right answer. This provides them with a set of worked out problems, using their own logic, before they are asked to tackle more difficult problems. The **Review** sections provide additional questions, often combining skills in the current chapter with previous concepts to help students climb to the next level of understanding. By providing these three types of practice, students are encouraged to reflect on their understanding in preparing for class, during class, and at the end of each chapter as they prepare to transfer their knowledge to other areas. Finally we have provided a series of **Umbrella Projects** to allow students to apply skills that they have mastered to larger-scope problems. We have found the use of these problems extremely helpful in providing context for the skills that they learn throughout a unit.

Understanding that every student learns differently, we have included several media components in addition to traditional text. Each section within each chapter has an accompanying set of **video lecture slides** . Within these slides, the examples presented are unique from those in the text to provide another set of sample solutions. The slides are presented with **voiceover**, which has allowed us to move away from traditional in-class lecture. We expect the students to listen to the slides outside of class, and then in class we typically spend time working problems, reviewing assigned problems, and providing **"wrap-up" lectures**, which are mini-versions of the full lectures to summarize what they should have gotten from the assignment. We expect the students to come to class with questions from the reading and lecture that we can then help clarify. We find with this method, the students pay more attention, as the terms and problems are already familiar to them, and they are more able to verbalize what they don't know. Furthermore, they can always go back and listen to the lectures again to reinforce their knowledge as many times as they need.

Some sections of this text are difficult to lecture, and students will learn this material best by **working through examples**. This is especially true with Excel and MATLAB, so you will notice that many of the lectures in these sections are shorter than previous material. The examples are scripted the first time a skill is presented, and students are expected to have their laptop open and work through the examples (not just read them). When students ask us questions in this section, we often start the answer by asking them to "show us your work from Chapter XX." If the student has not actually worked the examples in that chapter, we tell them to do so first; often, this will answer their questions.

After the first few basic problems, in many cases where we are discussing more advanced skills than data entry, we have **provided starting worksheets and code** ▣ ▣ in the online version by "hanging" the worksheets within the online text. Students can access the starting data through the online copy of the book. In some cases, though, it is difficult to explain a skill on paper, or even with slides, so for these instances we have included **videos** ▶.

Finally, for the communication section, we have provided **templates** ▣ ▣ for several types of reports and presentations. These can also be accessed in the Pearson eText version, available with adoption of MyEngineeringLab™. Visit www.pearsonhighered.com/TLAE for more information.

MyEngineeringLab™

Thinking Like an Engineer, Third Edition, together with MyEngineeringLab provides an engaging in-class experience that will inspire your students to stay in engineering, while also giving them the practice and scaffolding they need to keep up and be successful in the course. It's a complete digital solution featuring:

- A customized study plan for each student with remediation activities provides an opportunity for self paced learning for students at all different levels of preparedness.
- Automatically graded homework review problems from the book and self study quizzes give immediate feedback to the student and provide comprehensive gradebook tracking for instructors.
- Interactive tutorials with additional algorithmically generated exercises provide opportunity for point-of-use help and for more practice.
- "Show My Work" feature allows instructors to see the entire solution, not only the graded answer.
- Learning objectives mapped to ABET outcomes provide comprehensive reporting tools.
- Selected spreadsheet exercises are provided in a simulated Excel environment; these exercises are automatically graded and reported back to the gradebook.
- Pre-built writing assignments provide a single place to create, track, and grade writing assignments, provide writing resources, and exchange meaningful, personalized feedback to students.
- Available with or without the full eText.

If adopted, access to MyEngineeringLab can be bundled with the book or purchased separately. For a fully digital offering, learn more at www.myengineeringlab.com or www.pearsonhighered.com/TLAE.

ADDITIONAL RESOURCES FOR INSTRUCTORS

Instructor's Manual—Available to all adopters, this provides a complete set of solutions for all activities and review exercises. For the In-Class Activities, suggested guided inquiry questions along with time frame guidelines are included. Suggested content sequencing and descriptions of how to couple assignments to the Umbrella Projects are also provided.

PowerPoints—A complete set of lecture PowerPoint slides make course planning as easy as possible.

Sample Exams—Available to all adopters, these will assist in creating tests and quizzes for student assessment.

MyEngineeringLab—Provides web-based assessment, tutorial, homework and course management. www.myengineeringlab.com

All requests for instructor resources are verified against our customer database and/or through contacting the requestor's institution. Contact your local Pearson/Prentice Hall representative for additional information.

WHAT DOES THINKING LIKE AN ENGINEER MEAN?

We are often asked about the title of the book. We thought we'd take a minute and explain what this means, to each of us. Our responses are included in alphabetical order.

For me, thinking like an engineer is about creatively finding a solution to some problem. In my pre-college days, I was very excited about music. I began my musical pursuits by learning the fundamentals of music theory by playing in middle school band and eventually worked my way into different bands in high school (orchestra, marching and, jazz band) and branching off into teaching myself how to play guitar. I love playing and listening to music because it gives me an outlet to create and discover art. I pursued engineering for the same reason; as an engineer, you work in a field that creates or improves designs or processes. For me, thinking like an engineer is exactly like thinking like a musician—through my fundamentals, I'm able to be creative, yet methodical, in my solutions to problems.

D. Bowman, Computer Engineer

Thinking like an engineer is about solving problems with whatever resources are most available—or fixing something that has broken with materials that are just lying around. Sometimes, it's about thinking ahead and realizing what's going to happen before something breaks or someone gets hurt—particularly in thinking about what it means to fail safe—to design how something will fail when it fails. Thinking like an engineer is figuring out how to communicate technical issues in a way that anyone can understand. It's about developing an instinct to protect the public trust—an integrity that emerges automatically.

M. Ohland, Civil Engineer

To me, understanding the way things work is the foundation on which all engineering is based. Although most engineers focus on technical topics related to their specific discipline, this understanding is not restricted to any specific field, but applies to everything! One never knows when some seemingly random bit of knowledge, or some pattern discerned in a completely disparate field of inquiry, may prove critical in solving an engineering problem. Whether the field of investigation is Fourier analysis, orbital mechanics, Hebert boxes, personality types, the Chinese language, the life cycle of mycetozoans, or the evolution of the music of Western civilization, the more you understand about things, the more effective an engineer you can be. Thus, for me, thinking like an engineer is intimately, inextricably, and inexorably intertwined with the Quest for Knowledge. Besides, the world is a truly fascinating place if one bothers to take the time to investigate it.

W. Park, Electrical Engineer

Engineering is a bit like the game of golf. No two shots are ever exactly the same. In engineering, no two problems or designs are ever exactly the same. To be successful, engineers need a bag of clubs (math, chemistry, physics, English, social studies) and then need to have the training to be able to select the right combination of clubs to move from the tee to the green and make a par (or if we are lucky, a birdie). In short, engineers need to be taught to THINK.

B. Sill, Aerospace Engineer

I like to refer to engineering as the color grey. Many students enter engineering because they are "good at math and science." I like to refer to these disciplines as black and white—there is one way to integrate an equation and one way to balance a chemical reaction. Engineering is grey, a blend of math and science that does not necessarily have one clear answer. The answer can change depending on the criteria of the problem. Thinking like an engineer is about training your mind to conduct the methodical process of problem solving. It is examining a problem from many different angles, considering the good, the bad and the ugly in every process or product. It is thinking creatively to discover ways of solving problems, or preventing issues from becoming problems. It's about finding a solution in the grey and presenting it in black and white.

E. Stephan, Chemical Engineer

Lead author note: When writing this preface, I asked each of my co-authors to answer this question. As usual, I got a wide variety of interpretations and answers. This is typical of the way we approach everything we do, except that I usually try and mesh the responses into one voice. In this instance, I let each response remain unique. As you progress throughout this text, you will (hopefully) see glimpses of each of us interwoven with the one voice. We hope that through our uniqueness, we can each reach a different group of students and present a balanced approach to problem solving, and, hopefully, every student can identify with at least one of us.

—Beth Stephan
Clemson University
Clemson, SC

ACKNOWLEDGMENTS

When we set out to formalize our instructional work, we wanted to portray engineering as a reality, not the typical flashy fantasy portrayed by most media forums. We called on many of our professional and personal relationships to help us present engineering in everyday terms. During a lecture to our freshman, Dr. Ed Sutt [PopSci's 2006 Inventor of the Year for the HurriQuake Nail] gave the following advice: *A good engineer can reach an answer in two calls: the first, to find out who the expert is; the second, to talk to the expert.* Realizing we are not experts, we have called on many folks to contribute articles. To our experts who contributed articles for this text, we thank: Dr. Lisa Benson, Dr. Neil Burton, Jan Comfort, Jessica (Pelfrey) Creel, Jason Huggins, Leidy Klotz, and Troy Nunmaker.

To Dr. Lisa Benson, thank you for allowing us to use "Science as Art" for the basis of many photos that we have chosen for this text. To explain "Science as Art": *Sometimes, science and art meet in the middle. For example, when a visual representation of science or technology has an unexpected aesthetic appeal, it becomes a connection for scientists, artists and the general public. In celebration of this connection, Clemson University faculty and students are challenged to share powerful and inspiring visual images produced in laboratories and workspaces for the "Science as Art" exhibit.* For more information, please visit www.scienceasart.org. To the creators of the art, thank you for letting us showcase your work in this text: Martin Beagley, Dr. Caye Drapcho, Eric Fenimore, Dr. Scott Husson, Dr. Jaishankar Kutty, Dr. Kathleen Richardson, and Dr. Ken Webb. A special thanks Russ Werneth for getting us the great Hubble teamwork photo.

To the Rutland Institute for Ethics at Clemson University: The four-step procedure outlined in Chapter 2 on Ethics is based on the toolbox approach presented in the Ethics Across the Curriculum Seminar. Our thanks to Dr. Daniel Wueste, Director, and the other Rutlanders (Kelly Smith, Stephen Satris and Charlie Starkey) for their input into this chapter.

To Jonathan Feinberg and all the contributors to the Wordle (http://www.wordle.net) project, thank you for the tools to create for the Wordle images in the introduction sections. We hope our readers enjoy this unique way of presenting information, and are inspired to create their own Wordle!

To our friends and former students who contributed their Wise Words: Tyler Andrews, Corey Balon, Ed Basta, Sergey Belous, Brittany Brubaker, Tim Burns, Ashley Childers, Jeremy Comardelle, Matt Cuica, Jeff Dabling, Christina Darling, Ed D'Avignon, Brian Dieringer, Lauren Edwards, Andrew Flowerday, Stacey Forkner, Victor Gallas Cervo, Lisa Gascoigne, Khadijah Glast, Tad Hardy, Colleen Hill, Tom Hill, Becky Holcomb, Beth Holloway, Selden Houghton, Allison Hu, Ryan Izard, Lindy Johnson, Darryl Jones, Maria Koon, Rob Kriener, Jim Kronberg, Rachel Lanoie, Mai Lauer, Jack Meena, Alan Passman, Mike Peterson, Candace Pringle, Derek Rollend,

Eric Roper, Jake Sadie, Janna Sandel, Ellen Styles, Adam Thompson, Kaycie (Smith) Timmons, Devin Walford, Russ Werneth, and Aynsley Zollinger.

To our fellow faculty members, for providing inspiration, ideas, and helping us find countless mistakes: Dr. Steve Brandon, Dr. Ashley Childers, Andrew Clarke, Dr. David Ewing, Dr. Sarah Grigg, Dr. Richard Groff, Dr. Apoorva Kapadia, Dr. Sabrina Lau, Dr. Jonathan Maier, Dr. William Martin, Jessica Merino, and John Minor. You guys are the other half of this team that makes this the best place on earth to work! We could not have done this without you.

To the staff of the GE program, we thank you for your support of us and our students: Kelli Blankenship, Lib Crockett, Chris Porter, and all of our terrific advising staff both past and present. To the administration at Clemson, we thank you for your continued support of our program: Associate Dean Dr. Randy Collins, Interim Director Dr. Don Beasley, Dean Dr. Anand Gramopadhye, Provost Nadim Aziz. Special thanks to President Jim Barker for his inspirational leadership of staying the course and giving meaning to "One Clemson." We wish him all the best as he retired from the Presidency this December.

To the thousands of students who used this text in various forms over the years—thanks for your patience, your suggestions, and your criticism. You have each contributed not only to the book, but to our personal inspirations to keep doing what we do.

To all the reviewers who provided such valuable feedback to help us improve. We appreciate the time and energy needed to review this material, and your thoughtful comments have helped push us to become better.

To the great folks at Prentice Hall—this project would not be a reality without all your hard work. To Eric Hakanson, without that chance meeting this project would not have begun! Thanks to Holly Stark for her belief in this project and in us! Thanks to Scott Disanno for keeping us on track and having such a great vision to display our hard work. You have put in countless hours on this edition—thanks for making us look great! Thanks to Tim Galligan and the fabulous Pearson sales team all over the country for promoting our book to other schools and helping us allow so many students to start "Thinking Like Engineers"! We would not have made it through this without all of the Pearson team efforts and encouragement!

FINALLY, ON A PERSONAL NOTE

DRB: Thanks to my parents and sister for supporting my creative endeavors with nothing but encouragement and enthusiasm. To my grandparents, who value science, engineering, and education to be the most important fields of study. To my co-authors, who continue to teach me to think like an engineer. To Dana, you are the glue that keeps me from falling to pieces. Thank you for your support, love, laughter, inspiration, and determination, among many other things. You are entirely too rad. I love you.

MWO: My wife Emily has my love, admiration, and gratitude for all she does, including holding the family together. For my children, who share me with my students—Charlotte, whose "old soul" touches all who take the time to know her; Carson, who is quietly inspiring; and Anders, whose love of life and people endears him to all. I acknowledge my father Theodor, who inspired me to be an educator; my mother Nancy, who helped me understand people; my sister Karen, who lit a pathway in engineering; my brother Erik, who showed me that one doesn't need to be loud to be a leader; and my mother-in-law Nancy Winfrey, who shared the wisdom of a long career. I recognize those who helped me create an engineering education career path: Fred Orthlieb, Civil and Coastal

Engineering at the University of Florida, Marc Hoit, Duane Ellifritt, Cliff Hays, Mary Grace Kantowski, and John Lybas, the NSF's SUCCEED Coalition, Tim Anderson, Clemson's College of Engineering and Science and General Engineering, Steve Melsheimer, Ben Sill, and Purdue's School of Engineering Education.

WJP: Choosing only a few folks to include in an acknowledgment is a seriously difficult task, but I have managed to reduce it to five. First, Beth Stephan has been the guiding force behind this project, without whom it would never have come to fruition. In addition, she has shown amazing patience in putting up with my shenanigans and my weird perspectives. Next, although we exist in totally different realities, my parents have always supported me, particularly when I was a newly married, destitute graduate student fresh off the farm. Third, my son Isaac, who has the admirable quality of being willing to confront me with the truth when I am behaving badly, and for this I am grateful. Finally, and certainly most importantly, to Lila, my partner of more than one-third century, I owe a debt beyond anything I could put into words. Although life with her has seldom been easy, her influence has made me a dramatically better person.

BLS: To my amazing family, who always picked up the slack when I was off doing "creative" things, goes all my gratitude. To Anna and Allison, you are wonderful daughters who both endured and "experienced" the development of many "in class, hands on" activities—know that I love you and thank you. To Lois who has always been there with her support and without whining for over 40 years, all my love. Finally, to my co-authors who have tolerated my eccentricities and occasional tardiness with only minimum grumbling, you make great teammates.

EAS: To my co-authors, for tolerating all my strange demands, my sleep-deprived ravings and the occasional "I need this now" hysteria—and it has gotten worse with the third edition—you guys are the best! To my mom, Kay and Denny—thanks for your love and support. To Khadijah & Steven, wishes for you to continue to conquer the world! To Brock and Katie, I love you both a bushel and a peck. You are the best kids in the world, and the older you get the more you inspire me to be great at my job. Thank you for putting up with all the late nights, the lack of home-cooked meals, and the mature-beyond-your-years requirements I've asked of you. Finally, to Sean . . . last time I swore the rough parts were done, but man this edition was tough to finish up! I love you more than I can say—and know that even when I forget to say it, I still believe in us. "Show a little faith, there's magic in the night . . ."

Part 3

SCRUPULOUS WORKSHEETS

Scrupulous: **scroop·yə·ləs** ~ adjective;
definition _____

LEARNING OBJECTIVES

The overall learning objectives for this part include:
Chapter 10:

- Use Microsoft Excel to enhance problem solution techniques, including entering, sorting, and formatting data in a worksheet;
- Applying functions, including mathematical, statistical, and trigonometric;
- Read, write, and predict conditional statements, lookup functions, and data validation statements;
- Use conditional formatting, sorting, and filtering to aid in problem solutions.

Chapter 11:

- Use graphical techniques to create "proper" plots, sketch functions, and determine graphical solutions to problems.
- Create and format data into graphs using Microsoft Excel.

Chapter 12:

- Describe and interpret mathematical models in terms of physical phenomena.
- Given a graph, determine the type of trendline shown and interpret the physical parameters of the experimental system.

Chapter 13:

- Determine an appropriate mathematical model to describe experimental data using physical knowledge and logarithmic plots, then apply the model to form graphical solutions to engineering problems.
- Given a logarithmic plot, determine the equation of the trendline.
- Use Microsoft Excel to model experimental data by creating logarithmic plots.

Chapter 14:

- Apply basic concepts of statistics to experimental data.
- Use statistical and graphical functions and in Microsoft Excel and MATLAB to enhance solution techniques.

Microsoft Excel is a worksheet computer program used internationally for an incalculable number of different applications. A **worksheet** is a document that contains data separated by rows and columns. The idea of using a worksheet to solve different types of problems originated before the advent of computers in the form of bookkeeping ledgers. The first graphical worksheet computer program for personal computers, VisiCalc, was released in 1979 for the Apple II® computer.

Figure P3-1 Comparison of VisiCalc and Excel interfaces.

Modern worksheet computer programs like Excel are significantly more powerful than earlier versions like VisiCalc; a comparison of the interface is shown in Figure P3-1. Excel contains text-formatting controls, built-in functions to perform common calculations, and a number of different plotting capabilities that make it an extremely powerful data analysis tool for engineers. Part 3 introduces the Microsoft Excel interface, the formatting controls used to create organized worksheets, and many built-in functions to assist in analyzing data or performing calculations on data contained in the worksheet.

A successful engineer must rely on knowledge of the way things work in order to develop solutions to problems, whether ameliorating climate change or trapping cockroaches. In many cases, the behavior of systems or phenomena can be described mathematically. These mathematical descriptions are often called mathematical models. The variables in the model vary with respect to one another in the same way that the corresponding parameters of the real physical system change.

As a very simple example, imagine you are driving your car on a country road at a constant speed of 30 miles per hour. You know that at this speed, you travel one-half mile every minute. If you drive at this speed for 44 minutes, you cover a distance of 22 miles.

A mathematical model for this is $d = 0.5t$, where d is distance in miles, t is time in minutes, and the value 0.5 has units of miles per minute. If you substitute *any* number of minutes in this equation for time (including 44), the distance (in miles) will be exactly half of the time numerical value. This allows you to predict what would happen in the "real world" of cars and roads without having to actually go out and drive down the road to determine what would happen if you drove 30 miles per hour for 44 minutes.

Needless to say, the mathematical descriptions for some physical systems can be extremely complicated, such as models for the weather, global economic fluctuations, or the behavior of plasma in an experimental fusion reactor.

As it turns out, a significant number of phenomena important in engineering applications can be described mathematically with only three simple types of models. Also in Part 3, we introduce these three models and their characteristics, as well as discuss the use of Excel to determine a mathematical model from a set of data determined by experimentation.

A few notes about this section of the book:

- Within the examples given in this portion of the text, note that any information you are asked to type directly into Excel will be found in quotations. Do not type the quotation marks, type only the information found within the quotation marks.
- In hardcopy, the data needed to create a chart will be shown in columns or rows, depending on the size of the data, to efficiently use space and save a few trees by using less textbook paper. In the worksheets containing the starting data online, the data will be shown in columns.
- Files available online are indicated by the symbol .
- ✎ This symbol indicates directions for an important process to follow. Step-by-step instructions are given once for each procedure.
- ⌘ This symbol indicates special instructions for Mac OS users.

TIME MANAGEMENT

If you are using this text sequentially, by this point you are probably starting to feel a bit overwhelmed with all you need to do. While many introductory textbooks cover time management during the first few weeks of the semester, the authors have found it more useful to cover it a little later. In week 2 of your first semester of college, you are probably feeling like you still have things under control and do not need help. By week 10, however, you may be struggling to keep everything together and are more open to try some time management suggestions. Please note these are just suggestions and each person must develop a time management system that works best for him or her. It may take you a few attempts to find a process you can actually use, so keep making adjustments until you find your own personal solution.

There are 24 hours in each day, and 7 days in a week. Each week, you have 168 hours, or an estimated 170 hours, to spend doing something—sleeping, going to class, doing homework, or attending a football game. How do you spend all this time?

> **NOTE**
>
> Total available hours = 170
>
> Sleep = 50
>
> Meals = 20
>
> Personal hygiene = 10
>
> Classes = 20
>
> Studying = 40
>
> "Free" hours = 30

- To get enough rest, you should sleep at least 7 hours every night, or about 50 hours every week.
- If you spend 1 hour for each meal during the day, about 20 hours of your week will be spent eating.
- If you allow 1 hour per day for personal hygiene and a few hours for laundry (your classmates will thank you for showering and having clean clothes), this takes about 10 hours per week.
- Attending class is critical, and with lectures and labs you are probably in the classroom for 20 hours.
- If you spend the maximum recommended study time on each course, this will take another 30–45 hours each week.

So what is left? Actually, quite a bit of time remains: 30 hours. While that may not seem like much, remember we assumed the maximum limits in our analysis.

- It may only take you 30 minutes each day to get showered and dressed, saving you 3.5 hours per week.
- Your lab may be canceled, freeing up an additional 3 hours.
- While there are weeks when it will be necessary to study the maximum amount, this will also be balanced by weeks when you can study the minimum amount.

How, exactly, can you balance this "free" time with the "required" time? To be successful at time management, you must plan. If you carve out 1 hour each week to determine your plan for the upcoming days, you will be able to find time to work in any activities you want to do and still find time to study, eat, and sleep. Here, we present a PLAN with four steps: Prioritize, Leave time for fun, Anticipate delays, and No—learn to say it.

Prioritize

Ask:

- What must be completed this week (required assignments)?
- What can I begin to work on for next week (upcoming project, exams)?
- What would be nice to do if I have the time (recommended problems, reading)?

Rules:

- Schedule all courses in your plan. Attend every class. Be sure to include travel time, especially if you are commuting.
- Select a study time for each class and stick to it. As a general rule, plan for 2–3 hours of studying for each hour in class. For a 15-credit-hour course load, this is 30–45 hours.
- Determine when you can study best. Are you an early riser or a night owl?
- Be specific in your plan. Listing "Read Chapter 2, pages 84–97" is much better than "Read chemistry." Break down large projects into smaller tasks, each with a deadline.
- Do not study more than 2 hours at a time without a break. Pay attention to how long it takes you to become distracted easily.
- Schedule time daily to read course e-mail and check any online course management system.
- If you are working during college, do not forget to schedule in this time. As a general rule, you should not plan to work more than 10 hours per week while taking a 15-credit-hour course load. If you are working more, you may want to consult your financial aid office for advice.

Leave Time for Fun (and Chores)

Ask:

- What has to get done this week (chores)?
- What activities do I want to take part in (fun stuff you really want to do)?
- What would be nice to do if I have time (fun stuff if you have time)?

Rules:

- Schedule time for planning each week. Adopt your weekly schedule to meet the upcoming week deadlines and assignments.
- Schedule time for meals. Relax and talk with friends, read an engrossing book. Do not study during meals!
- Schedule time for sleep. Stick to this schedule—you will feel better if you go to sleep and awake each day at the same time . . . yes, even on weekends!
- Schedule time for physical activity. This can be hitting the gym, playing intramurals, or taking a walk. Staying healthy will help you stay on track.
- Schedule time for chores, such as laundry and paying bills.

- Allow time for technology on a limited basis. If you have a favorite TV show, schedule time to watch. If you want to surf on a social network, do so for a limited time each day.
- Plan outings. Colleges are wonderful resources for arts, music, theater, and athletics. Explore and find activities to enjoy, but do not compromise study time.
- Leave some open time. It is not necessary to schedule every minute of every day. Free time is a wonderful stress reliever!

Anticipate Delays

Ask:

- What can go wrong this week?
- What activities will alter my plans?

Rules:

- Plan time for "Murphy's Law": broken computers, running out of paper, getting sick, or helping a friend. If none occur, you will have extra hours in your plan.
- Leave time to proofread your work, or better yet, have someone else help you. Utilize your course teaching assistants, professor, or college academic facilities to assist you in polishing your final product.
- Plan to finish large projects 1 week before they are due to allow for any unexpected delays.

NO—Learn to Say it!

Ask:

- Will this activity help me reach my goal?
- If I do this activity, what will alter in my plan?

Rules:

- Schedule social activities around academics. Say "no" if you are not finished with your coursework.
- Remember, you are here to get an education. Employers will not care that you attended every basketball game or that you have 10,000 online friends if you have poor grades.

CHAPTER 10
EXCEL WORKBOOKS

The following is an example of the level of knowledge of Excel needed to proceed with this chapter. *If you are not able to quickly recreate an Excel Worksheet similar to the one shown, including equations and formatting, please review worksheet basics in the appendix materials online before proceeding.*

Begin with a new worksheet. Add correct header information (date, name, course, purpose / problem statement).

In Row 5, add the following headers:

- Mass (m) [g]
- Height (H) [ft]
- Potential Energy (PE) [J]
- Time (t) [min]
- Power (P) [W]

Color the cells of Row 5 the cell shade and font color of your choice.

Add the following data:

Mass [g]	Height [ft]	Time [min]
10	5	1
50	8	0.5
75	10	2.5

Calculate the corresponding potential energy and power terms in Row 6. Be sure to watch your units!

Choose an appropriate (reasonable) way to display the data in terms of number format.

Copy the equations from Row 6 down to Row 8 using the fill handle.

Add a border to all cells in Columns A – E, Rows 5 – 8.

Center all the information within each column.

A sample worksheet is shown below.

	A	B	C	D	E
1	Date		Course - Section		Name
2	Purpose: This worksheet demonstrates the skills necessary to proceed with the Excel Workbooks chapter.				
3					
4					
5	Mass (m) [g]	Height (H) [ft]	Potential Energy (PE) [J]	Time (t) [min]	Power (P) [W]
6	10	5	0.15	1	0.002
7	50	8	1.20	0.5	0.040
8	75	10	2.24	2.5	0.015

10.1 CELL REFERENCES

● **EXAMPLE 10-1**

Suppose we are given a list of XY coordinates in a worksheet. We want to calculate the distance between each point. We can find the distance between two XY coordinates by using Pythagoras' theorem:

$$d = \sqrt{(x_2 - x_1)^2 + (y_2 - y_1)^2}$$

	A	B	C	D	E	F	G	H	I
2	This example demonstrates how to handle Excel's order of operations and cell references.								
3									
4									
5	Point 1			Point 2					
6	X	Y		X	Y				
7	27	20		25	10				
8	25	4		7	8				
9	4	6		24	3				
10	25	26		13	24				
11	19	24		26	1				
12	29	10		0	5				
13	7	29		13	13				
14	3	20		19	16				
15	20	7		5	17				
16	20	26		19	3				
17	13	15		13	14				
18	23	22		17	25				
19	3	27		10	22				
20	30	16		30	17				
21									

To solve this problem, we must adhere to the default behavior of Excel to properly calculate the distance between the coordinates. First, we must observe the order of operations that Excel follows to determine how we need to write our equations. Second, we must determine how to use **cell references** to translate the $x_2, x_1, y_2,$ and y_1 values in the equation shown above into locations in our worksheet.

Let us rewrite Pythagoras' theorem in the notation shown above using what we know about order of operations in Excel:

$$d = ((x_2 - x_1)\text{^}2 + (y_2 - y_1)\text{^}2)\text{^}(1/2)$$

Let us calculate the distance between Point 1 and Point 2 in column G. In cell G7, we need to translate the equation into an equation that replaces the x_1, y_1 and x_2, y_2 variables with addresses to cells in the worksheet. Since each row represents a single calculation, we know that for the first data pair, x_1 is located in cell A7, y_1 is in B7, x_2 is in D7, and y_2 is in E7.

The equation we need to type into cell G7 becomes

$$= ((D7 - A7)\text{^}2 + (E7 - B7)\text{^}2)\text{^}(1/2)$$

If we copy that equation down for the other pairs of XY coordinates, our sheet should now contain a column of all the distance calculations.

	A	B	C	D	E	F	G	H	I
1	Distance Between XY Coordinates								
2	This example demonstrates how to handle Excel's order of operations and cell references.								
3									
4									
5		Point 1			Point 2				
6	X	Y		X	Y		Distance		
7	27	20		25	10		10.20		
8	25	4		7	8		18.44		
9	4	6		24	3		20.22		
10	25	26		13	24		12.17		
11	19	24		26	1		24.04		
12	29	10		0	5		29.43		
13	7	29		13	13		17.09		
14	3	20		19	16		16.49		
15	20	7		5	17		18.03		
16	20	26		19	3		23.02		
17	13	15		13	14		1.00		
18	23	22		17	25		6.71		
19	3	27		10	22		8.60		
20	30	16		30	17		1.00		
21									

Suppose we start off with a slightly modified worksheet that requires us to calculate the distance between all the points in the first column of XY values to a single point in the second column.

We can calculate the distance between all the points in the first column to the single point through the use of absolute addressing. An **absolute address** allows an equation to reference a single cell that will remain constant regardless of where the equation is copied in the worksheet. An absolute reference is indicated by a dollar sign ($) in front of the row and column designators. In this example, we want to use an absolute reference on cells D7 and E7 in all distance calculations. The equation we need to type in cell G7 becomes:

$$= ((\$D\$7 - A7)\text{^}2 + (\$E\$7 - B7)\text{^}2)\text{^}(1/2)$$

	A	B	C	D	E	F	G	H	I
1	Distance Between XY Coordinates								
2	This example demonstrates how to handle Excel's order of operations and cell references.								
3									
4									
5		Point 1			Point 2				
6	X	Y		X	Y		Distance		
7	27	20		25	10		10.20		
8	25	4					6.00		
9	4	6					21.38		
10	25	26					16.00		
11	19	24					15.23		
12	29	10					4.00		
13	7	29					26.17		
14	3	20					24.17		
15	20	7					5.83		
16	20	26					16.76		
17	13	15					13.00		
18	23	22					12.17		
19	3	27					27.80		
20	30	16					7.81		
21									

Relative Addressing

- A **relative cell address** used in a formula will always *refer to the cell in the same relative position* to the cell containing the formula, no matter where the formula is copied in the worksheet. For example, if "=B2" is typed into cell C4 and then copied to cell C7, the formula in cell C7 would read "=B5". In this case, the cell reference is to call the cell two rows up and one cell to the left.
- When we insert or change cells, the formulas automatically update. This is one of a worksheet's major advantages: easily applying the same calculation to many different sets of data.

Absolute Addressing

- Absolute addressing is indicated by the presence of a dollar sign ($) immediately before both the column and row designators in the formula (e.g., $C$5; $AB$10).
- An **absolute cell address** will *always refer to the same cell* if the formula is copied to another location. For example, if "=$B$2" is typed into cell C4 and then copied to cell C7, the formula in cell C7 would read "=$B$2".

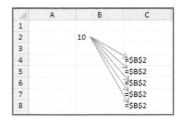 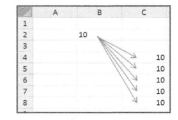

Mixed Addressing

- In **mixed addressing**, *either the row or the column designator is fixed* (by the $), but the other is relative (e.g., $C5; AB$10; $AB10).
- It may not be immediately obvious why this capability is desirable, but many problems are dramatically simplified with this approach. We will study this in more detail later.

COMPREHENSION CHECK 10-1

Type "5" in cell E22 and "9" in cell E23; type "=E22 + 4" in cell F22. Copy cell F22 to cell F23.

- Is this an example of absolute, mixed, or relative addressing?
- What is displayed in cell F23?

COMPREHENSION CHECK 10-2

Type "20" into cell G22 and "=$G$22 + 10" in cell H22. Copy cell H22 down to row 26 using the fill handle.

■ Is this an example of absolute, mixed, or relative addressing?
■ What is displayed in cell H26?

COMPREHENSION CHECK 10-3

Type "25" into cell A28 and "=A$28 + 5" in cell D28. Copy cell D28 down to row 30 using the fill handle. Copy cell D28 across to column F using the fill handle.

■ Is this an example of absolute, mixed, or relative addressing?
■ What is displayed in cell D30? What is displayed in cell F28?

COMPREHENSION CHECK 10-4

Type "=$A28 + 5" in cell G28. Copy cell G28 down to row 30 using the fill handle. Copy cell G28 across to column J using the fill handle.

■ Is this an example of absolute, mixed, or relative addressing?
■ What is displayed in cell G30? What is displayed in cell J28?

10.2   FUNCTIONS IN EXCEL

LEARN TO: Properly use Excel functions, especially those listed in tables in this section
Understand limitations of certain functions, especially trig function arguments
Given an Excel equation with built-in functions, predict the output

Hundreds of functions are built into Excel. Tables 10-1 through 10-4 list a few functions commonly used in engineering applications. Table 10-5 contains common error messages you may encounter. There are several things you should note when using these functions.

■ You must make certain to *use the correct name of the function.* For example, the average function is written as AVERAGE and cannot be abbreviated AVE or AVG.

■ *All functions must be followed by parentheses.* For example, the value of π is given as PI(), with nothing inside the parentheses.

■ The *argument* of the function (the stuff in the parentheses) can include numbers, text, expressions, or cell references, as long as they are appropriate for the function.

■ Many functions can *accept a list or range of cells as the argument.* These can be expressed as a list separated by commas [e.g., A6, D7, R2, F9], as a rectangular block designated by the top-left cell and bottom-right cell separated by a colon [e.g., D3:F9], or as a mixed group [e.g., A6, R2, D3:F9]. To insert cells into a formula, type the formula up to the open parenthesis and select the desired cells. You can also type in the references directly into the formula.

- Most functions will also *accept another function as the argument*. These can be fairly simple [e.g., SIN (RADIANS (90))] or more complicated [e.g., AVERAGE (SQRT(R2), COS(S4 + C4), MIN (D3:F9) + 2)].

- Some functions, such as trigonometric functions, require specific arguments. *Trigonometric functions must have an argument in units of radians, not units of degrees.* Be sure you are aware of any limitations of the functions you are using. Look up an unfamiliar function in the **HELP** menu.

- Note that *some functions can be expressed in several different ways.* For example, raising the number 2 to the fifth power can be written as = 2 ^ 5 or as POWER(2,5).

Table 10-1 Trigonometric functions in Excel

Function as Written in Excel	Definition
ACOS (cell)	Calculates the inverse cosine of a number (also ASIN)
COS (angle in radians)	Calculates the cosine of an angle (also SIN)
DEGREES (angle in radians)	Converts radians to degrees
PI()	Calculates pi (π) to about 15 significant figures
RADIANS (angle in degrees)	Converts degrees to radians

Table 10-2 Mathematical functions in Excel

Function as Written in Excel	Definition
EXP (cell)	Raises e (base of the natural log) to the power "cell"
POWER (cell, power)	Raises the cell to "power"
PRODUCT (cells)	Finds the product of a list of cells
SQRT (cell)	Finds the square root of cell
SUM (cells)	Finds the sum of a list of cells

Table 10-3 Statistical functions in Excel

Function as Written in Excel	Definition
AVERAGE (cells)	Finds the mean or average value of a list of cells
MAX (cells)	Finds the maximum value in a list of cells
MEDIAN (cells)	Finds the median value of a list of cells
MIN (cells)	Finds the minimum value in a list of cells
STDEV.P (cells)	Finds the standard deviation value of a list of cells
VAR.P (cells)	Finds the variance value of a list of cells

Table 10-4 **Miscellaneous functions in Excel**

Function as Written in Excel	Definition
COUNT (cells)	Counts number of cells that are not blank and that do not contain an error
COUNTIF (cells, criteria)	Counts number of cells that meet the stated criteria, such as a numerical value, text, or a cell reference
COUNTIFS (cells1, criteria1, cells2, criteria2, . . .)	Counts number of cells that meet multiple stated criteria, such as a numerical value, text, or a cell reference
INTERCEPT (*y* values, *x* values)	Calculates linear line for range of (*x*, *y*) pairs and returns the intercept value of *y* (where *x* = 0)
ROUND (cell, number of decimal places)	Rounds a number to a specific number of decimal places
SLOPE (*y* values, *x* values)	Calculates linear line for range of (*x*, *y*) pairs and returns the slope value
TRUNC (cell, number of digits)	Truncates a number to a specific number of digits

Table 10-5 **Common error messages in Excel and possible solutions**

Error	Explanation	Possible Fix	Example
#####	Column is not wide enough to display a number	Make column wider	−125,000,500 will not fit in a cell with a standard width
#DIV/0!	Formula has resulted in division by zero	Check values in denominator of formula contained in the cell	If cell A1 contains 12 and cell A2 is empty, the formula =A1/A2 will return #DIV/0!
#NAME?	Excel does not recognize something you have typed	Check spelling! Check operators for missing : Check for missing " " around text	Formula names: MXA should be MAX PI should be PI() Range of cells: A2B3 should be A2:B3
#NULL!	You specify a set of cells that do not intersect	Check formulas for spaces, missing commas	= SUM(A2:A5 B4:B6) will return this error; fix as = SUM(A2:A5,B4:B6)
#VALUE!	Formula contains invalid data types	Arguments of functions must be numbers, not text Sometimes, part of a required function is missing; check for all required elements	If cell A2 contains "2 grams" and cell A3 contains 3, the formula = A2 + A3 will result in this error since A2 is text (the word grams makes the cell text, not a number) = VLOOKUP(A2:B5,2,FALSE) will result in this error since a lookup function must contain four parts in the argument, not three
#N/A	Formula has called a value that is not available	Check for lookup value in data table (see Section 10.4)	If A2 contains 11, and the data table contains values 1 to 10 in the first column, this error will appear since the value 11 is not in the first column of the data table
#REF!	Invalid cell reference	Check operators for missing * or / Check formula for data table size and number of column to return (see Section 10.4)	Operators: (A7)(B6) should be (A7)*(B6) = VLOOKUP(A2,A2:B5,3,FALSE) will return this error because there are not three columns available in the lookup table
#NUM!	Formula results invalid numeric values	Check numerical result expected is between -1×10^{307} and 1×10^{307}	If the calculation results in a value outside the range given, such as 2×10^{400}, this error will appear

Handling Calculation Errors: IFERROR

Especially when dealing with worksheets that rely on user interaction to create meaningful information or analysis, there are often scenarios that will result in calculations that are not possible or might result in an error in a cell calculation. If you see cells in your worksheet that contain values like `#DIV/0!`, `#N/A`, or other messages that begin with the # symbol, that means that Excel was not able to calculate or look up the expression typed into the cell. The IFERROR function will allow the programmer of an Excel worksheet to specify what value should appear in a cell if there is a calculation error in the worksheet. The IFERROR function is often used when dealing with lookup statements or iterative expressions where error messages in cells might throw off the intended result of the calculation. For example, if you type = A1/A2 into cell B1 and it results in `#DIV/0!` you could type the following instead:

$$= \text{IFERROR(A1/A2,0)}$$

This function will check to see if A1/A2 results in an error message. If it does not generate an error, the resulting value of A1/A2 will appear in the cell, otherwise the value 0 will appear in the cell. It is worth noting that "0" in the formula above can be replaced with any valid Excel commands, including function calls, conditional statements, lookup statements, or simple hardcoding a value like 0 as shown above. For example, all of the following are valid IFERROR expressions:

$$= \text{IFERROR(A1/A2,MAX(A1,A2))}$$

$$= \text{IFERROR(IF(B2<3,A1/A2,B2),0)}$$

$$= \text{IFERROR(VLOOKUP(B2,A15:F20,3,FALSE),0)}$$

In the final example, if the lookup value of B2 is not found in the table located in A15:F20, the formula will return the value 0 rather than the error message `#N/A`.

● **EXAMPLE 10-2**

Assume we are studying the number of accidents that occur during different times of the day. Using the data given in the Excel workbook collected each week for two years, we want to use Excel to analyze our data to determine the average, minimum, or maximum number of accidents, as well as a few other items that might be of significance.

	A	B	C	D	E	F	G
1	Vehicular Accidents						
2	This worksheet demonstrates the proper use of Excel functions						
3							
4	Week	Number Accidents	Total Accidents		Samples Greater than Mean		
5	Y1 - 1	161	Total Samples				
6	Y1 - 2	209	Mean				
7	Y1 - 3	212	Median		Samples Between	180	200
8	Y1 - 4	62	Variance				
9	Y1 - 5	154	Standard Deviation				
10	Y1 - 6	68					
11	Y1 - 7	249					
12	Y1 - 8	33					
13	Y1 - 9	86					

NOTE

The ROUND function refers to number of decimal places, although the Excel help menu calls this "num_digits." Be sure to always read ALL the help menu file when using a new function.

Total accidents:	= SUM (B5:B108)
Total samples:	= COUNT (B5:B108)
Mean:	= AVERAGE (B5:B108)
Median:	= MEDIAN (B5:B108)
Variance:	= VAR.P (B5:B108)
Standard deviation:	= STDEV.P (B5:B108)

Note that decimal values appear when we calculate the mean, median, variance, and standard deviation of the accident data. Since it makes sense to round these values up to the nearest whole number, we need to type those functions as the argument to a rounding function. Start by modifying the equation for the mean by typing the **ROUND** *function. Notice that as you start typing the ROUND function in the cell, a drop-down menu with a list of all of the functions that start with the letters ROUND appears below the cell. Note that Excel contains a function called* **ROUNDUP** *that will round a number up to the nearest whole value away from zero.*

Total Accidents	15124	Samples Greater than Mean
Total Samples	104	
Mean	=round	
Median	ROUND	Rounds a number to a specified number of digits 2
Variance	ROUNDDOWN	
Standard Deviation	ROUNDUP	

After we select the ROUNDUP function, a new box below the cell documents the arguments the function requires. Note that we need to provide the value we want to round as the first argument and the number of decimal places to which we want to round the number (in this case, 0).

	Total Accidents	15124	Samples Greater than Mean
	Total Samples	104	
	Mean	=roundup(	
	Median	ROUNDUP(number, num_digits) Between	
	Variance	4229.95562	
	Standard Deviation	65.038109	

The new function we need to type ultimately becomes

= ROUNDUP (AVERAGE (B5:B108), 0)

Repeat this with the equations for calculating the median, variance, and the standard deviation.

Suppose we want to determine how many of the samples reported accidents greater than the calculated average number of accidents. Note that the **COUNTIF** *function requires a "criteria" argument, which can take on a number of different values. For example, if we want to count the number of values greater than 200 in the range B5:B108, we need to type the criteria ">200" (in double quotes) as the 2nd argument to the COUNTIF function.*

= COUNTIF (B5:B108,">200")

In this example, we want to compare our COUNTIF result to a value calculated in a different cell. Since we cannot type cell references inside of double quotes (">E21"), we need to use the **ampersand** *operator (&) to* **concatenate** *the logical operator to the cell reference (">"&E21).*

Samples Greater than Mean: = COUNTIF (B5:B108,">"&D6)

Similarly, we could use the **COUNTIFS** *function to calculate the number of samples that have a number of accidents between (and including) 180 and 200. COUNTIFS is a*

NOTE

Concatenate means to join things together. In Excel, the ampersand sign (&) will join two elements together.

=3&75 will result in 375

=3& "grams" will result in 3 grams

special function that contains a variable number of arguments, with a minimum of two arguments required (range1, criteria1) to use the function. Since we have two criteria that must be met (>180 and <200), we must pass in four arguments to the COUNTIFS function (range1, critera1, range2, criteria2). In this example, range1 and range2 must be the same range of cells since we are enforcing the criteria on the same set of data. We will place the bounds in the worksheet as follows:

Lower Bound in F7: 180 Upper Bound in G7: 200

Samples Between: = COUNTIFS (B5:B108,">="&F7, B5:B108, "<="&G7)

Your final worksheet should appear as shown.

	A	B	C	D	E	F	G
1	Vehicular Accidents						
2	This worksheet demonstrates the proper use of Excel functions						
3							
4	Week	Number Accidents	Total Accidents	15124	Samples Greater than Mean		
5	Y1 - 1	161	Total Samples	104	56		
6	Y1 - 2	209	Mean	146			
7	Y1 - 3	212	Median	152	Samples Between	180	200
8	Y1 - 4	62	Variance	4230	9		
9	Y1 - 5	154	Standard Deviation	66			
10	Y1 - 6	68					
11	Y1 - 7	249					
12	Y1 - 8	33					

COMPREHENSION CHECK 10-5

Launch a new worksheet. Type the following Excel expressions into the specified cells. Be certain you understand *why* each of the following yields the specific result. Note that not all functions shown in this table are valid Excel functions. If the formula returns an error, how can the formula be changed to correctly display the desired result?

In Cell . . .	Enter the Formula . . .	The Cell Will Display . . .
A1	= SQRT (144)	
A2	= MAX (5, 8, 20/2, 5 + 6)	
A3	= AVERAGE (5, SQRT(100), 15)	
A4	= POWER (2, 5)	
A5	= PI()	
A6	= PI	
A7	= PRODUCT (2, 5, A2)	
A8	= SUM (2 + 7, 3 * 2, A1:A3)	
A9	= RADIANS (90)	
A10	= SIN (RADIANS (90))	
A11	= SIN (90)	
A12	= ACOS (0.7071)	
A13	= DEGREES(ACOS(0.7071))	
A14	= CUBRT(27)	

● EXAMPLE 10-3

The maximum height (H) an object can achieve when thrown can be determined from the velocity (v) and the launch angle with respect to the horizontal (θ):

$$H = \frac{v^2 \sin(\theta)}{2g}$$

Note the use of a cell (E7) to hold the value of the acceleration due to gravity. This cell will be referenced in the formulae instead of our inserting the actual value into the formulae. This will allow us to easily work the problem in a different gravitational environment (e.g., Mars) simply by changing the one cell containing the gravitational constant.

	A	B	C	D	E	F	G
1	Basic Examples of Trig Functions and Cell Addressing						
2	The following data is used to illustrate built-in trig functions and mixed references						
3							
4							
5							
6							
7	Planet	Earth		Gravity (g)	9.8	[m/s²]	
8							
9	Velocity		Angle (θ) [degrees]				
10	(v)[m/s]	50	60	70	80		
11	10						
12	12						
13	14						
14	16						
15	18						
16	20						
17							

For the following, assume that the angle 50° is in cell B10. After setting up the column of velocities and the row of angles, we type the following into cell B11 (immediately below 50°)

= $A11^2 * SIN (RADIANS (B$10)) / (2*$E$7)

Note the use of absolute addressing (for gravity) and mixed addressing (for angle and velocity). For the angle, we allow the column to change (since the angles are in different columns) but not the row (since all angles are in row 10). For the velocity, we allow the row to change (since the velocities are in different rows) but the column is fixed (since all velocities are in column A). This allows us to write a single formula and replicate it in both directions.

The sine function requires an argument in units of radians, and the angle is given in units of degrees in the problem statement. In this example, we used the RADIANS function to convert from degrees into radians. Another method is to use the relationship 2π radians is equal to 360 degrees, or

= $A11^2 * SIN ((2 * PI() / 360) * B$10) / (2*$E$7)

We replicate the formula in cell B11 across the row to cell E11, selecting all four formulae in row 11 and replicating to row 16. If done correctly, the values should appear as shown.

Velocity (v) [m/s]	Angle (θ) [°]			
	50	60	70	80
20	3.91	4.42	4.79	5.02
12	5.63	6.36	6.90	7.24
14	7.66	8.66	9.40	9.85
16	10.01	11.31	12.27	12.86
18	12.66	14.32	15.53	16.28
20	15.63	17.67	19.18	20.10

Here, we consider the planet to be Mars with a gravity of 3.7 meters per second squared in cell E7. The worksheet should automatically update, and the values should appear as shown.

Velocity (v) [m/s]	Angle (θ) [°]			
	50	60	70	80
10	10.35	11.70	12.70	13.31
12	14.91	16.85	18.29	19.16
14	20.29	22.94	24.89	26.08
16	26.50	29.96	32.51	34.07
18	33.54	37.92	41.14	43.12
20	41.41	46.81	50.79	53.23

Now, we consider the planet to be Moon with a gravity of 1.6 meters per second squared in cell E7. The worksheet should automatically update, and the values should appear as shown.

Velocity (v) [m/s]	Angle (θ) [°]			
	50	60	70	80
10	23.94	27.06	29.37	30.78
12	34.47	38.97	42.29	44.32
14	46.92	53.04	57.56	60.32
16	61.28	69.28	75.18	78.78
18	77.56	87.69	95.14	99.71
20	95.76	108.25	117.46	123.10

COMPREHENSION CHECK 10-6

As part of the design of a high performance engine, you are analyzing properties of spherical ceramic ball bearings. Since many ceramic materials are considerably less dense than the metals typically used in such applications, the centrifugal load added by the bearings can be significantly reduced by the use of ceramics.

	A	B	C	D	E	F	G
1							
2		Mass of Ball Bearings (m) [g]					
3		Specific Gravity					
4	Radius (r) [cm]	3.12	3.18	3.22	3.31	3.37	
5	1.00	13.1	13.3	13.5	13.9	14.1	
6	1.05	15.1	15.4	15.6	16.1	16.3	
7	1.10	17.4	17.7	18.0	18.5	18.8	
8	1.15	19.9	20.3	20.5	21.1	21.5	
9	1.20	22.6	23.0	23.3	24.0	24.4	
10	1.25	25.5	26.0	26.3	27.1	27.6	
11	1.30	28.7	29.3	29.6	30.5	31.0	

Which of the following could be typed in cell B5 and copied across to cell F5, then down to cell F11 to calculate the masses of the various ball bearings shown in the table? If more than one answer is correct, indicate all that apply.

A. $= 4/3 * PI * \$A5\^3 * \$B4$
B. $= 4/3 * PI() * \$A5\^3 * B\$4$
C. $= 4/3 * PI() * \$A\$5\^3 * \$B\$4$
D. $= 4/3 * PI * A\$5\^3 * B\$4$
E. $= 4/3 * PI() * A5\^3 * B4$

10.3 LOGIC AND CONDITIONALS

LEARN TO: Create IF statements in Excel to create conditional results
Generate compound logic to develop complex conditions
Predict the output of an IF statement

Outside of the realm of computing, logic exists as a driving force for decision making. Logic transforms a list of arguments into outcomes based on a decision.

Arguments ⟶ Decision ⟶ Outcomes

Some examples of everyday decision making:

- If the traffic light is red, stop. If the traffic light is yellow, slow down. If the traffic light is green, go.

  Argument: three traffic bulbs   Decision: is bulb lit?   Outcomes: stop, slow, go

- If the milk has passed the expiration date, throw it out; otherwise, keep the milk

  Argument: expiration date   Decision: before or after?   Outcomes: garbage, keep

To bring decision making into our perspective on problem solving, we need to first understand how computers make decisions. **Boolean logic** exists to assist in the decision-making process, where each argument has a binary result and our overall outcome exhibits binary behavior. **Binary behavior**, depending on the application, is any sort of behavior that results in two possible outcomes.

In computing, we often refer to the outcome of Boolean calculations as "yes" and "no." Alternatively, we may refer to the outcomes as "true" and "false," or "1" and "0."

To determine the relationship between two cells (containing numbers or text), we have a few operators, listed in Table 10-6, that allow us to compare two cells to determine whether or not the comparison is true or false.

Table 10-6 **Relational operators in Excel**

Operator	Meaning
>	Greater than
<	Less than
> =	Greater than or equal to
< =	Less than or equal to
=	Equal to
< >	Not equal to

These relational operators are usually placed between two different cells to determine the relationship between the two values. This expression of **cell–operator–cell** is typically called a **relational expression**. If more than two relational expressions are needed to form a decision, relational expressions can be combined by means of logical operators to create a **logical expression**. To connect the Boolean arguments to make a logical decision, we have a few logical operators that allow us to relate our arguments to determine a final outcome.

NOTE

AND is true if and only if all arguments are true.

OR is true if at least one of the arguments is true.

- **AND:** The AND logical operator enables us to connect two Boolean arguments and return the result as TRUE if and only if *both* Boolean arguments have the value of TRUE. In Excel, the AND function accepts more than two arguments and is TRUE if all the arguments are TRUE.
- **OR:** The OR logical operator enables us to connect two Boolean arguments and return the result as TRUE if *only one* of the Boolean arguments has the value of TRUE. In Excel, the OR function accepts two or more arguments and is TRUE if at least one of the arguments is TRUE.
- **NOT:** The NOT logical operator enables us to invert the result of a Boolean operation. In Excel, the NOT function accepts one argument. If the value of that argument is TRUE, the NOT function returns FALSE. Likewise, if the argument of the function is FALSE, the NOT function returns TRUE.

Conditional statements are commands that give some decision-making authority to the computer. Specifically, the user asks the computer a question using conditional statements, and then the computer selects a path forward based on the answer to the question. Sample statements are given below:

- If the water velocity is fast enough, switch to an equation for turbulent flow!
- If the temperature is high enough, reduce the allowable stress on this steel beam!

- If the RPM level is above red line, issue a warning!
- If your grade is high enough on the test, state: You Passed!

In these examples, the comma indicates the separation of the condition and the action that is to be taken if the condition is true. The exclamation point marks the end of the statement. Just as in language, more complex conditional statements can be crafted with the use of "else" and "otherwise" and similar words. In these statements, the use of a semicolon introduces a new conditional clause, known as a nested conditional statement. For example:

- If the collected data indicate the process is in control, continue taking data; otherwise, alert the operator.
- If the water temperature is at or less than 10 degrees Celsius, turn on the heater; or else if the water temperature is at or greater than 80 degrees Celsius, turn on the chiller; otherwise, take no action.

Single Conditional Statements

In Excel, conditional statements can be used to return a value within a cell based upon specified criteria. The IF conditional statement within Excel takes the form

$$= \text{IF (logical test, value if true, value if false)}$$

Every statement must contain three and only three parts:

1. **A logical test, or the question to be answered**
   The answer to the logical test must be TRUE or FALSE.
   Is the flow rate in Reactor #1 higher than Reactor #5?

2. **A TRUE response**, if the answer to the question is yes
   Show the number 1 to indicate Reactor #1.

3. **A FALSE response**, if the answer to the question is no
   Show the number 5 to indicate Reactor #5.

The whole statement for the above example would read:

$$= \text{IF } (B3 > B4, 1, 5)$$

	A	B	C
1			
2			
3	Reactor #1 Flowrate	10	[gpm]
4	Reactor #5 Flowrate	25	[gpm]
5	Maximum Flowrate in Reactor #	5	

Special Things to Note

- **To leave a cell blank, type a set of quotations with nothing in between ("").** For example, the statement = IF (C3>10, 5,"") is blank if C3 is less than 10.
- **For display of a text statement, the text must be stated within quotes** (*"text goes in here"*). For example, the statement = IF (E5 > 10, 5,"WARNING") would display the word WARNING if E5 is less than 10.

● **EXAMPLE 10-4**   For the following scenarios, write a conditional statement to be placed in cell B5 to satisfy the conditions given. Below each statement are sample outcomes of the worksheet in different scenarios.

(a) Display the pressure difference between upstream station 1 (displayed in cell B3) and downstream station 2 (displayed in cell B4) if the pressure difference is positive; otherwise, display the number 1.

	A	B	C
1			
2			
3	Station #1 Pressure	2.4	[atm]
4	Station #2 Pressure	2.8	[atm]
5	Pressure Difference	1	[atm]

	A	B	C
1			
2			
3	Station #1 Pressure	3.2	[atm]
4	Station #2 Pressure	2.8	[atm]
5	Pressure Difference	0.4	[atm]

Answer: = IF ((B3 − B4) > 0, B3 − B4, 1)

(b) Display the value of the current tank pressure if the current pressure is less than the maximum tank pressure; otherwise, display the word "MAX".

	A	B	C
1			
2			
3	Maximum Tank Pressure	5	[atm]
4	Current Tank Pressure	2	[atm]
5	Pressure Status	2	[atm]

	A	B	C
1			
2			
3	Maximum Tank Pressure	5	[atm]
4	Current Tank Pressure	10	[atm]
5	Pressure Status	MAX	[atm]

Answer: = IF (B3 > B4, B4, "MAX")

(c) If the sum of the temperature values shown in cells B2, B3, and B4 is greater than or equal to 100, leave the cell blank; otherwise, display a warning to the operator that the temperature is too low.

	A	B	C
1			
2	Temperature Reading #1	25	[°C]
3	Temperature Reading #2	50	[°C]
4	Temperature Reading #3	45	[°C]
5	Cumulative Temperature		

	A	B	C
1			
2	Temperature Reading #1	25	[°C]
3	Temperature Reading #2	10	[°C]
4	Temperature Reading #3	45	[°C]
5	Cumulative Temperature	Too Low	

Answer: = IF (SUM(B2:B4) >= 100, "", "Too Low")

COMPREHENSION CHECK 10-7

Evaluate the following expressions. What is the final results that would occur when the formula is evaluated using the worksheet shown?

Comparison A: = IF (B5 > B6, B7, " ")

Comparison B: = IF (B2 + B3 <= 2*B9, B3 + B4, MIN(B2:B9))

Comparison C: = IF (B9 <> B8, "B9", B9 / B8)

	A	B	C	D	E	F
1						
2	Value 1	4				
3	Value 2	13			Comparison A	
4	Value 3	19			Comparison B	
5	Value 4	18			Comparison C	
6	Value 5	21				
7	Value 6	10				
8	Value 7	6				
9	Value 8	17				

Nested Conditional Statements

If more than two outcomes exist, the conditional statements in Excel can be nested. The nested IF conditional statement within Excel can take the form

> = IF(logical test #1, value if #1 true, IF (logical test #2, value if #2 true, value if both false))

Note that the number of parenthesis must match (open and closed) and must be placed in the proper location. Recall that every statement must contain three and only three parts. For the first IF statement, they are:

1. **The first logical test, or the first question to be answered**
   The answer to the logical test must be TRUE or FALSE.
   Is the score for Quiz #1 less than the score for Quiz #2?

2. **A true response**, or what to do if the answer to the first question is yes
   Show the score for Quiz #1.

3. **A false response**, or what to do if the answer to the first question is no
   Proceed to the logical question for the second IF statement.

For the second IF statement, the three parts are:

1. **The second logical test, or the second question to be answered**
   The answer to the logical test must be TRUE or FALSE.
   Is the score for Quiz #2 less than the score for Quiz #1?

2. **A true response**, or what to do if the answer to the second question is yes
   Show the score for Quiz #2.

3. **A false response**, or what to do if the answer to the second question, and by default both questions, is no
   Show the text "Equal".

The whole statement typed in cell B5 for the above example would read

$$= \text{IF (B3} < \text{B4, B3, IF (B3} > \text{B4, B4, "Equal"))}$$

	A	B	C
1			
2			
3	Quiz Grade #1	70	
4	Quiz Grade #2	70	
5	Lowest Quiz Score	Equal	

	A	B	C
1			
2			
3	Quiz Grade #1	90	
4	Quiz Grade #2	70	
5	Lowest Quiz Score	70	

	A	B	C
1			
2			
3	Quiz Grade #1	50	
4	Quiz Grade #2	70	
5	Lowest Quiz Score	50	

There can be a maximum of 64 nested IF statements within a single cell. The nested IF can appear as either the true or false response to the first IF logical test. In the above example, only the false response option is shown.

● **EXAMPLE 10-5**   Write the conditional statement to display the state of water (ice, liquid, or steam) based upon temperature displayed in cell B4, given in degrees Celsius. Below are sample outcomes of the worksheet in different scenarios.

	A	B	C
1			
2			
3			
4	Temperature of Mixture	75	[°C]
5	State of Mixture	Liquid	

	A	B	C
1			
2			
3			
4	Temperature of Mixture	110	[°C]
5	State of Mixture	Steam	

	A	B	C
1			
2			
3			
4	Temperature of Mixture	10	[°C]
5	State of Mixture	Ice	

Here, there must be two conditional statements because there are three responses:

■ *If the temperature is less than or equal to zero, display "Ice";*
■ *If the temperature is greater than or equal to 100, display "Steam";*
■ *Otherwise, display "Liquid".*

Answer: $= \text{IF(B4} <= 0, \text{"Ice", IF (B4} >= 100, \text{"Steam", "Liquid"))}$

COMPREHENSION CHECK 10-8

Continue the example in CC 10-6 above. The following is typed into cell G5, then copied down to cell G11:

$$= \text{IF(MAX(B5:F5)} > \text{AVERAGE(\$D\$5:\$D\$11), IF} \\ \text{MIN(B5:F5)} > \text{AVERAGE(\$D\$5:\$D\$11),"X","Z"),"Y")}$$

(a) Which of the following will appear in cell G7?
(b) Which of the following will appear in cell G8?
(c) Which of the following will appear in cell G9?

Choose from:

A. X
B. Y
C. Z
D. An error message will appear
E. The cell will be blank

	A	B	C	D	E	F	G
1							
2		Mass of Ball Bearings (m) [g]					
3		Specific Gravity					
4	Radius (r) [cm]	3.12	3.18	3.22	3.31	3.37	
5	1.00	13.1	13.3	13.5	13.9	14.1	
6	1.05	15.1	15.4	15.6	16.1	16.3	
7	1.10	17.4	17.7	18.0	18.5	18.8	
8	1.15	19.9	20.3	20.5	21.1	21.5	
9	1.20	22.6	23.0	23.3	24.0	24.4	
10	1.25	25.5	26.0	26.3	27.1	27.6	
11	1.30	28.7	29.3	29.6	30.5	31.0	

Compound Conditional Statements

If more than two logic tests exist for a single condition, conditional statements can be linked together by AND, OR, and NOT functions. Up to 255 logical tests can be compared in a single IF statement (only two are shown in the box below). The compound IF conditional statement takes the form

= IF (AND (logical test #1, logical test #2), value if both tests are true, value if either test is false)

= IF (OR (logical test #1, logical test #2), value if either test is true, value if both tests are false)

● **EXAMPLE 10-6**

Write the conditional statement that meets the following criteria:

(a) If the product has cleared all three quality checks (given in cells B2, B3, and B4) with a score of 80 or more on each check, mark the product as "OK" to ship; otherwise, mark the product as "Recycle."

	A	B	C
1			
2	Quality Check #1 Rating	90	
3	Quality Check #2 Rating	80	
4	Quality Check #3 Rating	85	
5	Mark Product	OK	

	A	B	C
1			
2	Quality Check #1 Rating	60	
3	Quality Check #2 Rating	80	
4	Quality Check #3 Rating	85	
5	Mark Product	Recycle	

Answer: = IF(AND (B2 >= 80, B3 >= 80, B4 >= 80),"OK", "Recycle")

(b) If the product has cleared all three quality checks (given in cells B2, B3, and B4) with a minimum score of 80 on each check, mark the product as "OK" to ship; otherwise, if the product scored a 50 or below on any check, mark the product as "Rejected"; otherwise, mark the product as "Rework."

	A	B	C
1			
2	Quality Check #1 Rating	90	
3	Quality Check #2 Rating	80	
4	Quality Check #3 Rating	85	
5	Mark Product	OK	

	A	B	C
1			
2	Quality Check #1 Rating	40	
3	Quality Check #2 Rating	80	
4	Quality Check #3 Rating	85	
5	Mark Product	Rejected	

	A	B	C
1			
2	Quality Check #1 Rating	60	
3	Quality Check #2 Rating	80	
4	Quality Check #3 Rating	85	
5	Mark Product	Rework	

Answer: = IF(AND (B2 >= 80, B3 >= 80, B4 >= 80), "OK", IF (OR (B2 <= 50, B3 <= 50, B4 <= 50), "Rejected", "Rework"))

COMPREHENSION CHECK 10-9

Continue the example in CC 10-6 above. Which of the following could be typed in cell H7 that will result in OK appearing in H7 if the mass in cell C7 is between 17.5 grams and 20 grams inclusive, but leave H7 blank otherwise? If more than one answer is correct, check all that apply.

A. =IF(C7<17.5 OR C7>20)," ","OK")

B. =IF(OR(C7<17.5,C7>20)," ","OK")

C. =(IF(C7<17.5) OR IF(C7>20)," ","OK")

D. =IF(C7<17.5,"", IF(C7>20,"","OK"))

E. =IF(C7<17.5,"OK", IF(C7>20,"OK",""))

◢	A	B	C	D	E	F	G
1							
2	Mass of Ball Bearings (m) [g]						
3		Specific Gravity					
4	Radius (r) [cm]	3.12	3.18	3.22	3.31	3.37	
5	1.00	13.1	13.3	13.5	13.9	14.1	
6	1.05	15.1	15.4	15.6	16.1	16.3	
7	1.10	17.4	17.7	18.0	18.5	18.8	
8	1.15	19.9	20.3	20.5	21.1	21.5	
9	1.20	22.6	23.0	23.3	24.0	24.4	
10	1.25	25.5	26.0	26.3	27.1	27.6	
11	1.30	28.7	29.3	29.6	30.5	31.0	

10.4 LOOKUP AND DATA VALIDATION

LEARN TO: Use a lookup function to merge data given two data tables with at least one common field

Predict the output if given a lookup statement

Create a validation protocol for data

The lookup function enables Excel to locate information from a table of data in a worksheet. There are two lookup functions: VLOOKUP, which searches vertically, and HLOOKUP, which searches horizontally. In the following example, we focus on VLOOKUP, but the same principles could easily be applied to HLOOKUP. To use the VLOOKUP function, we need to pass in four different arguments:

VLOOKUP (lookup_value, table_array, col_index_num, [range_lookup])

- The *lookup_value* argument is the value we want to look up in the table. Typically, this value is a string, but it can be a numerical value. Note that whatever we use as the *lookup_value*, Excel will perform a case-insensitive search of the data for the value, which means that any special characters used in the string, like punctuation or spaces, must appear the same in the *lookup_value* and the table, and must be a unique identifier in the first column of the table.
- The *table_array* is the range of cells that encapsulates the entire data table we want to search. Since we are using VLOOKUP, it is important to realize that our *table_array* must have at least two columns of data. Note that the *lookup_value* we are passing in to the VLOOKUP function will only search the first column of the *table_array*, so it might be necessary to move the data around.
- The *col_index_num* argument is the column number that contains the data we want as a result of our search. By default, Excel will refer to the first column where the *lookup_value* is located as the number 1, so the *col_index_num* will typicallly be a number greater than 1.

■ The last argument, [***range_lookup***], is an optional argument as indicated by the square brackets. This argument tells the function what type of search to perform and can only take on two values: TRUE or FALSE. In most cases, you will want to list this as FALSE.

- Passing in TRUE tells Excel to conduct an approximate search of the data. That is, Excel will search the data table for the largest value that is less than the *lookup_value* and use that result as the selected value. Note that for an approximate search, the first column of the *table_array* must be sorted in ascending order.
- Passing in FALSE tells Excel to conduct an exact search of the data. The data need not be sorted for this option. If an exact match is not found, the function returns an error.
- If we do not specify TRUE or FALSE, Excel attempts to match the data exactly, and if a match is not found, Excel returns an approximate value. This may give undesired results. It is good practice to tell Excel which searching algorithm to use to search the *table_array*.

Assume we are given the following table of data on students. To determine what Sally's eye color is from (column C) in cell A5, we could type

$$= \text{VLOOKUP ("Sally", A1:D4, 3, FALSE)}$$

since the data are unsorted and we are looking for an exact match on Sally.

	A	B	C	D
1	Joe	18	Blue	EE
2	John	19	Brown	ME
3	Sally	18	Brown	IE
4	Julie	18	Blue	CE

● **EXAMPLE 10-7**

Digital audio is a relatively new medium for storing and reproducing music. Before albums were sold on CD and other digital media formats, analog recordings were commonly sold as vinyl records, 8-track tapes, and cassette tapes. We want to build a worksheet to help us compare these different media formats to observe how information storage has progressed over the past 50 years. Note the following media equivalencies:

- A 74-minute CD (44.1 kilohertz, 2 channel, 16-bit digital audio) can hold 650 MB of data.
- A single-sided, single-layer DVD can hold 4.7 GB of data (~4,813 MB, 547 minutes of 44.1 kilohertz, 2 channel, 16-bit digital audio).
- A single-sided, single-layer Blu-ray disc can hold 25 GB of data (~25,600 MB, 2,914 minutes of 44.1 kilohertz, 2 channel, 16-bit digital audio).
- A 7-inch vinyl record recorded at 45 rpm can hold 9 minutes of music.
- A 7-inch vinyl record recorded at $33\frac{1}{3}$ rpm can hold 12 minutes of music.
- A 12-inch vinyl record recorded at 45 rpm can hold 24 minutes of music.
- A 12-inch vinyl record recorded at $33\frac{1}{3}$ rpm can hold 36 minutes of music.
- An 8-track tape can hold 46 minutes of music.
- A typical cassette tape can hold 60 minutes of music.

To determine audio equivalencies between these different storage formats, we first create a worksheet. We want to allow the user to input the media type and quantity of the desired format to be converted. To complete the comparison, it would seem like each calculation requires a statement with nine questions to ask (Is it a CD? Is it a DVD? Is it a Blu-ray? . . .).

	A	B	C	D	E
1	Digital Audio Media				
2	This worksheet demonstrates the use of VLOOKUP and data validation				
3					
4					
5	Quantity	Format	is equivalent to	Quantity	Format
6					CD
7					DVD
8					Blu-ray Disc
9	Storage Information				7" @ 45 rpm
10	Format	Length [min]			7" @ 33 1/3 rpm
11	CD	74			12" @ 45 rpm
12	DVD	547			12" @ 33 1/3 rpm
13	Blu-ray Disc	2914			8-track tape
14	7" @ 45 rpm	9			Cassette tape
15	7" @ 33 1/3 rpm	12			
16	12" @ 45 rpm	24			
17	12" @ 33 1/3 rpm	36			
18	8-track tape	46			
19	Cassette tape	60			

Rather than requiring the user to type the name of the media each time (CD, DVD, Blu-ray, etc), Excel can do **data validation**, *so we can give the user of our worksheet a drop-down menu from which to select the media. We need to add a table that contains the name of each media type along with the length of the audio we can fit on each media. We will place this table below our initial data, in cells A10:B19.*

Next, we need to calculate the quantity of each item. Since the name of the media will appear in cell B6, we use that as the lookup value in our VLOOKUP statement. To calculate the quantity for each equivalent media, we look up the length of the format specified in B6, divide that by the length of each media given in column E, and multiply that by the number of the original media provided in A6. Note that we need to round this number up since it does not make sense to have a noninteger value in our count.

For CDs, the calculation in Cell D6 should be

$$= \text{ROUNDUP (VLOOKUP (\$B\$6, \$A\$11:\$B\$19, 2, FALSE)/}$$
$$\text{VLOOKUP (E6, \$A\$11:\$B\$19, 2, FALSE) *\$A\$6, 0)}$$

The next step to finish our worksheet is to include a drop-down menu of the different media formats. To insert data validation on the media format, we click Cell B6 and go to **Data > Data Tools > Data Validation.**

The **Data Validation** *window is displayed. Under the* **Settings** *tab, the* **Allow:** *menu lets us specify the type of data that can be provided in the cell we selected. Since we want to restrict the data to a list of values, we select* **List**.

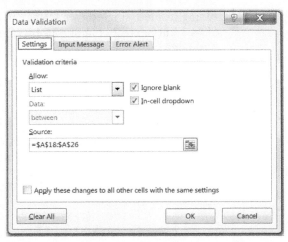

Under the **Source**: option, we select the range of all of the media types, $A$11:$A$19, and click **OK** to close the Data Validation window.

Notice the drop-down handle next to cell B6. When the user of the worksheet clicks B6, a drop-down menu appears that lists all of the possible media types so that the user can quickly select an item from the list. Furthermore, this feature prevents the user from typing items that are not on the list, making a typo, or entering any other information that will cause an error in calculations that rely on the value in B6.

5	Quantity	Format	is equivalent to	Quantity	
6	100	Blu-ray Disc		3938	
7		CD		533	
8		DVD		100	Bl
		Blu-ray Disc			
9		7" @ 45 rpm		32378	7"
10		7" @ 33 1/3 rpm		24284	7" @
11		12" @ 45 rpm		12142	12
		12" @ 33 1/3 rpm			
12		8-track tape		8095	12" @

In addition to controlling the input type to a cell, it is also possible to give feedback to the person using the worksheet using pop up messages. In this example, the quantity cannot be a negative number, so we need to bring up the Data Validation window again and restrict the input to only allow whole numbers that are greater than or equal to zero.

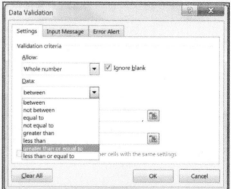

Next, we need to click the Input Message tab to type in a message that will appear below the cell when the person using our worksheet clicks on the cell to type in a quantity.

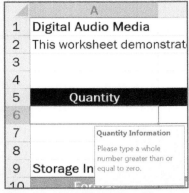

Finally, we need to click the Error Alert tab to provide the message that should pop up when an invalid number is typed into the cell.

COMPREHENSION CHECK 10-10

This is a continuation of the worksheet you created in Example 10-3. Modify it to use VLOOKUP and data validation to allow the user of the worksheet to select the planet and automatically fill in the gravity for each planet.

Planet	Gravity (g) [m/s²]
Earth	9.8
Jupiter	24.8
Mars	3.7
Mercury	3.7
Moon	1.6
Neptune	11.2
Pluto	0.7
Saturn	10.4
Uranus	8.9
Venus	8.9

10.5 CONDITIONAL FORMATTING

LEARN TO: Use conditional formatting in Excel to facilitate data analysis
Use conditional formatting to apply multiple rules to create compound logic analysis

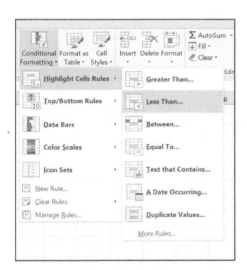

You can use conditional formatting to change the font color or background of a cell based upon the values found in that cell. As an example:

- On a blank worksheet, type the value of 20 in cell A4, a value of 30 in cell B4, and a value of 50 in cell C4.
- Select cells A4 to C4.
- Select **Home > Styles > Conditional Formatting**.
- On the first drop-down menu, choose **Highlight Cells Rules**.
- On the second drop-down menu, choose **Less Than**.

The choice of "less than" will combine the next two boxes into a single box. You can enter a number or formula, or reference a cell within the worksheet.

For this example, enter the value "25." Note: If you enter a formula, the same rules apply for absolute and relative referencing. In addition, if you select a cell within the worksheet, the program automatically defaults to an absolute reference.

- Select the formatting you want to apply when the cell value meets the condition or the formula returns the value TRUE using the dropdown menu shown after the word "with". The default is set to "Light Red Fill with Dark Red Text". You can change the font, border, or background of the cell using the **Custom Format** option. For this example, choose a green background on the Fill tab. When you are finished, click **OK**.

- To add another condition, simply repeat the process. As another example, make it greater than 40, with a font of white, bolded on a red background.

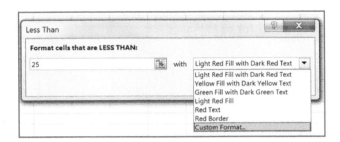

Your worksheet should now look like the one shown. If none of the specified conditions are TRUE, the cells keep their existing formats.

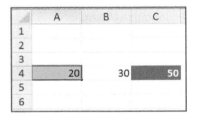

● **EXAMPLE 10-8**

Let us assume we want to build an interactive worksheet that changes the format of a cell to model the behavior of a traffic light. We want the user to input the number of seconds it takes for a light (which is initially green) to turn red. In addition, the user must also be able to provide the "warning" so that the light can switch from green to yellow and then to red.

- The green light (bottom) will only be lit if the time remaining is greater than the warning time.
- The yellow light (middle) will only be lit if the time remaining is greater than 0 seconds, but less than the warning time.
- The red light (top) will only be lit if the time remaining is 0 seconds.

Before we set up the conditional formatting for each cell, we need to write IF statements in the light cells that will be used as a trigger for conditional formatting.

For Cell E5 (the red light): = IF(A5 = 0, "R", "")
For Cell E9 (the yellow light): = IF(AND (A5 <= B5, A5 > 0), "Y", "")
For Cell E13 (the green light): = IF(A5 > B5, "G", "")

Next, we add a set of conditional formatting rules for each cell.
For the red light, we click E5 and create two rules:

- *Highlight Cells Rules* > *Text that Contains* *and enter a letter R in the appropriate field, setting the formatting to red color and red text. Note the text and fill are the SAME color red.*

- *Highlight Cells Rules > New Rule. Under Select a Rule Type: choose Format only cells that contain. Under the Edit the Rule Description: in the first drop down menu choose Blanks. Set the format to black fill with black text.*

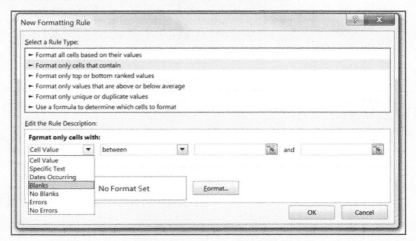

For the yellow light, we click E9 and repeat this process to turn the fill color yellow when cell has the letter "Y" in the text. For the green light, we click E13 and repeat this process to turn the fill color green when cell has the letter "G" in the text.

The final worksheet should appear as shown. Note that cell formats should change when the time remaining changes.

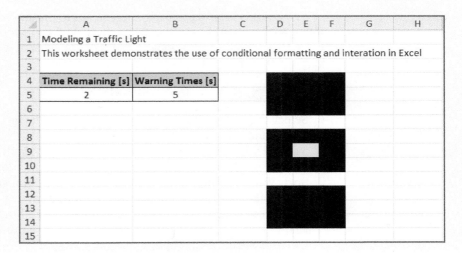

This is a continuation of the worksheet you created in Example 10.3. Modify it to highlight all heights greater than 100 meters with a light blue background and all heights less than 25 meters with a dark blue background with a white font.

10.6 SORTING AND FILTERS

LEARN TO: Use Excel to sort data with multiple levels of sorting
Use Excel to filter data based on specified criteria
Use the SUBTOTAL function to analyze filtered data

Excel provides a number of built-in tools for sorting and filtering data in a worksheet. This section describes how to use these tools effectively without causing unintended side effects.

Each year, the federal government publishes a list of fuel economy values. The complete lists for recent years can be found at www.fueleconomy.gov/feg. A partial list of 2013 vehicles is shown below. In the table, MPG = miles per gallon.

Make	Model	MPG City	MPG Highway	Annual Fuel Cost
Jeep	Grand Cherokee 4WD	16	23	$2,900
BMW	X5 xDrive 35i	16	23	$3,100
Honda	Civic Hybrid	44	44	$1,250
Volkswagen	Jetta 2.5L	24	31	$2,100
Ford	Mustang	15	26	$2,900
Bentley	Continental GTC	14	24	$3,450
Honda	Fit	28	35	$1,800

Given this information, assume you are to present it with some sort of order. What if you want to sort the data on text values (Make or Model) or numerical values (MPG City, MPG Highway, Annual Fuel Cost), or what if you want to view only certain vehicles that meet a certain condition?

Sorting Data in a Worksheet

- Select the cells to be sorted. You can select cells in a single column or row, or in a rectangular group of cells.
- Select **Home** > **Editing** > **Sort & Filter**. By default, two commonly used sorting tools (Sort A to Z and Sort Z to A) appear, in addition to a button for Custom Sort. With a group of cells selected, the common sorting tools will sort according to the values in the leftmost column. If the leftmost column contained numerical values, the options would have read Sort Smallest to Largest/Largest to Smallest. Since it is often desired to involve multiple sorting conditions, click **Custom Sort**.
- The sorting wizard is displayed as shown below. If your selected group of cells had a header row (a row that displays the names of the columns and not actual data) the "My data has headers" checkbox should be selected.

By default, Excel automatically detects whether the top row of your selected data is a header or a data row. Since you selected the data including the header rows, the "Sort by" drop-down menu will contain the header names. If you had not included the header row, the "Sort by" drop-down menu would show the column identifiers as options. It is good practice to select the headers in addition to the data to make sorting easier to understand.

■ Assume you want to sort the list alphabetically (A to Z) by the make, then by smallest-to-largest annual fuel cost. Click the **Add Level** button to add two levels of sorting since there are two conditions. In the sorting wizard, the topmost sorting level will be the sort applied first, and then the next level will sort each data group that forms from the first sort. In the example, there is more than one Honda vehicle, so the second level will place the Civic Hybrid above the Fit, since the Civic Hybrid has a smaller annual fuel cost.

The resulting sorted data appear as shown.

	A	B	C	D	E
1	Fuel Economy of Vehicles				
2	This worksheet demonstrates the use of sorting and filtering in Excel				
3					
4	**Make**	**Model**	**MPG City**	**MPG Highway**	**Annual Fuel Cost**
5	Bentley	Continental GTC	14	24	$3,450
6	BMW	X5 xDrive 35i	16	23	$3,100
7	Ford	Mustang	15	26	$2,900
8	Honda	Civic Hybrid	44	44	$1,250
9	Honda	Fit	28	35	$1,800
10	Jeep	Grand Cherokee 4WD	16	23	$2,900
11	Volkswagen	Jetta 2.5L	24	31	$2,100

NOTE

To "undo" a sort, either choose the "Undo" arrow button on the top menu or use CTRL+Z.

It is important to be sure to select all of the data when using the sort functions because it is possible to corrupt your data set. To demonstrate, select only the first three columns (Make, Model, MPG City) and sort the data smallest to largest on the MPG City column.

Notice after sorting that the last two columns (MPG Highway, Annual Fuel Cost) are not the correct values for the vehicle. There is no way to recover the original association if you were to save the file and open it at a later time, so it is critical that when using the built-in sorting functions, you verify the correctness of your data before saving your workbook. In this case, you can click Excel's Undo button or CTRL+Z to unapply the last sort.

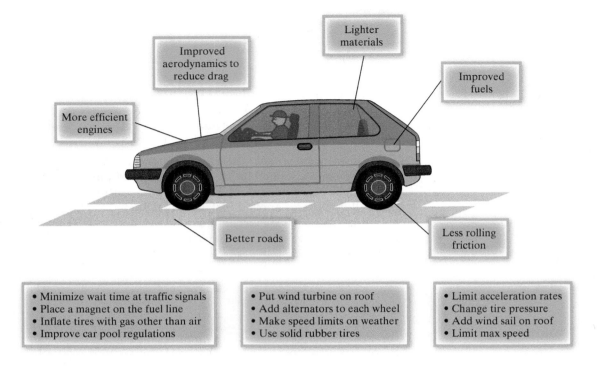

The following labels appear in the diagram:

- Lighter materials
- Improved aerodynamics to reduce drag
- Improved fuels
- More efficient engines
- Better roads
- Less rolling friction

- Minimize wait time at traffic signals
- Place a magnet on the fuel line
- Inflate tires with gas other than air
- Improve car pool regulations

- Put wind turbine on roof
- Add alternators to each wheel
- Make speed limits on weather
- Use solid rubber tires

- Limit acceleration rates
- Change tire pressure
- Add wind sail on roof
- Limit max speed

Improving automotive gas mileage, while keeping costs under control, is a complex puzzle, involving many different types of engineers. Above are some ways to possibly improve fuel efficiency. Some really work, some are false claims, and some are fictitious. Can you tell the difference? What other ways can you think of to improve today's automobiles?

COMPREHENSION CHECK 10-12

In 1980, the Environmental Protection Agency (EPA) began the Superfund Program to help cleanup highly polluted areas of the environment. There are over 1,300 Superfund sites across the country. Not all Superfund sites are from deliberate pollution. Some sites are old factories, where chemicals were dumped on the ground; landfills where garbage was dumped along with other poisonous waste; remote places where people secretly dumped hazardous waste because they did not know what to do with it; or old coal, iron ore, or silver mines.

According to the EPA (http://www.epa.gov/superfund/index.htm), the following groundwater contaminants were found in South Carolina Superfund sites in Greenville, Pickens, Oconee, and Anderson counties.

- Sort by city in ascending order. Examine the result: Which city appears first?
- Sort again: first by city in descending order, then by site name in descending order. Examine the results: Which site name now appears first?

- Sort again by contaminant in ascending order, then by site name in ascending order. Examine the results: Which site name appears last?

Contaminants	Site Name	City
Polycyclic aromatic hydrocarbons	Sangamo Weston	Pickens
Volatile organic compounds	Beaunit Corporation	Fountain Inn
Polycyclic aromatic hydrocarbons	Beaunit Corporation	Fountain Inn
Polycyclic aromatic hydrocarbons	Para-Chem Southern, Inc.	Simpsonville
Volatile organic compounds	Golden Strip Septic Tank Service	Simpsonville
Volatile organic compounds	Para-Chem Southern, Inc.	Simpsonville
Metals	Para-Chem Southern, Inc.	Simpsonville
Polycyclic aromatic hydrocarbons	Rochester Property	Travelers Rest
Volatile organic compounds	Sangamo Weston	Pickens
Polychlorinated biphenyl	Sangamo Weston	Pickens
Metals	Rochester Property	Travelers Rest
Metals	Golden Strip Septic Tank Service	Simpsonville
Metals	Beaunit Corporation	Fountain Inn
Volatile organic compounds	Rochester Property	Travelers Rest

Filtering Data in a Worksheet

Assume you want to look only at a specific portion of the data set and hide all the other rows of data. For example, you might want to look only at Honda vehicles or all vehicles that have an MPG City rating between 10 and 15 MPG. Excel has a built-in filtering capability by which you can conditionally display rows in a data set.

- Select the header row for a data set and click the **Sort & Filter** button in the **Home** > **Editing** ribbon. Click the **Filter** option to enable filtering for each column of data. Each column label contains a drop-down menu with various sorting options, as well as a number of different approaches for filtering.

  - For data sets that contain a small number of options, use the checkboxes in the drop-down filter to manually check certain options to display.
  - For numerical values, use the Number Filters submenu to filter on certain conditional expressions. The Custom Filter option in the Number Filters submenu lets you combine up to two logical expressions to filter a single column of data.

Assume you want to revisit your fuel economy data set and add in a number of statistical functions to assist in analysis.

	A	B	C	D	E
1	Fuel Economy of Vehicles				
2	This worksheet demonstrates the use of sorting and filtering in Excel				
3					
4	Make	Model	MPG City	MPG Highway	Annual Fuel Cost
5	Jeep	Grand Cherokee 4WD	16	23	$2,900
6	BMW	X5 xDrive 35i	16	23	$3,100
7	Honda	Civic Hybrid	44	44	$1,250
8	Volkswagen	Jetta 2.5L	24	31	$2,100
9	Ford	Mustang	15	26	$2,900
10	Bentley	Continental GTC	14	24	$3,450
11	Honda	Fit	28	35	$1,800
12					
13		Average	22	29	$2,500
14		Min	14	23	$1,250
15		Max	44	44	$3,450

Suppose you filter the data set to look only at the Honda vehicles.

	A	B	C	D	E
1	Fuel Economy of Vehicles				
2	This worksheet demonstrates the use of sorting and filtering in Excel				
3					
4	Make	Model	MPG City	MPG Highway	Annual Fuel Cost
7	Honda	Civic Hybrid	44	44	$1,250
11	Honda	Fit	28	35	$1,800
12					
13		Average	22	29	$2,500
14		Min	14	23	$1,250
15		Max	44	44	$3,450

Notice that the statistical calculations at the bottom are still referencing the entire data set, even though, because of the filter, only a subset of the data is displayed. For data comparisons, this will be a valuable side effect; however, if you want the calculations to apply only to the visible data, you will need to use built-in functions other than the traditional functions (AVERAGE, MIN, MAX).

Using the SUBTOTAL Function

The **SUBTOTAL** function allows the worksheet to dynamically recalculate expressions generated with a filtered list. In the example where only Honda vehicles are selected, only the two visible vehicles will be used in the calculations, if you modify your worksheet to use the SUBTOTAL function instead of the traditional statistical functions. To use the SUBTOTAL function, pass in two different arguments:

= SUBTOTAL (function_num, range)

- The *function_num* argument is a number associated to various built-in Excel functions. Table 10-7 lists the available functions for use with the SUBTOTAL function.
- The *range* argument is the range of cells to which the function should be applied.

Table 10-7 **Available functions in SUBTOTAL**

function_num	Function	Definition
1	AVERAGE	Computes the average value of the range
2	COUNT	Counts the number of cells in the range that contain numbers
3	COUNTA	Counts the number of nonempty cells in the range
4	MAX	Calculates the maximum value of the range
5	MIN	Calculates the minimum value of the range
6	PRODUCT	Calculates the product of each number in the range
7	STDEVP	Calculates the standard deviation of the numbers in the range
8	SUM	Calculates the sum of all of the numbers in the range
9	VARP	Calculates the variance of the numbers in the range

In the example, use the following calculation in cell C13 to calculate the average of MPG City:

$$= \text{AVERAGE}(C5:C11)$$

The AVERAGE function corresponds to function_num 1, so the resulting calculation in cell C13 using the SUBTOTAL function would appear as follows:

$$= \text{SUBTOTAL}(1, C5:C11)$$

After you modified all of the statistical calculations in the worksheet to use the SUBTOTAL function, the sheet should appear as shown in the examples below. Note that the values recalculate automatically according to the filtered data.

Filter on Make: Honda Only

	A	B	C	D	E
1	Fuel Economy of Vehicles				
2	This worksheet demonstrates the use of sorting and filtering in Excel				
3					
4	Make	Model	MPG City	MPG Highway	Annual Fuel Cost
7	Honda	Civic Hybrid	44	44	$1,250
11	Honda	Fit	28	35	$1,800
12					
13		Average	36	40	$1,525
14		Min	28	35	$1,250
15		Max	44	44	$1,800

Filter on Annual Fuel Cost: Less than $3,000

	A	B	C	D	E
1	Fuel Economy of Vehicles				
2	This worksheet demonstrates the use of sorting and filtering in Excel				
3					
4	Make	Model	MPG City	MPG Highway	Annual Fuel Cost
5	Jeep	Grand Cherokee 4WD	16	23	$2,900
7	Honda	Civic Hybrid	44	44	$1,250
8	Volkswagen	Jetta 2.5L	24	31	$2,100
9	Ford	Mustang	15	26	$2,900
11	Honda	Fit	28	35	$1,800
12					
13		Average	25	32	$2,190
14		Min	15	23	$1,250
15		Max	44	44	$2,900

In-Class Activities

ICA 10-1

The worksheet shown below was designed to calculate the total pressure felt by an object submerged in a fluid as a function of the depth the object is submerged. The user will enter the surface pressure (in units of atmospheres), specific gravity of the fluid, and the gravity of the planet (in units of meters per second squared) – all user input is shown in red. The worksheet will calculate the surface pressure in units of pascals, density of the fluid in kilograms per cubic meter, and depth in units of feet – all conversions are shown in orange. Finally, the worksheet will calculate the total pressure in units of atmospheres.

	A	B	C	D
1				
2				
3				
4	Surface Pressure	(Psurface)	2	[atm]
5	Specific Gravity of Fluid	(SG)	1.26	[–]
6	Gravity	(g)	9.8	[m / s^2]
7				
8	Surface Pressure	(Psurface)		[Pa]
9	Density of Fluid	(ρ)		[kg / m^3]
10				
11	Depth (H) [ft]	Depth (H) [m]	Total Pressure (P) [atm]	
12	1			
13	10			
14	20			
15	30			
16	40			
17	50			
18	60			
19	70			
20	80			
21	90			
22	100			

(a) What formula should be typed in cell C8 to convert the surface pressure in cell C4 from atmospheres to pascals?

(b) What formula should be typed in cell C9 to determine the density in units of kilograms per cubic meter?

(c) What formula should be typed into cell B12 that can then be copied down Column B to convert the depth from units of feet to units of meters?

(d) What formula should be typed into cell C12 that can then be copied down Column C to calculate the total pressure in units of atmospheres?

ICA 10-2

The worksheet provided was designed to calculate the total pressure felt by an object submerged in a fluid as a function of the depth the object is submerged.

The user will enter the surface pressure (in units of atmospheres), specific gravity of the fluid, and the gravity of the planet (in units of meters per second squared) – all user input is shown in red.

The worksheet will calculate the surface pressure in units of pascals, density of the fluid in kilograms per cubic meter, and depth in units of feet – all conversions are shown in orange. Format the pressure and density to a whole number, and the height in meters to three decimal places.

Finally, the worksheet will calculate the total pressure in units of atmospheres; format to two decimal places.

Complete the starting Excel file to meet these criteria. A sample worksheet is shown below for comparison.

	A	B	C	D
1				
2				
3				
4	Surface Pressure	(Psurface)	2	[atm]
5	Specific Gravity of Fluid	(SG)	1.26	[–]
6	Gravity	(g)	9.8	[m / s^2]
7				
8	Surface Pressure	(Psurface)	202650	[Pa]
9	Density of Fluid	(ρ)	1260	[kg / m^3]
10				
11	Depth (H) [ft]	Depth (H) [m]	Total Pressure (P) [atm]	
12	1	0.30	2.04	
13	10	3.05	2.37	
14	20	6.10	2.74	
15	30	9.15	3.11	
16	40	12.20	3.49	
17	50	15.24	3.86	
18	60	18.29	4.23	
19	70	21.34	4.60	
20	80	24.39	4.97	
21	90	27.44	5.34	
22	100	30.49	5.72	

ICA 10-3

Some alternate energy technologies, such as wind and solar, produce more energy than needed during peak production times (windy and sunny days), but produce insufficient energy at other times (calm days and nighttime). Many schemes have been concocted to store the surplus energy generated during peak times for later use when generation decreases. One scheme is to use the energy to spin a massive flywheel at very high speeds, then use the rotational kinetic energy stored to power an electric generator later.

The worksheet shown below was designed to calculate how much energy is stored in flywheels of various sizes. The speed of the flywheel (revolutions per minute) is to be entered in cell B2, and the density of the flywheel in cell B4. A formula in cell B3 converts the speed into units of radians per second. There are 2π radians per revolution of the wheel.

To simplify the computations, the stored energy was calculated in three steps. The first table calculates the volumes of the flywheels, the second table uses these volumes to calculate the masses of the flywheels, and the third table uses these masses to determine the stored rotational kinetic energy.

Note that in all cases, changing the values in cells B2 and/or B4 should cause all appropriate values to be automatically recalculated.

	A	B	C	D	E	F	G	H	I
1									
2	Speed (v) [rpm]	15,000		Volume (V) [m³]			Height (H) [m]		
3	Speed (ω) [rad/s]	1571		Diameter (D) [m]	0.3	0.6	0.9	1.2	1.5
4	Density (ρ) [kg/m³]	8000		0.2	0.009	0.019	0.028	0.038	0.047
5				0.4	0.038	0.075	0.113	0.151	0.188
6				0.6	0.085	0.170	0.254	0.339	0.424
7				0.8	0.151	0.302	0.452	0.603	0.754
8				1.0	0.236	0.471	0.707	0.942	1.178
9									
10				Mass (m) [kg]			Height (H) [m]		
11				Diameter (D) [m]	0.3	0.6	0.9	1.2	1.5
12				0.2	75	151	226	302	377
13				0.4	302	603	905	1206	1508
14				0.6	679	1357	2036	2714	3393
15				0.8	1206	2413	3619	4825	6032
16				1.0	1885	3770	5655	7540	9425
17									
18				Kinetic Energy (KE) [J]			Height (H) [m]		
19				Diameter (D) [m]	0.3	0.6	0.9	1.2	1.5
20				0.2	4.65E+05	9.30E+05	1.40E+06	1.86E+06	2.33E+06
21				0.4	7.44E+06	1.49E+07	2.23E+07	2.98E+07	3.72E+07
22				0.6	3.77E+07	7.53E+07	1.13E+08	1.51E+08	1.88E+08
23				0.8	1.19E+08	2.38E+08	3.57E+08	4.76E+08	5.95E+08
24				1.0	2.91E+08	5.81E+08	8.72E+08	1.16E+09	1.45E+09
25				Average KE [J]	9.11E+07	1.82E+08	2.73E+08	3.64E+08	4.55E+08
26				Max - Min KE [J]	1.08E+09				

(a) What should be typed in cell B3 to convert revolutions per minute in cell B2 into radians per second?

(b) What should be typed into cell E4 that can then be copied through the rest of the first table to calculate the flywheel volumes? Assume the shape of the flywheel to be a cylinder.

(c) What should be typed into cell E12 that can then be copied through the rest of the second table to calculate the flywheel masses?

(d) What should be typed into cell E20 that can then be copied through the rest of the third table to calculate the kinetic energies stored in the flywheels? The rotational kinetic energy is given by the formula: $KE_{Rot} = (I\omega^2)/2 = (mr^2\omega^2)/4$

(e) What should be typed into cell E25 that can then be copied through Row 25 to determine the average kinetic energy at each height (in each column)?

(f) What should be typed into cell E26 to determine the difference between the maximum kinetic energy and 800 times the minimum kinetic energy given in the table?

ICA 10-4

The worksheet shown was designed to calculate the cost of material necessary to purchase to produce a given number of parts. The user will enter the specific gravity of the material, the diameter of the cylindrical part in units of inches, the cost of the raw material in dollars per pound-mass, and the number of parts to be manufactured – all user input is shown in red. The worksheet will calculate the radius of the cylindrical part in units of centimeters and the density of the fluid in grams per cubic centimeter – all conversions are shown in orange.

The worksheet will determine the volume and mass of a single part for a given height. Finally, the worksheet will determine the total mass of material needed to produce the desired number of parts in units of pounds-mass, and the total material cost.

The total material cost appears twice. In cells E13 to E20, a formula is written to determine the cost. In cells B26 to B33, the cells simply reference the corresponding cell in the table above. For example, in cell B26 the formula = E13 appears.

In the bottom table, the total cost for "N" parts is determined by the formula:

Total Cost = Total Material Cost + (Energy Cost + Labor Cost) × Number of Parts

Specific Gravity of Material	(SG)	1.50	[-]		
Diameter	(D)	4.0	[in]		
Cost of Raw Material	(C)	$2.25	[$ / lbm]		
Number of Parts	(N)	150	[-]		
Radius	(R)		[cm]		
Density of Fluid	(ρ)		[g / cm^3]		
Height (H) [cm]	Volume (V) [cm^3]	Mass (m) [g]	Mass (M_N) [lbm] for N parts	Total Material Cost (MC) [$]	
1					
2					
3					
5					
6					
8					
10					
12					
Labor Cost	(LC)	$1.50	[$ / part]		

	Total Cost of N Parts	Energy Cost (EC) [$ / part]			
Height (H) [cm]	Total Material Cost (MC) [$]	$0.05	$0.10	$0.20	$0.40
1					
2					
3					
5					
6					
8					
10					
12					

(a) What should be typed in cell C9 to determine the radius in the correct units?

(b) What should be typed into cell B13 that can then be copied down Column B to determine the volume of a cylindrical part in units of cubic centimeters?

(c) What should be typed into cell C13 that can then be copied through down Column C to calculate the mass of each part in unit of grams?

(d) What should be typed into cell D13 that can then be copied down Column D to calculate the total mass needed to produce N parts in units of pounds-mass?

(e) What should be typed into cell E13 that can then be copied down Column E to calculate the total material cost?

(f) What should be typed into cell C26 that can then be copied through C26 to F33 given the energy cost in row 25 and labor cost in cell C22 to calculate the total cost of producing N parts?

ICA 10-5

The worksheet shown was designed to calculate the cost of material necessary to purchase to produce a given number of parts. The user will enter the specific gravity of the material, the diameter of the cylindrical part in units of inches, the cost of the raw material in dollars per pound-mass, and the number of parts to be manufactured – all user input is shown in red. The worksheet will calculate the radius of the cylindrical part in units of centimeters and the density of the fluid in grams per cubic centimeter – all conversions are shown in orange.

The worksheet will determine the volume and mass of a single part for a given height. Finally, the worksheet will determine the total mass of material needed to produce the desired number of parts in units of pounds-mass, and the total material cost.

The total material cost appears twice. In cells E13 to E20, a formula is written to determine the cost. In cells B26 to B33, the cells simply reference the corresponding cell in the table above. For example, in cell B26 the formula = E13 appears.

In the bottom table, the total cost for "N" parts is determined by the formula:

$$\text{Total Cost} = \text{Total Material Cost} + (\text{Energy Cost} + \text{Labor Cost}) \times \text{Number of Parts}$$

A sample worksheet is shown below for comparison.

	A	B	C	D	E	F
4	Specific Gravity of Material	(SG)	1.50	[--]		
5	Diameter	(D)	4.0	[in]		
6	Cost of Raw Material	(C)	$2.25	[$ / lb_m]		
7	Number of Parts	(N)	150	[--]		
9	Radius	(R)	5.08	[cm]		
10	Density of Fluid	(ρ)	1.5	[g / cm^3]		
12	Height (H) [cm]	Volume (V) [cm^3]	Mass (m) [g]	Mass (M_N) [lb_m] for N parts	Total Material Cost (MC) [$]	
13	1	81.07	121.61	40	$90.50	
14	2	162.15	243.22	80	$181.00	
15	3	243.22	364.83	121	$271.50	
16	5	405.37	608.05	201	$452.50	
17	6	486.44	729.66	241	$543.00	
18	8	648.59	972.88	322	$724.00	
19	10	810.73	1216.10	402	$905.00	
20	12	972.88	1459.32	483	$1,086.01	
22	Labor Cost	(LC)	$1.75	[$ / part]		

		Total Cost of N Parts		Energy Cost (EC) [$ / part]		
25	Height (H) [cm]	Total Material Cost (MC) [$]	$0.05	$0.10	$0.20	$0.40
26	1	$90.50	$360.50	$368.00	$383.00	$413.00
27	2	$181.00	$451.00	$458.50	$473.50	$503.50
28	3	$271.50	$541.50	$549.00	$564.00	$594.00
29	5	$452.50	$722.50	$730.00	$745.00	$775.00
30	6	$543.00	$813.00	$820.50	$835.50	$865.50
31	8	$724.00	$994.00	$1,001.50	$1,016.50	$1,046.50
32	10	$905.00	$1,175.00	$1,182.50	$1,197.50	$1,227.50
33	12	$1,086.01	$1,356.01	$1,363.51	$1,378.51	$1,408.51

ICA 10-6

Refer to the following worksheet. The following expressions are typed into the Excel cells indicated. Write the answer that appears in the cell listed. If the cell will be blank, write "BLANK" in the answer space. If the cell will return an error message, write "ERROR" in the answer space.

	A	B	C	D	E	F	G	H
1								
2								
3	Fluid Type	Benzene			Fluid Type	Olive Oil		
4	Density (ρ)	0.879	[g / cm^3]		Density (ρ)	0.703	[g / cm^3]	
5	Viscosity (μ)	6.47E-03	[g / (cm s)]		Viscosity (μ)	1.01	[g / (cm s)]	
6								
7	Velocity (v)	15	[cm / s]		Velocity (v)	50	[cm / s]	
8								
9	Pipe Diameter	Reynolds Number			Pipe Diameter	Reynolds Number		
10	(D) [cm]	(Re) [--]			(D) [cm]	(Re) [--]		
11	1.27	2,588			1.27	44		
12	2.54	5,176			2.54	88		
13	3.81	7,764			3.81	133		
14	5.08	10,352			5.08	177		
15	6.35	12,940			6.35	221		
16	7.62	15,529			7.62	265		

	Expression	Typed into Cell
(a)	= IF (B4 > F4, B3, "F3")	D4
(b)	= IF (B7/2 > F7/10, " ", B7*2)	H7
(c)	= IF (B11 < F11, "B11", IF (B11 > F11, SUM(B11, F11), F11))	D11
(d)	= IF (AND(B4 < F4,B5 < F5), B3, MAX(F11:F16))	D9
(e)	= IF(OR(E16/2^2 > E15*2,E11+E12 < E14),F4*62.4,F4*1000)	H16

ICA 10-7

Write the output value that would appear in a cell if the equation was executed in Excel. You should answer these questions WITHOUT actually using Excel, as practice for the exam. If the cell will appear blank, write "BLANK" in the space provided.

= IF (AND (A1 /A2 > 2, A2 > 3), A1, A2)		Output
(a) A1 = 30 A2 = 5		
(b) A1 = 5 A2 = 1		

= IF (SIN (A1*B1/180) < 0.5, PI(), IF (SIN (A1*B1/180) > 1, 180/A1,""))	Output
(c) A1 = 30 B1 = PI()	
(d) A1 = 5 B1 = PI()	

ICA 10-8

Write the output value that would appear in a cell if the equation was executed in Excel. You should answer these questions WITHOUT actually using Excel, as practice for the exam. If the cell will appear blank, write "BLANK" in the space provided.

= IF (OR (C1 > D3, D3 < E1), "YES", "NO")			Output
(a) C1 = 10	E1 = −5	D3 = 0.1*C1^(−5*E1)	
(b) C1 = 10	E1 = 5	D3 = 0.1*C1^(−5*E1)	

= IF (AND (G4/H3 > 2, H3 > 3), G4, MAX (2, G4, H3, 5*J2-10))			Output
(c) G4 = 30	H3 = 5	J2 = 2	
(d) G4 = 10	H3 = 8	J2 = 10	

ICA 10-9

Refer to the following worksheet. In all questions, give the requested answers in Excel notation, indicating EXACTLY what you would type into the cell given to properly execute the required procedures.

	A	B	C	D	E	F	G
1							
2							
3	Height (H) [ft]	5				Width (W) [ft]	
4					1	1.5	2
5							
6	Volume (V)	Radius (r)	Area (A)		Length [ft]		
7	[ft³]	[ft]	[ft²]	[cm²]	(L1)	(L2)	(L3)
8	79		70.5				
9	1		7.9				
10	55		58.8				
11	13		28.6				
12	39		49.5				
13	9		23.8				
14	63		62.9				
15	23		38.0				
16	72		67.3				
17	27		41.2				
18	67		64.9				

(a) In Column B, you wish to determine the radius of a cylinder. The volume (Column A) and height (Cell B3) have been provided. Recall the volume of a cylinder is given by $V = \pi r^2 H$. Assume you will write the formula in Cell B8 and copy it down the column to Cell B100. In the expression, fill in the blanks with any Excel functions and fill in the boxes with any dollar signs necessary for relative, mixed or absolute references.

$$= \underline{\quad}(\square A\square 8\,/\,(\underline{\quad}*\square B\square 3)\underline{\quad})\underline{\quad}$$

(b) In Column C, the area of a cylinder corresponding to the radius (in Column B) and the height (Cell B3) has been determined in units of square feet. In Column D, you wish to express these values in units of square centimeters. Fill in any Excel mathematical operators or parenthesis for the expression to correctly complete this conversion.

$$= \text{C8}\underline{\quad}2.54\underline{\quad}2\underline{\quad}12\underline{\quad}2$$

(c) In Columns E-G, we wish to determine the dimensions of a rectangular container with the same volume as the cylinders given in Column A. The rectangle will be the same height as the cylinder (Cell B3) but have three possible widths (contained in Cells E_4–G_4). Fill in the boxes below with any dollar signs necessary for relative, mixed, or absolute references to allow the expression to determine the length in Cell E8, and by copied across to Columns F and G, then down all three columns to Row 100.

$$= \square A\square 8/(\square B\square 3*\square E\square 4)$$

(d) In Column H, we wish to tell the user how the length and radius of the different containers compare. Fill in the IF-statement below for Cell H8 to display the maximum value of the length calculations (Cells E8 through G8) if the maximum value of the length calculations is greater than the corresponding radius calculation, otherwise display the letter R.

$$= \text{IF}(\_(1)\_,\ \_(2)\_,\ \_(3)\_)$$

(e) Fill in the if-statement below for Cell J8 to display the sum of Length 1 and Length 2 if the sum of these lengths is greater than Length 3; otherwise, leave it blank.

$$\text{IF}(\_(1)\_,\ \_(2)\_,\ \_(3)\_)$$

ICA 10-10

Give all answers in EXACT Excel notation, as if you were instructing someone EXACTLY what to type into Excel. Be sure to use the values given in the worksheet as cell references and not actual numerical values in the formula. Use absolute, mixed or relative addressing as required.

	A	B	C	D	E	F	G	H
1								
2		Ideal Gas Constant (R)	8,314	[(Pa L)/(K mol)]				
3		Amount of substance (n)	2	[mol]				
4		Molecular weight (MW)	28	[g / mol]				
5		Mass of substance (m)		[g]				
6								
7		Temperature (T) [°F]	Temperature (T) [K]	Volume (V) [ft³]	Volume (V) [L]	Pressure (P) [Pa]	Pressure Warning	Volume Warning
8		25		1				
9		30		1.2				
10		35		1.4				
11		40		0.84				
12		45		0.75				

(a) What would you type into cell C5 to calculate the mass of gas in the container?

(b) What would you type into cell C8 so that you could copy the cell down to cell C12 to calculate all corresponding values of temperature, converting the temperatures given in Column B from units of degrees Fahrenheit to units of kelvins?

(c) What would you type into cell E8 so that you could copy the cell down to cell E12 to calculate all corresponding values of volume, converting the volumes given in Column D from units of cubic feet to units of liters?

(d) What would you type into cell F8 so that you could copy the cell down to cell F12 to calculate all corresponding values of pressure using the ideal gas law, solving for pressure in units of pascals?

(e) What conditional statement would you type in cell G8 so that you could copy the cell down to cell G12 to display the words "Too High" if the pressure from the ideal gas calculation is equal to or greater than 500,000 pascals? If the pressure is less than this value, the cell should remain blank.

(f) What conditional statement would you type in cell H8 so that you could copy the cell down to cell H12 to display the words "Bigger" if the corresponding value in Column E is greater than 5 gallons, "Smaller" if the value in Column E is less than 1 gallon, or display the actual value of the volume, in units of gallons, if the value is between 1 and 5 gallons?

ICA 10-11

A bioengineer conducts clinical trials on stressed-out college students to see if a sleep aid will help them fall asleep faster. She begins the study by having 20 students take a sleep aid for seven days and records through biofeedback the time when they fall asleep. To analyze the data, she sets up the following worksheet. Evaluate the expressions below; state what will appear in the cell when the command is executed. Column I contains the average time each student took to fall asleep during the seven-day trial. Column J contains any adverse reactions the students experienced (H = headache; N = nausea).

(a) Column K will contain the rating of the time it took the student to fall asleep compared with the control group, who did not take the medication. The statement as it appears in cell K14 is given below. What will appear in cell K14 when this statement is executed?

= IF > (I14 > $I$2 + $I$3, "MORE", IF (I14 < $I$2 − $I$3, "LESS", ""))

(b) Column L groups the participants into three groups according to their reaction to the drug and the time it took them to fall asleep. Assume the statement for part (a) is executed in Column K. The statement as it appears in cell L7 is given below. What will appear in cell L7 when this statement is executed?

= IF (AND (K7 = "MORE", J7 = "H"), "MH", IF (AND (K7 = "MORE", J7 = "N"), "MN", ""))

(c) Suppose the formula in Column L was changed to regroup the participants. The statement as it appears in cell L9 is given below. In Excel, this statement would appear as a continuous line, but here it is shown on two lines for space. What will appear in cell L9 when this statement is executed?

= IF (AND (K9 = "MORE", OR (J9 = "H", J9 = "N")), "SEVERE",

IF (OR (J9 = "H", J9 = "N"), "MILD", IF (K9 = "LESS", "HELPFUL", "")))

(d) Suppose the formula in part (c) was copied into cell L16. What would appear in cell L16 when this statement is executed?

(e) Suppose the formula in part (c) was copied into cell L18. What would appear in cell L18 when this statement is executed?

	A	B	C	D	E	F	G	H	I	J	K	L
1						Control Group Data						
2						Overall Average			35	[min]		
3						Standard Deviation			4	[min]		
4												
5					Number of Minutes to Fall Asleep							
6	Patient	Day 1	Day 2	Day 3	Day 4	Day 5	Day 6	Day 7	Average	Reaction	Time	Group
7	A	45	39	83	47	39	25	42	46	H		
8	B	35	75	15	36	42	12	29	35			
9	C	42	32	63	45	37	34	31	41	N		
10	D	14	25	65	38	53	33	32	37	H		
11	E	14	71	48	18	29	14	24	31			
12	F	14	25	29	24	18	24	15	21	H N		
13	G	31	14	42	19	28	17	21	25			
14	H	12	24	32	42	51	12	16	27	H N		
15	I	28	29	44	15	43	15	22	28	N		
16	J	21	19	35	41	34	25	18	28	H		
17	K	44	36	51	39	30	26	25	36			
18	L	38	43	36	59	14	34	18	35	N		
19	M	19	15	63	50	55	27	31	37	H		

ICA 10-12

Refer to the worksheet shown, set up to calculate the displacement of a spring. Hooke's law states the force (F, in newtons) applied to a spring is equal to the stiffness of the spring (k, in newtons per meter) times the displacement (x, in meters): $F = kx$.

	A	B	C	D	E	F	G	H
1								
2	Spring Code	Stiffness [N/m]	Maximum Displacement [mm]			Spring Code	Stiffness [N / m]	Maximum Displacement [mm]
3	3-Blue	50	20			1-Blue	10	40
4						1-Black	25	60
5	Mass [g]	Displacement [cm]	Warning			2-Blue	30	25
6	25	0.49				2-Black	40	60
7	50	0.98				2-Red	20	30
8	75	1.47				3-Blue	50	20
9	100	1.96				3-Red	40	30
10	125	2.45	Too Much Mass			3-Green	60	10
11	150	2.94	Too Much Mass					
12	175	3.43	Too Much Mass					
13	200	3.92	Too Much Mass					
14	225	4.41	Too Much Mass					
15	250	4.90	Too Much Mass					
16	275	5.39	Too Much Mass					
17	300	5.88	Too Much Mass					
18								

Cell A3 contains a data validation list of springs. The stiffness (cell B3) and maximum displacement (cell C3) values are found using a VLOOKUP function linked to the table shown at the right side of the worksheet. These data are then used to determine the displacement of the spring at various mass values. A warning is issued if the displacement determined is greater than the maximum displacement for the spring. Use this information to determine the answers to the following questions.

(a) Write the expression, in Excel notation, that you would type into cell B6 to determine the displacement of the spring. Assume you will copy this expression to cells B7 to B17.

(b) Fill in the following information in the VLOOKUP function used to determine the maximum displacement in cell C3 based on the choice of spring in cell A3.

$$= \text{VLOOKUP}(\_\_\_(1)\_\_\_, \_\_\_\_(2)\_\_\_\_, \_\_\_\_(3)\_\_\_\_, \_\_\_(4)\_\_\_)$$

(c) Fill in the following information in the IF function used to determine the warning given in cell C6, using the maximum displacement in cell C3. Assume you will copy this expression to cells C7 to C17.

$$= IF(\_\_\_(1)\_\_\_, \_\_\_\_(2)\_\_\_\_, \_\_\_\_(3)\_\_\_\_)$$

ICA 10-13

You are interested in analyzing different implant parts being made in a bioengineering production facility. The company has the ability to make 9 different parts for shoulder, knee, or hip replacement.

On the worksheet shown, you have created a place for the user to choose the body location (shoulder, knee, or hip) in cell B5 using a data validation list. Once the body location is set, a list of material choices will appear in cells D5 to F5. The user can choose a material in cell B6 using a data validation list. If the material chosen does not match one of the possible choices in cell D5 to F5, a warning will be issued for the user to choose another material.

In cell B9, the user will choose if the part is size small (S), medium (M), or large (L) using a data validation list. Based upon body location and size, the part number will adjust automatically using a VLOOKUP function. After the part number has been determined, the material weight (cell B11) and part volume (cell B12) will adjust automatically using a VLOOKUP function.

The user will enter the number of desired parts in cell B14. If the user requests more than 250 parts, a warning of "Too Many" will be issued; if the user requests less than 20 parts, a warning of "Too Small" will be issued in cell C14.

The amount of material to be ordered will be determined in cell B16 by multiplying the number of parts and the material weight. The cost of the material to be ordered will be determined in cell B17. If the order cost is greater than $1000, a request to "Check with Purchasing" will appear; otherwise, the cost of the order will appear. Finally, in cell B18 the amount of boxes needed for shipping will appear determined by number of parts requested and number of parts per box, based on the part number chosen in cell B10.

Lookup functions in Excel contain four parts.

$$= VLOOKUP(\_\_(1)\_\_, \_\_(2)\_\_, \_\_(3)\_\_, \_\_(4)\_\_)$$

(a) Fill in the following information in the VLOOKUP function used to determine third possible material choice in cell F5 based on the choice of body location in cell B5.

An IF statement in Excel contains three parts. Fill in the following information in the IF function used to determine the following conditions:

$$= IF(\_\_(1)\_\_, \_\_(2)\_\_, \_\_(3)\_\_)$$

(b) In cell C6, the a warning is issued to the user if the material chosen in cell B6 does not match the list of materials provided in cell D5 to F5. Fill in the IF statement used to create this error message, containing a complex IF test using AND or OR.

A nested IF statement in Excel contains three parts per IF statement. Fill in the following information in the IF function used to determine the following conditions:

$$= IF(\_\_(1a)\_\_, \_\_(2a)\_\_, IF(\_\_(1b)\_\_, \_\_(2b)\_\_, \_\_(3b)\_\_))$$

(c) In cell B14, the user can enter the number of parts needed in production. If this value is more than 250 parts, a warning will appear in Cell C14 telling the user the quantity is too high; if the value is less than 20, a warning will tell the user the quantity is too small; otherwise, the cell remains blank.

(d) In order for Excel to display the correct number of boxes needed, the following functions are tried. Which one will correctly display the number of boxes needed to ship the parts?

(A) `= B14/VLOOKUP(B10,J1:L10,3,FALSE)`

(B) `= ROUND(B14/VLOOKUP(B10,J1:L10,3,FALSE),0)`

(C) `= ROUNDDOWN(B14/VLOOKUP(B10,J1:L10,3,FALSE),0)`

(D) `= ROUNDUP(B14/VLOOKUP(B10,J1:L10,3,FALSE),0)`

(E) `= TRUNC(B14/VLOOKUP(B10,J1:L10,3,FALSE),0)`

	A	B	C	D	E	F	G	H	I	J	K	L	M	N
1								Body Location	Part Size	Part Number	Material Weight [lbm]	Number / Box	Part Volume [cin]	Energy Cost / Part
2								Shoulder	S	JB2	0.45	78	5.5	0.1
3								Shoulder	M	JB3	0.15	24	3.5	0.04
4								Shoulder	L	JB5	0.15	55	3.5	0.09
5	Body Location	Shoulder	Material Choices:	AuZn-4	WC-2	CuAg-5		Hip	L	KA9	0.05	64	1.5	0.02
6	MATERIAL	PdSi-3	Wrong Material Match / Choose Again					Hip	M	KA11	0.1	82	2.5	0.05
7	Cost / lbm of material	$ 22.00						Hip	S	KA2	0.4	36	6	0.02
8								Knee	M	DS3	0.5	65	1.5	0.07
9	Part Size	L						Knee	S	DS7	0.3	98	1.5	0.05
10	Part Number	JB5						Knee	L	DS8	0.4	93	5	0.04
11	Material Weight [lbm]	0.15												
12	Part Volume [cin]	3.5						Material	Material Cost / lbm			Body Location		Material Choice
13								AuZn-4	$ 5.00			Shoulder	AuZn-4	WC-2	CuAg-5
14	Number of Parts	300	Too Many					WC-2	$ 17.00			Knee	ZnCd-2	CoNi-7	PtC-9
15								CuAg-5	$ 7.00			Hip	PtZn-4	PtC-9	MnPd-8
16	Amount of Mat'l to Order [lbm]	45						PdSi-3	$ 22.00						
17	Cost of Mat'l to Order [$]	$990.00						PdSi-5	$ 2.00						
18	Amount of Boxes Needed	6						ZnCd-2	$ 18.00						
19								CoNi-7	$ 24.00						
20								CoAg-12	$ 8.00						
21								CdAl-2	$ 13.00						
22								PtZn-4	$ 19.00						
23								PtC-9	$ 6.00						
24								MnPd-8	$ 25.00						
25								WTi-3	$ 3.00						
26								ScCo-4	$ 6.00						
27								ZrW-8	$ 7.00						
28								MnRh-5	$ 13.00						
29								PdCd-7	$ 11.00						

ICA 10-14

You have a large stock of several values of inductors and capacitors, and are investigating how many possible combinations of a single capacitor and a single inductor chosen from the ones you have in stock will give a resonant frequency between specified limits.

Create two cells to hold a minimum and maximum frequency the user can enter.

	Allowable Range				Allowable Range	
Incorrect Data:	f_{min} [Hz]	f_{max} [Hz]		Correct Data:	f_{min} [Hz]	f_{max} [Hz]
	2,500	1,000			2,500	7,777

Calculate the resonant frequency (f_R) for all possible combinations of one inductor and one capacitor, rounded to the nearest integer. For a resonant inductor/capacitor circuit, the resonant frequency in hertz [Hz] is calculated by

$$f_R = \frac{1}{2\pi\sqrt{LC}}$$

In this equation, L is the inductance in units of henry [H] and C is the capacitance in units of farads [F]. Note that the capacitance values in the table are given in microfarads. Automatically format each result to indicate its relation to the minimum and maximum frequency values as listed below.

■ $f_R > f_{MAX}$: The cell should be shaded white with light grey text and no border.

■ $f_R < f_{MIN}$: The cell should be shaded light grey with dark grey text and no border.

■ $f_{MIN} < f_R < f_{MAX}$: The cell should be shaded white with bold black text and a black border.

If done properly, the table should appear similar to the table below for $f_{MIN} = 2,500$ and $f_{MAX} = 7,777$.

After you have this working properly, modify the frequency input cells to use data validation to warn the user of an invalid value entry.

Resonant Frequency (f_R) [Hz]	Capacitance (C) [μF]							
Inductance (L) [H]	0.0022	0.0082	0.05	0.47	0.82	1.5	3.3	10
0.0005	151748	78601	31831	10382	7860	**5812**	**3918**	2251
0.002	75874	39301	15915	**5191**	**3930**	**2906**	1959	1125
0.01	33932	17576	**7118**	2322	1758	1299	876	503
0.05	15175	7860	**3183**	1038	786	581	392	225
0.068	13012	**6740**	2729	890	674	498	336	193
0.22	**7234**	**3747**	1517	495	375	277	187	107
0.75	**3918**	2029	822	268	203	150	101	58

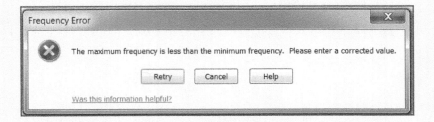

Frequency Error

The maximum frequency is less than the minimum frequency. Please enter a corrected value.

Retry   Cancel   Help

Was this information helpful?

ICA 10-15

We accidentally drop a tomato from the balcony of a high-rise apartment building. As it falls, the tomato has time to ponder some physics and says, "You know, the distance I have fallen equals $\frac{1}{3}$ gravity times the time I have fallen squared." Create a worksheet to solve the question of when the tomato goes splat.

■ The user will input the initial balcony height in units of feet. Use data validation to set a limit for the height of 200 feet.

■ Place the acceleration due to gravity in a cell under the balcony height and not within the formulas themselves. *Be sure to watch the units for this problem!*

■ Column A will be the distance the tomato falls, starting at a distance of zero up to a distance of 200 feet, in 5-foot increments.

■ Column B will show the calculated time elapsed at each distance fallen.

■ Column C will display the status of the tomato as it falls.
  • If the tomato is still falling, the cell should display the distance the tomato still has to fall.
  • If the tomato hits the ground, the cell should display "SPLAT" on a red background.
  • SPLAT should appear once; the cells below are blank.

Test your worksheet using the following conditions:

I.   At a balcony height of 200 feet, the tomato should splat at a time of 3.52 seconds.

II. At a balcony height of 50 feet, the tomato should splat at a time of 1.76 seconds.

ICA 10-16

You are interested in calculating the best place to stand to look at a statue. Where should you stand so that the angle subtended by the statue is the largest?

At the top of the worksheet, input the pedestal height (P) and the statue height (S).

In Column A, create a series of distances (d) from the foot of the statue, from 2 feet to 40 feet by 2-foot increments.

In Column B, calculate the subtended angle in radians using the following equation:

$$\theta = \tan^{-1}\left(\frac{P + S}{d}\right) - \tan^{-1}\left(\frac{P}{d}\right)$$

Photo courtesy of E. Stephan

In Column C, write a function to change the angles in Column B from radians to degrees. At the bottom of Column C, insert a function to display the maximum value of all the angles.

In Column D, use a conditional statement whose output is blank except at the single distance where the angle is a maximum; at the maximum, print "Stand Here." This font should be in the color of your choice, not the default black text.

Test your worksheet using the following conditions:

I.   At a pedestal height of 20 feet and a statue height of 10 feet, the subtended angle is 11.5 degrees and you should stand 24 feet from the statue.

II.   At a pedestal height of 30 feet and a statue height of 20 feet, the subtended angle is 14.5 degrees and you should stand 38 feet from the statue.

ICA 10-17

Many college students have compact refrigerator-freezers in their dorm room. The data set provided is a partial list of energy efficient models less than 3.6 cubic feet [cft], according to the American Council for an Energy Efficient Economy (www.aceee.org). Complete the analysis below.

We would like to compute the cost to run each model for a year. Assume that it costs $0.086 per kilowatt-hour [kWh]. Create a new column, "Annual Energy Cost [$/year]," that calculates the annual energy cost for each refrigerator.

(a)   Sort the first table by energy usage, with the model with the highest kilowatt-hour rating listed first. Which model appears first?

(b)   Sort by the volume in ascending order and the annual energy cost in ascending order. Which model appears first?

(c)   Assume we want to restrict our selection to refrigerators that can contain more than 2.5 cubic feet. Which models appear in the list?

(d)   Assume we want to restrict our selection to refrigerators that can contain more than 2.5 cubic feet and only require between 0 and 300 kilowatt-hours per year. Which models appear in the list?

ICA 10-18

The complexity of video gaming consoles has evolved over the years. The data set provided is a list of energy usage data on recent video gaming consoles, according to the Sust-It consumer energy report data (www.sust-it.net).

Compute the cost to run each gaming console for a year, including the purchase price. Assume that it costs $0.086 per kilowatt-hour [kWh]. Create a new column, "Cost + Energy [$/yr]," that calculates the total (base + energy) cost for each gaming console.

On average, a consumer will own and operate a video gaming console for four years. Calculate the total carbon emission [kilograms of carbon dioxide, or kg CO_2] for each gaming console over the average lifespan; put the result in a column labeled "Average Life Carbon Emission [kg CO_2]." If these steps are completed correctly, the first year cost for the Microsoft Xbox 360 should be $410.36 and the Average Life Carbon Emissions should be 207.88 kilograms of carbon dioxide.

(a) Sort the table by total cost, with the console with the highest total cost listed first. Which console appears first?

(b) Sort by the original cost in ascending order and the average life carbon emission in ascending order. Which console appears last?

(c) Restrict your selection to video game consoles that originally cost $300. Which models appear in the list?

(d) Restrict your selection to video game consoles that originally cost less than or equal to $300 and have an average life carbon emission less than or equal to 25 kg CO_2. Which models appear in the list?

Chapter 10 REVIEW QUESTIONS

1. With current rocket technology, the cost to lift one kilogram of mass to geosynchronous orbit (GSO) is about $20,000. Several other methods of lifting mass into space for considerably less cost have been envisioned, including the Lofstrom loop, the orbital airship, and the space elevator.

   In space elevators, a cargo compartment (climber) rides up a slender tether attached to the Earth's surface and extending tens of thousands of miles into space. Many designs provide power to the climber by beaming it to a collector on the climber using a laser of maser.

   The leftmost column of the table should contain efficiencies from 0.5% to 2% in 0.25% increments. The top row of the table should list electricity prices from 4 cents to 14 cents per kilowatt-hour with 2 cent increments. Each row of the table thus represents a specific efficiency and each column represents a specific electricity cost. The intersection of each row and column should contain the corresponding total cost of the electricity used to lift one kilogram to GSO.

   Assume that the total change in the potential energy of an object lifted from sea level to GSO is 50 megajoules per kilogram.

   Any constants and conversion factors used should appear as properly labeled constants in individual cells, and your formulae should reference these. Conversions and constants should NOT be directly coded into the formulae. You are expected to use absolute, relative, and mixed cell addressing as appropriate.

   Test case: If electricity costs 18 cents per kilowatt-hour and the conversion efficiency is 3%, the electricity to lift one kilogram to GSO would cost $83.33.

2. A history major of your acquaintance is studying agricultural commerce in nineteenth century Wales. He has encountered many references to "hobbits" of grain, and thinking that this must be some type of unit similar to a bushel (rather than a diminutive inhabitant of Middle Earth), he has sought your advice because he knows you are studying unit conversions in your engineering class.

   He provides a worksheet containing yearly records for the total number of hobbits of three commodities sold by a Mr. Thomas between 1817 and 1824, and has asked you to convert these to not only cubic meters, but also both U.S. and imperial bushels.

	A	B	C	D	E	F	G	H	I	J	K	L	M
1													
2													
3													
4													
5			Barley				Wheat				Oats		
6	Year	Hobbits	Imp. Bushels	US Bushels	Cubic Meters	Hobbits	Imp. Bushels	US Bushels	Cubic Meters	Hobbits	Imp. Bushels	US Bushels	Cubic Meters
7	1817	106				154				203			
8	1818	118				145				187			
9	1819	98				167				167			
10	1820	137				124				199			
11	1821	102				105				210			
12	1822	142				168				147			
13	1823	93				132				186			
14	1824	117				136				193			
15													
16		Hobbit	Imp. Bushels	US Bushels	Cubic Meters								
17		1											

   After a little research, you find that the hobbit was equal to two and a half imperial bushels, the imperial bushel equals 2,219 cubic inches, and the U.S. bushel equals 2,150 cubic inches.

First, you create a table showing the conversion factors from hobbits to the other units, including comments documenting the conversion. You then use these calculated conversion factors to create the rest of the table.

3. You want to set up a worksheet to investigate the oscillatory response of an electrical circuit. Create a worksheet similar to the one shown, including the proper header information.

4			
5			
6			
7	Neper Frequency (α_0)	25	[rad/s]
8	Resonant Frequency (ω_0)	400	[rad/s]
9	Initial Voltage (V_0)	15	[V]
10			
11	Damped Frequency (ω_d)		[rad/s]
12			
13			
14	Time (t) [s]	Voltage (V) [V]	
15			

First, calculate another constant, the damped frequency ω_d, which is a function of the neper frequency (α_0) and the resonant frequency (ω_0). This can be calculated with the formula

$$\omega_d = \sqrt{\omega_0^2 - \alpha_0^2}$$

Next, create a column of times (beginning in A15) used to calculate the voltage response, ranging from 0 to 0.002 seconds at an increment of 0.0002 seconds.

In column B, calculate the voltage response with the following equation, formatted to one decimal place:

$$V = V_0 e^{-\alpha_0 t} \cos (\omega_d t)$$

Test Cases: Use the following to test your worksheet.

I. Change neper frequency to 200 radians per second, resonant frequency to 800 radians per second, and initial voltage to 100 volts. At a time of 0.0008 seconds, the voltage should be 69.4 V.

II. Change neper frequency to 100 radians per second, resonant frequency to 600 radians per second, and initial voltage to 100 volts. At a time of 0.0008 seconds, the voltage should be 82.2 V.

4. A phase diagram for carbon and platinum is shown. Assuming the lines shown are linear, we can say the mixture has the following characteristics:

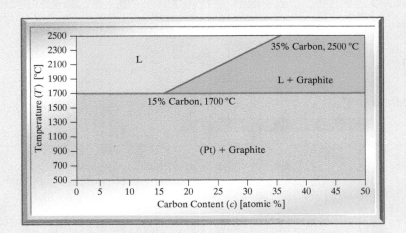

- Below 1,700°C, it is a mixture of solid platinum and graphite.
- Above 1,700°C, there are two possible phases: a liquid (L) phase and a liquid (L) + graphite phase. The endpoints of the division line between these two phases are labeled on the diagram.

Use the workbook provided to determine the phase of a mixture, given the temperature and carbon content.

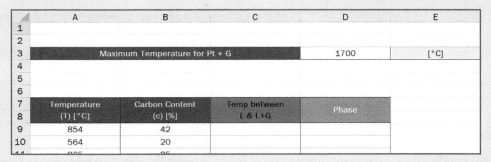

	A	B	C	D	E
1					
2					
3	Maximum Temperature for Pt + G			1700	[°C]
4					
5					
6					
7	Temperature	Carbon Content	Temp between	Phase	
8	(T) [°C]	(c) [%]	L & L+G		
9	854	42			
10	564	20			

(a) Write the equation to describe the temperature of the dividing line between the liquid (L) region and the liquid (L) + graphite region in Column C. Reference the carbon content found in Column B as needed. Add any absolute reference cells you feel are needed to complete this calculation.

(b) Write the conditional statement to determine the phase in Column D. For simplicity, call the phases Pt + G, L, and L + G. For points on the line, YOU can decide which phase they are included in.

(c) Use conditional formatting to indicate each phase. Provide a color key.

5. A simplified phase diagram for cobalt and nickel is shown. Assuming the lines shown are linear, we can say the mixture has the following characteristics:

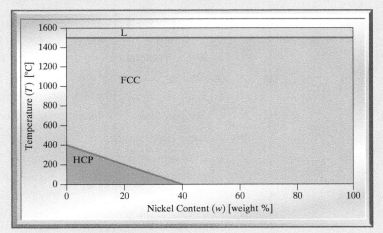

- Above 1,500°C, it is a liquid.
- Below 1,500°C, there are two possible phases: face-centered cubic (FCC) phase and hexagonal close-packed (HCP) phase.

Use the workbook provided to determine the phase of a mixture, given the temperature and nickel content.

	A	B	C	D	E
1					
2					
3		Minimum Temperature for Liquid		1500	[°C]
4					
5					
6					
7	Temperature	Nickel Content	Temp Between	Phase	
8	(T) [°C]	(w) [%]	HCP & FCC		
9	543	74			
10	1028	4			
11	1326	69			

(a) Write the mathematical equation to describe the dividing line between the HCP region and the FCC region in Column C. Reference the nickel content found in Column B as needed. Add any absolute reference cells you feel are needed to complete this calculation.

(b) Write the conditional statement to determine the phase in Column D. For simplicity, call the phases HCP, FCC, and L. For points on the line, YOU can decide which phase they are included in.

(c) Use conditional formatting to indicate each phase. Provide a color key.

6. You enjoy drinking coffee but are particular about the temperature (T) of your coffee. If the temperature is greater than or equal to 70 degrees Celsius [°C], the coffee is too hot to drink; less than or equal to 45°C is too cold by your standards. Your coffee pot produces coffee at the initial temperature (T_0). The cooling of your coffee can be modeled by the equation below, where time (t) and the cooling factor (k) are in units per second:

$$T = T_0 e^{-kt}$$

(a) At the top of the worksheet, create an area where the user can modify four properties of the coffee. For a sample test case, enter the following data.

- Initial temperature (T_0); for the initial problem, set to 80°C.
- Cooling factor (k); set to 0.001 per second [s^{-1}].
- Temperature above which coffee is "Too Hot" to drink (T_{hot}); set to 70°C.
- Temperature below which coffee is "Too Cold" to drink (T_{cold}); set to 45°C.

(b) Create a temperature profile for the coffee:

- In column A, generate a time range of 0–300 seconds, in 15-second intervals.
- In column B, generate the temperature of the coffee, using the equation given and the input parameters set by the user (T_0 and k).

(c) In column B, the temperature values should appear on a red background if the coffee is too hot to drink, and a blue background if it is too cold using conditional formatting.

(d) In column C, create a warning next to each temperature that says "Do not Drink" if the calculated temperature in column B is too hot or too cold in comparison with the temperature values the user enters.

A sample worksheet is shown below for the test case described in Part (a).

Coffee Parameters		
Initial Temperature (T_0)	80	[°C]
Cooling Factor (k)	0.001	[1/s]
Too Hot Temperature (T_{hot})	70	[°C]
Too Cold Temperature (T_{cold})	45	[°C]
Time [s]	Temperature [deg C]	Warning!
0	80	Do not Drink
15	79	Do not Drink
30	78	Do not Drink
45	76	Do not Drink
60	75	Do not Drink
75	74	Do not Drink
90	73	Do not Drink
105	72	Do not Drink
120	71	Do not Drink
135	70	
150	69	
165	68	
180	67	

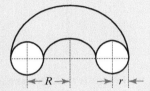

7. In the 1950s, a team at Los Alamos National Laboratories built several devices they called "Perhapsatrons," thinking that PERHAPS they might be able to create controllable nuclear fusion. After several years of experiments, they were never able to maintain a stable plasma and abandoned the project.

The perhapsatron used a toroidal (doughnut-shaped) plasma confinement chamber, similar to those used in more modern Tokamak fusion devices. You have taken a job at a fusion research lab, and your supervisor asks you to develop a simple spreadsheet to calculate the volume of a torus within which the plasma will be contained in a new experimental reactor.

(a) Create a simple calculator to allow the user to type in the radius of the tube (r) in meters and the radius of the torus (R) in meters and display the volume in cubic meters.

(b) Data validation should be used to assure that $R > r$ in part (a).

(c) Create a table that calculates the volumes of various toruses with specific values for r and R. The tube radii (r) should range from 5 centimeters to 100 centimeters in increments of 5 centimeters. The torus radii (R) should range from 1.5 meters to 3 meters in increments of 0.1 meters.

The volume of a torus can be determined using $V = 2\pi^2 R r^2$. A sample worksheet for parts (a) and (b) is shown below.

Tube Radius (r) [m]	Torus Radius (R) [m]	Torus Volume (V) [m³]
2	1	79.0

Microsoft Excel   ☒

✕ The value you entered is not valid.

A user has restricted values that can be entered into this cell.

[Retry]   [Cancel]   [Help]

Was this information helpful?

Use the following phase diagram for Questions 8–9.

The phase diagram below for the processing of a polymer relates the applied pressure to the raw material porosity.

- Region A or B = porosity is too high or too low for the material to be usable.
- Region C = combinations in this region yield material with defects, such as cracking or flaking.
- Region D = below a pressure of 15 pound-force per square inch [psi] the polymer cannot be processed.
- Region E = optimum region to operate.

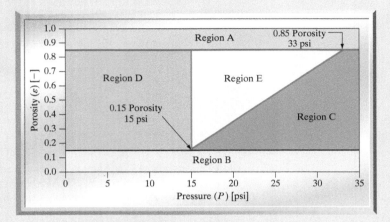

There are often multiple ways to solve the same problem; here we look a few alternative ways to determine the phase of the material and the processibility of the material.

8. **(a)** In Column C, develop the equation for the line dividing the phases of Region E and Region C. Assume it was written in cell C9 and copied to Column C.

(b) In Column D, write an expression to determine the phase of the material (Phase A–Phase E).

(c) In Column E, write an expression to determine if the material is processable.

(d) When the conditions of Phase E are met, the cell should be highlighted by conditional formatting. Provide a color key.

	A	B	C	D	E
1					
2					
3		Porosity Upper Limit [%]		85	
4		Porosity Lower Limit [%]		15	
5		Pressure Limit [psi]		15	
6					
7	Pressure	Porosity	Porosity between	Phase	Is Material able to
8	(P) [psi]	(ε) [%]	C and E		be Processed?
9	16	91			
10	17	60			
11	18	30			

9. **(a)** In Column A and Column B, use data validation to restrict the user from entering values outside the valid parameter ranges—pressure: 0–35 psi and porosity: 0–100%.

(b) In Column C, develop the equation for the line dividing the phases of Region E and Region C.

(c) In Column D, write an expression to determine the phase of the material (Phase A–Phase E).

(d) In Column E, write an expression to determine if the material is processable.

(e) When the conditions of Phase E are met, the cell should be highlighted by conditional formatting.

(f) Write an expression in Column F to tell the user why the material was rejected. For example, under the conditions of pressure $= 25$ psi and porosity $= 40\%$, the statement might say "Porosity too low."

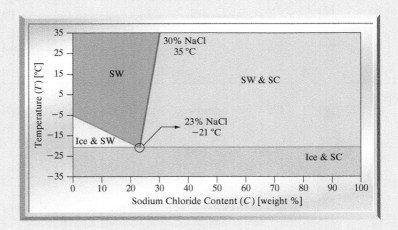

Use the following phase diagram for Questions 10–11.

The following phase diagram is for salt water. There are four possible phases, which depend on the temperature and the sodium chloride content (NaCl).

- Ice and SC = Mixed ice and salt crystals.
- Ice and SW = Ice and saltwater.
- SW = Saltwater.
- SW and SC = Saltwater and salt crystals.

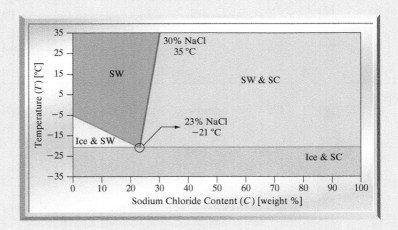

There are often multiple ways to solve the same problem; here we look a few alternative ways to determine the phase of the mixture.

10. (a) In Column C, develop the equation for the line dividing the phases of the ice–saltwater mix and the saltwater. Assume it was written in cell C11 and copied down.

(b) In Column D, develop the equation for the line dividing the phases of the saltwater and the saltwater–salt crystals mix. Assume it was written in cell D11 and copied down.

(c) In Column E, write an expression to determine the phase of the mixture.

(d) Use conditional formatting to highlight the various phases. Provide a color key.

	A	B	C	D	E
1					
2					
3					
4					
5					
6					
7	Upper Limit of Mixed Ice and Salt Crystals			-21	[°C]
8					
9	NaCl [%]	Temp [°C]	Dividing Temp [° C]		Phase
10			Ice and SW to SW	SW to SW and SC	
11	84	31			
12	60	-17			
13	81	-17			
14	41	17			

11. **(a)** In Column A and Column B, use data validation to restrict the user from entering values outside the valid parameter ranges: NaCl (%): 0–100%; Temp [°C]: −35°C to 35°C.
    (b) In Column C, develop the equation for the line dividing the phases of the ice–saltwater mix and the saltwater.
    (c) In Column D, develop the equation for the line dividing the phases of the saltwater and the saltwater–salt crystals mix.
    (d) In Column E, write an expression to determine the phase of the mixture.
    (e) Use conditional formatting to highlight the various phases. Provide a color key.

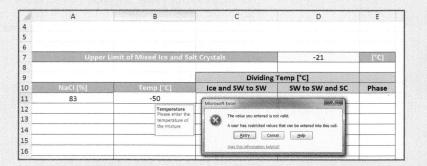

12. When liquid and vapor coexist in a container at equilibrium, the pressure is called vapor pressure. Several models predict vapor pressure. One, called the **Antoine equation**, first introduced by Ch. Antoine in 1888, yields vapor pressure in units of millimeters of mercury [mm Hg].

$$P = 10^{\left(A - \frac{B}{T+C}\right)}$$

The constants A, B, and C are called the *Antoine constants*; they depend on both fluid type and temperature. Note that "B" and "C" must be in the same units as temperature and "A" is a dimensionless number, all determined by experiment.

	A	B	C	D	E	F
1						
2						
3						
4						
5						
6						
7			Constants		Validity Range	
8	Compound	A	B [°C]	C [°C]	T_{min}[°C]	T_{max}[°C]
9						
10						
11						
12						
13						
14						
15	Temperature (T) [°C]	Pressure (P) [mm Hg]		Compound		Constants
16					A	B [°C]
17				Acetic Acid	7.5596	1644.05	2
18				Acetone	7.1327	1219.97	2
19				Cyclohexane	6.85146	1206.47	2
20				Ethanol	8.20417	1642.89	
21				Hexadecane	7.0287	1830.51	

Create a worksheet using the provided template. The Antoine constants, located in cells D17 to I24 of the workbook provided, should automatically fill in after the user selects one from a drop-down menu in Cell A9 of the compounds shown below. (*Hint:* Use data validation and lookup expressions.)

Next, create a column of temperature (T) beginning at –100 degrees Celsius and increasing in increments of 5 degrees Celsius until a temperature of 400 degrees Celsius.

In column B, calculate the vapor pressure (P, in millimeters of mercury, [mm Hg]) using the Antoine equation, formatted to four decimal places. If the equation is outside the valid temperature range for the compound, the pressure column should be blank.

13. The ideal gas law assumes that molecules bounce around and have negligible volume themselves. This is not always true. To compensate for the simplifying assumptions of the ideal gas law, the Dutch scientist Johannes van der Waals developed a "real" gas law that uses several factors to account for molecular volume and intermolecular attraction. He was awarded the Nobel Prize in 1910 for his work. The **van der Waals equation** is as follows:

$$\left(P + \frac{an^2}{V^2}\right)(V - bn) = nRT$$

$P, V, n, R,$ and T are the same quantities as found in the ideal gas law. The constant "a" is a correction for intermolecular forces [atm L^2/mol^2], and the constant "b" accounts for molecular volume [L/mol]. Each of these factors must be determined by experiment.

	A	B	C	D	E	F
1						
2						
3						
4						
5						
6						
7	Type of Gas				Compound	a
8	Quantity [g]					[atm L^2 / mol
9	Temperature (T) [°C]				Acetic Acid	17.587
10					Acetone	13.906
11					Ammonia	4.170
12	Molecular Weight (MW) [g/mol]				Argon	1.345
13	vdW Constant "a" [atm L^2/mol^2]				Benzene	18.001
14	vdW Constant "b" [L/mol]				Chlorobenzene	25.433
15					Diethyl ether	17.380
16	Ideal Gas Constant (g) [(atm L)/mol K)]		0.08206		Ethane	5.489
17					Ethanol	12.021
18					Hexane	24.387
19		Ideal Gas	van der Waals		Methanol	9.523
20	Volume (V) [L]	Pressure (P) [atm]			Neon	0.211
21					Oxygen	1.360

Create a worksheet using the provided template. The molecular weight, "a," and "b" should automatically fill in after the user selects the type of gas in cell B7. (*Hint:* Use data validation and lookup expressions using the data found in the table located in E7 to H26 in the workbook provided.) The user will also set the quantity of gas and the temperature of the system.

Next, create a column of volume beginning in A21 at 0.5 liters and increasing in increments of 0.1 liters to a volume of 5 liters.

In column B, calculate the pressure (*P*, in atmospheres [atm]) using the ideal gas law.

In column C, calculate the pressure (*P*, in atmospheres [atm]) using the van der Waals equation.

NOTE

The astronomical unit (AU) is the average distance from the Earth to the Sun.

14. One of the NAE Grand Challenges for Engineering is **Engineering the Tools of Scientific Discovery**. According to the NAE website: "Grand experiments and missions of exploration always need engineering expertise to design the tools, instruments, and systems that make it possible to acquire new knowledge about the physical and biological worlds."

Solar sails are a means of interplanetary propulsion using the radiation pressure of the sun to accelerate a spacecraft. The table contained in the starting Excel file shows the radiation pressure at the orbits of the eight planets.

Create a table showing the area in units of square meters of a solar sail needed to achieve various accelerations for various spacecraft masses at the distances from the sun of the various planets. Your solution should use data validation and VLOOKUP to select a planet and the corresponding radiation pressure. The columns of your table should list masses of the spacecraft (including the mass of the sail) ranging from 100 to 1,000 kilograms in increments of 100 kilograms. The rows should list accelerations from 0.0001 to 0.001 g in increments of 0.001 g, where "g" is the acceleration of Earth's gravity, 9.8 meters per second squared. All constants and conversion factors should be placed in individual cells using appropriate labels, and all formulae should reference these cells and NOT be directly coded into the formulae. You should use absolute, relative, and mixed addressing as appropriate.

15. A hands-on technology museum has hired you to do background research on the feasibility of a new activity to allow visitors to assemble their own ferrite core memory device—a technology in common use until the 1970s, and in specialized applications after that. The computers onboard the early space shuttle flights used core memory due to their durability, non-volatility, and resistance to radiation—core memory recovered from the wreck of the Challenger still functioned.

Ferrite core memory comprises numerous tiny ferrite rings ("cores") in a grid, each of which has either two or three wires threaded through it in a repeating pattern and can store a single bit, or binary digit—a 0 or a 1. Since the cores were typically on the order of one millimeter in diameter, workers had to assemble these under microscopes.

After investigating ferrite materials, you find several that would be suitable for fabrication of the cores. The museum staff has decided to have the visitors assemble a 4 × 4 array (16 cores—actual devices were MUCH larger) and anticipate that 2,500 people will assemble one of these over the course of the project. Assuming that the cores are each cylindrical rings with a hole diameter half that of the outside diameter of the ring and a thickness one-fourth the outside diameter, you need to know how many grams of ferrite beads you need to purchase with 10% extra beyond the specified amount for various core diameters and ferrite materials. You also wish to know the total cost for the beads.

Photo courtesy of W. Park

Using the provided online worksheet that includes a table of different ferrite material densities and costs, use data validation to select one of the materials from the list, then create a table showing the number of pounds of cores for core diameters of 1.2 to 0.7 millimeter in 0.1 millimeter increments as well as the total cost. For cores with a diameter less than 1 millimeter, there is a 50% manufacturing surcharge, thus the smallest cores cost more per gram. Include table entries for individual core volume and total volume of all cores. Your worksheet should resemble the example below.

	A	B	C	D	
1					
2					
3					
4			Cost of Ferrite Cores for Ha		
5					
6	Ferrite Compound	Specific Gravity	Cost per Gram [$/g]		Fer Comp
7	CMP C	3.73	$ 32.50		CM
8					CM
9	Sets needed	2500			CM
10	Cores per set	16			CM
11	Total Cores	40,000			CM
12	Total + 10%	44,000			CM
13					
14				Core Outs	
15			0.7	0.8	0
16	Volume of one core [mm^3]		0.0505	0.0754	0.1
17	Volume of all Cores [mm^3]		2,222	3,318	4,7
18	Mass of Cores [g]		8.29	12.37	17
19	Cost of Cores [$]		$ 404.11	$ 603.21	$ 8

16. A substance used to remove the few remaining molecules from a near vacuum by reacting with them or adsorbing them is called a getter. There are numerous materials used and several ways of deploying them within a system enclosing a vacuum, but here we will look at a common method used in vacuum tubes, once the workhorse of electronics but now relegated to high-end audio systems and other niche markets. In vacuum tubes, after the air is evacuated with a vacuum pump, getters are usually deposited on the inside of the tube, often at the top, by flash deposition.

Assume we are investigating getter materials for use in vacuum tubes with various inside diameters and hemispherical tops. The getter will be flash deposited on this hemispherical area.

We wish to set up a worksheet that will allow the user to select a getter material from a menu using data validation, and produce a table showing the number of moles of that material and the thickness of the deposited film for various masses of material from 20 to 300 milligram with 20 milligram increments and various tube inside diameters from 0.6 to 1.2 inches by 0.1 inch. Your final worksheet should appear similar to the example shown below. A starting worksheet including the table of possible materials and their specific gravities and atomic weights is available online.

Photo courtesy of W. Park

	A	B	C	D	E	
1						
2						
3						
4	Getter Material	Specific Gravity	Atomic Weight [g/mol]		Getter Material	
5	Sodium	0.968	22.99		Barium	
6					Aluminum	
7					Sodium	
8					Strontium	
9					Calcium	
10					Magnesium	
11						
12	Getter Thickness [μm]				Vacuum Tube	
13	Mass [mg]	Moles	0.6	0.7	0.8	
14	20	8.70E-04	56.6	41.6	31.9	
15	40	1.70E-03	113.3	83.2	63.7	
16	60	2.60E-03	169.9	124.8	95.6	

17. Create an Excel worksheet that will allow the user to type in the radius of a sphere and select from a drop-down menu the standard abbreviation for the units used.

Standard Unit Abbreviations						
Unit	meter	centimeter	millimeter	yard	foot	inch
Abbreviation	m	cm	mm	yd	ft	in

The volume of the sphere should then be calculated and expressed by the following units: cubic meters, cubic centimeters, cubic millimeters, liters, gallons, cubic yards, cubic feet, and cubic inches. Your worksheet should appear similar to the sample shown below, although you will probably need additional information in the worksheet not shown here.

		Volume							
Enter Radius Value Here	Enter Radius Units Here	m^3	cm^3	mm^3	liters	gallons	yd^3	ft^3	in^3
1.7	in	3.372E-04	3.372E+02	3.372E+05	3.372E-01	8.910E-02	4.416E-04	1.191E-02	2.058E+01

HINT

The built-in function =LEFT(text,[num_char]) returns a given number of charaters out of a text string, starting on the left side of the text string. For example, if cell A6 contains the word "Resistor", the formula "=LEFT(A6,3)" typed into cell B6 would return "Res". The formula "=RIGHT(A6,5)" would return "istor".

18. Most resistors are so small that the actual value would be difficult to read if printed on the resistor. Instead, colored bands denote the value of resistance in ohms. Anyone involved in constructing electronic circuits must become familiar with the color code, and with practice, one can tell at a glance what value a specific set of colors means. For the novice, however, trying to read color codes can be a bit challenging.

Begin with the worksheet template provided. In the worksheet, the user will enter a resistance value as the first two digits and a multiplier, both selected using a drop-down menu created through data validation. The resistance should be calculated as the first two digits times the multiplier.

The worksheet should automatically determine the First Digit and the Second Digit of the value entered in cell E7, using the built-in functions LEFT and RIGHT. The number of zeros should be determined using the lookup function.

Finally, the worksheet should determine the corresponding resistance band color using the Color Code table. The cells should automatically change to the correct color when the digits or multiplier are changed using conditional formatting.

For example, a resistance of 4,700 ohms [Ω] has first digit 4 (yellow), second digit 7 (violet), and 2 zeros following (red). A resistance of 56 Ω would be 5 (green), 6 (blue), and 0 zeros (black); 1,000,000 Ω is 1 (brown), 0 (black), and 5 zeros (green). Particularly note that if the second digit is zero, it does not count in the multiplier value. There are numerous explanations of the color code on the web if you need further information or examples.

	A	B	C	D	E	F	G	H	I	J	K	L	M	N
1														
2														
3														
4		Resistor Values				Enter Values Below							Color Code	
5		Standard	Multipliers	Zeros		First Two Digits	Multiplier		Resistance	First Digit	Second Digit	Number of zeros	Value	Color
6														
7		10	1	0		47	100		4700	4	7	2	0	Black
8		12	10	1						Yellow	Violet	Red	1	Brown
9		15	100	2									2	Red
10		18	1,000	3									3	Orange

19. Download the starting file, and complete the following commands using the data provided.

(a) Indicate the following using conditional formatting commands of your choice. Each condition below should appear in a unique format.
- Length shown in Column B is greater than 6 inches or less than 4 inches.
- Width shown in Column C is less than 2.5 inches.
- Inner radius shown in Column D is above average for the inner radius values.
- Outer radius shown in Column E is below average for the outer radius values.
- Volume shown in Column F is less than 10 cubic inches or greater than 20 cubic inches.

(b) For the following conditions, in Column H use an IF statement to indicate the Status:
- If length is less than 4 inches or width is less than 2.5 inches, list the status as "Too Small."
- Otherwise, if twice the inner radius is greater than the outer radius, list the status as "Off Center."
- Otherwise, if the volume is greater than 20 cubic inches or the mass is greater than 3,000 grams, list the status as "Too Large."
- Otherwise, if none of these conditions are true, leave the cell blank.

(c) For the following conditions, in Column J use an IF statement to indicate the Action Code:
- If the status is "Too Small" or "Too Large," list as action code as a numerical value of one.
- If the status is "Off Center," list as action code as a numerical value of two.
- If none of these conditions are met, list as action code as a numerical value of three.

(d) Use a conditional formatting icon set in Column I to indicate the following:
- Status as green for action code 3.
- Status as yellow for action code 2.
- Status as red for action code 1.

(e) Count the following items, showing the results somewhere above the data table. Be sure to indicate each counted item with an appropriate label.
- Indicate the number of items classified as each action code, such as how many items are listed as 1.
- Indicate number of parts when the length is greater than 6 inches.
- Indicate number of parts when the volume is less than 10 cubic inches or greater than 20 cubic inches. As a hint, use two "COUNT" functions and add them together.

(f) Sort the worksheet in the following order: Length, increasing and simultaneously then Outer Radius, decreasing. Be careful to select only the data and not the entire worksheet.

(g) Set the worksheet controls to be filtered in the header row. Filter the worksheet so only parts of length 2.80, 5.20, and 7.15 inches are shown.

CHAPTER 11
GRAPHICAL SOLUTIONS

Often, the best way to present technical data is through a "picture." But if not done properly, it is often the worst way to display information. As an engineer, you will have many opportunities to construct such pictures. If technical data are presented properly in a graph, it is often possible to explain a point in a concise and clear manner that is impossible any other way.

11.1 GRAPHING TERMINOLOGY

LEARN TO: Identify the abscissa and the ordinate of a graph
Identify the independent and dependent variables in a problem

MNEMONIC

Within the alphabet:

a comes before o

h comes before v

x comes before y

Therefore:

Abscissa = Horizontal axis

Ordinate = Vertical axis

Abscissa is the horizontal axis; **ordinate** is the vertical axis. Until now, you have probably referred to these as "x" and "y." This text uses the terms *abscissa* and *ordinate*, or *horizontal* and *vertical*, since x and y are only occasionally used as variables in engineering problems.

The **independent** variable is the parameter that is controlled or whose value is selected in the experiment; the **dependent** variable is the parameter that is measured corresponding to each set of selected values of the independent variable. Convention usually shows the independent variable on the abscissa and the dependent variable on the ordinate.

Data sets given in tabular form are commonly interpreted and graphed with the leftmost column or topmost row as the independent variable and the other columns or rows as the dependent variable(s). For the remainder of this text, if not specifically stated, assume that the abscissa variable is listed in the leftmost column or topmost row in a table of data values.

Time	Distance (d) [m]	
(t) [s]	Car 1	Car 2
Abscissa	Ordinate	Ordinate

Time (t) [s]		Abscissa
Distance	Car 1	Ordinate
(d) [m]	Car 2	Ordinate

11.2 PROPER PLOTS

LEARN TO:	Create a graph utilizing the "proper plot" rules

We call graphs constructed according to the following rules **proper plots**:

- **Label both axes clearly.** Three things are required unless the information is unavailable: category (e.g., Time), symbol used (t), and units [s]. Units should accompany all quantities when appropriate, enclosed in square brackets [ ].
- **Select scale increments (both axes) that are easy to read and interpolate between.** With a few exceptions, base your scale on increments of 1, 2, 2.5, and 5. You can scale each value by any power of 10 as necessary to fit the data. Avoid unusual increments (such as 3, 7, 15, or 6.5).

Increment	Sequence				
1	0	10	20	30	40
5	0.05	0.10	0.15	0.20	0.25
2.5	−2,500	0	2,500	5,000	7,500
2	6×10^{-5}	8×10^{-5}	1×10^{-4}	1.2×10^{-4}	1.4×10^{-4}

In this final case, reading is easier if the axis is labeled something like Time (t) [s] $\times 10^{-4}$ so that only the numbers 0.6, 0.8, 1.0, 1.2, and 1.4 show on the axis.

- **Provide horizontal and vertical gridlines** to make interpolation easier to aid the reader in determining actual numerical values from the graph.

    When minor gridlines are present, the reader should be able to easily determine the value of each minor increment. For example, examine the graphs shown in Figure 11-1. In which graph is it easier to determine the abscissa value for the blue point? In the graph on the left, the abscissa increment can easily be determined as 0.1 meters. In the graph on the right, it is more difficult to determine the increment as 0.08 meters.

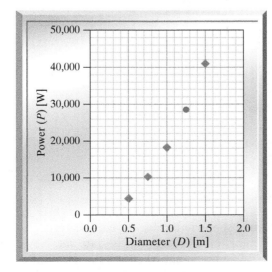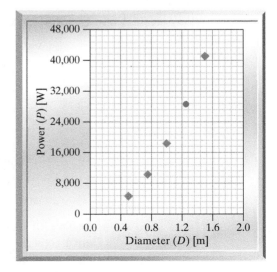

Figure 11-1 Example of importance of minor gridline spacing.

- **Provide a clear legend** describing each data set of multiple data sets shown. Do not use a legend for a single data set. Legends may be shown in a stand-alone box or captioned next to the data set. Both methods are shown in Figure 11-2.
- **Show measurements as symbols. Show calculated or theoretical values as lines.** Do not display symbols for calculated or theoretical values. A symbol shown on a graph indicates that an experimental measurement has been made (see Figure 11-3).

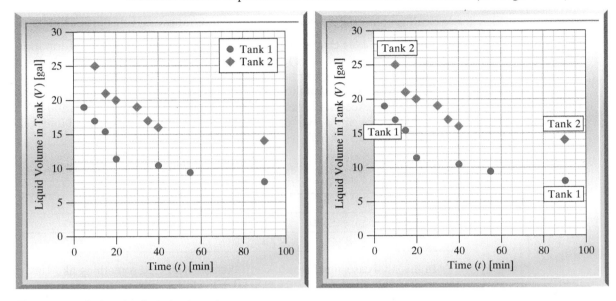

Figure 11-2 Options for displaying legends.

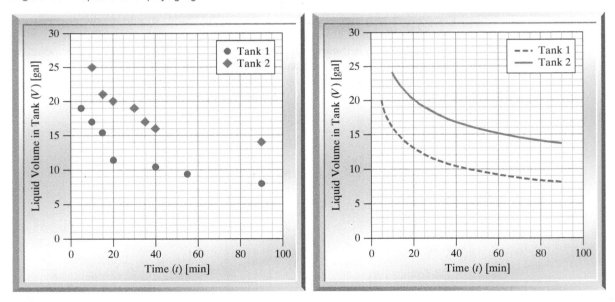

Figure 11-3 Illustration of experimental data (shown as points) versus theoretical data (shown as lines).

- **Use a different symbol shape and color** for each experimental data set and a different line style and color for each theoretical data set. **Never use yellow and other light pastel colors.** Remember that when graphs are photocopied, all colored lines become black lines. Some colors disappear when copied and are hard to see in a projected image. For example, in Figure 11-4, left, it is much easier to distinguish between the different lines than in the figure on the right.

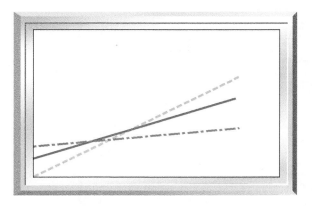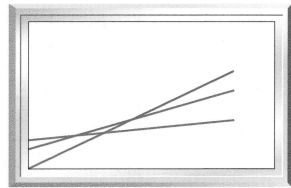

Figure 11-4 Example of importance of different line types.

- When placing a graph within a document:
  - **Produce graphs in portrait orientation** whenever possible within a document. Portrait orientation does not necessarily mean that the graph is distorted to be taller than it is wide; it means that readers can study the graph without turning the page sideways.
  - **Be sure the graph is large enough to be easily read.** The larger the graph, the more accurate the extracted information.
  - **Caption with a brief description.** The restating of "*d* versus *t*" or "distance versus time" or even "the relationship between distance and time" does not constitute a proper caption. The caption should give information about the graph to allow the graph to stand alone, without further explanation. It should include information about the problem that does not appear elsewhere on the graph. For example, instead of stating "distance versus time," better choices would be "Lindbergh's Flight across the Atlantic," "The Flight of Voyager I," or "Walking between Classes across Campus, Fall 2008." When including a graph as part of a written report, place the caption below the graph.

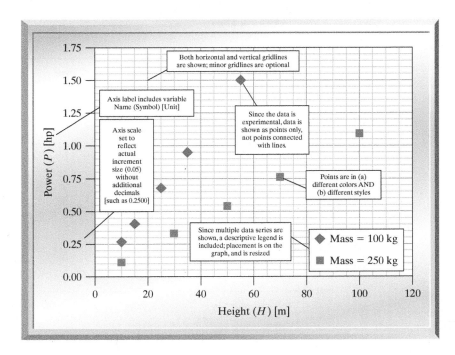

Figure 11-5 Example of a proper plot, showing multiple experimental data sets.

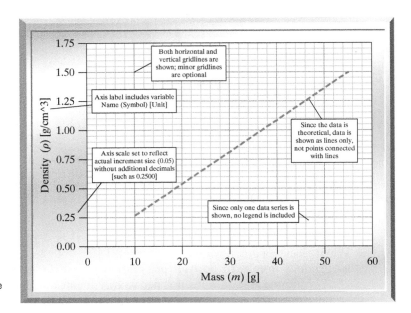

Figure 11-6 Example of a proper plot, showing a single theoretical data set.

Figure 11-7 below is an example of a poorly constructed plot. Some problems with this plot are listed below:

- It is a plot of distance versus time, but is it the distance of a car, a snail, or a rocket? What are the units of distance—inches, meters, or miles? What are the units of time—seconds, days, or years? Is time on the horizontal or vertical axis?
- Two data sets are shown, or are there three? Why is the one data set connected with a line? Is it a trendline? Is the same data set shown in the triangles? What do the shaded and open triangles represent—different objects, different trials of the same object, or modifications to the same object?
- Lack of gridlines and strange axis increments makes it difficult to interpolate between values. What is the location of the blue dot?

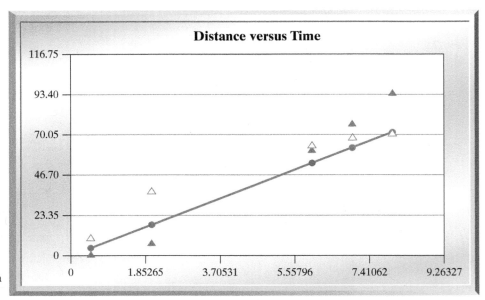

Figure 11-7 Example of a poorly constructed graph.

● **EXAMPLE 11-1**

When attempting to stop a car, a driver must consider both the reaction time and the braking time. The data are taken from www.highwaycode.gov.uk. Create a proper plot of these experimental data, with speed on the abscissa.

Vehicle Speed (v) [mph]	Distance	
	Reaction (d_r) [m]	Braking (d_b) [m]
20	6	6
30	9	14
40	12	24
50	15	38
60	18	55
70	21	75

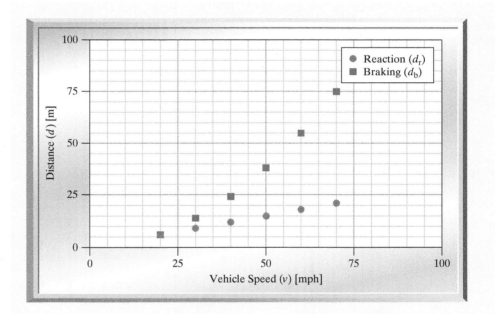

Figure 11-8 At various speeds, the necessary reaction time and braking time needed to stop a car.

● **EXAMPLE 11-2**

Ohm's law describes the relationship between voltage, current, and resistance within an electrical circuit, given by the equation $V = IR$, where V is the voltage [V], I is the current [A], and R is the resistance [Ω]. Construct a proper plot of the theoretical voltage on the ordinate versus current, determined from the equation, for the following resistors: 3,000 Ω, 2,000 Ω, and 1,000 Ω. Allow the current to vary from 0 to 0.05 A.

Note that while the lines were probably generated from several actual points along each line for each resistor, the points are not shown; only the resulting line is shown since the values were developed from theory and not from experiment. If you create a plot like this by hand, you would first put in a few points per data set, then draw the lines and erase the points so that they are not shown on the final graph.

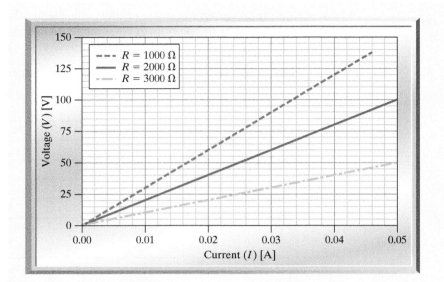

Figure 11-9 Ohm's law determined for a simple circuit to compare three resistor values.

COMPREHENSION CHECK 11-1

In the following experimental data plot, identify violations of the proper plot rules.

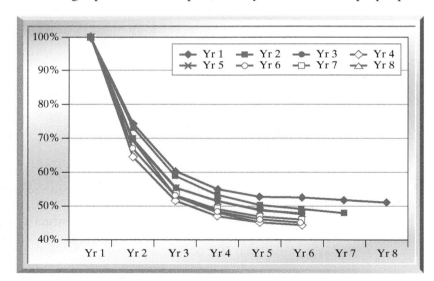

**COMPREHENSION
CHECK** 11-2

In the following experimental data plot, identify violations of the proper plot rules.

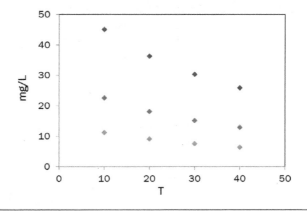

**COMPREHENSION
CHECK** 11-3

In the following theoretical data plot, identify violations of the proper plot rules.

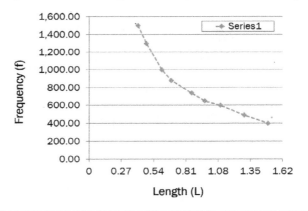

**COMPREHENSION
CHECK** 11-4

In the following theoretical data plot, identify violations of the proper plot rules.

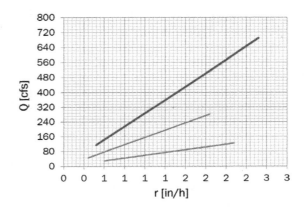

11.3 AVAILABLE GRAPH TYPES IN EXCEL

LEARN TO: Recognize the different types of graph available in Excel, and when to use each type
Understand the difference between a scatter plot and a line plot
Understand the concept of categorical data

The following is an example of the level of knowledge of Excel needed to proceed. *If you are not able to quickly recreate the following exercise in Excel, please review graphing basics in the appendix materials online before proceeding.*

Two graphs are given here; they describe the draining of tanks through an orifice in the bottom. When the tank contains a lot of liquid, the pressure on the bottom is large and the tank empties at a higher rate than when there is less liquid. The first graph shows actual data obtained from two different tanks. These data are given in the table below. The second plot shows curves (developed from theoretical equations) for two tanks. The equations for these curves are also given. Create these graphs exactly as shown, with matching legend, axis limits, gridlines, axis labels, symbol and line types and colors.

Experimental data for first graph:

Time (*t*) [min]	5	10	15	20	40	55	90
Volume Tank #1 (*V1*) [gal]	19.0	17.0	15.5	11.5	10.5	9.5	8.0

Time (*t*) [min]	10	15	20	30	35	40	90
Volume Tank #2 (*V2*) [gal]	25	21	20	19	17	16	14

Theoretical equations for second graph (with *t* in minutes):

- Tank 1: Volume remaining in tank 1 [gal] $V = 33\, t^{-0.31}$
- Tank 2: Volume remaining in tank 2 [gal] $V = 44\, t^{-0.26}$

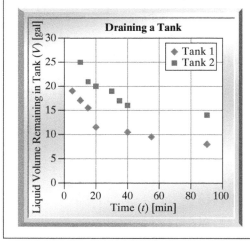

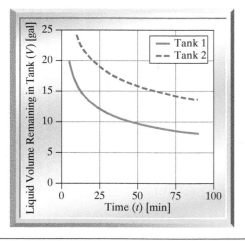

You can create many different types of charts in Excel. Usually, you will only be concerned with a few main types, shown in Table 11-1.

Table 11-1 **Common chart types available in Excel**

A **scatter plot** is a graph that numerically represents two-dimensional (2-D) theoretical or experimental data along the abscissa and ordinate of the graph. It is most commonly used with scientific data. To create a scatter plot, you specify each pair in the graph by selecting two identically sized columns or rows of data that represent the (x, y) values of each experimental symbol or point on a theoretical expression.

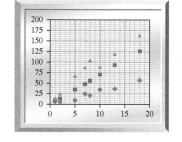

A scatter plot can be shown as discrete data points (used to show experimental data) or lines (used to show theoretical expressions). Excel will also show discrete data points connected by lines; the authors of this text do not find this type of chart particularly useful and do not discuss this type of chart.

The step size of both axes is evenly spaced as determined by the user and can be customized to show all or part of a data set plotted on a graph.

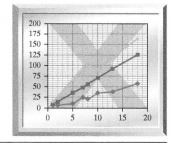

Use a scatter plot to visualize your data when you want to:

- Observe mathematical phenomena and relationships among different data sets
- Interpolate or extrapolate information from data sets
- Determine a mathematical model for a data set, using trendlines

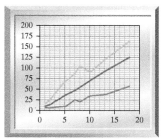

A **line plot** is a graph that visualizes a one-dimensional (1-D) set of theoretical or experimental data.

A line plot can be shown as points connected by lines, lines only, or in three dimensions (3-D).

The y-axis values of a line plot are spaced as determined by the user; however, the x-axis of a line plot is not. As shown in the graphs to the right, a line plot places each discrete element evenly along the x-axis regardless of the actual step-spacing of the data.

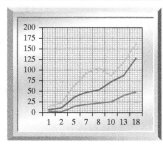

Use a line plot to visualize your data when you want to:

- Display any evenly spaced data
- Visualize time-series data taken at even intervals
- Display categorical data (e.g., years, months, days of the week)

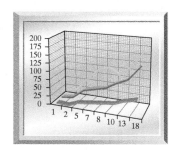

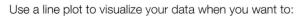

(continued)

Table 11-1 Common chart types available in Excel (*continued*)

A **column graph** is used for displaying various types of categorical data.

The *y*-axis increments are spaced evenly, but the *x*-axis spacing has no meaning since the items are discrete categories. As a rule of thumb, a column graph can be used to represent the same information shown on a line plot.

A column plot can be shown as bars, cylinders, or cones; as a clustered group or stacked; or in 1-D or 3-D.

Use a column graph to visualize your data when you want to:

- Display any categorical data
- Observe differences between categories

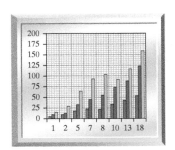

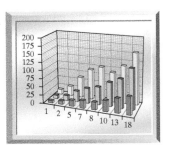

A **bar graph** is identical to a column graph, with the *x*- and *y*-categories reversed; the *x*-category appears on the ordinate and the *y*-category appears on the abscissa. Because of the similarity, only column graphs are covered in this text.

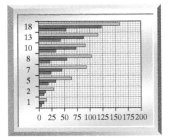

A **pie graph** is used on a single column or row of nonnegative numbers, graphed as a percentage of the whole. It is typically used for categorical data, with a maximum of seven categories possible.

A pie graph can be shown in 1-D or 3-D, with either the percentages or the raw data displayed with the category names.

Use a pie graph to visualize your data when you want to:

- Display categorical data as part of a whole
- Observe differences between categories

Pie charts are similar in form to column and bar charts; they are not covered in this text.

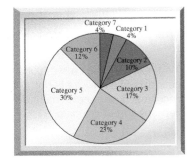

11.4 GRAPH INTERPRETATION

> **LEARN TO:** Calculate the area under a curve and describe its meaning
> Calculate the slope of a line and describe its meaning
> Understand the technical terms derivative and integral, with respect to graph interpretation

A graph conveys a great deal of information in a small amount of space. By being able to interpret a graph, you can infer the story behind the lines. In addition to the value of the slope of the line, the shape of the line contains useful information.

● **EXAMPLE 11-3**

Hourglass. *Courtesy of Thayer's Gifts, Greenwood, SC. Photo: W. Park*

Assume your company is designing a series of hourglasses for the novelty market, such as tourist attraction sales. You have determined that your prototype hourglass allows 275 cubic millimeters of sand to fall from the top to the bottom chamber each second. What volume of sand would be needed if the "hourglass" really measured a period of 10 minutes?

There are 60 seconds per minute, thus 10 minutes is 600 seconds. The sand flows at a rate of 275 cubic millimeters per second for 600 seconds, thus the total volume of sand is 165,000 cubic millimeters.

$$(275 \text{ mm}^3/\text{s})(600 \text{ s}) = 165,000 \text{ mm}^3 \text{ or } 165 \text{ cm}^3$$

Let us consider the same problem graphically. Since the flow rate of sand is constant, a graph of flow rate with respect to time is simply a horizontal line. Now consider the area under the flow rate line. The area of a rectangle is simply the width times the height. If we make a point of using the units on each axis as well as the numeric values, we get

$$((275-0) \text{ mm}^3/\text{s})((10-0) \text{ min}*60 \text{ s/min}) = (275 \text{ mm}^3/\text{s})(600 \text{ s}) = 165,000 \text{ mm}^3$$

This is exactly the same result we got above. In other words, the volume of sand is the area under the line.

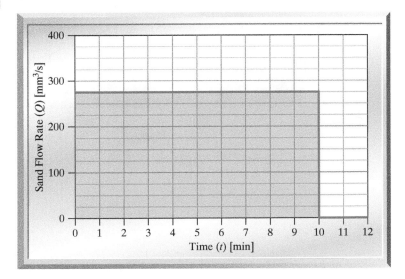

Figure 11-10 Sand in an hourglass.

This seems like much more effort than the straightforward calculation we did originally, so why should we bother with the graph? Let us look at a slightly more complicated situation.

● **EXAMPLE 11-4**

Assume a container is being filled with sand. Initially, the sand enters the container at 100 grams per second, but the rate of filling decreases linearly for 20 seconds, then stops. The final rate of sand into the container just before it stops is 25 grams per second. How much sand enters the container during the 20 seconds involved?

Let us compute the area under the line shown in Figure 11-11, being sure to include units, and see what we get. We can break this area into a rectangle and a triangle, which will make the calculation a bit easier.

■ *The area of the rectangle at the base (below $\dot{m}$ = 25) is ((25−0) grams/second) ((20−0) seconds) = 500 grams.*
■ *The area of the triangle is 0.5 ((100−25) grams per second) ((20−0) seconds) = 750 grams.*
■ *The total area is 1,250 grams, the total mass of sand in the container after 20 seconds.*

Again, many of you have realized that there is a much easier way to obtain this result. Simply find the average flow rate (in this case: 62.5 grams per second) and multiply by the total time.

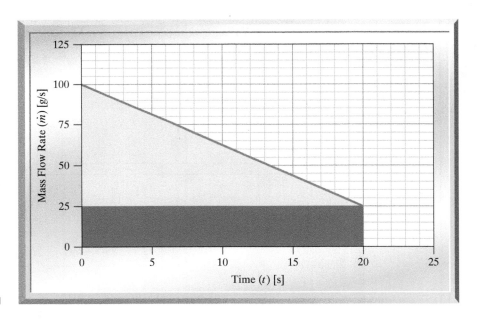

Figure 11-11

However, what if the parameter plotted on the vertical axis was not a simple straight line? Consider the following example.

● **EXAMPLE 11-5**

What if the parameter plotted on the vertical axis was not a simple straight line or straight-line segments? For example, the flow rate of liquid out of a pipe at the bottom of a cylindrical barrel follows an exponential relationship. Assume the flow rate out of a tank is given by $Q = 4\,e^{-t/8}$ gallons per minute. A graph of this is shown in Figure 11-12.

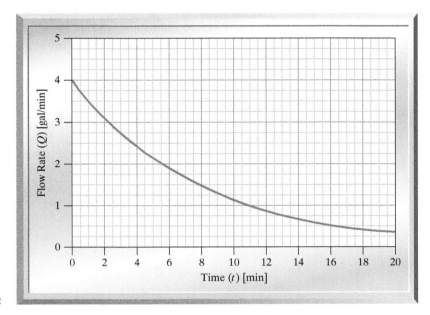

Figure 11-12

Although we might be able to make a reasonable estimate of the area under the curve (the total volume of water that has flowed out of the tank) simple algebra is insufficient to arrive at an accurate value. Those of you who have already studied integral calculus should know how to solve this problem. However, some students using this text may not have progressed this far in math, so we will have to leave it at that. It is enough to point out that there are innumerable problems in many engineering contexts that require calculus to solve. To succeed in engineering, you must have a basic understanding of calculus.

● **EXAMPLE 11-6**

From the past experience of driving an automobile down a highway, you should under-stand the concepts relating acceleration, velocity, and distance. As you slowly press the gas pedal toward the floor, the car accelerates, causing both the speed and the distance to increase. Once you reach a cruising speed, you turn on the cruise control. Now, the car is no longer accelerating and travels at a constant velocity while increasing in dis-tance. These quantities are related through the following equations:

$$\text{velocity} = (\text{acceleration})(\text{time}) \quad v = (a)(t)$$
$$\text{distance} = (\text{velocity})(\text{time}) \qquad d = (v)(t)$$

If we create a graph of velocity versus time, the form of the equation tells us that acceleration is the slope of the line. Likewise, a graph of distance versus time has velocity as the slope of the line.

However, if we had a graph of velocity versus time and we wanted to determine distance, how can we do this? The distance is determined by how fast we are traveling times how long we are traveling at that velocity; we can find this by determining the area under the curve of velocity versus time. Likewise, if we had a graph of acceleration versus time, we could determine the velocity from the area under the curve. In technical terms, the quantity determined by the slope is referred to as the **derivative**; the quantity determined by the area under the curve is referred to as the **integral**.

In the graph shown in Figure 11-13, we drive our car along the road at a constant velocity of 60 miles per hour [mph]. After 1.5 hours, how far have we traveled?

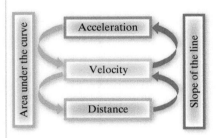

The area under the curve, shown by the rectangular box, is:

$$\text{Area of the rectangle} = (\text{height of rectangle})(\text{width of rectangle})$$
$$= (60 - 0\,\text{mph})(1.5 - 0\,\text{h})$$
$$= 90\,\text{miles}$$

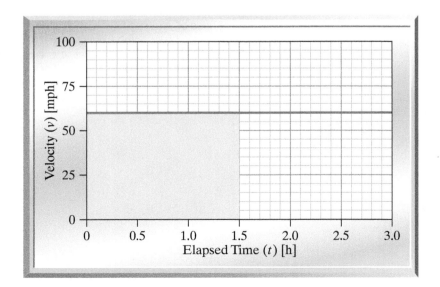

Figure 11-13 Example of distance calculation from area under velocity versus time graph.

COMPREHENSION CHECK 11-5

Use the graph to answer the following questions.

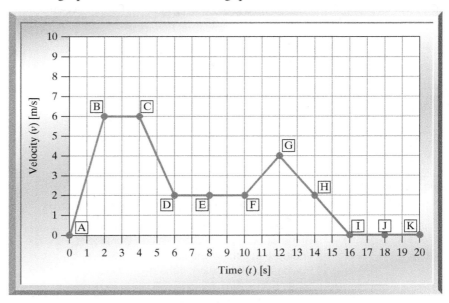

(a) What is the distance traveled by the vehicle when it reaches point C?
(b) What is the distance traveled by the vehicle when it reaches point F?

11.5 MEANING OF LINE SHAPES

LEARN TO: Recognize linear and non-linear curves, and interpret the slope and area of the curve
Understand the special linear cases, vertical lines and horizontal lines
Understand the physical meanings of the four combinations of curves with concavity

In addition to the value of the slope of the line, the shape of the line contains useful information. In Figure 11-13, the speed is shown as a horizontal line. This implies that it has a constant value; it is not changing over time. The slope of this line is zero, indicating that the acceleration is zero. Table 11-2 contains the various types of curve shapes and their physical meanings.

Table 11-2 What do the lines on a graph mean?

If the graph shows a . . .	. . . it means that the dependent variable . . .	Sketch
horizontal line	The variable is not changing. The slope (the derivative) is zero. The area under the curve (the integral) is increasing at a constant rate.	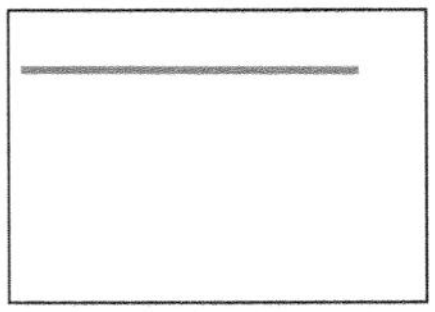
vertical line	The variable has changed "instantaneously." The slope (the derivative) is "undefined" (infinite). The area under the curve is undefined (zero).	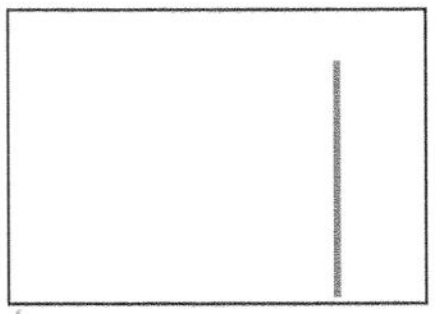
straight line, positive or negative slope neither horizontal nor vertical	The variable is changing at a constant rate. The slope (the derivative) is constant and non-zero. The area under the line (the integral) is increasing. If the slope is positive, the rate of increase is increasing. If the slope is negative, the rate of increase is decreasing. If the negative slope line goes below zero, the area will begin to decrease.	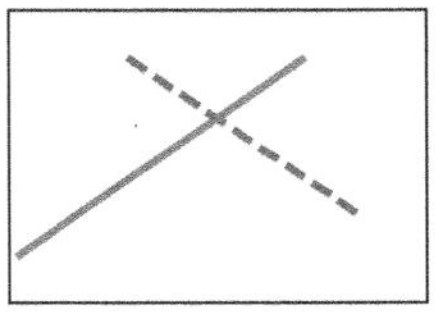
curved line concave up, increasing trend	The variable is increasing at an increasing rate. The slope of the curve (the derivative) is positive and increasing. The area under the curve (the integral) is increasing at an increasing rate.	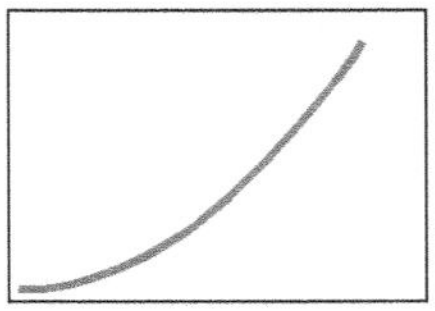
curved line concave down, increasing trend	The variable is increasing at a decreasing rate. The slope of the curve (the derivative) is positive and decreasing. The area under the curve (the integral) is increasing at an increasing rate.	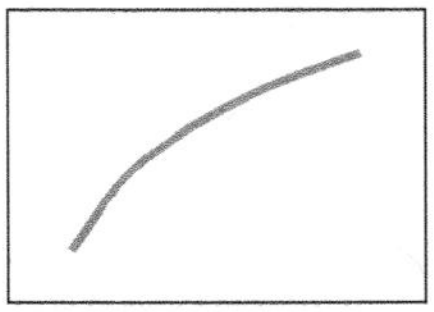
curved line concave up, decreasing trend	The variable is decreasing at a decreasing rate. The slope of the curve (the derivative) is negative with a decreasing magnitude. The area under the curve (the integral) is increasing at a decreasing rate.	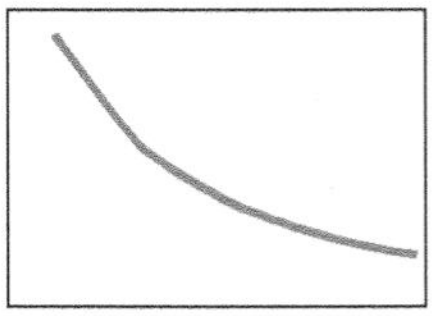
curved line concave down, decreasing trend	The variable is decreasing at an increasing rate. The slope of the curve (the derivative) is negative with an increasing magnitude. The area under the curve (the integral) is increasing at a decreasing rate.	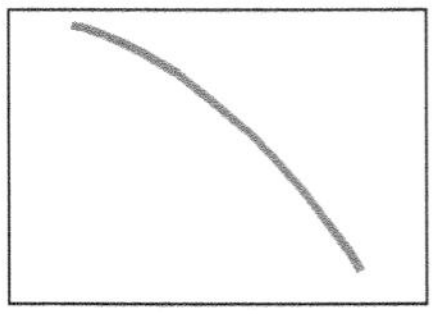

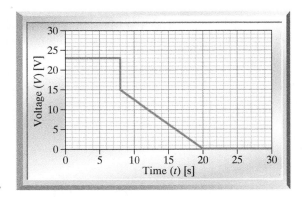

Figure 11-14

In Figure 11-14, the voltage is constant from time = 0 to 8 seconds, as indicated by the horizontal line at 23 volts. At time = 8 seconds, the voltage changes instantly to 15 volts, as indicated by the vertical line. Between time = 8 seconds and 20 seconds, the voltage decreases at a constant rate, as indicated by the straight line, and reaches 0 volts at time = 20 seconds, where it remains constant.

In Figure 11-15, the force on the spring increases at an increasing rate from time = 0 until 2 minutes, then remains constant for 1 minute, after which it increases at a decreasing rate until time = 5 minutes. After 5 minutes, the force remains constant at about 6.8 newtons.

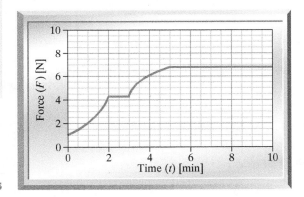

Figure 11-15

The height of a blimp is shown in Figure 11-16. The height decreases at an increasing rate for 5 minutes, then remains constant for 2 minutes. From time = 7 to 10 minutes, its height decreases at a decreasing rate. At time = 10 minutes, the height remains constant at 10 meters.

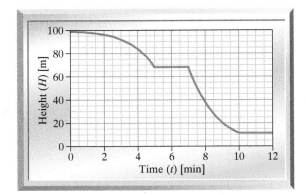

Figure 11-16

● EXAMPLE 11-7 The Mars Rover travels slowly across the Martian terrain collecting data, yielding the following velocity profile. Use this graph to answer the following questions.

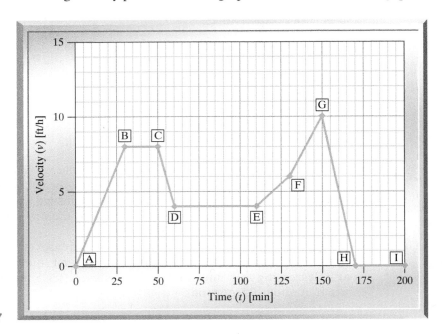

Figure 11-17

Between points (D) and (E), the acceleration of the Rover is _____.

The velocity profile between points (D) and (E) is flat, indicating that the velocity is not changing. Acceleration is the derivative of velocity with respect to time; so acceleration is ZERO.

If the graph shows a . . .	. . . it means that the dependent variable . . .	Sketch
horizontal line	The variable is not changing.	
	The slope (the derivative) is zero.	
	The area under the curve (the integral) is increasing at a constant rate.	

The value of acceleration of the Rover between points (G) and (H) is _____ ft/h².

Acceleration is the slope of the line of the velocity versus time graph. The slope between (G) and (H) is found by:

$$((10-0)\ ft/h)/(((170-150)\ min)*60\ min/h) = 30\ ft/h^2$$

Between points (E) and (F), the distance traveled by the Rover is _____.

The velocity profile between points (E) and (F) is increasing at a constant rate. Distance is the integral of velocity with respect to time; so the distance is INCREASING at an INCREASING rate.

If the graph shows a . . .	. . . it means that the dependent variable . . .	Sketch
straight line, positive or negative slope neither horizontal nor vertical	The variable is changing at a constant rate. The slope (the derivative) is constant and non-zero. The area under the line (the integral) is increasing. If the slope is positive, the rate of increase is increasing.	

The distance the Rover has traveled from the start of the trip to point (C) is _____ ft.

Distance is the area under the curve of the velocity versus time graph. The area defined from point (A) to point (C) can be divided into two geometric shapes:

*From (A) to (B) = Area is a Triangle = 1/2 base * height*
Area #1 = 1/2 (8−0) ft/h (30−0) min* 1h/60 min = 2 ft*

*From (B) to (C) = Area is a Rectangle = base * height*
Area #2 = (8−0) ft/h (50−30) min * 1h/60 min = 2.67 ft*

Total distance = Area #1 + Area #2 = 2 ft + 2.67 ft = 4.67 ft

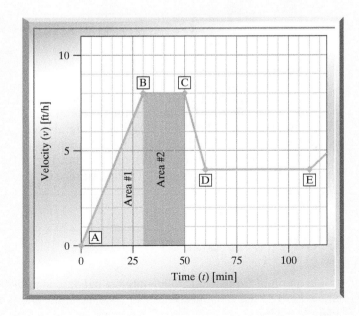

Figure 11-18

**COMPREHENSION
CHECK 11-6**

Use the graph to answer the following questions. Choose from the following answers:

1. Zero
2. Positive and constant
3. Positive and increasing
4. Positive and decreasing
5. Negative and constant
6. Negative with increasing magnitude
7. Negative with decreasing magnitude
8. Cannot be determined from information given

NOTE

The rate of change (derivative) of acceleration is called JERK.

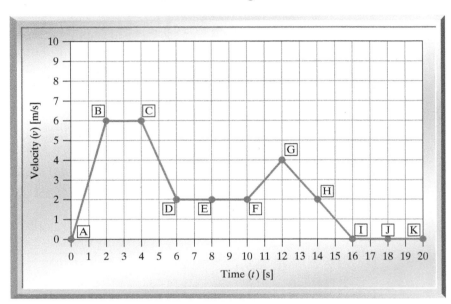

(a) Between points (A) and (B), the acceleration is ___
(b) Between points (B) and (C), the acceleration is ___
(c) Between points (C) and (D), the acceleration is ___
(d) Between points (D) and (E), the distance is ___
(e) Between points (F) and (G), the distance is ___
(f) Between points (G) and (H), the distance is ___

11.6   GRAPHICAL SOLUTIONS

LEARN TO: Use a graph of expressions to identify the overlapping points
Show fixed costs, variable cost, sales price, revenue, and profit graphically
Identify the breakeven point of an economic process (if one exists)

When you have two equations containing the same two variables, it is sometimes desirable to find values of the variables that satisfy both equations. Most of you have studied methods for solving simultaneous linear equations—however, most of these methods apply only to linear equations and do not work if one or both of the equations is nonlinear. It also becomes problematic if you are working with experimental data.

For systems of two equations, or data sets in two variables, you can use a graphical method to determine the value or values that satisfy both. The procedure is simply to graph the two equations and visually determine where the curves intersect. This may be nowhere, at one point, or at several points.

● **EXAMPLE 11-8**

We assume that the current through two electromagnets is given by the following equations

$$\text{Electromagnet A: } I = 5t + 6$$
$$\text{Electromagnet B: } I = -3t + 12$$

We want to determine when the value of the current through the electromagnets is equal.

Graphing both equations gives Figure 11-19. Recall that data derived from a theoretical equation is shown as lines only, without any points.

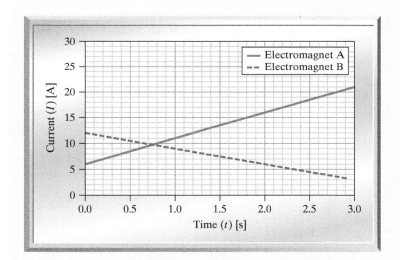

Figure 11-19

The two lines cross at time 0.75 seconds (approximately), and the current at this time is approximately 9.7 amperes. The larger we make this graph and the more gridlines we include, the more accurately we can determine the solution.

Solution: $t = 0.75$ seconds, $I = 9.7$ amperes.

Using Graphs in Economic Analysis

Breakeven analysis determines the quantity of product a company must make before they begin to earn a profit. Two types of costs are associated with manufacturing: fixed and variable. **Fixed costs** include equipment purchases, nonhourly employee salaries, insurance, mortgage or rent on the building, etc., or "money we must spend just to open the doors." **Variable costs** depend on the production volume, such as material costs, hourly employee salaries, and utility costs. The more product produced, the higher the variable costs become.

Total cost = Fixed cost + Variable cost * Amount produced

The product is sold at a **selling price**, creating **revenue**.

Revenue = Selling price * Amount sold

Any excess revenue remaining after all production costs have been paid is **profit**. Until the company reaches the breakeven point, they are operating at a **loss** (negative profit), where the money they are bringing in from sales does not cover their expenses.

Profit = Revenue − Total cost

The **breakeven point** occurs when the revenue and total cost lines cross, or the point where profit is zero (not negative or positive). These concepts are perhaps best illustrated through an example.

● **EXAMPLE 11-9**

Let the amount of product we produce be G [gallons per year]. Consider the following costs:

- Fixed cost: $1 million
- Variable cost: 10 cents/gallon of G
- Selling price: 25 cents/gallon of G

Plot the total cost and the revenue versus the quantity produced. Determine the amount of G that must be produced to breakeven. Assume we sell everything we make.

The plot of these two functions is shown in Figure 11-20. The breakeven point occurs when the two graphs cross, at a production capacity of 6.7 million gallons of G.

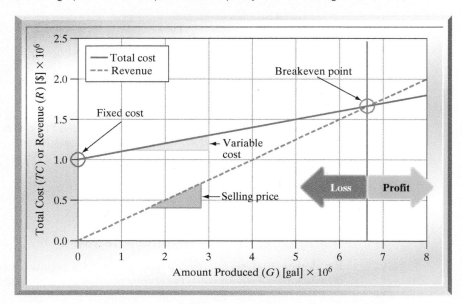

Figure 11-20 Breakeven analysis definitions.

● **EXAMPLE 11-10**

In creating electrical parts for a Mars excursion module, you anticipate the costs of production shown in the graph. In your analysis, you assume the following costs of production:

- Labor cost = $1.20 / part
- Energy cost = $0.60 / part

Use this graph to answer the following questions.

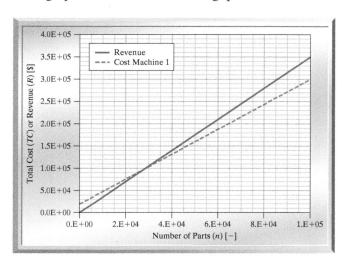

Figure 11-21

What is the material cost per part?

Variable cost is the slope of the total cost line.
   *Total cost = Fixed cost + Variable cost * Amount produced*

$$Slope\ total\ cost = \frac{3E5 - 2E4}{1E5 - 0} = \frac{\$2.80}{part}$$

The material cost is one of three costs that make up the variable cost.
Variable cost = Material cost + Labor cost + Energy cost
Solving for Material cost:

$$Material\ cost = \frac{\$2.80}{part} - \frac{\$1.20}{part} - \frac{\$0.60}{part} = \frac{\$1.00}{part}$$

What is the selling price of each part?

Selling price is the slope of the revenue line.
   *Revenue = Selling price * Amount sold*

$$Slope\ revenue = \frac{3.5E5 - 0}{1E5 - 0} = \frac{\$3.50}{part}$$

You decide to consider a second option, with a fixed cost of $50,000 and a variable cost of $2.00 / part. Draw the total cost line for Machine #2 on the graph.

To draw the total cost line, two points are needed if the line is linear.
   At n = 0 parts, the total cost = fixed cost = $50,000.
   At n = 100,000 parts,
   the total cost = $50,000 + ($2.00/part) (100,000 parts) = $250,000.

To ensure the line is linear, it is a good idea to test at least one more point to make sure if falls along this line.

At n = 40,000 parts,
the total cost = $50,000 + ($2.00/part)(40,000 parts) = $130,000.

Connecting a line through these points yields the green, dot-dash line shown below.

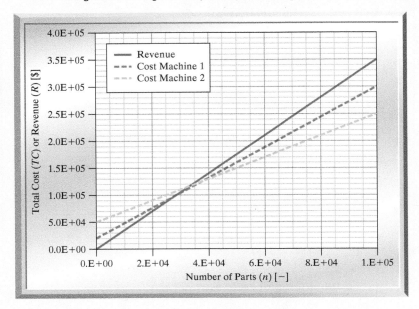

Figure 11-22

What is the profit of each machine at 80,000 parts?

Profit is the difference between the cost and revenue lines. If the cost line is above the revenue line, the process is operating at a loss. If the cost line is below the revenue line, the process is operating at a profit. Examining the graph at 80,000 parts, both cost lines are below the revenue line, so both machines are operating at a profit.

The difference for Machine 1 is 4 minor gridlines. Each ordinate minor gridline on the graph is $1E4. The profit for Machine 1 is $40,000.

The difference for Machine 2 is 7 minor gridlines. The profit for Machine 2 is $70,000.

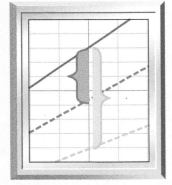

Figure 11-23

If the selling price is decreased by $0.50 per part, what will happen to the breakeven point for Machine #1?

(A) It will move to the left, indicating the breakeven will occur sooner than originally shown

(B) It will move to the right, indicating the breakeven will occur later than originally shown

(C) It will not change the breakeven point

In the revenue line, the larger the slope, the higher the angle of line, the higher the selling price. A decrease in selling price translates graphically to a slope at a lower angle. If the slope of the revenue line decreases, the number of parts required to breakeven will increase, shifting the breakeven point to the right.

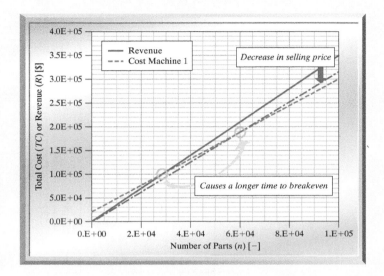

Figure 11-24

COMPREHENSION CHECK 11-7

You are working for a tire manufacturer, producing wire to be used in the tire as a strengthening agent. You are considering implementing a new machining system, and you must present a breakeven analysis to your boss. You develop the graph, showing two possible machines that you can buy.

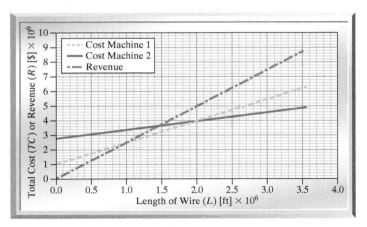

(a) Which machine has a higher fixed cost?
(b) Which machine has a lower variable cost?
(c) How much wire must be produced on Machine 1 to breakeven?
(d) If you make 3 million feet of wire, which machine will yield the highest profit?
(e) Which machine has the lower breakeven point?

You want to install a solar panel system on your home. According to one source, if you install a 40-square foot system, the cost curve is shown in the graph.

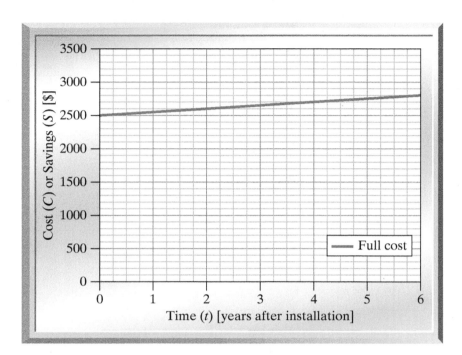

(a) List the fixed cost and the variable cost for this system.

(b) If the source claims that you can breakeven in 3.5 years, how much savings are you generating per year (or, what is the slope of the savings curve or the "revenue" that you generate by installing the system)? Draw the "revenue" curve on the graph and use it to answer this question.

(c) If you receive a Federal Tax Credit for "going green," you can save 30% on the initial fixed cost. With this savings, how long does it take to breakeven? Draw this operating cost curve, labeled "Credit Cost" on the graph and use it to answer this question.

(d) With the new tax credit, at what time do you reach a savings of $1000?

● **EXAMPLE 11-11**

The semiconductor diode is sort of like a one-way valve for electric current: it allows current to flow in one direction, but not the other. In reality, the behavior of a diode is considerably more complicated. In general, the current through a diode can be found with the **Shockley equation**,

$$I = I_0 \left(e^{\frac{V_D}{nV_T}} - 1 \right)$$

where I is the current through the diode in amperes; I_0 is the saturation current in amperes, constant for any specific diode; V_D is the voltage across the diode in volts; and V_T is the thermal voltage in volts, approximately 0.026 volts at room temperature. The emission coefficient, n, is dimensionless and constant for any specific diode; it usually has a value between 1 and 2.

The simple circuit shown has a diode and resistor connected to a battery. For this circuit, the current through the resistor can be given by:

$$I = \frac{V - V_D}{R}$$

where I is the current through the resistor in milliamperes [mA], V is the battery voltage in volts [V], V_D is the voltage across the diode in volts, and R is the resistance in ohms [Ω].

In this circuit, the diode and resistor are in series, which implies that the current through them is the same. We have two equations for the same parameter (current), both of which are a function of the same parameter (diode voltage). We can find a solution to these two equations, and thus the current in the circuit, by graphing both equations and finding the point of intersection. For convenience of scale, the current is expressed in milliamperes rather than amperes.

Plot these two equations for the following values and determine the current.

$$I_0 = 0.01 \text{ mA}$$
$$V = 3 \text{ V}$$
$$R = 24 \ \Omega$$
$$nV_T = 0.04 \text{ V}$$

NOTE

This example demonstrates the graphical solution of simultaneous equations when one of the equations is nonlinear. We do not expect you to know how to perform the involved circuit analyses. Those of you who eventually study electronics will learn these techniques in considerable detail.

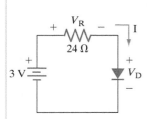

The point of intersection shown in Figure 11-25 is at $V_D = 0.64$ V and $I = 100$ mA; thus, the current in the circuit is 100 mA or 0.1 A.

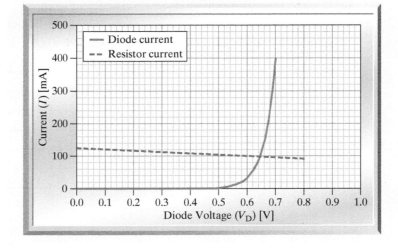

Figure 11-25

In-Class Activities

For questions ICA 11-1 to ICA 11-9, your instructor will determine if you should complete this question by hand or using Excel. If you must complete this problem by hand, a blank graph has been provided online.

ICA 11-1

Joule's first law relates the heat generated to current flowing in a conductor. It is named after James Prescott Joule, the same person for whom the unit of Joule is named. Use the following experimental data to create a scatter graph of the power (P, on the ordinate) and current (I, on the abscissa).

Current (I) [A]	0.50	1.25	1.50	2.25	3.00	3.20	3.50
Power (P) [W]	1.20	7.50	11.25	25.00	45.00	50.00	65.00

ICA 11-2

Data for a wind turbine is shown below. Use the following experimental data to create a scatter plot of the power (P, on the ordinate) and velocity (v, on the abscissa).

Velocity (v) [m/s]	5	8	12	15	19	23
Power (P) [W]	15	60	180	400	840	1500

ICA 11-3

There is a large push in the United States currently to convert from incandescent light bulbs to compact fluorescent bulbs (CFLs). The lumen [lm] is the SI unit of luminous flux (LF), a measure of the perceived power of light. To test the power usage, you run an experiment and measure the following data. Create a proper plot of these experimental data, with electrical consumption (EC) on the ordinate and LF on the abscissa.

Luminous Flux [lm]	Electrical Consumption [W]	
	Incandescent 120 V	Compact Fluorescent
80	16	
200		4
400	38	8
600	55	
750	68	13
1,250		18
1,400	105	19

ICA 11-4

Your team has designed three tennis ball launchers, and you have run tests to determine which launcher best meets the project criteria. Each launcher is set to three different launch angles, and the total distance the ball flies through the air is recorded. These experimental data are summarized in the table. Plot all three sets of data on a scatter plot, showing one data set for each of the three launchers on a single graph. Launch angle should be plotted on the horizontal axis.

Launcher 1		Launcher 2		Launcher 3	
Launch Angle (θ) [°]	Distance (d) [ft]	Launch Angle (θ) [°]	Distance (d) [ft]	Launch Angle (θ) [°]	Distance (d) [ft]
20	5	10	10	20	10
35	10	45	25	40	20
55	12	55	18	50	15

ICA 11-5

Plot the following pairs of functions on a single graph. The independent variable (angle) should vary from 0 to 360 degrees on the horizontal axis.

(a) $\sin\theta, -2\sin\theta$ **(c)** $\sin\theta, \sin\theta + 2$

(b) $\sin\theta, \sin 2\theta$ **(d)** $\sin\theta, \sin(\theta + 90)$

ICA 11-6

Plot the following pairs of functions on a single graph. The independent variable (angle) should vary from 0 to 360 degrees on the horizontal axis.

(a) $\cos\theta, \cos 3\theta$ **(c)** $\cos\theta, \cos(2\theta) + 1$

(b) $\cos\theta, \cos\theta - 3$ **(d)** $\cos\theta, 3\cos(2\theta) - 2$

ICA 11-7

You need to create a graph showing the relationship of an ideal gas between pressure (P) and temperature (T). The ideal gas law relationship: $PV = nRT$. The ideal gas constant (R) is 0.08206 atmosphere liter per mole kelvin. Assume the tank has a volume (V) of 12 liters and is filled with nitrogen. The initial temperature (T) is 270 kelvin and the initial pressure (P) is 2.5 atmospheres. First, determine the number of moles of gas (n). Then, create a graph to model the gas as the temperature increases from 270 to 350 kelvin.

ICA 11-8

The decay of a radioactive isotope can be modeled using the following equation, where C_0 is the initial amount of the element at time zero and k is the half-life of the isotope. Create a graph of the decay of Isotope A [$k = 1.48$ hours]. Allow time to vary on the abscissa from 0 to 5 hours with an initial concentration of 10 grams of Isotope A.

$$C = C_0 e^{-t/k}$$

ICA 11-9

In researching alternate energies, you find that wind power is calculated by the following equation:

$$P = \frac{1}{2} A\rho v^3$$

where

- P = power [watts]
- A = sweep area (circular) of the blades [square meters]
- ρ = air density [kilograms per cubic meter]
- v = velocity [meters per second]

The specific gravity of air is 0.00123 and the velocity is typically 35 meters per second. Create a graph of the theoretical power (P, in units of watts) as a function of the blade diameter (D, in units of meters). Allow the diameter to be graphed on the abscissa and vary from 0.5 to 1.5 meters. The following graph applies to ICA 11-10 to 11-13.

ICA 11-10

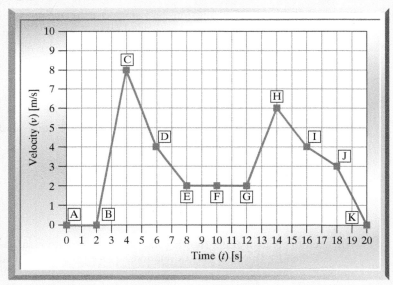

Answer the following questions using the graph. Choose from the following answers.

1. Zero
2. Positive and constant
3. Positive and increasing
4. Positive and decreasing
5. Negative and constant
6. Negative with increasing magnitude
7. Negative with decreasing magnitude
8. Cannot be determined from information given

(a) Between points (A) and (B), the acceleration is
(b) Between points (C) and (D), the acceleration is
(c) Between points (G) and (H), the acceleration is
(d) Between points (B) and (C), the distance is
(e) Between points (F) and (G), the distance is
(f) Between points (I) and (J), the distance is

ICA 11-11

Answer the following questions using the graph. Choose from the following answers.

1. Zero
2. Positive and constant
3. Positive and increasing
4. Positive and decreasing
5. Negative and constant
6. Negative with increasing magnitude
7. Negative with decreasing magnitude
8. Cannot be determined from information given

(a) Between points (B) and (C), the acceleration is
(b) Between points (F) and (G), the acceleration is
(c) Between points (I) and (J), the acceleration is
(d) Between points (A) and (B), the distance is
(e) Between points (C) and (D), the distance is
(f) Between points (G) and (H), the distance is

ICA 11-12

Use the graph to determine the following numerical values and appropriate units:

(a) Between points (A) and (B), the acceleration is
(b) Between points (I) and (J), the acceleration is
(c) At point (G), the total distance traveled is
(d) At point (K), the total distance traveled is

ICA 11-13

Use the graph to determine the following numerical values and appropriate units:

(a) Between points (C) and (D), the acceleration is
(b) Between points (F) and (G), the acceleration is
(c) At point (E), the total distance traveled is
(d) At point (I), the total distance traveled is

ICA 11-14

Use the graph on the next page to determine which statements about the two vehicles are true?

(a) At point B, the distance traveled by Vehicle 1 is equal to the distance traveled by Vehicle 2.
(b) At point B, the velocity of Vehicle 1 is equal to the velocity of Vehicle 2.
(c) The average acceleration of Vehicle 1 between points B and C is equal to the average acceleration of Vehicle 2 between points D and E.
(d) At point E, the distance traveled by Vehicle 1 is greater than the distance traveled by Vehicle 2.
(e) At point E, the velocity of Vehicle 1 is greater than the velocity of Vehicle 2.
(f) The average acceleration of Vehicle 1 between points E and F is greater than to the average acceleration of Vehicle 2 between points E and F.

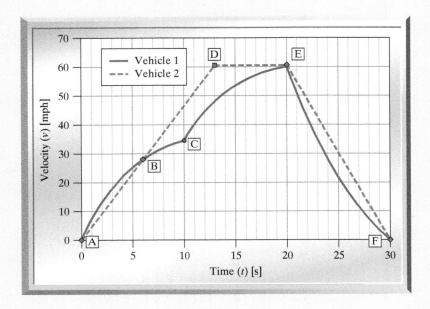

ICA 11-15

The graph shows the power delivered to a motor over a period of 50 seconds. The power gradually increases to 200 watts and then remains constant until the power is turned off at 50 seconds.

(a) What is the total energy absorbed by the motor during the 50 second period shown?

(b) What is the rate of change of power delivery during the first 10 seconds?

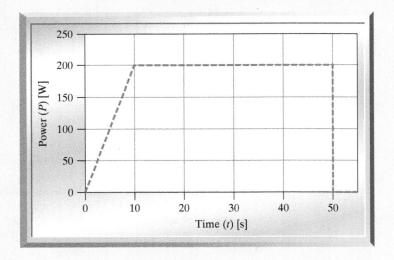

ICA 11-16

The music industry in the United States has had a great deal of fluctuation in profit over the past 20 years due to the advent of new technologies such as peer-to-peer file sharing and mobile devices such as the iPod and iPhone. The following graph displays data from a report published by eMarketer in 2009 about the amount U.S. consumers spend on digital music files and physical music formats (CDs, records, cassette tapes, etc.), where the values for 2009–2013 are reported as projections and for 2008 is reported using actual U.S. spending measurements.

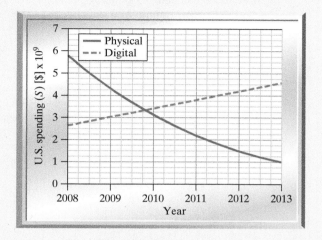

(a) According to the study, when will the sale of physical media be equivalent to the sale of digital audio files?

(b) When will the sales of digital audio files exceed that of physical media by $1 billion?

(c) If the physical media sales were $2 billion higher than the trend displayed on the graph, when would the sale of digital audio files exceed physical media?

(d) If the digital audio file sales were $1 billion lower than the trend displayed on the graph, when would the sale of digital audio files exceed physical media?

ICA 11-17

You are working for a chemical manufacturer, producing solvents used to clean lenses for microscopes. You are working on determining the properties of three different solvent blends. You develop the following chart, showing the evaporation of the three blends.

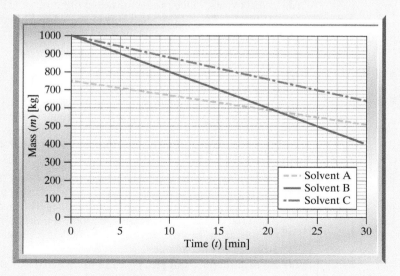

(a) Which solvent evaporates at the slowest rate?

(b) Which solvent evaporates at the fastest rate?

(c) What is the initial mass of Solvent A? Be sure to include units.

(d) What is the rate of solvent evaporation of Solvent A? Be sure to include units.

ICA 11-18

Use the accompanying graph to answer the following questions. Assume the company makes 30,000 parts per month of Product A and 17,500 parts per month of Product B.

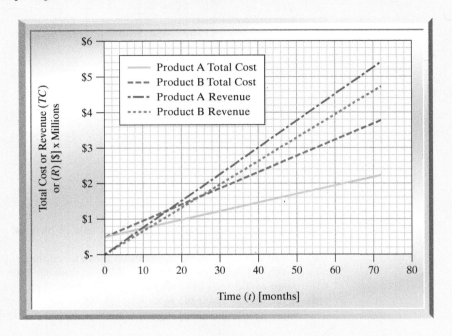

(a) Which product has the higher variable cost, and what is this value in units of dollars per part?

(b) Which product has the higher selling price, and what is this value in units of dollars per part?

(c) Which product has the faster breakeven time, and what is this value in units of months?

(d) At six years, which product makes more profit and what is this value in units of dollars?

(e) If the fixed cost of product B is increased to $1,000,000 and the selling price is increased by $0.75 / part, what is the new breakeven point in units of months?

ICA 11-19

A company designs submersible robots with a new design for the robots that increases the rate of production. A new facility for manufacturing the submersible robots is constructed at a cost of $100,000,000. A contract is negotiated with a materials supplier (Supplier A) to provide all of the raw material and construction labor necessary for $250 per robot. The robots will be sold for $500 each.

(a) How many robots must be manufactured and sold to breakeven?

(b) How many robots must be manufactured and sold to make a profit of $100,000,000?

(c) An alternative materials supplier (Supplier B) comes along with a quote for the labor and material cost at $400 per robot, but only requires $50,000,000 to build a submersible robot construction facility. How many robots must be manufactured and sold to breakeven for this alternative supplier?

(d) Which supplier will generate a profit of $20,000,000 with fewer robots produced?

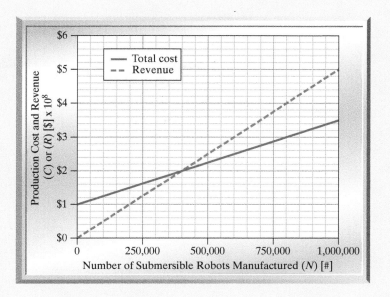

ICA 11-20

Your company is manufacturing a complex part from an advanced material. Assume the initial setup cost to manufacture these parts is $750,000, and each part costs $500 to make.

(a) Create a proper plot of this total cost curve, labeled "Cost Proposal A."
(b) If the company wishes to break even after selling 1,000 parts, sketch the revenue curve on the graph.
(c) What is the sales price per unit in this case?
(d) How many units must the company sell in order to make a profit of $500,000? Indicate this location on graph.
(e) The company is considering a change in the process to reduce the manufacturing cost by $100 per part, with the same fixed cost as Proposal A. Sketch the total cost curve for this situation, labeled "Cost Proposal B."
(f) What is the breakeven point for Cost Proposal B if the revenue curve remains the same for the new processing change? Indicate this location on the graph.

ICA 11-21

Using the list provided, you may be assigned a topic for which to create a graph. You must determine the parameters to graph and imagine a set of data to show on the chart. A blank grid has been provided below and online; you may use one of these grids, or use graph paper as directed by your instructor.

1. Air temperature
2. Airplane from airport to airport
3. Baking bread
4. Bird migration
5. Boiling water in a whistling teapot
6. Bouncing a basketball
7. Brushing your teeth
8. Burning a pile of leaves
9. Burning candle
10. Climbing a mountain
11. Cooking a Thanksgiving turkey
12. Daily electric power consumption
13. Detecting a submarine by using sonar
14. Diving into a swimming pool
15. Drag racing
16. Driving home from work

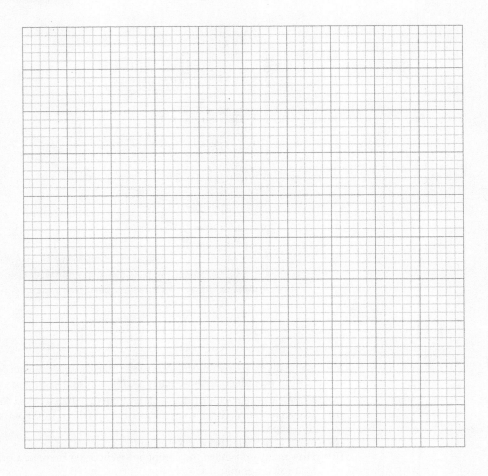

17. Dropping ice in a tub of warm water
18. Engineer's salary
19. Exercising
20. Feedback from an audio system
21. Fishing
22. Flight of a hot air balloon
23. Football game crowd
24. Formation of an icicle
25. A glass of water in a moving vehicle
26. Hammering nails
27. Leaves on a tree
28. Letting go of a helium balloon
29. Marching band
30. Moving a desk down a staircase
31. Oak tree over the years
32. Oil supply
33. Person growing up
34. Playing with a yo-yo
35. Plume from a smokestack
36. Pony Express
37. Popping corn
38. Pouring water out of a bottle

39. Power usage on campus
40. Pumping air into a bicycle tire
41. Rain filling a pond
42. Recycling
43. River in a rainstorm
44. Skipping a stone on water
45. Sleeping
46. Snoring
47. Snow blowing over a roof
48. Solar eclipse
49. Sound echoing in a canyon
50. Space station
51. Spinning a hula-hoop
52. Student attention span during class
53. Studying for an exam
54. The moon
55. Throwing a ball
56. Thunderstorm
57. Traffic at intersections
58. Train passing through town
59. Using a toaster
60. Washing clothes

ICA 11-22

Materials

Balloons (2)   Stopwatch (2)   String (40 inches)   Tape measure

Part I: Blowing Up a Balloon

One team member is to inflate one balloon, a second team member is to time the inhalation stage (how long it takes to inhale a single breath), and a third team member is to time the exhalation stage (how long it takes to exhale a single breath into the balloon). A fourth team member is to measure the balloon size at the end of each inhale/exhale cycle, using the string to measure the balloon circumference.

Record the observations on a worksheet similar to the following one for three complete inhale/exhale cycles or until the balloon appears to be close to maximum volume, whichever occurs first. Repeat the entire balloon inflation process for a second balloon; average the times from the balloons to obtain the time spent at each stage and the average circumference at each stage. Calculate the balloon volume at each stage, assuming the balloon is a perfect sphere.

Balloon	Stage	Inhale Time	Exhale Time	Circumference
1	1			
	2			
	3			
2	1			
	2			
	3			

	Stage	Inhale Time	Exhale Time	Circumference	Volume
Average Balloon	1				
	2				
	3				

Part II: Analysis

Graph the balloon volume (V, ordinate) versus time (t, time). A blank grid has been provided below and online; you may use one of these grids, or use graph paper as directed by your instructor. Allow the process to be continuous, although in reality it was stopped at various intervals for measurements. The resulting graph should contain only the time elapsed in the process of inhaling and exhaling, not the time required for recording the balloon size. For this procedure, assume that the air enters the balloon at a constant rate and the balloon is a perfect sphere.

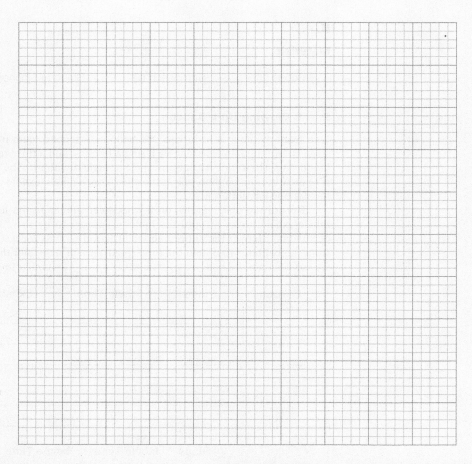

(a) What does the assumption of the air entering the balloon at a constant rate indicate about the slope?

(b) Calculate the following graphically.

- The rate at which the air enters the balloon in the first stage.
- The rate at which the air enters the balloon in the third stage.

(c) On the same graph, sketch the balloon volume (V, ordinate) versus time (t, time) if you were inflating a balloon that contained a pinhole leak.

(d) On the same graph, sketch the balloon volume (V, ordinate) versus time (t, time) if you were inflating a balloon from a helium tank.

Chapter 11 REVIEW QUESTIONS

For questions Review 11-1 to 11-10, your instructor will determine if you should complete this question by hand or using Excel. If you must complete this problem by hand, a blank graph has been provided online.

1. A computer engineer has measured the power dissipated as heat generated by a prototype microprocessor running at different clock speeds. Create a proper plot of the following experimental data set.

Speed (S) [GHz]	0.8	1.3	1.8	2.5	3.1
Power dissipated as heat (P) [W]	135	217	295	405	589

2. Due to increased demand, an industrial engineer is experimenting with increasing the speed (S) of a machine used in the production of widgets. The machine is normally rated to produce five widgets per second, and the engineer wants to know how many defective parts (D) are made at higher speeds, measured in defective parts per thousand. Create a proper plot of the following experimental data set.

Speed (S) [parts/min]	5.5	5.9	6.5	7.2	8.0
Defects in parts per thousand (D)	1	3	7	13	21

3. An engineer is conducting tests of two prototype toothbrush sanitizers that use ultraviolet radiation to kill pathogenic organisms while the toothbrush is stored. The engineer is trying to determine the minimum power needed to reliably kill pathogens on toothbrushes. Several toothbrushes are treated with a mix of bacteria, fungi, and viruses typically found in the human mouth, and then each is placed in one of the sanitizers for six hours at a specific power level (P). After six hours in the sanitizers, the viable pathogens remaining (R) on each toothbrush is assayed. Create a proper plot of the following experimental data set.

Power (P) [W]		10	18	25	40
Pathogens remaining (R) [%]	Sanitizer A	46	35	14	2
	Sanitizer B	58	41	21	7

4. Several reactions are carried out in a closed vessel. The following data are taken for the concentration (C) in units of grams per liter of solvent processed for compounds A and B as a function of time (t). Create a proper plot of the following experimental data set.

Time (t) [min]	Concentration [g/L]	
	A (C_A)	B (C_B)
36	0.145	0.160
65	0.120	0.155
100	0.100	0.150
160	0.080	0.140

5. The following experimental data are collected on the current (I, in units of milliamperes) in the positive direction and voltage (V, in units of volts) across the terminals of two different thermionic rectifiers. Create a proper plot of the following experimental data set.

| | Current (I) [mA] | |
Voltage (V) [V]	Rectifier A	Rectifier B
18	5	15
30	18	26
40	24	34
45	30	50

6. If an object is heated, the temperature of the body will increase. The energy (Q) associated with a change in temperature (ΔT) is a function of the mass of the object (m) and the specific heat (C_p). Specific heat is a material property, and values are available in literature. In an experiment, heat is applied to the end of an object, and the temperature change at the other end of the object is recorded. This leads to the theoretical relationship shown. An unknown material is tested in the lab, yielding the following results:

$$\Delta T = \frac{Q}{mC_p}$$

Heat applied (Q) [J]	12	17	25	40	50	58
Temp change (ΔT) [K]	1.50	2.00	3.25	5.00	6.25	7.00

Graph the experimental temperature change (ΔT, ordinate) versus the heat applied (Q).

7. Eutrophication is the result of excessive nutrients in a lake or other body of water, usually caused by runoff of nutrients (animal waste, fertilizers, and sewage) from the land, which causes a dense growth of plant life. The decomposition of the plants depletes the supply of oxygen, leading to the death of animal life. Sometimes, these excess nutrients cause an algae bloom— or rapid growth of algae, which normally occur in small concentrations in the water body.

The following table contains data to illustrate the relationship between pressure (depth of fluid), the temperature of the water, and the solubility of oxygen in the water. Create a proper plot of the data.

| Solubility of O_2 [mg/L] | Pressure (P) [mm Hg] | | |
Temperature (T) [°C]	760	1520	3040
10	11.3	22.6	45.1
20	9.1	18.2	36.4
30	7.6	15.2	30.3
40	6.5	12.9	25.9

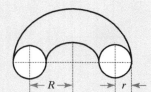

8. In the 1950s, a team at Los Alamos National Laboratories built several devices called "Perhapsatrons," thinking that PERHAPS they might be able to create controllable nuclear fusion. After several years of experiments, they were never able to maintain stable plasma and abandoned the project.

The perhapsatron used a toroidal (doughnut-shaped) plasma confinement chamber, similar to those used in more modern Tokamak fusion devices. You have taken a job at a fusion research lab, and your supervisor asks you to develop a simple spreadsheet to calculate the volume of a torus within which the plasma will be contained in a new experimental reactor.

(a) Create a table that calculates the volumes of various toruses with specific values for r and R. The tube radii (r) should range from 10 to 100 centimeters in increments of 10 centimeters. The torus radii (R) should range from 1.5 to 3 meters in increments of 0.5 meters. The volume of a torus can be determined using $V = 2\pi^2 R r^2$.

(b) Using the table of volumes, create a graph showing the relationship between volume (ordinate) and tube radius (r) for torus radii (R) of 2 and 3 meters.

(c) Using the table of volumes, create a graph showing the relationship between volume (ordinate) and torus radius (R) for tube radii (r) of 40, 70, and 100 centimeters.

9. Generally, when a car door is opened, the interior lights come on and turn off again when the door is closed. Some cars turn the interior lights on and off gradually. Suppose that you have a car with 25 watts of interior lights. When a door is opened, the power to the lights increases linearly from 0 to 25 watts over 2 seconds. When the door is closed, the power is reduced to zero in a linear fashion over 5 seconds.

(a) Create a proper plot of power (P, on the ordinate) and time (t).

(b) Using the graph, determine the total energy delivered to the interior lights if the door to the car is opened and then closed 10 seconds later.

10. One of the 22 named, derived units in the metric system is the volt, which can be expressed as 1 joule per coulomb ($V = J/C$). A coulomb is the total electric charge on approximately 6.24×10^{18} electrons. The voltage on a capacitor is given by $V = \Delta Q/C + V_0$ volts, where ΔQ is the change in charge [coulombs] stored, V_0 is the initial voltage on the capacitor, and C is the capacitance [farads].

(a) Create a proper plot of voltage (V, on the ordinate) and total charge (ΔQ) for a 5-farad capacitor with an initial voltage of 5 volts for $0 < \Delta Q < 20$.

(b) Using the graph, determine the total energy stored in the capacitor for an addition of 15 coulombs.

11. Below is a graph of the vertical position of a person bungee jumping, in meters. A copy of this graph has been provided online; you may use one of these graphs, or use graph paper as directed by your instructor.

(a) What is the closest this person gets to the ground?

(b) When this person stops bouncing, how high off the ground will the person be?

(c) If the person has a mass of 70 kilograms, how would the graph change for a jumper of 50 kilograms? Approximately sketch the results on the graph.

(d) If the person has a mass of 70 kilograms, how would the graph change for a jumper of 80 kilograms? Approximately sketch the results on the graph.

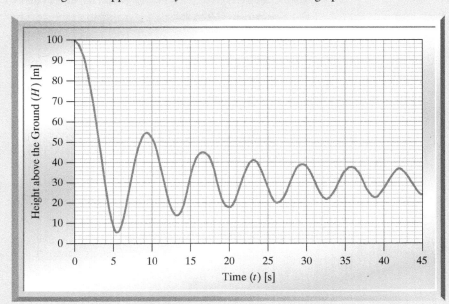

12. Shown are graphs of the altitude in meters, and velocity in meters per second, of a person skydiving. A copy of these graphs has been provided online; you may use one of these graphs, or use graph paper as directed by your instructor.

(a) When does the skydiver reach the ground?

(b) How fast is he moving when he reaches the ground?

(c) At what altitude does he open the parachute?

(d) Terminal velocity is the velocity at which the acceleration of gravity is exactly balanced by the drag force of air. How long does it take him to reach his terminal velocity without the parachute open?

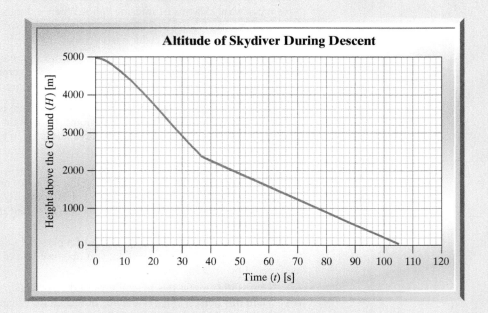

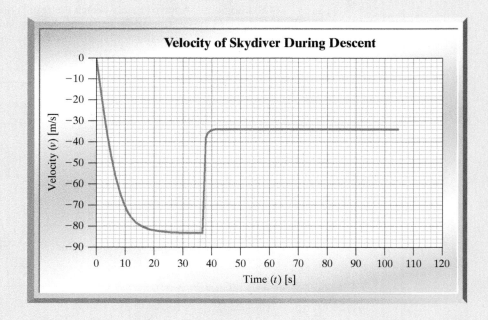

13. The graph below shows the current used to charge a capacitor over a period of 25 milliseconds [ms]. Choose from the following answers for (a)–(b).

1. Zero
2. Positive and constant
3. Positive and increasing
4. Positive and decreasing
5. Negative and constant
6. Negative with increasing magnitude
7. Negative with decreasing magnitude
8. Cannot be determined from information given

  (a) At time $t = 10$ to 12 ms, classify the manner in which the **current** is changing.
  (b) At time $t = 16$ to 18 ms, classify the manner in which the **charge** on the capacitor is changing.
  (c) What is the total charge on the capacitor at time $t = 20$ ms?
  (d) If the voltage on the capacitor at time 25 ms is 20 volts, what is the value of the capacitance? Express your answer using an appropriate prefix.

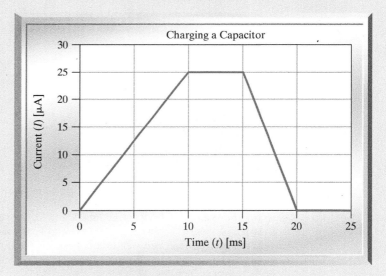

14. Answer the following questions using the graph. Choose from the following answers for (a)–(c):

1. Zero
2. Positive and constant
3. Positive and increasing
4. Positive and decreasing
5. Negative and constant
6. Negative with increasing magnitude
7. Negative with decreasing magnitude
8. Cannot be determined from information given

  (a) Between points A and B, the total energy produced is:
  (b) Between points A and B, the power generated is:
  (c) Between points B and C, the power generated is:
  (d) What is the power being generated at $t = 7$ minutes? State your answer in units of kilowatts.

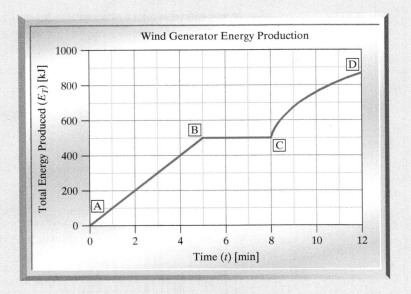

15. Answer the following questions using the graph. Choose from the following answers for (a)–(d):

1. Zero
2. Positive and constant
3. Positive and increasing
4. Positive and decreasing
5. Negative and constant
6. Negative with increasing magnitude
7. Negative with decreasing magnitude
8. Cannot be determined from information given

(a) For vehicle 2, between points A and D, the velocity is:
(b) For vehicle 2, between points D and E, the acceleration is:
(c) For vehicle 2, between points E and F, the distance is:
(d) What is the total distance traveled by vehicle 2 between points A and E? Give your answer in miles.
(e) Which vehicle travels the farthest distance between points A and F?

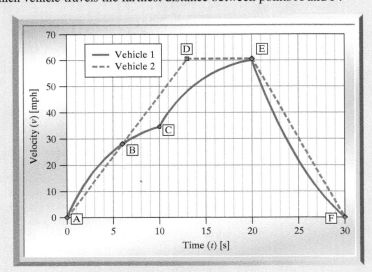

For questions Review 11-16 to 11-19, your instructor will determine if you should complete this question by hand or using Excel. If you must complete this problem by hand, a blank graph has been provided online.

16. In a simple electric circuit, the current (I) must remain below 40 milliamps ($I < 40$ mA), and must also satisfy the function $I > 10^{-6}\, e^{25V}$, where V is the voltage across a device called a diode.

   (a) Create a proper plot of these two inequalities with current on the ordinate. The values on the vertical axis should range from 0 to 50 milliamperes, and the values on the horizontal axis should range from 0 to 1 volt.

   (b) If graphing part **(a)** by hand, shade the region of the graph where *both* inequalities are satisfied.

   (c) Graphically determine the maximum allowable voltage across the diode. Indicate the location of this answer on your graph.

17. In a hard drive design, the faster the disk spins, the faster the information can be read from and written to the disk. In general, the more information to be stored on the disk, the larger the diameter of the disk must be. Unfortunately, the larger the disk, the lower the maximum rotational speed must be to avoid stress-related failures. Assume the minimum allowable rotational speed (S) of the hard drive is 6,000 revolutions per minute [rpm], and the rotational speed must meet the criterion $S < 12{,}000 - 150\, D^2$, where D is the diameter of the disk in inches.

   (a) Create a proper plot of these two inequalities with rotational speed on the ordinate and diameter on the abscissa. The values on the vertical axis should range from 0 to 12,000 rpm, and the values on the horizontal axis should range from 0 to 7 inches.

   (b) If graphing part **(a)** by hand, shade the region of the graph where both inequalities are satisfied.

   (c) Graphically determine the range of allowable rotational speeds for a 4-inch diameter disk. Indicate the location of this answer on your graph.

   (d) Graphically determine the largest diameter disk that meets the design criteria. Indicate the location of this answer on your graph.

18. We have decided to become entrepreneurs by raising turkeys for the Thanksgiving holiday. We already have purchased some land in the country with buildings on it, so that expense need not be a part of our analysis. A study of the way turkeys grow indicates that the mass of a turkey (m) from the time it hatches (at time zero) until it reaches maturity is:

$$m = K(1 - e^{-bt})$$

Here, we select values of K and b depending on the breed of turkey we decide to raise. The value (V) of our turkey is simply the mass of the turkey times the value per pound-mass (S) when we sell it, or:

$$V = Sm$$

Here, S is the value per pound-mass (in dollars). Finally, since we feed the turkey the same amount of food each day, the cumulative cost (C) to feed the bird is:

$$C = Nt$$

Here, N is the cost of one day's supply of food [$/day].

    Create a graph of this situation, showing three lines: cumulative food cost, bird value, and profit on a particular day. For the graph, show the point after which you begin to lose money, and show the time when it is most profitable to sell the bird, indicating the day on which that occurs. Use values of $K = 21$ pound-mass, $b = 0.03$ per day, $S = \$1$ per pound-mass, and $N = \$0.12$ per day.

19. As an engineer, suppose you are directed to design a pumping system to safely discharge a toxic industrial waste into a municipal reservoir. The concentrated wastewater from the plant will be mixed with freshwater from the lake, and this mixture is to be pumped into the center of the lake. You realize that the more water you mix with the waste, the more dilute it will be and thus will have a smaller impact on the fish in the lake. On the other hand, the more water you use, the more it costs in electricity for pumping. Your objective is to determine the optimum amount of water to pump so the overall cost is a minimum.

  ■ Assume that the cost of pumping is given by the expression $C_{pump} = 10 \, Q^2$. The cost C_{pump} [$/day] depends on the pumping rate Q [gallons per minute, or gpm] of the water used to dilute the industrial waste.

  ■ Now, suppose that some biologists have found that as more and more water dilutes the waste, the fish loss C_{fish} [$/day] can be expressed as $C_{fish} = 2{,}250 - 150 \, Q$.

  With this information, construct a graph, with pumping rate on the abscissa showing the pumping cost, the fish-loss cost, and total cost on the ordinate. For the scale, plot 0 to 15 gallons per minute for flow rate.

  Determine both the minimum cost and the corresponding flow rate. Indicate the location of this answer on your graph.

20. We have obtained a contract to construct metal boxes (square bottom, rectangular sides, no top) for storing sand. Each box is to contain a specified volume and all edges are to be welded. Each box will require the following information: a volume (V, in units of cubic inches), the length of one side of the bottom (L, in units of inches), the box height (H, in units of inches), and the material cost (M, in units of dollars per square inch). To determine the total cost to manufacture a box, we must include not only the cost of the material, but also the cost of welding all the edges. Welding costs depend on the number of linear inches that are welded (W, in units of dollars per inch). The client does not care what the box looks like, but it should be constructed at the minimum cost possible.

  (a) Construct a worksheet that will depict the cost of the material for one box, the welding cost for one box, and the total cost for the box. First, create at the top of your worksheet a section to allow the user to specify as absolute references the variables V, M, and W. Next, create a column for length ranging from 2 to 20 inches in increments of 2 inches. Finally, determine the material cost per box, welding cost per box, and total cost.

  (b) Create a proper plot of the material cost, welding cost, and total cost (all shown as ordinate values) versus the box length.

  For the following values, use the graph to determine the box shape for minimum cost: $V = 500$ cubic inches, $M = \$1.00$ per square inch, and $W = \$3.00$ per inch. Indicate the location of this answer on your graph.

  (c) Below the table created in part (a), create a row to determine the minimum value for the material cost, the welding cost, and the total cost shown in the table. Use the information to create conditional formatting in the table to show the minimum values in the table as cells with a dark color background and white text. The highlighted cells should verify the solution found in part (b) using the graph.

21. Your company has developed a new high-mileage automobile. There are two options for manufacturing this new vehicle.

  ■ Process A: The factory can be completely retooled and workers trained to use the new equipment.

  ■ Process B: The old equipment can be modified.

  A graph of the costs of each process and the revenues from sales of the vehicles is shown.

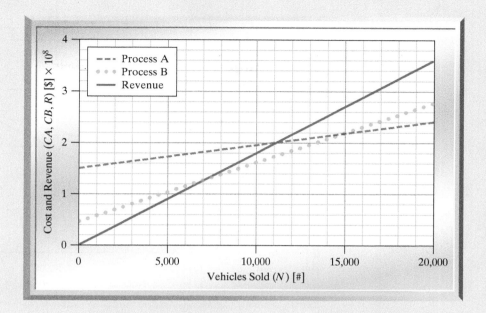

Use the chart to answer the following questions.

(a) What is the sales price per vehicle?

(b) What is the breakeven point (number of vehicles) for each of the two processes?

(c) Which process yields the most profit if 18,000 vehicles are sold? How much profit is made in this case?

(d) If the sales price per vehicle is reduced by $2,000 with a rebate offer, what is the new breakeven point (number of vehicles) for each of the two processes?

22. One of the fourteen Grand Challenges for Engineering as determined by the National Academy of Engineering committee is **Make Solar Energy Economical**. According to the NAE website: The solar "share of the total energy market remains rather small, well below 1 percent of total energy consumption, compared with roughly 85 percent from oil, natural gas, and coal." "... today's commercial solar cells ... typically convert sunlight into electricity with an efficiency of only 10 percent to 20 percent." "Given their manufacturing costs, modules of today's cells ... would produce electricity at a cost roughly 3 to 6 times higher than current prices." "To make solar economically competitive, engineers must find ways to improve the efficiency of the cells and to lower their manufacturing costs."

The following graph shows a breakeven analysis for a company planning to manufacture modular photoelectric panels. A copy of this graph has been provided online; you may use one of these graphs, or use graph paper as directed by your instructor.

(a) What is the fixed cost incurred in manufacturing the photoelectric panels?

(b) How much does it cost to manufacture each photoelectric panel?

(c) What is the sales price of one photoelectric panel?

(d) If the company makes and sells 30,000 panels, is there a net loss or profit, and how much?

While the company is still in the planning stages, the government starts a program to stimulate the economy and encourage green technologies. In this case, the government agrees to reimburse the company $250 for each of the first 10,000 units sold.

(e) Sketch a modified revenue curve for this situation.

(f) Using this new revenue curve, how many units must the company make to break even? Be sure to clearly indicate this point on the graph.

(g) Also using the new revenue curve, how many units must the company make and sell to make a profit of $1,500,000? Be sure to clearly indicate this point on the graph.

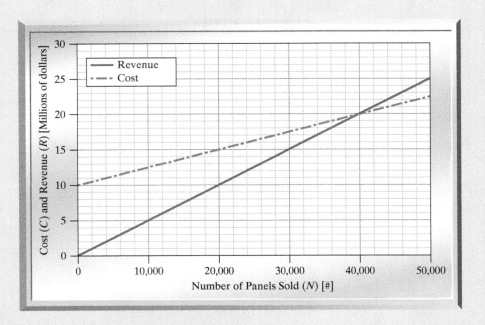

23. You are an engineer for a plastics manufacturing company. In examining cost-saving measures, your team has brainstormed the following ideas (labeled Idea A and Idea B). It is your responsibility to evaluate these ideas and recommend which one to pursue. You have been given a graph of the current process. A copy of this graph has been provided online; you may use one of these graphs, or use graph paper as directed by your instructor.

(a) What is the selling price of the product?

Current Cost: The current process has been running for a number of years, so there are no initial fixed costs to consider.

In the operating costs, the process requires the following:

- Material cost: $2.00/pound-mass of resin
- Energy cost: $0.15/pound-mass of resin
- Labor cost: $0.10/pound-mass of resin

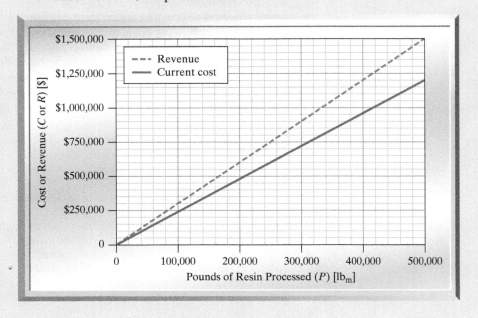

(b) There is also a cost associated with taking the scrap material to the landfill. Using the total cost determined from the graph, find the cost of landfill, in dollars per pounds-mass of resin.

Idea (A): Your customer will allow you to use regrind (reprocessed plastic) in the parts instead of 100% virgin plastic. Your process generates 10% scrap. Evaluate using all your scrap materials as regrind, with the regrind processed at your plant.

(c) You will need to purchase a regrind machine to process the plastic, estimated at a cost of $100,000. Using the regrind will alter the following costs, which account for using 10% scrap material:

- Material cost: $1.80/pound-mass of resin
- Energy cost: $0.16/pound-mass of resin
- Labor cost: $0.11/pound-mass of resin

This idea will eliminate the landfill charge required in the current process (see part **(b)**). Draw the total cost curve for Idea (A) on the graph or on a copy.

(d) How long (in pounds of resin processed) before the company reaches breakeven on Idea A?

(e) At what minimum level of production (in pound-mass of resin processed) will Idea (A) begin to generate more profit than the current process?

Idea (B): Your customer will allow you to use regrind (reprocessed plastic) in the parts instead of 100% virgin plastic. Evaluate using 25% regrind purchased from an outside vendor.

(f) Using the regrind from the other company will alter the following costs, which account for using 25% scrap material purchased from the outside vendor:

- Material cost: $1.85/pound-mass of resin
- Energy cost: $0.15/pound-mass of resin
- Labor cost: $0.11/pound-mass of resin

This idea will eliminate the landfill charge required in the current process (see part **(b)**) and will not require the purchase of a regrind machine as discussed in Idea (A). Draw the total cost curve for Idea (B) on the graph or on a copy.

(g) At what minimum level of production (in pound-mass of resin processed) will Idea (B) begin to generate more profit than the current process?

(h) At a production level of 500,000 pound-mass of resin, which Idea (A, B, or neither) gives the most profit over the current process?

(i) If the answer to part **(h)** is neither machine, list the amount of profit generated by the current process at 500,000 pound-mass of resin. If the answer to part **(h)** is Idea A or Idea B, list the amount of profit generated by that idea at 500,000 pound-mass of resin.

24. When a wind generator is installed there is a substantial initial cost, but daily operation requires no further cash payment. However, to keep the generator in proper operating condition, it must undergo maintenance once a year. Each maintenance cycle requires a cash payment of $5,000. The solid lines on the graph below show this situation. The stepped blue line shows the cost over time and the straight brown line shows the revenue derived from the generator.

As the second yearly maintenance approaches, you are informed by the manufacturer that a significant upgrade is available for additional cost. The upgrade will make the generator far more efficient, thus the revenue would increase substantially. The yearly maintenance cost after the upgrade would still be $5,000. The dashed lines show the cost and revenue projections if the upgrade is installed.

(a) What is the amount of revenue per year without the upgrade?

(b) What is the initial cost of the wind generator?

(c) How many years after the initial installation do you breakeven if the upgrade is installed? List your answer as number of years + number of months.

(d) What is the cost of the upgrade completed at the two-year maintenance cycle? Note that this figure includes the standard $5,000 maintenance fee.

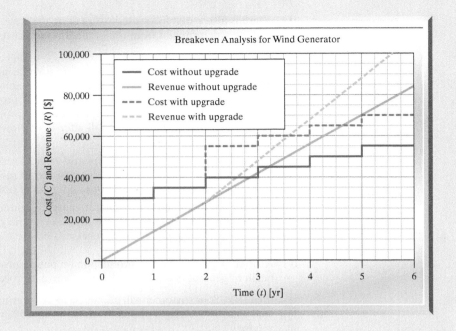

(e) How many years after the initial installation would the profit be the same whether you upgrade or not? List your answer as number of years + number of months.

(f) How many years after the initial installation will you have made a profit of $25,000 if the upgrade is NOT installed? List your answer as number of years + number of months.

(g) If the upgrade results in increased reliability thus increasing the maintenance interval to two years, though still at a cost of $5,000 per maintenance, how many years after the initial installation will you breakeven after the upgrade? List your as number of years + number of months.

CHAPTER 12
MODELS AND SYSTEMS

A **model** is an abstract description of the relationship between variables in a system. A model allows the categorization of different types of mathematical phenomena so that general observations about the variables can be made for use in any number of applications.

For example, if we know that $t = v + 5$ and $M = z + 5$, any observations we make about v with respect to t also apply to z with respect to M. A specific model describes a *system* or *function* that has the same *trend* or *behavior* as a generalized model. In engineering, many specific models within different subdisciplines behave according to the same generalized model.

This section covers three general models of importance to engineers: **linear**, **power**, and **exponential**. It is worth noting that many applications of models within these three categories contain identical math but apply to significantly different disciplines.

Linear models occur when the dependent variable changes in direct relationship to changes in the independent variable. We discuss such systems, including springs, resistive circuits, fluid flow, and elastic materials, in this chapter by relating each model to Newton's generalized law of motion.

Power law systems occur when the independent variable has an exponent not equal to 1 or 0. We discuss these models by addressing integer and rational real exponents.

Exponential models are used in all engineering disciplines in a variety of applications. We discuss these models by examining the similarities between growth and decay models.

The following is an example of the level of knowledge of Excel needed to proceed. *If you are not able to quickly recreate the following exercise in Excel, including trend-lines and formatting, please review trendline basics in appendix materials online before proceeding.*

Energy (E) stored in an **inductor** is related to its inductance (L) and the current (I) passing through it by the following equation:

$$E = \frac{1}{2} L I^2$$

The SI unit of inductance, **henry** [H], is named for Joseph Henry (1797–1878), credited with the discovery of self-inductance of electromagnets.

Three inductors were tested and the results are given here. Create a proper plot of the data and add a properly formatted power law trendline to each data set.

Current (I) [A]	2	6	10	14	16
Energy of Inductor 1 ($E$1) [J]	0.002	0.016	0.050	0.095	0.125
Energy of Inductor 2 ($E$2) [J]	0.010	0.085	0.250	0.510	0.675
Energy of Inductor 3 ($E$3) [J]	0.005	0.045	0.125	0.250	0.310

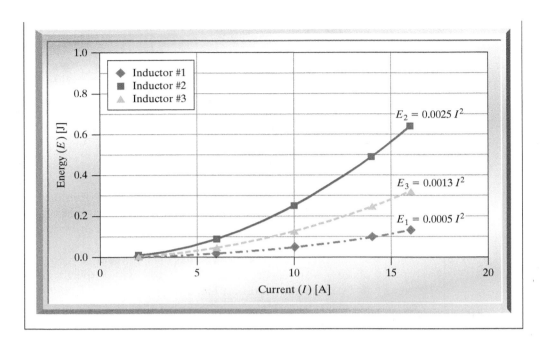

Figure 12-1 is an example of a properly formatted graph, showing an experimental data series with linear trendlines.

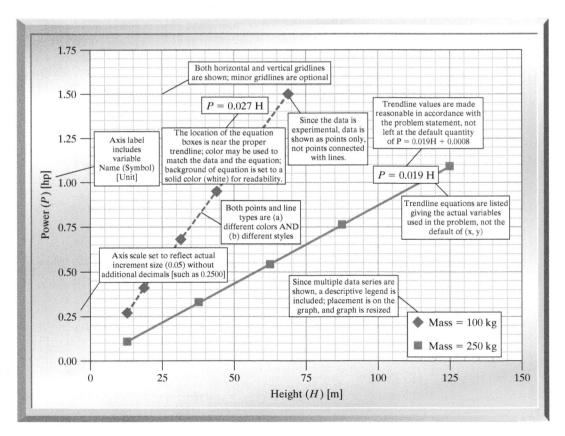

Figure 12-1
Example of a proper plot, showing multiple experimental data sets with linear trendlines.

12.1 LINEAR FUNCTIONS

LEARN TO: Recognize the shape and boundaries of a linear function shown graphically
Recognize when an equation is a linear model
Determine the physical meaning and units of parameters of a linear function

Trend	Equation	Data Form	Graphical Example
Linear	$y = mx + c$	Defined value at $x = 0$ ($y = c$) ——————— Data appears as a linear (straight) line	

One of the most common models is **linear**, taking the form $y = mx + c$, where the ordinate value (y) is a function of the abscissa value (x) and a constant factor called the **slope** (m). At an initial value of the abscissa ($x = 0$), the ordinate value is equal to the **intercept** (c). Examples include

■ Distance (d) traveled at constant velocity (v) over time (t) from initial position (d_0):

$$d = vt + d_0$$

■ Total pressure (P_{total}), relating density (ρ), gravity (g), liquid height (H), and the pressure above the surface ($P_{surface}$):

$$P_{total} = \rho g H + P_{surface}$$

■ Newton's second law, relating force (F), mass (m), and acceleration (a):

$$F = ma$$

Note that the intercept value (c) is zero in the last example.

General Model Rules

Given a linear system of the form $y = mx + c$ and assuming $x \geq 0$:

■ When $m = 1$, the function is equal to $x + c$.

■ When $m = 0$, $y = c$, regardless of the value of x (y never changes).

■ When $m > 0$, as x increases, y increases, regardless of the value of c.

■ When $m < 0$, as x increases, y decreases, regardless of the value of c.

● EXAMPLE 12-1

We want to determine the effect of depth of a fluid on the total pressure felt by a submerged object. Recall that the total pressure is

$$P_{total} = P_{surface} + P_{hydro} = P_{surface} + \rho g H$$

where P_{total} = total pressure [atm]; $P_{surface}$ = pressure at the surface [atm]; ρ = density [kg/m^3]; g = gravity [m/s^2]; H = depth [m]. We enter the lab, take data, and create the following chart.

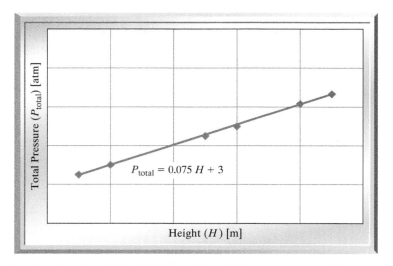

Determine the density of the fluid, in units of kilograms per cubic meter.

*We can determine the parameters by matching the trendline generated in Excel with the theoretical expression. In theory: total pressure = density * gravity * height of fluid + pressure on top of the fluid*
*From graph: total pressure = 0.075 * height + 3*
*By comparison: density * gravity = 0.075 [atm/m]*

$$\frac{0.075 \text{ atm}}{m} \left| \frac{101{,}325 \text{ Pa}}{1 \text{ atm}} \right| \frac{1 \frac{kg}{ms^2}}{1 \text{ Pa}} = \rho \left(\frac{9.8 \text{ m}}{s^2} \right)$$

$$\frac{7{,}600 \text{ kg}}{m^2 s^2} = \rho \left(\frac{9.8 \text{ m}}{s^2} \right)$$

$$\rho = \frac{7{,}600 \text{ kg}}{m^2 s^2} \left| \frac{s^2}{9.8 \text{ m}} \right. = \frac{775 \text{ kg}}{m^3}$$

Determine if the tank is open to the atmosphere or pressurized, and determine the pressure on the top of the fluid in units of atmospheres.

*Once again, we can compare the Excel trendline to the theoretical expression. In theory: total pressure = density * gravity * height of fluid + pressure on top of the fluid*
*From graph: total pressure = 0.075 * height + 3*
By comparison, the top of the tank is pressurized at 3 atm.

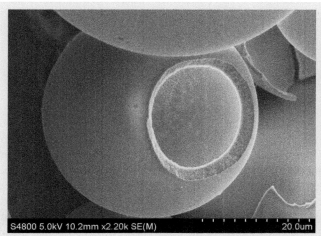

Increasingly, engineers are working at smaller and smaller scales. Tiny beads made of glass are on the order of 50 micrometers in diameter. They are manufactured so that they become hollow, allowing the wall thickness to be a few nanometers. The compositions of the glass were engineered, so when processed correctly, they would sustain a hollow structure and the glass walls would be infiltrated with hundreds of thousands of nanometer-sized pores. These beads can possibly revolutionize the way fluids and gases are stored for use. The pores are small enough that fluids and even gases could be contained under normal conditions. However, if activated properly, the pores would allow a path for a gas to exit the "container" when it is ready to be used.

S4800 5.0kV 10.2mm x2.20k SE(M)   20.0um

Photo courtesy of K. Richardson

COMPREHENSION CHECK 12-1

The graph shows the ideal gas law relationship ($PV = nRT$) between pressure (P) and temperature (T).

(a) What are the units of the slope (0.0087)?

(b) If the tank has a volume of 12 liters and is filled with nitrogen (formula, N_2; molecular weight, 28 grams per mole), what is the mass of gas in the tank in units of grams?

(c) If the tank is filled with 48 grams of oxygen (formula, O_2; molecular weight, 32 grams per mole), what is the volume of the tank in units of liters?

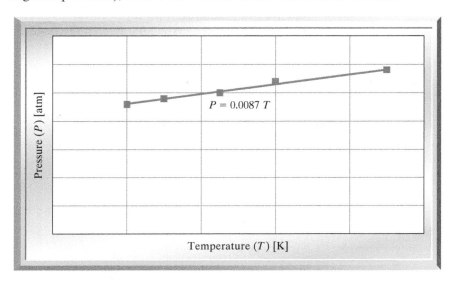

$P = 0.0087\ T$

Pressure (P) [atm]

Temperature (T) [K]

12.2   LINEAR RELATIONSHIPS

LEARN TO: Identify linear systems that are analogous to Newton's second law
Define dynamic and kinematic viscosity; identify units of centipoise and stokes
Determine equivalency in systems of springs, circuits, capacitors, and inductors

Most physics textbooks begin the study of motion ignoring how that object came to be moving in the first place. This is appropriate to the way physicists study the world, by observing the world as it is. Engineering is about changing the way things are. The fact that "engineer" is a verb as well as a noun is a reminder of this. As a result, engineers are concerned with forces and the changes those forces cause. While physicists study how far a car travels through the air when hit by a truck, engineers focus on stopping the truck before it hits the car or on designing an air-bag system or crush-proof doors. Engineering has many diverse branches because of the many different kinds of forces and ways to apply them.

NOTE

Newton's First Law: A system keeps doing what it is doing unless the forces acting on the system change.

Another Way of Looking at Newton's Laws

Newton's first law is given as "An object at rest remains at rest and an object in motion will continue in motion with a constant velocity unless it experiences a net external force." As we consider variables other than motion, we want to expand this definition: **A system keeps doing what it is doing unless the forces acting on the system change**.

NOTE

Newton's Second Law: When a force influences a change to a system parameter, the system opposes the change according to its internal resistance.

Newton's second law is given as "The acceleration of an object is directly proportional to the net force acting on it and inversely proportional to its mass." This can be interpreted as follows: When an external force acts on a system to cause acceleration, the system resists that acceleration according to its mass. Expanding Newton's second law, we can generalize it for use with variables other than motion: **When a force influences a change to a system parameter, the system opposes the change according to its internal resistance**.

In generalizing these relationships, we can start to establish a pattern observed in a wide variety of phenomena, summarized in Table 12-1.

Table 12-1 Generalized Newton's second law

When a "system"...	...is acted upon by a "force"...	...to change a "parameter"...	...the "system" opposes the change by a "resistance"	Equation
Physical object	External push or pull (F)	Acceleration (a)	Object mass (m)	$F = ma$

Springs

When an external force (F), such as a weight, is applied to a spring, it will cause the spring to stretch a distance (x), according to the following expression:

$$F = kx$$

This equation is called **Hooke's law**, named for Robert Hooke (1635–1703), an English scientist. Among other things, he is credited with creating the biological term "cell." The comparison of Hooke's Law and Newton's Second Law is shown in Table 12-2.

Table 12-2 Generalized second law . . . applied to springs

When a "system" . . .	. . . is acted upon by a "force" . . .	. . . to change a "parameter". . .	. . . the "system" opposes the change by a "resistance"	Equation
Physical object	External push or pull (F)	Acceleration (a)	Object mass (m)	$F = ma$
Spring	External push or pull (F)	Elongation (x)	Spring stiffness (k)	$F = kx$

The variable k is the **spring constant**, a measure of the stiffness of the spring. Stiff springs are hard to stretch and have high k values; springs with low k values are easy to stretch. The constant k is a material property of the spring, determined by how it is made and what material it is made from. The spring constant has units of force per distance, typically reported in newtons per meter.

● **EXAMPLE 12-2**

Two springs were tested; a weight was hung on one end and the resulting displacement measured. The results were graphed. Using the graph shown below, give the spring constant of each spring and determine which spring is stiffer.

Spring 1 has a linear trendline of F = 66x. The slope of the line is the spring constant:

$$k_1 = 66 \ N/m$$

Spring 2 has a linear trendline of F = 8x, which corresponds to:

$$k_2 = 8 \ N/m$$

Spring 1 is stiffer since it has a higher spring constant.

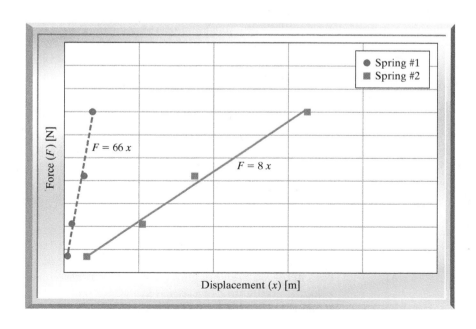

Electric Circuits

Electric current (I) is a measure of how many charges (normally electrons) flow through a wire or component in a given amount of time. This is analogous to measuring water flowing through a pipe as amount per time, whether the units are tons per hour, gallons per minute, or molecules per second.

NOTE

A now outdated term for voltage was actually "electromotive force" or EMF.

Voltage (V) is the "force" that pushes the electrons around. Although its effects on charged particles are similar to those of a true force, voltage is quite different dimensionally. The unit of voltage is the **volt** [V], described as the potential difference (voltage) across a conductor when a current of one ampere dissipates one watt of power.

Resistance (R) is a measure of how difficult it is to push electrons through a substance or device. When a voltage is applied to a circuit, a current is generated. This current depends on the equivalent resistance of the circuit. Resistance has units of volts per ampere, which is given the special name **ohm** [Ω]. It is named for Georg Ohm (1789–1854), the German physicist who developed the theory, called **Ohm's Law**, to explain the relationship between voltage, current, and resistance. The similarities between Ohm's Law and Newton's Second Law are given in Table 12-3.

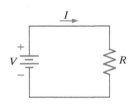

$$V = IR$$

Table 12-3 Generalized second law . . . applied to circuits

When a "system" . . .	. . . is acted upon by a "force" . . .	. . . to change a "parameter" . . .	. . . the "system" opposes the change by a "resistance"	Equation
Physical object	External push or pull (F)	Acceleration (a)	Object mass (m)	$F = ma$
Electrical circuit	Circuit voltage (V) (electromotive force)	Circuit current (I)	Circuit resistance (R)	$V = IR$

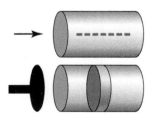

Fluid Flow

To create motion in a solid object, we can apply a force to that object by pushing on it. Imagine you have a small cube on the desk in front of you. If you take your pencil and push on that object at a single point, the entire object will move. For motion in a fluid to be created, a force must be applied over an area of the fluid. While both liquids and gases can be defined as fluids, we focus on liquids in this section. Imagine a section of fluid-filled pipe placed on the desk in front of you. If we apply a force at a single point in the fluid, only the particles at that point will move. To move the entire fluid uniformly, we must apply the force at all points at the pipe entrance simultaneously. Applying a force over the cross-sectional area of the pipe results in the application of a pressure to the fluid. The pressure that results in fluid flow has a special name: **shear stress** (τ, Greek letter tau).

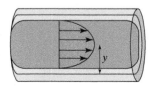

As the fluid moves, we find that the fluid molecules in contact with the wall adhere to the wall and do not move. The motion of the fluid can be visualized as occurring in layers; as the distance from the wall increases, the fluid moves faster. The fluid moves fastest at the farthest point from the wall, which is the center of the pipe. Since the velocity changes depend on the location in the pipe from the wall, the parameter we are changing cannot be expressed as a simple velocity, but rather as a **velocity gradient**, given as ($\Delta v/\Delta y$ or $\dot{\gamma}$). This is sometimes called the **shear rate** or **strain rate**.

Not all fluids respond equally to an applied pressure. The fluid property that represents the resistance of a fluid against flow is called the **dynamic viscosity** (μ, Greek letter mu). The relationship between shear stress and the velocity profile of a fluid is called **Newton's law of viscosity**, named after Isaac Newton. Fluids that behave in this way are called **Newtonian fluids** (e.g., water and oil). The comparison between Newton's Law of Viscosity and Newton's Second Law is given in Table 12-4.

$$\tau = \mu \frac{\Delta v}{\Delta y}$$

Table 12-4 Generalized second law . . . applied to fluid flow

When a "system" . . .	. . . is acted upon by a "force" . . .	. . . to change a "parameter" . . .	. . . the "system" opposes the change by a "resistance"	Equation
Physical object	External push or pull (F)	Acceleration (a)	Object mass (m)	$F = ma$
Fluid	Shear stress (τ)	Shear rate ($\Delta v/\Delta y$)	Dynamic viscosity (μ)	$\tau = \mu \dfrac{\Delta v}{\Delta y}$

Sometimes, a fluid must have a certain amount of stress (called the **yield stress**, τ_0) applied before it will begin to move like a Newtonian fluid. These fluids are called **Bingham plastics**, named after Eugene Bingham, a chemist who made many contributions to the field of **rheology** (the science of deformation and flow of matter, a term he, along with Markus Reiner, is credited in creating). Examples of Bingham plastics include toothpaste and slurries.

$$\tau = \mu \frac{\Delta v}{\Delta y} + \tau_0$$

Common units of dynamic viscosity are **centipoise** [cP], named after the French physician Jean Louis Poiseuille (1799–1869) who studied the flow of blood in tubes. Dynamic viscosity is a function of temperature. In most instances, viscosity decreases with increasing temperature; as the fluid heats up, it becomes easier to move.

Property	Symbol	Typical Units	Equivalent Units
Dynamic viscosity	μ	cP	$1P = 1g/(cm\ s)$
Kinematic viscosity	ν	St	$1St = 1cm^2/s$

Another useful term in describing a fluid is **kinematic viscosity** (ν, Greek letter nu). The kinematic viscosity is the ratio of dynamic viscosity to density and is given the unit of **stokes** [St], named after George Stokes (1819–1903), the Irish mathematician and physicist who made important contributions to science, including Stokes' law, optics, and physics. Several values of dynamic and kinematic viscosity are given in Table 12-5.

$$\nu = \frac{\mu}{\rho}$$

Table 12-5 Summary of material properaties for several liquids

Liquid	Specific Gravity	Dynamic Viscosity (μ) [cP]	Kinematic Viscosity (ν) [cSt]
Acetone	0.791	0.331	0.419
Corn syrup	1.36	1,380	1,015
Ethanol	0.789	1.194	1.513
Glycerin	1.260	1,490	1,183
Honey	1.36	5,000	3,676
Mercury	13.600	1.547	0.114
Molasses	1.400	8,000	5,714
Olive oil	0.703	101	143
SAE 30W oil	0.891	290	325
Water	1.000	1.000	1.000

COMPREHENSION CHECK 12-2

Fluid A has a dynamic viscosity of 0.5 centipoise and a specific gravity of 1.1. What is the density of Fluid A in units of pound-mass per cubic foot?

COMPREHENSION CHECK 12-3

Fluid A has a dynamic viscosity of 0.5 centipoise and a specific gravity of 1.1. What is the dynamic viscosity of Fluid A in units of pound-mass per foot second?

COMPREHENSION CHECK 12-4

Fluid A has a dynamic viscosity of 0.5 centipoise and a specific gravity of 1.1. What is the kinematic viscosity of Fluid A in units of stokes?

Elastic Materials

Elasticity is the property of an object or material that causes it to be restored to its original shape after distortion. A rubber band is easy to stretch and snaps back to near its original length when released, but it is not as elastic as a piece of piano wire. The piano wire is harder to stretch, but would be said to be more elastic than the rubber band because of the precision of its return to its original length. The term elasticity is quantified by **Young's modulus** or **modulus of elasticity** (E), the amount of deformation resulting from an applied force. Young's modulus is named for Thomas Young (1773–1829), a British scientist, who contributed to several fields: material elongation theory; optics, with his "double slit" optical experiment that led to the deduction that light travels in waves; and fluids, with the theory of surface tension and capillary action.

Like fluids, elastic materials accept a force applied over a unit area rather than a point force. **Stress** (σ, Greek letter sigma) is the amount of force applied over a unit area of the material, which has units of pressure [Pa]. The **strain** (ε, Greek letter epsilon) is the ratio of the elongation to the original length, yielding a dimensionless number. Since the modulus values tend to be large, they are usually expressed in units of Gigapascals [GPa]. The generalized second law as applied to an elastic material is shown in Table 12-6.

$$\sigma = E\varepsilon$$

Table 12-6 Generalized second law . . . applied to elastic materials

When a "system" . . .	. . . is acted upon by a "force" . . .	. . . to change a "parameter" . . .	. . . the "system" opposes the change by a "resistance"	Equation
Physical object	External push or pull (F)	Acceleration (a)	Object mass (m)	$F = ma$
Elastic object	Stress (σ)	Strain (ε)	Modulus of elasticity (E)	$\sigma = E\varepsilon$

From this discussion, you can see examples from many areas of engineering that are similar to Newton's second law. We often want to change something and find that it resists this change; this relationship is often linear. In all of these situations, we discover a coefficient that depends on the material encountered in the particular situation (mass, spring stiffness, circuit resistance, fluid viscosity, or modulus of elasticity).

Many other examples are not discussed here, such as Fourier's law of heat transfer, Fick's law of diffusion, and Darcy's law of permeability. You can enhance your understanding of your coursework by attempting to generalize the knowledge presented in a single theory to other theories that may be presented in other courses. Many different disciplines of engineering are linked by common themes, and the more you can connect these theories across disciplines, the more meaningful your classes will become.

Combinations of Springs and Circuits

When connected, both springs and circuits form a resulting system that behaves like a single spring or single resistor. In a combination of springs, the system stiffness depends on the stiffness of each individual spring and on the configuration, referred to as the effective spring constant (k_{eff}). In a network of circuits, the system resistance depends on the value of the individual resistors and on the configuration, referred to as the effective resistance (R_{eff}).

Springs in Parallel

When springs are attached in *parallel*, they must *displace the same distance* even though they may have different spring constants. The derivation below shows how this leads to an effective spring constant that is the sum of the individual spring constants in the system. Each spring is responsible for supporting a proportional amount of the force.

Writing Hooke's law for two springs each displacing the same distance (x):

$$F_1 = k_1 x \tag{a}$$
$$F_2 = k_2 x \tag{b}$$

NOTE

Springs in parallel both displace the same distance.

Solve for F_1 in terms of F_2 since the displacement is the same:

$$F_1 = k_1 \frac{F_2}{k_2} = F_2 \frac{k_1}{k_2} \tag{c}$$

Writing Hooke's law as applied to the overall system:

$$F = k_{eff} x \tag{d}$$

The total force applied to the configuration (F) is the sum of the force supported by each spring:

$$F = F_1 + F_2 \tag{e}$$

Eliminating force (F) from Equation (e) with Equation (d):

$$k_{eff} x = F_1 + F_2 \tag{f}$$

Eliminating displacement (x) with Equation (b):

$$k_{eff} \frac{F_2}{k_2} = F_1 + F_2 \tag{g}$$

Substituting for F_1 with Equation (c):

$$k_{eff} \frac{F_2}{k_2} = F_2 \frac{k_1}{k_2} + F_2 \tag{h}$$

Dividing Equation (h) by F_2:

NOTE

A system of two springs in parallel will always be stiffer than either spring individually.

$$\frac{k_{eff}}{k_2} = \frac{k_1}{k_2} + 1 \tag{i}$$

Multiplying Equation (i) by k_2 gives:

$$\boldsymbol{k_{eff} = k_1 + k_2} \tag{j}$$

Springs in Series

When two springs are attached in *series*, the *force is the same for both springs*. The effective spring constant is derived below. The applied force affects each spring as though the other spring did not exist, and each spring can stretch a different amount.

Writing Hooke's law for two springs each under the same applied force (F):

$$F = k_1 x_1 \tag{k}$$
$$F = k_2 x_2 \tag{l}$$

Solve for x_1 in terms of x_2 since the force is the same:

$$x_1 = \frac{k_2}{k_1} x_2 \tag{m}$$

Writing Hooke's law as applied to the overall system:

$$F = k_{eff} x \tag{n}$$

The total distance stretched by the configuration (x) is the sum of the distance stretched by each spring:

$$x = x_1 + x_2 \tag{o}$$

Eliminating force (F) from Equation (n) with Equation (l):

$$k_2 x_2 = k_{eff} x \tag{p}$$

Eliminating displacement (x) with Equation (o):

$$k_2 x_2 = k_{eff}(x_1 + x_2) \tag{q}$$

Substituting for x_1 with Equation (m):

$$k_2 x_2 = k_{eff}\left(\frac{k_2}{k_1} x_2 + x_2\right) \tag{r}$$

Dividing Equation (r) by x_2:

$$k_2 = k_{eff}\left(\frac{k_2}{k_1} + 1\right) \tag{s}$$

Dividing Equation (s) by k_2 gives:

$$1 = k_{eff}\left(\frac{1}{k_1} + \frac{1}{k_2}\right) \tag{t}$$

Thus,

$$k_{eff} = \frac{1}{\left(\frac{1}{k_1} + \frac{1}{k_2}\right)} = \left(\frac{1}{k_1} + \frac{1}{k_2}\right)^{-1} \tag{u}$$

These equations for two springs connected in parallel and series generalize to any number of springs. For N springs in parallel, the effective spring constant is

$$k_{eff} = k_1 + k_2 + \cdots + k_{N-1} + k_N \tag{v}$$

For N springs in series, the effective spring constant is

$$k_{eff} = \left(\frac{1}{k_1} + \frac{1}{k_2} + \cdots + \frac{1}{k_{N-1}} + \frac{1}{k_N}\right)^{-1} \tag{w}$$

● **EXAMPLE 12-3**

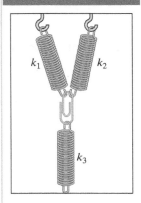

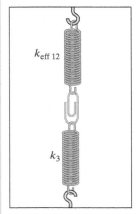

Find the displacement (x) in the spring combination shown, where Spring 1 (with a stiffness k_1) and Spring 2 (with a stiffness k_2) are connected in parallel, and the combination is then connected to Spring 3 (with a stiffness k_3) in series. Use the following values:

$$F = 0.2 \text{ N}$$
$$k_1 = 10 \text{ N/m}$$
$$k_2 = 5 \text{ N/m}$$
$$k_3 = 8 \text{ N/m}$$

First, we recognize that k_1 and k_2 are in parallel, so we can solve for an effective spring constant, using Equation (j).

$$k_{eff12} = k_1 + k_2 = 10 \text{ N/m} + 5 \text{ N/m} = 15 \text{ N/m}$$

The combination can then be redrawn to show k_{eff12} and k_3 in series.
Next, we solve for the effective spring constant using Equation (u).

$$k_{eff} = \left(\frac{1}{k_{eff12}} + \frac{1}{k_3} \right)^{-1} = \left(\frac{1}{15 \text{ N/m}} + \frac{1}{8 \text{ N/m}} \right)^{-1} = 5.2 \text{ N/m}$$

We can now solve for the displacement, using Hooke's law:

$$F = k_{eff} \, x$$
$$x = \frac{F}{k_{eff}} = \frac{0.2 \text{ N}}{5.2 \text{ N/m}} = 0.04 \text{ m} = 4 \text{ cm}$$

COMPREHENSION CHECK 12-5

You have three springs, with stiffness 1, 2, and 3 newtons per meter [N/m], respectively. How many unique spring stiffnesses can be formed with these springs? Consider each spring alone, pairs of springs in both parallel and series, and all springs used at once.

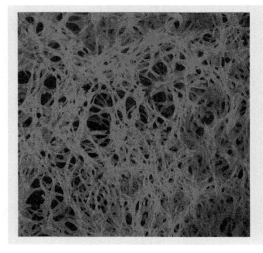

Human fibroblasts are connective tissue cells present in organs throughout the body. In this image, these cells can be seen spreading within a semi-interpenetrating network made of a polymer called polyethylene glycol diacrylate-hyaluronic acid (Pegda-HA). This material can be injected in a minimally invasive manner and cross-linked inside the body to form an insoluble gel with mechanical properties similar to many soft tissues in the human body. Such materials are being widely studied as "scaffolds" for cell transplantation in tissue engineering and regenerative medicine. The material degrades within 4–6 weeks, yielding physiological metabolites and water soluble polymers that are readily excreted through the kidneys.

Photo courtesy of K. Webb and J. Kutty

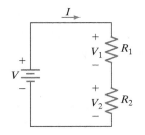

Resistors in Series

When two resistors are connected in *series*, the *current through both of the resistors is the same*, even though the value of each resistor may be different. The derivation below shows the effective resistance of two resistors connected in series. Note that the voltage is applied to the entire system.

Writing Ohm's law for two resistors each with the same current:

$$V_1 = IR_1 \tag{A}$$
$$V_2 = IR_2 \tag{B}$$

Solving for V_1 in terms of V_2 since the current is the same:

$$V_1 = R_1 \frac{V_2}{R_2} = V_2 \frac{R_1}{R_2} \tag{C}$$

Writing Ohm's law as applied to the overall system:

$$V = IR_{\text{eff}} \tag{D}$$

The total voltage applied to the configuration (V) is the sum of the voltage applied to each resistor:

$$V = V_1 + V_2 \tag{E}$$

Eliminating voltage (V) from Equation (E) with Equation (D):

$$IR_{\text{eff}} = V_1 + V_2 \tag{F}$$

Eliminating current (I) from Equation (F) with Equation (B):

$$R_{\text{eff}} \frac{V_2}{R_2} = V_1 + V_2 \tag{G}$$

Substitution for V_1 with Equation (C):

$$R_{\text{eff}} \frac{V_2}{R_2} = V_2 \frac{R_1}{R_2} + V_2 \tag{H}$$

Dividing Equation (H) by V_2:

$$R_{\text{eff}} \frac{1}{R_2} = \frac{R_1}{R_2} + 1 \tag{I}$$

Multiplying Equation (I) by R_2:

$$\boldsymbol{R_{eff} = R_1 + R_2} \tag{J}$$

NOTE

Resistors in series have the same current through both of the resistors.

NOTE

A system of two resistors in series will always provide more resistance than either resistor individually.

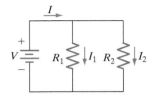

Resistors in Parallel

When two resistors are connected in *parallel*, the *voltage across both of the resistors is the same*. The current through each resistor may be different. The voltage is applied to the entire system.

Writing Ohm's law for two resistors each with the same voltage:

$$V = I_1 R_1 \tag{K}$$

$$V = I_2 R_2 \tag{L}$$

Solving for I_1 in terms of I_2 since the current is the same:

$$I_1 = \frac{R_2}{R_1} I_2 \tag{M}$$

Writing Ohm's law as applied to the overall system:

$$V = I R_{\text{eff}} \tag{N}$$

The total current (I) is the sum of the current flowing through each resistor:

$$I = I_1 + I_2 \tag{O}$$

Eliminating voltage (V) from Equation (N) using Equation (L):

$$I_2 R_2 = I R_{\text{eff}} \tag{P}$$

Eliminating current (I) using Equation (O):

$$I_2 R_2 = (I_1 + I_2) R_{\text{eff}} \tag{Q}$$

Substituting for I_1 using Equation (M):

$$I_2 R_2 = \left(\frac{R_2}{R_1} I_2 + I_2 \right) R_{\text{eff}} \tag{R}$$

Dividing Equation (R) by I_2:

$$R_2 = R_{\text{eff}} \left(\frac{R_2}{R_1} + 1 \right) \tag{S}$$

Dividing Equation (S) by R_2 gives:

$$1 = R_{\text{eff}} \left(\frac{1}{R_1} + \frac{1}{R_2} \right) \tag{T}$$

> **NOTE**
>
> Resistors in parallel have the same voltage through both of the resistors.

> **NOTE**
>
> A system of two resistors in parallel will always have less resistance than either resistor individually.

Thus,

$$\boldsymbol{R_{\text{eff}}} = \frac{1}{\frac{1}{R_1} + \frac{1}{R_2}} = \left(\frac{1}{R_1} + \frac{1}{R_2} \right)^{-1} \tag{U}$$

These equations for two resistors connected in parallel and series generalize to any number of resistors. For N resistors in parallel, the effective resistance is

$$R_{\text{eff}} = \left(\frac{1}{R_1} + \frac{1}{R_2} + \cdots + \frac{1}{R_{N-1}} + \frac{1}{R_N} \right)^{-1} \tag{V}$$

This form, along with spring equation (w) shown earlier, is sometimes referred to as the "reciprocal of the sum of the reciprocals."

For N resistors in series, the effective resistance is

$$R_{\text{eff}} = R_1 + R_2 + \cdots + R_{N-1} + R_N \tag{W}$$

WARNING!

Some of you may have seen a "simpler" form of the equation for two springs in series or two resistors in parallel.

For two springs in series: $k_{eff} = \dfrac{k_1 k_2}{k_1 + k_2}$

For two resistors in parallel: $R_{eff} = \dfrac{R_1 R_2}{R_1 + R_2}$

These forms are sometimes referred to as "the product over the sum."

THESE FORMS *DO NOT GENERALIZE* TO MORE THAN TWO ELEMENTS.

If you have three or more elements, then you must use the "reciprocal of the sum of the reciprocals" form given earlier.

● **EXAMPLE 12-4**

Find the current (I) in the circuit shown. Resistor 1 (with resistance R_1) and Resistor 2 (with resistance R_2) are connected in series, and the combination is then connected to Resistor 3 (with resistance R_3) in parallel. Use the following values:

$$V = 12 \text{ V}$$
$$R_1 = 7.5 \text{ k}\Omega$$
$$R_2 = 2.5 \text{ k}\Omega$$
$$R_3 = 40 \text{ k}\Omega$$

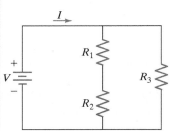

First, we recognize that R_1 and R_2 are in series, so we reduce R_1 and R_2 to a single effective resistor by using Equation (J).

$$R_{eff12} = R_1 + R_2 = 7.5 \text{ k}\Omega + 2.5 \text{ k}\Omega = 10 \text{ k}\Omega$$

Next, we can redraw the circuit so R_{eff12} and R_3 are in parallel. We solve for the effective resistance by using Equation (U).

$$R_{eff} = \left(\frac{1}{R_{eff12}} + \frac{1}{R_3} \right)^{-1} = \left(\frac{1}{10 \text{ k}\Omega} + \frac{1}{40 \text{ k}\Omega} \right)^{-1} = 8 \text{ k}\Omega$$

We can now solve the problem with Ohm's law:

$$V = IR_{eff}$$

$$I = \frac{V}{R_{eff}} = \frac{12 \text{ V}}{8 \text{ k}\Omega} = 0.0015 \text{ A} = 1.5 \text{ mA}$$

COMPREHENSION CHECK 12-6

You have three resistors with resistance 2, 2, and 3 ohms [Ω], respectively. How many unique resistances can be created with these resistors? Consider each resistor alone, pairs of resistors both in parallel and in series, and all resistors used at once.

When Are Components Connected in Series, Parallel, or Neither?

Note that in each diagram, the lines with one end loose indicate where the circuit or spring configuration is connected to other things.

Series

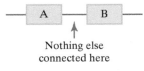

When one end (but not both) of each of two components is connected together with NOTHING ELSE CONNECTED AT THAT POINT, they are in series.

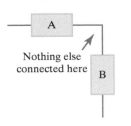

Note that they do not necessarily have to be in a straight line as shown. Electrical components can be physically mounted in any position relative to one another, and as long as a wire connects one end of each together (with nothing else connected there), they would be in series. Two springs can be connected by a string, so that the string makes a right angle direction change over a pulley, and the two springs would be in series.

Parallel

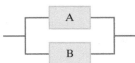

When each end of one component is connected to each of the two ends of another component, they are in parallel.

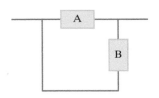

Similar to the series connection, the components do not have to be physically mounted parallel to each other or side by side, as long both ends are connected directly together with no intervening components. This is simple to do with electrical components since wire can be easily connected between any two points. Can you determine a method to physically connect two springs in parallel so that one is vertical and the other horizontal?

Sample Combinations

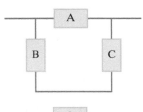

In the figure at left, B and C are in series. A is neither in series nor parallel with B or C since the lines extending to the left and right indicate connection to other stuff. A is, however, in parallel with the series combination of B and C.

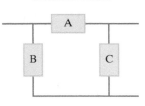

In the figure at left, no components are in series or parallel with anything since the lines extending to the left and right indicate connection to other stuff. Note the extra line at lower right.

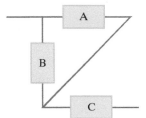

In the figure at left, A and B are in parallel. C is neither in series nor parallel with A or B. C is, however, in series with the parallel combination of A and B.

Capacitors and Inductors

In a capacitor, the **voltage** depends not only on the total charge stored, but also on the physical construction of the device, particularly the surface area of the plates. The charge (Q) stored in a capacitor is proportional to the voltage (V) across it, where C is the proportionality constant.

$$Q = CV$$

Note that C must have units of coulombs per volt, and is called **capacitance**. Capacitance is measured in units of **farads** [F], where one farad equals one coulomb per volt, or $1\ F = 1\ C/V$.

In its simplest form, an **inductor** is just a coil of wire. **Inductance** (L) is measured in units of **henrys** [H]. The voltage across an inductor is equal to the inductance of the device times the instantaneous rate of change of current through the inductor

$$V = L\frac{dI}{dt}$$

Dimensionally, the henry is one volt second per ampere [V s/A]. This can be shown to be dimensionally equal to resistance times time [Ω s] or energy per current squared [J/A^2].

For both systems, we can write a generalized form of Newton's second law, shown in Table 12-7.

Table 12-7 Generalized second law . . . applied to capacitors and inductors

When a "system" . . .	. . . is acted upon by a "force" . . .	. . . to change a "parameter" . . .	. . . the "system" opposes the change by a "resistance"	Equation
Physical object	External push or pull (F)	Acceleration (a)	Object mass (m)	$F = ma$
Capacitor	Charge (Q)	Voltage (V)	Capacitance (C)	$Q = CV$
Inductor	Voltage (V)	Rate of change of current (dI/dt)	Inductance (L)	$V = L\dfrac{dI}{dt}$

Combining Capacitors and Inductors

Mathematically, capacitors in series or parallel combine like springs, and inductors combine like resistors.

For two capacitors, C_1 and C_2 in **parallel**, the equivalent capacitance is given by

$$C_{eq} = C_1 + C_2$$

In general, for any number of capacitors in parallel, the equivalent capacitance is

$$C_{eq} = \sum_{i=1}^{N} C_i$$

On the other hand, two capacitors in **series** combine as the reciprocal of the sum of the reciprocals, given by

$$C_{eq} = \cfrac{1}{\cfrac{1}{C_1} + \cfrac{1}{C_2}}$$

or in general for any number of series capacitors

$$C_{eq} = \frac{1}{\sum\limits_{i=1}^{N} \frac{1}{C_i}}$$

To help you remember which configuration matches which mathematical form, consider that the larger the area of the plates of the capacitor, the larger the capacitance. If capacitors are connected in parallel, the total plate area connected to each terminal is greater, thus the capacitance increases. This is represented by the sum, not the reciprocal of the sum of the reciprocals.

COMPREHENSION CHECK 12-7

You have four 60 nanofarad [nF] capacitors. Using two or more of these capacitors in parallel or series, how many different equivalent capacitances can you form that are greater than 110 nF? Show the circuits for each such connection and list the resulting capacitances.

For two inductors, L_1 and L_2 in **series**, the equivalent inductance is given by

$$L_{eq} = L_1 + L_2$$

In general, for any number of inductors in series, the equivalent inductance is

$$L_{eq} = \sum_{i=1}^{N} L_i$$

On the other hand, two inductors in **parallel** combine as the reciprocal of the sum of the reciprocals, given by

$$L_{eq} = \frac{1}{\frac{1}{L_1} + \frac{1}{L_2}}$$

or in general for any number of parallel inductors

$$L_{eq} = \frac{1}{\sum\limits_{i=1}^{N} \frac{1}{L_i}}$$

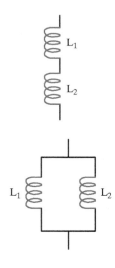

To help you remember which configuration matches which mathematical form, consider that the more turns of wire the current has to go through in an inductor, the larger the inductance. If inductors are connected in series, the total number of turns of wire the current must go through is larger, thus the inductance is larger, so this must be the sum, not the reciprocal of the sum of the reciprocals.

COMPREHENSION
CHECK 12-8

You have three 120 millihenry [mH] inductors. Can you connect two or three of these in a way that will yield an equivalent inductance of 180 mH? If not, what is the closest equivalent inductance to 180 mH you can achieve without going over 180 mH. Show the resulting connection and list the resulting inductance.

12.3 POWER FUNCTIONS

LEARN TO: Recognize the shape and boundaries of a power function shown graphically
Recognize when an equation is a power model
Determine the physical meaning and units of parameters of a power function

Trend	Equation	Data Form	Graphical Example
Power	$y = bx^m$	Positive m Value of zero at $x = 0$ ─────────────── Negative m Value of infinity at $x = 0$	

Generalized power models take the form $y = bx^m + c$. One example:

- One expression for the volume (V) of a conical frustrum with base radius (r) is

$$V = \frac{\pi (H + h)}{3} r^2 - V_T$$

where H is the height of the frustrum, h is the height of the missing conical top, and V_T is the volume of the top part of the cone that is missing. In this case, $b = \dfrac{\pi (H + h)}{3}$ and $c = -V_T$.

In this chapter, we will only consider power law models, where c is zero. In the next chapter we will discuss ways of dealing with data when the value of c is non-zero. Examples of a power model where $c = 0$:

- Many geometric formulae involving areas, volumes, etc., such as the volume of a sphere (V) as a function of radius (r):

$$V = 4/3\pi r^3$$

- Distance (d) traveled by a body undergoing constant acceleration (a) over time (t), starting from rest:

$$d = at^2$$

- Energy calculations in a variety of contexts, both mechanical and electrical, such as the kinetic energy (KE) of an object as a function of the object's velocity (v), where the constant (k) depends upon the object shape and type of motion:

$$KE = kmv^2$$

- Ideal gas law relationships, such as Boyle's law, relating volume (V) and pressure (P) of an ideal gas, holding temperature (T) and quantity of gas (n) constant:

$$V = (nRT)P^{-1}$$

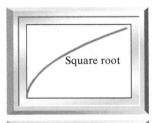

Square root

General Model Rules

Given a power system of the form $y = bx^m + c$, assuming $x \geq 0$:

- When $m = 1$, the model is a linear function.

- When $m = 0$, $y = b + c$, regardless of the value of x (y never changes).

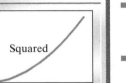

Squared

- When m is rational, the function will contain a rational exponent or may be described with a radical symbol ($\sqrt{}$). Certain rational exponents have special names ($1/2$ is "square root," $1/3$ is "cube root").

- When m is an integer, the function will contain an integer exponent on the independent variable. Certain exponents have special names (2 is "squared," 3 is "cubed").

- When $0 < |m| < 1$ and $x < 0$, the function may contain complex values.

● EXAMPLE 12-5

NOTE

With a positive integer exponent, the dependent variable (volume) increases as the independent variable (radius) increases. This observation is true with any power model with a positive integer exponent.

The volume (V) of a cone is calculated in terms of the radius (r) and height (H) of the cone. The relationship is described by the following equation:

$$V = \frac{\pi r^2 H}{3}$$

Given a height of 10 centimeters, calculate the volume of the cone when the radius is 3 centimeters.

$$V = \frac{\pi (3 \text{ cm})^2 (10 \text{ cm})}{3} \approx 94.2 \text{ cm}^3$$

What is the volume of the cone when the radius is 8 centimeters?

$$V = \frac{\pi (8 \text{ cm})^2 (10 \text{ cm})}{3} \approx 670 \text{ cm}^3$$

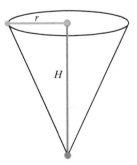

● **EXAMPLE 12-6**

The resistance (R [g/(cm^{4}s)]) of blood flow in an artery or vein depends upon the radius (r [cm]), as described by **Poiseuille's equation**:

$$R = \frac{8\mu L}{\pi} r^{-4}$$

The dynamic viscosity of blood (μ [g/(cm s)]) and length of the artery or vein (L [cm]) are constants in the system. In studying the effects of a cholesterol-lowering drug, you mimic the constricting of an artery being clogged with cholesterol, shown in the illustration. You use the data you collect to create the following graph.

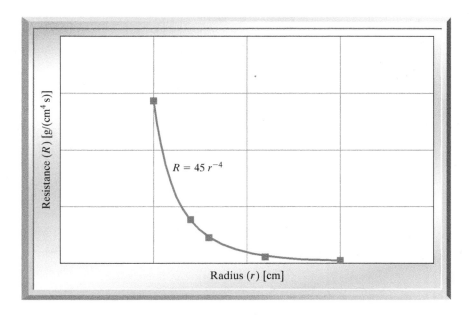

NOTE

With a negative integer exponent, the dependent variable (resistance) decreases as the independent variable (radius) increases. This trend is true for any power model with a negative integer exponent.

If the length of the artificial artery tested was 505 centimeters, what is the dynamic viscosity of the sample used to mimic blood, in units of grams per centimeter second [g/(cm s)]?

The constant "45" has physical meaning, found by comparison to the theoretical expression.

In theory: $R = \dfrac{8\,\mu L}{\pi} r^{-4}$ and from graph: $R = 45r^{-4}$

By comparison:

$$45\frac{g}{s} = \frac{8\,\mu L}{\pi} = \frac{8\,\mu\,(505\text{ cm})}{\pi}$$

$$\mu = 0.035 \text{ g/(cm s)}$$

**COMPREHENSION
CHECK 12-9**

The graph shows the ideal gas law relationship ($PV = nRT$) between pressure (P) and volume (V). If the tank is at a temperature of 300 kelvins and is filled with nitrogen (formula, N_2; molecular weight, 28 grams per mole), what is the mass of gas in the tank in units of grams?

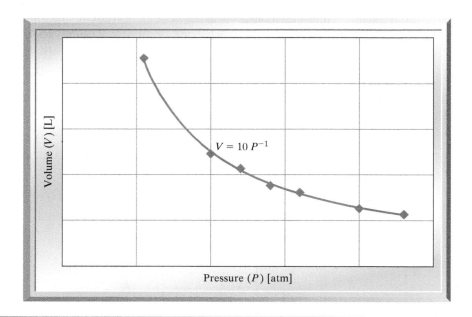

$V = 10\,P^{-1}$

Volume (V) [L]

Pressure (P) [atm]

**COMPREHENSION
CHECK 12-10**

The graph above shows the ideal gas law relationship ($PV = nRT$) between pressure (P) and volume (V). If the tank is filled with 10 grams of oxygen (formula, O_2; molecular weight, 32 grams per mole), what is the temperature of the tank in units of degrees Celsius?

12.4 EXPONENTIAL FUNCTIONS

Trend	Equation	Data Form	Graphical Example
Exponential	$y = be^{mx} + c$	Defined value at $x = 0$ ($y = b + c$) Positive m: asymptotic to c for large negative values of x Negative m: asymptotic to c at large positive values of x	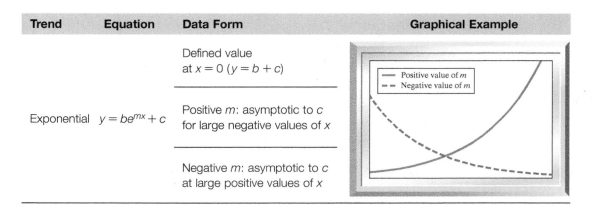

Exponential models take the form $y = be^{mx} + c$. Examples include

- A newly forged ingot has an initial temperature (T_0) and is left to cool at room temperature (T_R). The temperature (T) of the ingot as it cools over time (t) is given by

$$T = (T_0 - T_R)\, e^{mt} + T_R$$

where m will be a negative value and $c = T_R$. Note that $b = T_0 - T_R$, so that at $t = 0$, $T = T_0$ as expected.

- The voltage (V) across a capacitor (C) as a function of time (t), with initial voltage (V_0) discharging its stored charge through resistance (R):

$$V = V_0 e^{-t/(RC)}$$

- The number (N) of people infected with a virus such as smallpox or H1N1 flu as a function of time (t), given the following: an initial number of infected individuals (N_0), no artificial immunization available and dependence on contact conditions between species (C):

$$N = N_0 e^{Ct}$$

- The transmissivity (T) of light through a gas as a function of path length (L), given an absorption cross-section (s) and density of absorbers (N):

$$T = e^{-sNL}$$

- The growth of bacteria (C) as a function of time (t), given an initial concentration of bacteria (C_0) and depending on growth conditions (g):

$$C = C_0 e^{gt}$$

Note that all exponents must be dimensionless, and thus unitless. For example, in the first equation, the quantity m *must have units of inverse time so that the quantity of* mt *will be unitless.*

Note that the intercept value (c) is zero in all of the above examples except the first one.

General Model Rules

Given an exponential system of the form $y = be^{mx} + c$:

- When $m = 0$, $y = b + c$ regardless of the value of x (y never changes).
- When $m > 0$, the model is a **growth function**. The minimum value of the growth model for $x \geq 0$ is $b + c$. As x approaches infinity, y approaches infinity.
- When $m < 0$, the model is a **decay function**. The value of the decay model approaches c as x approaches infinity. When $x = 0$, $y = b + c$.

What Is "e"?

The **exponential constant** "e" is a transcendental number, thus also an irrational number, that can be rounded to 2.71828. It is defined as the base of the natural logarithm function. Sometimes, e is referred to as **Euler's number** or the **Napier constant**. The reference to Euler comes from the Swiss mathematician Leonhard Euler (pronounced "oiler," 1707–1783), who made vast contributions to calculus, including the notation and terminology used today. John Napier (1550–1617) was a Scottish mathematician credited with inventing logarithms and popularizing the use of the decimal point.

Growth Functions

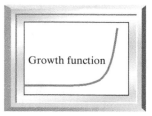

Growth function

An exponential **growth function** is a type of function that increases without bound as the independent variable increases. For a system to be considered an exponential growth function, the exponential growth model ($y = be^{mx} + c$) with m is a positive value that represents the **growth rate**.

A more general exponential growth function can be formed by replacing the Napier constant with an arbitrary constant, or $y = ba^{mx} + c$. In general, a must be greater than 1 for the system to be a growth function. The value of a is referred to as the *base*, m is the *growth rate*, b is the *initial value*, and c is a *vertical shift*. Note that when $a = 1$ or $m = 0$, the system is reduced to $y = b + c$, which is a constant.

● EXAMPLE 12-7

In 1965, Gordon E. Moore, co-founder of Intel Corporation, claimed in a paper that the number of transistors on an integrated circuit will double every 2 years. This idea by Moore was later referred to as **Moore's law**. The Intel 4004 CPU was released in 1971 as the first commercially available microprocessor. The Intel 4004 CPU contained 2,300 transistors. This system can be modeled with the following growth function:

$$T = T_0 2^{t/2}$$

In the equation, T_0 represents the initial number of transistors, and t is the number of years since T_0 transistors were observed on an integrated circuit. Predict the number of transistors on an integrated circuit in 1974 using the Intel 4004 CPU as the initial condition.

$$t = 1974 - 1971 = 3 \text{ years}$$
$$T = T_0 2^{t/2} = 2,300\left(2^{3/2}\right) = 2,300\left(2^{1.5}\right) \approx 6,505 \text{ transistors}$$

In 1974, the Intel 8080 processor came out with 4,500 transistors on the circuit.

Predict the number of transistors on integrated circuits in 1982 using the Intel 4004 CPU as the initial condition.

$$t = 1982 - 1971 = 11 \text{ years}$$
$$T = T_0 2^{t/2} = 2,300\left(2^{11/2}\right) = 2,300\left(2^{5.5}\right) \approx 104,087 \text{ transistors}$$

In 1982, the Intel 286 microprocessor came out with 134,000 transistors in the CPU.

Predict the number of transistors on integrated circuits in 2007 using the Intel 4004 CPU as the initial condition.

$$t = 2007 - 1971 = 36 \ years$$

$$T = T_0 2^{t/2} = 2{,}300\left(2^{36/2}\right) = 2{,}300\left(2^{18}\right) \approx 603{,}000{,}000 \ transistors$$

In 2007, the NVIDIA G80 came out with 681,000,000 transistors in the CPU.

No one really knows how long Moore's law will hold up. It is perhaps interesting to note that claims have consistently been made for the past 30 years that Moore's law will only hold up for another 10 years. Although many prognosticators are still saying this, some are not. There is, however, a limit to how small a transistor can be made. Any structure has to be at least one atom wide, for example, and as they become ever smaller, quantum effects will probably wreak havoc. Of course, chips can be made larger, multilayer structures can be built, new technologies may be developed (the first functional memristor was demonstrated in 2008), and so forth.

● **EXAMPLE 12-8**

An environmental engineer has obtained a bacteria culture from a municipal water sample and allowed the bacteria to grow. After several hours of data collection, the following graph is created. The growth of bacteria is modeled by the following equation, where B_0 is the initial concentration of bacteria at time zero, and g is the growth constant.

$$B = B_0 \, e^{gt}$$

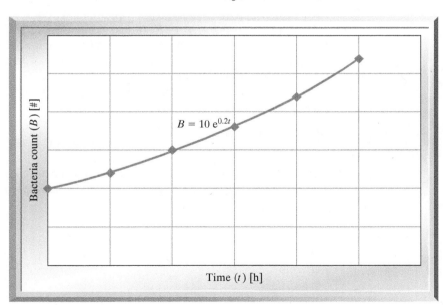

What was the initial concentration of bacteria?

In theory: $B = B_0 e^{gt}$ and from graph: $B = 10e^{0.2t}$

By comparison: $B_0 = 10$ bacteria

What was the growth constant (g) of this bacteria strain?

In theory: $B = B_0 \, e^{gt}$ and from graph: $B = 10e^{0.2t}$

By comparison: $g = 0.2$ per hour. Recall that exponents must be unitless, so the quantity of ($g\,t$) must be a unitless group. To be unitless, g must have units of inverse time.

The engineer wants to know how long it will take for the bacteria culture population to grow to 30,000.

To calculate the amount of time, plug in 30,000 for B and solve for t:

$$30{,}000 = 10e^{0.2t}$$

$$3{,}000 = e^{0.2t}$$

$$\ln(3{,}000) = \ln(e^{0.2t}) = 0.2t$$

$$t = \frac{\ln(3{,}000)}{0.2\left[\frac{1}{h}\right]} = 40 \text{ h}$$

Decay Functions

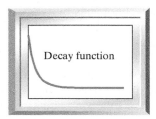

Decay function

A **decay function** is a type of function that decreases and asymptotically approaches a value as the independent variable increases. In the exponential decay model $(y = be^{-mx} + c)$, m is a positive value that represents the **decay rate**.

● EXAMPLE 12-9

An electrical engineer wants to determine how long it will take for a particular capacitor in a circuit to discharge. The engineer wired a voltage source across a capacitor (C, farads) and a resistor (R, ohms) connected in series. After the capacitor is fully charged, the circuit is completed between the capacitor and resistor, and the voltage source is removed from the circuit. The product of R and C in a circuit like this is called the "time constant" and is usually denoted by the Greek letter tau ($\tau = RC$).

The following equation can be used to calculate the voltage across a discharging capacitor at a particular time:

$$V = V_0 e^{-\frac{t}{\tau}} = V_0 e^{-\frac{t}{RC}}$$

Assuming a resistance of 100 kiloohms [kΩ], a capacitance of 100 microfarads [μF], and an initial voltage (V_0) of 20 volts [V], determine the voltage across the capacitor after 10 seconds.

$$V = 20 \text{ [V] } e^{-\frac{10\text{ s}}{(100\text{ k}\Omega)(100\text{ }\mu\text{F})}}$$

$$= 20 \text{ [V] } e^{-\frac{10\text{ s}}{(100 \times 10^3\Omega)(100 \times 10^{-6}\text{F})}} \approx 7.36 \text{ V}$$

Assuming a resistance of 200 kiloohms [kΩ], a capacitance of 100 microfarads [μF], and an initial voltage (V_0) of 20 volts [V], determine the voltage across the capacitor after 20 seconds.

$$V = 20[V]e^{-\frac{20\text{ s}}{(200\text{ k}\Omega)(100\text{ }\mu\text{F})}} \approx 7.36 \text{ V}$$

Note that doubling the resistance in the circuit doubles the amount of time required to discharge the capacitor. In RC circuits, it is easy to increase the discharge time of a capacitor by increasing the resistance in the circuit.

NOTE

Exponential models are often given in the form $y = be^{-t/\tau} + c$, where t is time; thus τ also has units of time. In this case, the constant τ is often called the **time constant**.

Basically, the time constant is a measure of the time required for the response of the system to go approximately two-thirds of the way from its initial value to its final value, as t approaches infinity. The exact value is not $2/3$, but $1 - e^{-1} \approx 0.632$ or 63.2%.

The decay of a radioactive isotope was tracked over a number of hours, resulting in the following data. The decay of a radioactive element is modeled by the following equation, where C_0 is the initial amount of the element at time zero, and k is the decay constant of the isotope.

$$C = C_0 e^{-kt}$$

Determine the initial concentration and decay constant of the isotope, including value and units.

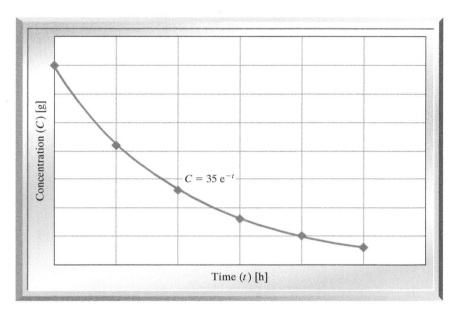

$C = 35\, e^{-t}$

Picture of a single mortar shot. The creation of fireworks involves knowledge of chemistry (what materials to include to get the desired colors), physics and dynamics (what amounts of combustible charge should be included to launch the object properly), and artistry (what colors, shapes, patterns, and sounds the firework should emit such that it is enjoyable to watch). This picture is a close-up of the instant when a firework is detonating.

Photo courtesy of E. Fenimore

In-Class Activities

ICA 12-1

The graph shows the ideal gas law relationship ($PV = nRT$) between volume (V) and temperature (T).

(a) What are the units of the slope (0.0175)?
(b) If the tank has a pressure of 1.2 atmospheres and is filled with nitrogen (formula, N_2; molecular weight, 28 grams per mole), what is the mass of gas in the tank in units of grams?
(c) If the tank is filled with 10 grams of oxygen (formula, O_2; molecular weight, 32 grams per mole), what is the pressure of the tank (P) in units of atmospheres?

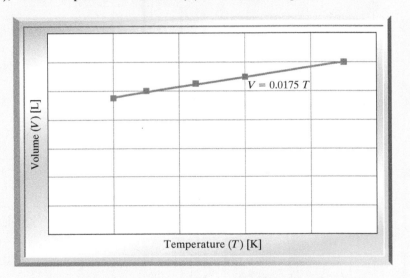

ICA 12-2

An inductor is an electrical device that can store energy in the form of a magnetic field. In the simplest form, an inductor is a cylindrical coil of wire, and its inductance (L), measured in henrys [H], can be calculated by

$$L = \frac{\mu_0 n^2 A}{\ell}$$

where

$\mu_0 =$ permeability of free space $= 4\pi \times 10^{-7}$ [newtons per ampere squared, N/A^2]
$n \ =$ number of turns of wire [dimensionless]
$A =$ cross-sectional area of coil [square meters, m^2]
$\ell \ =$ length of coil [meters, m]
$L =$ inductance [henrys, H] $= [J/A^2]$

Several inductors were fabricated with the same number of turns of wire (n) and the same length (ℓ), but with different diameters, thus different cross-sectional areas (A). The inductances were measured and plotted as a function of cross-sectional area, and a mathematical model was developed to describe the relationship, as shown on the graph below.

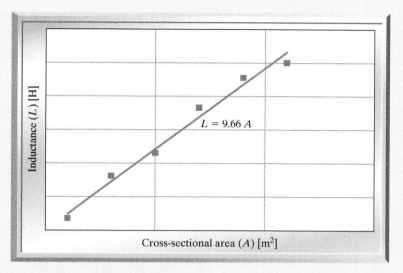

$L = 9.66\,A$

(a) What are the units of the slope (9.66)?
(b) For an inductor fabricated as described above, what is its diameter if its inductance is 0.2 henrys? Give your answer in centimeters.
(c) If the length of the coil (ℓ) equals 0.1 meter, how many turns of wire (n) are in the inductor?

ICA 12-3

Solid objects, such as your desk or a rod of aluminum, can conduct heat. The magnitude of the thermal diffusivity of the material determines how quickly the heat moves through a given amount of material. The equation for thermal diffusivity (α) is given by:

$$\alpha = \frac{k}{\rho\, C_p}$$

Experiments are conducted to change the thermal conductivity (k) of the material while holding the specific heat (C_p) and the density (ρ) constant. The results are shown graphically.

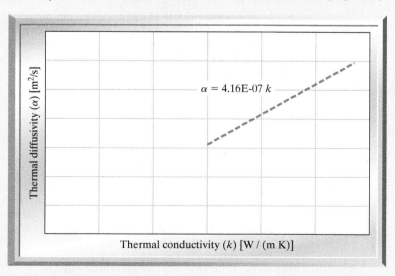

$\alpha = 4.16\text{E-07}\,k$

(a) What are the units of the constant 4.16×10^{-7}? Simplify your answer.
(b) If the specific heat of the material is 890 joules per kilogram kelvin, what is the density of the material?
(c) If the material has a density of 4,500 kilograms per cubic meter, what is the specific heat of the material in units of joules per kilogram kelvin?

ICA 12-4

Mercury has a dynamic viscosity of 1.55 centipoises and a specific gravity of 13.6.

(a) What is the density of mercury in units of kilograms per cubic meter?
(b) What is the dynamic viscosity of mercury in units of pound-mass per foot second?
(c) What is the dynamic viscosity of mercury in units of pascal seconds?
(d) What is the kinematic viscosity of mercury in units of stokes?

ICA 12-5

SAE 10W30 motor oil has a dynamic viscosity of 0.17 kilograms per meter second and a specific gravity of 0.876.

(a) What is the density of the motor oil in units of kilograms per cubic meter?
(b) What is the dynamic viscosity of the motor oil in units of pound-mass per foot second?
(c) What is the dynamic viscosity of the motor oil in units of centipoise?
(d) What is the kinematic viscosity of the motor oil in units of stokes?

ICA 12-6

You have two springs each of stiffness 1 newton per meter [N/m] and one spring of stiffness 2 newtons per meter [N/m].

(a) There are ___ configurations possible, with ___ unique combinations, resulting in ___ different stiffness values.
   A "configuration" is a way of combining the springs. For example, two springs in parallel is one configuration; two springs in series is a second configuration.
   A "combination" is the specific way of combining given springs to form an effective spring constant. For example, combining Spring #1 and #2 in parallel is one combination; combining Spring #1 and #3 in parallel is a second combination. These combinations may or may not result in a unique effective spring constant.
(b) What is the stiffest combination, and what is the spring constant of this combination?
(c) What is the least stiff combination, and what is the spring constant of this combination?

ICA 12-7

You have three resistors of resistance 30 ohm [Ω].

(a) There are ___ configurations possible, with ___ unique combinations, resulting in ___ different resistance values.
   A "configuration" is a way of combining the resistors. For example, two resistors in parallel is one configuration; two resistors in series is a second configuration.
   A "combination" is the specific way of combining given resistors to form an effective resistance. For example, combining Resistor #1 and #2 in parallel is one combination; combining Resistor #1 and #3 in parallel is a second combination. These combinations may or may not result in a unique effective resistance.
(b) What is the greatest resistance that can be made from a combination of resistors, and what is the effective resistance of this combination?
(c) What is the least resistance that can be made from a combination of resistors, and what is the effective resistance of this combination?

ICA 12-8

Four springs were tested, with the results shown graphically below. Use the graph to answer the following questions.

(a) Which spring is the stiffest?
(b) Which spring, if placed in parallel with Spring C, would yield the stiffest combination?
(c) Which spring, if placed in series with Spring C, would yield the stiffest combination?
(d) Rank the following combinations in order of stiffness:

Spring A and Spring D are hooked in parallel
Spring B and Spring C are hooked in series, then connected with Spring D in parallel
Spring A
Spring D

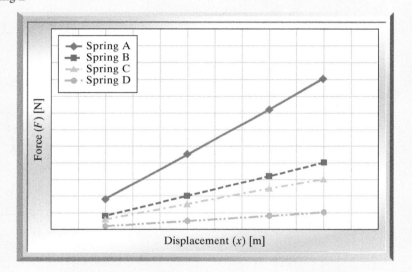

ICA 12-9

Four circuits were tested, with the results shown graphically below. Use the graph to answer the following questions.

(a) Which resistor gives the most resistance?
(b) What is the resistance of Resistor A?
(c) Which resistor, if placed in parallel with Resistor C, would yield the highest resistance?
(d) Which resistor, if placed in series with Resistor C, would yield the highest resistance?

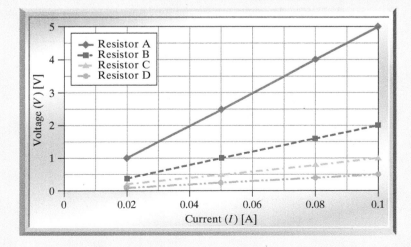

ICA 12-10

Assume you have an unlimited number of inductors all with the same inductance L.

(a) How would you connect 4 of these inductors so that the equivalent inductance equals L?

(b) How would you connect N^2 of these inductors so that the equivalent inductance equals L?

ICA 12-11

(a) The equivalent capacitance of the circuit shown is 6 nF. Determine the value of C.

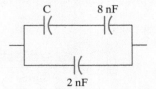

(b) The equivalent capacitance of the circuit shown is 5 nF. Determine the value of C.

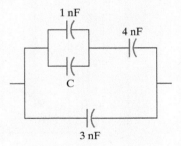

ICA 12-12

A standard guitar, whether acoustic or electric, has six strings, all with essentially the same total length between the bridge and the nut at the tuning head. Each string vibrates at a different frequency determined by the tension on the string and the mass per unit length of the string. In order to create pitches (notes) other than these six, the guitarist presses the strings down against the fretboard, thus shortening the length of the strings and changing their frequencies. In other words, the vibrating frequency of a string depends on tension, length, and mass per unit length of the string.

The equation for the fundamental frequency of a vibrating string is given by

$$f = \frac{\sqrt{T/\mu}}{2L}$$

where

f = frequency [Hz]
T = string tension [N]
μ = mass per unit length [kg/m]
L = string length [m]

Many electric guitars have a device often called a "whammy" bar or a "tremolo" bar that allows the guitarist to change the tension on the strings quickly and easily, thus changing the frequency of the strings. (Think of Jimi Hendrix simulating "the rockets' red glare, the bombs bursting in air" in his rendition of *The Star Spangled Banner* – a true *tour de force*.) In designing a new whammy bar, we test our design by collecting data using a single string on the guitar and creating a graph of the observed frequency at different string tensions as shown.

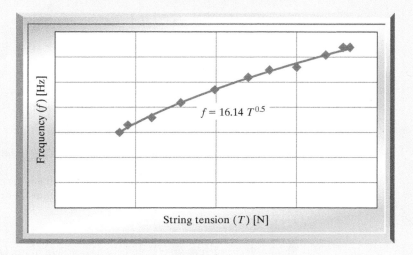

(a) What are the units of the coefficient (16.14)?
(b) If the observed frequency is 150 hertz, what is the string tension in newtons?
(c) If mass per unit length is 2.3 grams per meter, what is the length of the string in meters?
(d) If the length of the string is 0.67 meters, what is the mass per unit length in kilograms per meter?

ICA 12-13

A standard guitar, whether acoustic or electric, has six strings, all with essentially the same total length between the bridge and the nut at the tuning head. Each string vibrates at a different frequency determined by the tension on the string and the mass per unit length of the string. In order to create pitches (notes) other than these six, the guitarist presses the strings down against the fretboard, thus shortening the length of the strings and changing their frequencies. In other words, the vibrating frequency of a string depends on tension, length, and mass per unit length of the string.

The equation for the fundamental frequency of a vibrating string is given by

$$f = \frac{\sqrt{T/\mu}}{2L}$$

where

f = frequency [Hz]
T = string tension [N]
μ = mass per unit length [kg/m]
L = string length [m]

Many electric guitars have a device often called a "whammy" bar or a "tremolo" bar that allows the guitarist to change the tension on the strings quickly and easily, thus changing the frequency of the strings. (Think of Jimi Hendrix simulating "the rockets red glare, the bombs bursting in air" in his rendition of *The Star Spangled Banner* – a true *tour de force*.) In designing a new whammy bar, we test our design by collecting data using a single string on the guitar and creating a graph of the observed frequency at different string lengths as shown.

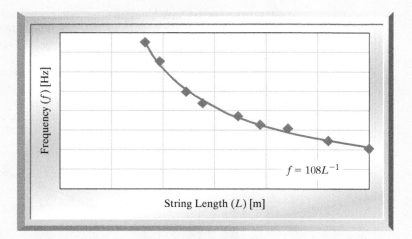

(a) Is the relationship between frequency and length linear, power, or exponential?
(b) What are the units of the coefficient (108)?
(c) If the tension on the string is 135 newtons, what is the mass per unit length in grams per meter?
(d) If the mass per length of the string is 3.5 grams per meter, what is the tension in newtons?

ICA 12-14

Solid objects, such as your desk or a rod of aluminum, can conduct heat. The magnitude of the thermal diffusivity of the material determines how quickly the heat moves through a given amount of material. The equation for thermal diffusivity (α) is given by:

$$\alpha = \frac{k}{\rho \, C_p}$$

Experiments are conducted to change the specific heat (C_p) of the material while holding the thermal conductivity (k) and the density (ρ) constant. The results are shown graphically.

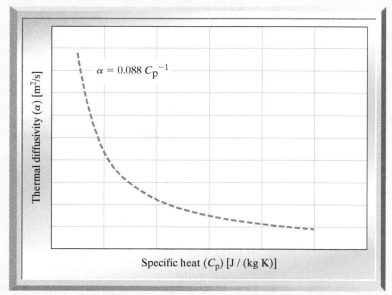

(a) What are the units of the constant 0.088? Simplify your answer.
(b) If the thermal conductivity of the material is 237 watts per meter kelvin, what is the density of the material?
(c) If the material has a density of 4,500 kilograms per cubic meter, what is the thermal conductivity of the material in units of watts per meter kelvin?

ICA 12-15

Eutrophication is a process whereby lakes, estuaries, or slow-moving streams receive excess nutrients that stimulate excessive plant growth. This enhanced plant growth, often called an algal bloom, reduces dissolved oxygen in the water when dead plant material decomposes and can cause other organisms to die. Nutrients can come from many sources, such as fertilizers; deposition of nitrogen from the atmosphere; erosion of soil containing nutrients; and sewage treatment plant discharges. Water with a low concentration of dissolved oxygen is called hypoxic. A biosystems engineering models the algae growth in a lake. The concentration of algae (C), measured in grams per milliliter [g/mL], can be calculated by

$$C = C_0 e^{\left(\frac{kt}{r}\right)}$$

where

C_0 = initial concentration of algae [?]
k = multiplication rate of the algae [?]
r = estimated nutrient supply amount [mg of nutrient per mL of sample water]
t = time [days]

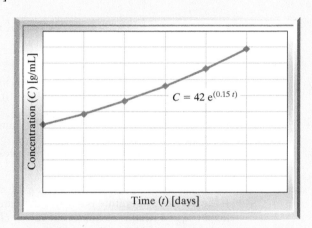

$C = 42\, e^{(0.15\,t)}$

(a) For the exponential model shown, list the value and units of the parameters m and b. You do not need to simplify any units. Recall that an exponential model has the form: $y = be^{mx}$.
(b) What are the units on the multiplication rate of the algae (k)?
(c) If the algae are allowed to grow for 10 days with an estimated nutrient supply of 3 milligrams of nutrient per milliliter of water sample, what is the multiplication rate of the algae (k)?

ICA 12-16

The graph below shows the relationship between current and voltage in a 1N4148 small signal diode (a semiconductor device that allows current to flow in one direction but not the other).

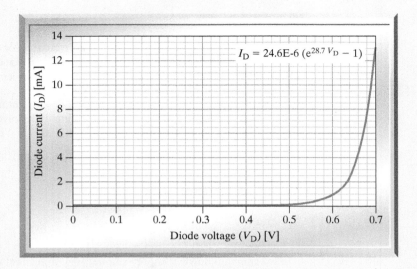

Semiconductor diodes can be characterized by the Shockley Equation:

$$I_D = I_0 \left(e^{\frac{qV_D}{nkT}} - 1 \right)$$

where

I_D is the diode current [amperes]

I_0 is the reverse saturation current, constant for any specific diode

q is the charge on a single electron, 1.602×10^{-19} coulombs

V_D is the voltage across the diode [volts]

n is the emission coefficient, having a numerical value typically between 1 and 2, and constant for any specific device.

k is Boltzmann's Constant, 1.381×10^{-23} joules per kelvin

T is the temperature of the device [kelvin]

(a) What are the units of the −1 following the exponential term? Justify your answer.

(b) If the device temperature is 100 degrees Fahrenheit, what are the units of the emission coefficient, n, and what is its numerical value? (*Hint: Electrical power [W] equals a volt times an ampere: $P = VI$. One ampere equals one coulomb per second.*)

(c) What is the numerical value and units of the reverse saturation current, I_0? Use an appropriate metric prefix in your final answer.

ICA 12-17

The total quantity (mass) of a radioactive substance decreases (decays) with time as

$$m = m_0 e^{-\frac{t}{\tau}}$$

where

$t = $ time [days]

$\tau = $ time constant

$m_0 = $ initial mass (at $t = 0$)

$m = $ mass at time t [mg]

A few milligrams each of three different isotopes of uranium were assayed for isotopic composition over a period of several days to determine the decay rate of each. The data was graphed and a mathematical model derived to describe the decay of each isotope.

(a) What are the units of τ if time is measured in days?

(b) What is the initial amount of each isotope at $t = 0$?

Isotope	Half-life [days]
230U	20.8
231U	4.2
237U	6.75
240U	0.59

(c) When will 1 milligram of the original isotope to remain in each sample?

(d) Four isotopes of uranium are shown in the table with their half-lives. Which isotope most likely matches each of the three samples? Note that one isotope does not have a match on the graph.

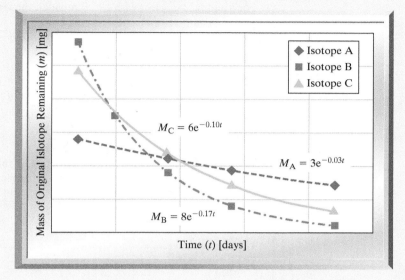

ICA 12-18

Match the data series from the options shown on the graph to the following model types. You may assume that power and exponential models do not have a constant offset. You may also assume that only positive values are shown on the two axes. For each match, write "Series X," where X is the appropriate letter, A through F. If no curve matches the specified criterion, write "No Match." If more than one curve matches a given specification, list both series.

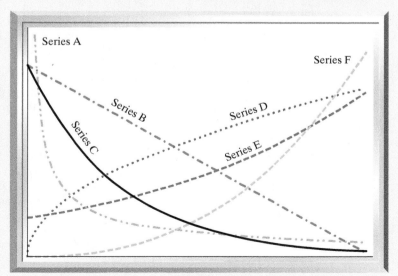

(a) Exponential, negative numeric value in exponent

(b) Power, negative numeric value in exponent

(c) Linear, negative slope

(d) Exponential, positive numeric value in exponent

(e) Power, positive numeric value in exponent

1. For a simple capacitor with two flat plates, the capacitance (C) [F] can be calculated by

$$C = \frac{\varepsilon_r \varepsilon_0 A}{d}$$

where

   $\varepsilon_0 = 8.854 \times 10^{-12}$ [F/m] (the permittivity of free space in farads per meter)
   ε_r = relative static permittivity, a property of the insulator [dimensionless]
   A = area of overlap of the plates [m^2]
   d = distance between the plates [m]

   Several experimental capacitors were fabricated with different plate areas (A), but with the same inter-plate distance ($d = 1.2$ mm) and the same insulating material, and thus the same relative static permittivity (ε_r). The capacitance of each device was measured and plotted versus the plate area. The graph and trendline are shown below. The numeric scales were deliberately omitted.

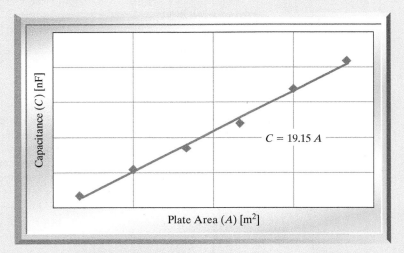

   (a) What are the units of the slope (19.15)?
   (b) If the capacitance is 2 nanofarads [nF], what is the area (A) of the plates?
   (c) What is the relative static permittivity of the insulating layer?
   (d) If the distance between the plates were doubled, how would the capacitance be affected?

2. When we wish to generate hydroelectric power, we build a dam to back up the water in a river. If the water has a height (H, in units of feet) above the downstream discharge, and we can discharge water through the turbines at a rate (Q, in units of cubic feet per second [cfs]), the maximum power (P, in units of kilowatts) we can expect to generate is:

$$P = CHQ$$

   For a small "run of the river" hydroelectric facility, we have obtained the following data.

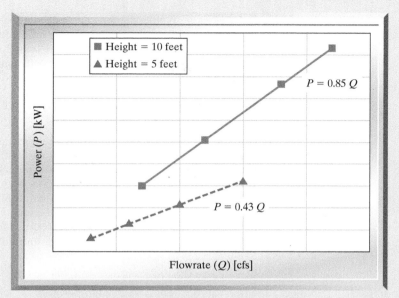

(a) Using the trendline results, and examining the general equation above, determine the value and units of the coefficient C for a height of 10 feet.

(b) If the flow rate was 15 cubic feet per second and the height is 3 meters, what would the power output be in units of horsepower?

(c) If the flow rate was 10 cubic feet per second and the height is 8 meters, what would the power output be in units of horsepower?

3. When rain falls over an area for a sufficiently long time, it will run off and collect at the bottom of hills and eventually find its way into creeks and rivers. A simple way to estimate the maximum discharge flow rate (Q, in units of cubic feet per second [cfs]) from a watershed of area (A, in units of acres) with a rainfall intensity (i, in units of inches per hour) is given by an expression commonly called the Rational Method, as

$$Q = CiA$$

Values of C vary between about 0 (for flat rural areas) to almost 1 (in urban areas with a large amount of paved area).

    A survey of a number of rainfall events was made over a 10-year period for three different watersheds. The data that resulted is given in the table below. Watershed A is 120 acres, B is 316 acres, and C is 574 acres.

Storm event	Watershed	Rainfall Intensity (i) [in/h]	Maximum Runoff (Q) [cfs]
1	A	0.5	30
2	A	1.1	66
3	A	1.6	96
4	A	2.1	126
5	B	0.3	47
6	B	0.7	110
7	B	1.2	188
8	B	1.8	283
9	C	0.4	115
10	C	1	287
11	C	1.5	430
12	C	2.4	690

(a) Create a graph containing all three watersheds, with flowrate on the ordinate and fit linear trendlines to obtain a simple model for each watershed.
From the information given and the trendline model obtained, answer the following:

(b) What is the value and units of the coefficient C?

(c) What would the maximum flow rate be from a watershed of 400 acres if the rainfall intensity was 0.6 inches per hour?

(d) How long would it take at this flowrate to fill an Olympic sized swimming pool that is 50 meters long, 20 meters wide, and 2 meters deep?

4. You are experimenting with several liquid metal alloys to find a suitable replacement for the mercury used in thermometers. You have attached capillary tubes with a circular cross-section and an inside diameter of 0.3 millimeters to reservoirs containing 5 cubic centimeters of each alloy. You mark the position of the liquid in each capillary tube when the temperature is 20 degrees Celsius, systematically change the temperature, and measure the distance the liquid moves in the tube as it expands or contracts with changes in temperature. Note that negative values correspond to contraction of the material due to lower temperatures. The data you collected for four different alloys is shown in the table below.

Alloy G1		Alloy G2		Alloy G3		Alloy G4	
Temperature (T) [°C]	Distance (d) [cm]	Temperature (T) [°C]	Distance (d) [cm]	Temperature (T) [°C]	Distance (d) [cm]	Temperature (T) [°C]	Distance (d) [cm]
22	1.05	21	0.95	24	2.9	25	5.1
27	3.05	29	7.65	30	7.2	33	13.8
34	6.95	33	10.6	34	9.8	16	−4.3
14	−3.5	17	−2.6	19	−0.6	13	−7.05
9	−5.1	3	−14.8	12	−6.15	6	−14.65
2	−8.7	−2	−19.8	4	−11.5	−2	−22.15
−5	−11.7	−8	−25.4	−5	−18.55	−6	−26.3
−11	−15.5					−12	−32.4

(a) In Excel, create two new columns for each compound to calculate the change in temperature (ΔT) relative to 20°C (for example, 25°C gives $\Delta T = 5$°C) and the corresponding change in volume (ΔV).
Plot the change in volume versus the change in temperature; fit a linear trendline to each data set.

(b) From the trendline equations, determine the value and units of the coefficient of thermal expansion, β, for each alloy. Note that $\Delta V = \beta V \Delta T$, where V is the initial volume.

(c) There is a small constant offset (C) in each trendline equation $(\Delta V = \beta V \Delta T + C)$. What is the physical origin of this constant term? Can it be safely ignored? In other words, is its effect on the determination of β negligible?

5. The resistance of a wire $(R$ [ohm]$)$ is a function of the wire dimensions $(A =$ cross-sectional area, $L =$ length$)$ and material $(\rho =$ resistivity$)$ according to the relationship

$$R = \frac{\rho L}{A}$$

The resistance of three wires was tested. All wires had the same cross-sectional area.

Length (L) [m]	0.01	0.1	0.25	0.4	0.5	0.6
Resistance Wire 1 (R1) [Ω]	8.00E-05	8.00E-04	2.00E-03	3.50E-03	4.00E-03	4.75E-03
Resistance Wire 2 (R2) [Ω]	4.75E-05	4.80E-04	1.00E-03	2.00E-03	2.50E-03	3.00E-03
Resistance Wire 3 (R3) [Ω]	1.50E-04	1.70E-03	4.25E-03	7.00E-03	8.50E-03	1.00E-02

(a) Plot the data and fit a linear trendline model to each wire.
(b) From the following chart, match each wire (1, 2, and 3) with the correct material according to the results of the resistivity determined from the trendlines, assuming a 0.2-centimeter diameter wire was used.

Material	Resistivity (ρ) [Ωm] $\times 10^{-8}$
Aluminum	2.65
Copper	1.68
Iron	9.71
Silver	1.59
Tungsten	5.60

6. Use the figure shown to answer the following questions.

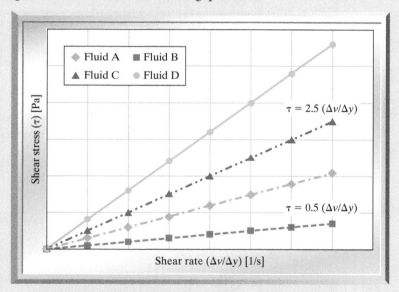

(a) Which fluid has the lowest dynamic viscosity?
(b) What is the dynamic viscosity of Fluid B in units of centipoise?
(c) If the specific gravity of Fluid C is 0.8, what is the kinematic viscosity of Fluid C in units of stokes?

7. You are given four springs, one each of 2.5, 5, 7.5, and 10 newtons per meter [N/m].

   (a) What is the largest equivalent stiffness that can be made using these four springs? Draw a diagram indicating how the four springs are connected.

   (b) What is the smallest equivalent stiffness that can be made using only three of these springs? Draw a diagram indicating how the three springs are connected.

   (c) How close an equivalent stiffness to the average of the four springs (6.25 newtons per meter) can you make using only these springs? You may use all four springs to do this, but you may use less if that will yield an equivalent stiffness closer to the average.

8. You have three springs. You conduct several tests and determine the following data.

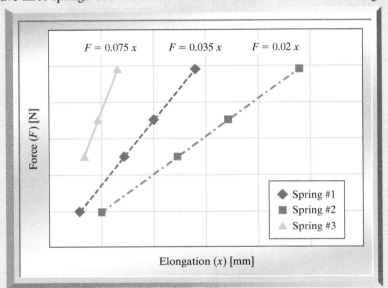

   Choose one correct spring or spring combination that will meet the following criteria as closely as possible. Assume you have one of each spring available for use. List the spring or spring combination and the resulting spring constant.

   (a) You want the spring or spring system to hold 95 grams and displace approximately 1 centimeter.

   (b) You want the spring or spring system to displace approximately 4 centimeter when holding 50 grams.

   (c) You want the spring or spring system to displace approximately 5 millimeter when holding 75 grams.

   (d) You want the spring or spring system to hold 20 grams and displace approximately 1 centimeter.

9. You are given four resistors, each of 7.5, 10, 15, and 20 kiloohms [kΩ].

   (a) What is the largest equivalent resistance that can be made using these four resistors? Draw a diagram indicating how the four resistors are connected.

   (b) What is the smallest equivalent resistance that can be made using only three of these resistors? Draw a diagram indicating how the three resistors are connected.

   (c) How close an equivalent resistance to the average of the four resistors (13.125 kΩ) can you make using only these resistors? You may use all four resistors to do this, but you may use less if that will yield an equivalent resistance closer to the average.

10. You have three resistors. You conduct several tests and determine the following data.

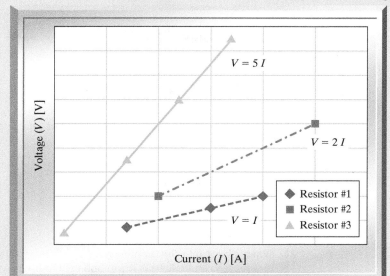

Choose one correct resistor or resistor combination that will meet the following criteria as closely as possible. Assume you have one of each resistor available for use. List the resistor or resistor combination and the resulting resistor constant.

(a) You want the resistor or resistor system to provide approximately 20 amperes when met with 120 volts.

(b) You want the resistor or resistor system to provide approximately 46 amperes when met with 30 volts.

(c) You want the resistor or resistor system to provide approximately 15 amperes when met with 120 volts.

(d) You want the resistor or resistor system to provide approximately 33 amperes when met with 45 volts.

11. Use the diagrams shown to answer the following questions.

(a) Determine the equivalent stiffness of four springs connected as shown.

(b) Determine the equivalent stiffness of four springs connected as shown.

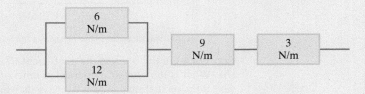

(c) Determine the equivalent resistance of four resistors connected as shown.

(d) Determine the equivalent resistance of four resistors connected as shown.

12. When a buoyant cylinder of height H, such as a fishing cork, is placed in a liquid and the top is depressed and released, it will bob up and down with a period T. We can conduct a series of tests and see that as the height of the cylinder increases, the period of oscillation also increases. A less dense cylinder will have a shorter period than a denser cylinder, assuming of course all the cylinders will float. A simple expression for the period is:

$$T = 2\pi\sqrt{\frac{\rho_{cylinder}}{\rho_{liquid}}\frac{H}{g}}$$

where g is the acceleration due to gravity, $\rho_{cylinder}$ is the density of the material, and ρ_{liquid} is the density of the fluid. By testing cylinders of differing heights, we wish to develop a model for the oscillation period, shown in the graph below.

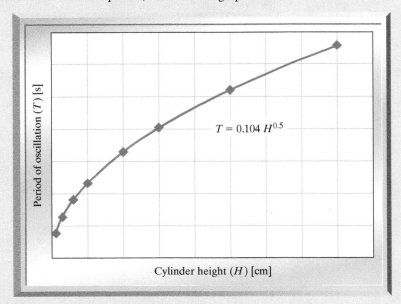

(a) What are the units of the coefficient (0.104) shown in the model?
(b) What is the oscillation period in units of seconds of a cylinder that is 4-inches tall?
(c) If the oscillation period is 0.2 seconds, what is the height of the cylinder in units of inches?
(d) We will conduct a series of tests with a new plastic (polystretchypropylene) that has a specific gravity of 0.6. What is the specific gravity of the fluid?

13. It is extremely difficult to bring the internet to some remote parts of the world. This can be inexpensively facilitated by installing antennas tethered to large helium balloons. To help analyze the situation, assume we have inflated a large spherical balloon. The pressure on the inside of the balloon is balanced by the elastic force exerted by the rubberized material. Since we are dealing with a gas in an enclosed space, the Ideal Gas Law will be applicable.

$$PV = nRT$$

where

P = pressure [atm]
V = volume [L]
n = quantity of gas [moles]
R = ideal gas constant [0.08206 (atm L)/(mol K)]
T = temperature [K]

If the temperature increases, the balloon will expand and/or the pressure will increase to maintain the equality. As it turns out, the increase in volume is the dominant effect, so we will treat the change in pressure as negligible.

The circumference of an inflated spherical balloon is measured at various temperatures; the resulting data are shown in the graph below.

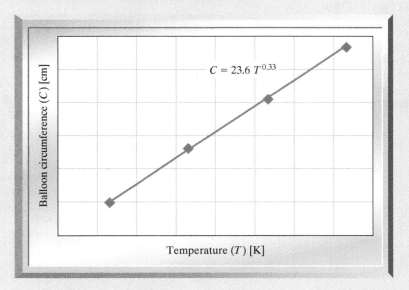

(a) What are the units of the constant 0.33?
(b) What are the units of the constant 23.6?
(c) What would the temperature of the balloon be if the circumference was 162 centimeters?
(d) If a circle with an area of 100 square centimeters is drawn on the balloon at 20 degrees Celsius, what would the area be at a temperature of 100 degrees Celsius?
(e) If the pressure inside the balloon is 1.2 atmospheres, how many moles of gas does it contain?

14. The data shown graphically below was collected during testing of an electromagnetic mass driver. The energy to energize the electromagnets was obtained from a bank of capacitors. The capacitor bank was charged to various voltages, and for each voltage, the exit velocity of the projectile was measured when the mass driver was activated.

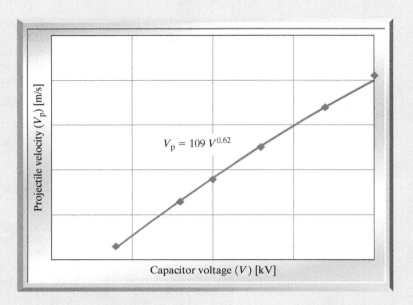

NOTE

Due to several complicated non-linear losses in the system that are far beyond the scope of this course, this is a case of a power model in which the exponent does not come out to be an integer or simple fraction, so rounding to two significant figures is appropriate. In fact, this model is only a first approximation—a really accurate model would be considerably more complicated.

(a) What would the velocity be if the capacitors were charged to 100,000 volts?
(b) What voltage would be necessary to accelerate the projectile to 1,000 meters per second?
(c) Assume that the total capacitance is 5 farads. If the capacitors are initially charged to 10,000 volts and are discharged to 2,000 volts during the launch of a projectile, what is the mass of the projectile if the overall conversion of energy stored in the capacitors to kinetic energy in the projectile has an efficiency of 20%? Recall that the energy stored in a capacitor is given by $E = 0.5\,CV^2$, where C is capacitance in farads and V is voltage in volts.

15. A standard guitar, whether acoustic or electric, has six strings, all with essentially the same total length between the bridge and the nut at the tuning head. Each string vibrates at a different frequency determined by the tension on the string and the mass per unit length of the string. In order to create pitches (notes) other than these six, the guitarist presses the strings down against the fretboard, thus shortening the length of the strings and changing their frequencies. In other words, the vibrating frequency of a string depends on tension, length, and mass per unit length of the string.

   The equation for the fundamental frequency of a vibrating string is given by

$$f = \frac{\sqrt{T/\mu}}{2L}$$

where

f = frequency [Hz] T = string tension [N]
μ = mass per unit length [kg/m] L = string length [m]

Many electric guitars have a device often called a "whammy" bar or a "tremolo" bar that allows the guitarist to change the tension on the strings quickly and easily, thus changing the frequency of the strings. (Think of Jimi Hendrix simulating "the rockets red glare, the bombs bursting in air" in his rendition of *The Star Spangled Banner* – a true *tour de force*.) In designing a new whammy bar, we test our design by collecting data on a single string of the observed frequency at different string lengths (using the fret board) with a specific setting of the whammy bar.

Length (L) [m]	0.25	0.28	0.32	0.36	0.40	0.45	0.51	0.57	0.64
Frequency (f) [Hz]	292	241	231	205	171	165	136	129	112

(a) Create a graph of the observed frequency data, including the power trendline and equation generated by Excel.

(b) If the tension was reduced to half of its original value, would the frequency increase or decrease and by what percentage of the original values?

(c) If the tension on the string is 125 newtons, what is the mass per unit length in grams per meter?

(d) If the mass per length of the string is 3 grams per meter, what is the tension in newtons?

16. Your supervisor has assigned you the task of designing a set of measuring spoons with a "futuristic" shape. After considerable effort, you have come up with two geometric shapes that you believe are really interesting.

    You make prototypes of five spoons for each shape with different depths and measure the volume each will hold. The table below shows the data you collected.

Depth (d) [cm]	Volume (V_A) [mL] Shape A	Volume (V_B) [mL] Shape B
0.5	1	1.2
0.9	2.5	3.3
1.3	4	6.4
1.4	5	7.7
1.7	7	11

Use Excel to plot and determine appropriate power models for this data. Use the resulting models to determine the depths of a set of measuring spoons comprising the following volumes for each of the two designs:

Volume Needed (V) [tsp or tbsp]	Depth of Design A (d_A) [cm]	Depth of Design B (d_B) [cm]
1/4 tsp		
1/2 tsp		
3/4 tsp		
1 tsp		
1 tbsp		

17. One of the NAE Grand Challenges for Engineering is **Engineering the Tools of Scientific Discovery**. According to the NAE website: "Grand experiments and missions of exploration always need engineering expertise to design the tools, instruments, and systems that make it possible to acquire new knowledge about the physical and biological worlds."

    Solar sails are a means of interplanetary propulsion using the radiation pressure of the sun to accelerate a spacecraft. The table below shows the radiation pressure at the orbits of several planets.

Planet	Distance from Sun (d) [AU]	Radiation Pressure (P) [μPa]
Mercury	0.46	43.3
Venus	0.72	17.7
Earth	1	9.15
Mars	1.5	3.96
Jupiter	5.2	0.34

NOTE

The astronomical unit (AU) is the average distance from the Earth to the Sun.

(a) Plot this data and determine the power law model for radiation pressure as a function of distance from the sun.
(b) What are the units of the exponent in the trendline?
(c) What are the units of the other constant in the trendline?
(d) What is the radiation pressure at Uranus (19.2 AU from sun)?
(e) At what distance from the sun is the radiation pressure 5 μPa?

18. When volunteers build a Habitat for Humanity house, it is found that the more houses that are completed, the faster each one can be finished since the volunteers become better trained and more efficient. A model that relates the building time and the number of homes completed can generally be given by

$$t = t_0\, e^{-N/\nu} + t_M$$

where

t = time required to construct one house [days]
t_0 = a constant related to (but not equal) the time required to build the first house
N = the number of houses completed [dimensionless]
ν = a constant related to the decrease in construction time as N increases
t_M = another constant related to construction time

A team of volunteers has built several houses, and their construction time was recorded for four of those houses. The construction time was then plotted as a function of number of previously built houses and a mathematical model derived as shown below. Using this information, answer the following questions:

(a) What are the units of the constants 8.2, 3, and 2.8?
(b) If the same group continues building houses, what is the minimum time to construct one house that they can expect to achieve?
(c) How long did it take for them to construct the first house?
(d) How many days (total) were required to build the first five houses?

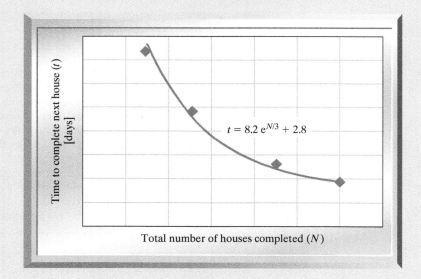

19. As part of an electronic music synthesizer, you need to build a gizmo to convert a linear voltage to an exponentially related current. You build three prototype circuits, make several measurements of voltage and current in each, and graph the results as shown below.

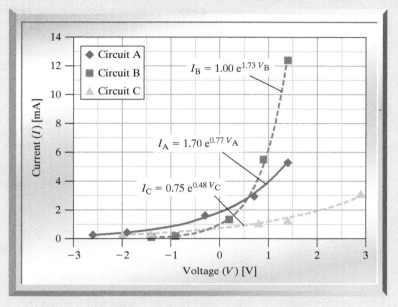

Assume that each circuit is modeled by the equation

$$I_X = A_X e^{(R_M/(R_X V_T))V_X}$$

where

I_X is the current in circuit X [milliamperers, mA]
A_X is a scaling factor associated with circuit X
R_M is a master resistor, and has the same value in all circuits [ohms, Ω]
R_X is a resistor in circuit X whose value is different in each circuit [ohms, Ω]
V_T is the thermal voltage, and has a value of 25.7 volts
V_X is the voltage in circuit X [volts, V]

(a) What are the units of A_X?
(b) If you wish $I_X = 1$ mA when $V_X = 0$, what should the value of A_X be?
(c) Using the trendline models, if $R_M = 10$ kΩ, what is the value of R_A?

20. Essentially all manufactured items are made to some "tolerance," or how close the actual product is to the nominal specifications. For example, if a company manufactures hammers, one customer might specify that the hammers should weigh 16 ounces. With rounding, this means that the actual weight of each hammer meets the specification if it weighs between 15.5 and 16.5 ounces. Such a hammer might cost 10 dollars. However, if the U.S. military, in its quest for perfection, specifies that an essentially identical hammer should have a weight of 16.000 ounces, then in order to meet specifications, the hammer must weigh between 15.9995 and 16.0005 ounces. In other words, the weight must fall within a range of one-thousandth of an ounce. Such a hammer might cost $1,000.

You have purchased a "grab bag" of 100 supposedly identical capacitors. You got a really good price, but there are no markings on the capacitors. All you know is that they are all the same nominal value. You wish to discover not only the nominal value, but the tolerance: are they within 5% of the nominal value, or within 20%? You set up a simple circuit with a known resistor and each of the unknown capacitors. You charge each capacitor to

10 volts, and then use an oscilloscope to time how long it takes for each capacitor to discharge to 2 volts. In a simple RC (resistor–capacitor) circuit, the voltage (V_C) across a capacitor (C) discharging through a resistor (R) is given by:

$$V_C = V_0 e^{-t/(RC)}$$

where t is time in seconds and V_0 is the initial voltage across the capacitor.

After measuring the time for each capacitor to discharge to from 10 to 2 V, you scan the list of times, and find the fastest and slowest. Since the resistor is the same in all cases, the fastest time corresponds to the smallest capacitor in the lot, and the slowest time to the largest. The fastest time was 3.3 microseconds and the slowest was 3.7 microseconds. For the two capacitors, you have the two pairs of data points.

(a) Enter these points into a worksheet, then plot these points in Excel, the pair for C_1 and the pair for C_2, on the same graph, using time as the independent variable. Fit exponential trendines to the data.

Time for C_1 (s)	Voltage of C_1	Time for C_2 (s)	Voltage of C_2
0	10	0	10
3.3×10^{-6}	2	3.7×10^{-6}	2

(b) Assuming you chose a precision resistor for these measurements that had a value of $R = 1,000.0$ ohms, determine the capacitance of the largest and smallest capacitors.

(c) You selected the fastest and slowest discharge times from a set of 100 samples. Since you had a fairly large sample set, it is not a bad assumption, according to the Laws of Large Numbers, that these two selected data sets represent capacitors near the lower and higher end of the range of values within the tolerance of the devices. Assuming the nominal value is the average of the minimum and maximum allowable values, what is the nominal value of the set of capacitors?

(d) What is the tolerance, in percent, of these devices? As an example, if a nominal 1 μF (microfarad) capacitor had an allowable range of 0.95 μF $< C <$ 1.05 μF, the tolerance would be 5%.

If standard tolerances of capacitors are 5%, 10%, and 20%, to which of the standard tolerances do you think these capacitors were manufactured? If you pick a smaller tolerance than you calculated, justify your selection. If you picked a higher tolerance, explain why the tolerance is so much larger than the measured value.

CHAPTER 13
MATHEMATICAL MODELS

As we have already seen, a large number of phenomena in the physical world obey one of the three basic mathematical models.

- Linear: $y = mx + b$
- Power: $y = bx^m + c$
- Exponential: $y = be^{mx} + c$

As we have mentioned previously, Excel can determine a mathematical model (trendline equation) for data conforming to all three of these model types, with the restriction that the constant c in the power and exponential forms must be 0.

Here, we consider how to determine the best model type for a specific data set, as well as learning methods of dealing with data that fit a power or exponential model best but have a nonzero value of c.

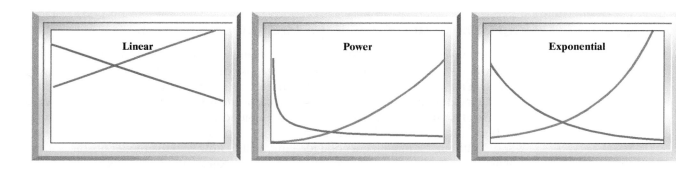

Except as otherwise noted, the entire discussion in this chapter assumes that the data fits one of the three trendlines models: linear, power, or exponential. You should always keep this in mind when using the techniques discussed here.

13.1 SELECTING A TRENDLINE TYPE

When you determine a trendline to fit a set of data, in general you want the line, which may be straight or curved, to be as close as is reasonable to most of the data points.

*The objective is **not** to ensure that the curve passes through every point.*

To determine an appropriate model for a given situation, we use five guidelines, presented in general order of importance:

1. Do we already know the model type that the data will fit?

2. What do we know about the behavior of the process under consideration, including initial and final conditions?

3. What do the data look like when plotted on graphs with logarithmic scales?

4. How well does the model fit the data?

5. Can we consider other model types?

Guideline 1: Determine if the Model Type Is Known

If you are investigating a phenomenon that has already been studied by others, you may already know which model is correct or perhaps you can learn how the system behaves by looking in appropriate technical literature. In this case, all you need are the specific values for the model parameters since you already know the form of the equation. As we have seen, Excel is quite adept at churning out the numerical values for trendline equations.

If you are certain you know the proper model type, you can probably skip Guidelines 2 and 3, although it might be a good idea to quantify how well the model fits the data as discussed in Guideline 4. For example, at this point you should know that the extension of simple springs has a linear relationship to the force applied.

At other times, you may be investigating situations for which the correct model type is unknown. If you cannot determine the model type from experience or references, continue to Guideline 2.

Guideline 2: Evaluate What Is Known About the System Behavior

The most important thing to consider when selecting a model type is whether the model makes sense in light of your understanding of the physical system being investigated. Since there may still be innumerable things with which you are unfamiliar, this may seem like an unreasonable expectation. However, by applying what you *do* know to the problem at hand, you can often make an appropriate choice without difficulty.

When investigating an unknown phenomenon, we typically know the answer to at least one of three questions:

1. How does the process behave in the initial state?

2. How does the process behave in the final state?

3. What happens to the process between the initial and the final states—if we sketch the process, what does it look like? Does the parameter of interest increase or decrease? Is the parameter asymptotic to some value horizontally or vertically?

● EXAMPLE 13-1

Suppose we do not know Hooke's law and would like to study the behavior of a spring. We hang the spring from a hook, pull downward on the bottom of the spring with varying forces, and observe its behavior. We know initially the spring will stretch a little under its own weight even before we start pulling on it, although in most cases this is small or negligible. As an extreme case, however, consider what would happen if you hang one end of a Slinky® from the ceiling, letting the other end fall as it will.

As we pull on the spring, we realize the harder we pull, the more the spring stretches. In fact, we might assume that in a simple world, if we pull twice as hard, the spring will stretch twice as far, although that might not be as obvious. In words we might say,
The distance the spring stretches (x) is directly proportional to the pulling force (F), *or we might express the behavior as an equation:*

$$x = kF + b$$

where b is the amount of stretch when the spring is hanging under its own weight. This is what we mean by using an "expected" form. Always remember, however, that what you "expect" to happen may be in error.

In addition, suppose we had tested this spring by hanging five different weights on it and measuring the stretch each time. After plotting the data, we realize there is a general trend that as the weight (force) increases, the stretch increases, but the data points do not lie exactly on a straight line. We have two options:

- *If we think our assumption of linear behavior may be in error, we can try nonlinear models.*
- *Or we can use a linear model, although the fit may not be as good as one or more of the nonlinear models.*

To bring order to these questions, we should ask the following sequence of questions:

Is the system linear?

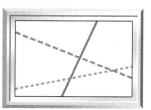

Linear systems have the following characteristics. If any of these is not true, then the system is not linear.

1. As the independent variable gets larger, the dependent variable continues to increase (positive slope) or decrease (negative slope) without limit. (See item 4 below.)

2. If the independent variable becomes negative, as it continues negative, the dependent variable continues to decrease (positive slope) or increase (negative slope) without limit unless one of the variables is constant. (See item 4 below.)

3. The rate of increase or decrease is constant; in other words, it will not curve upward or downward, but is a straight line.

4. There are no horizontal or vertical asymptotes unless the dependent variable is defined for only *one* value of the independent variable *or* if the dependent variable is the same value for *all* values of the independent variable.

Examples illustrating if a system is or is not linear:

- You are driving your car at a constant speed of 45 miles per hour [mph]. The longer you drive, the farther you go, without limit. In addition, your distance increases by the same amount each hour, regardless of total time elapsed. This is a linear system.

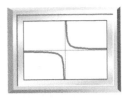

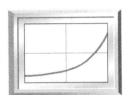

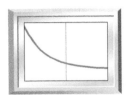

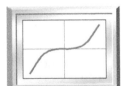

■ You observe the temperature of the brake disks on your car to be slowly decreasing. If it continued to decrease without limit, the temperature would eventually be less than absolute zero; thus, it is not linear. The temperature will eventually approach the surrounding air temperature; thus, there is a horizontal asymptote.

If the system is not linear, is there a vertical asymptote?

If there *is* a vertical asymptote, it will also have a horizontal asymptote. This is a power law model with a negative exponent. REMEMBER: We are assuming that our data fit one of the three models being considered here, and the previous statement is certainly not true for all other models. For example, $y = \tan x$ has multiple vertical asymptotes, but no horizontal asymptote.

If there is not a vertical asymptote, is there a horizontal asymptote?

If there is a horizontal asymptote (but not a vertical one), then the model is exponential. If the horizontal asymptote occurs for positive values of the independent variable, then the exponent is negative. If the horizontal asymptote occurs for negative values of the independent variable, then the exponent is positive.

What if there is not a horizontal asymptote or a vertical asymptote?

It is a power law model with a positive exponent. Such models can have a variety of shapes.

This sequence of questions can be represented pictorially as shown below. Remember, this is only valid if we assume the data fits one of the three models being discussed.

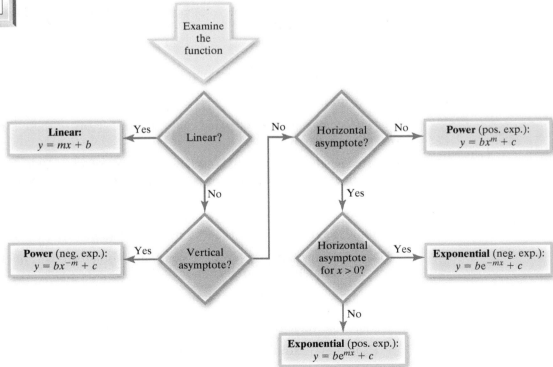

Guideline 3: Convert Axes to a Logarithmic Scale

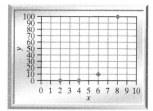

If the logarithm of the dependent or independent variable is plotted instead of the variable itself, do the modified data points appear to lie on a straight line?

To see how logarithmic axes are constructed, let us consider a simple case. Plotting the data points below gives the graph shown to the left.

x	2	4	6	8
y	0.1	1	10	100

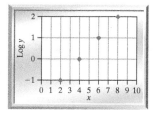

One way to linearize the data is to take the logarithm (base 10) of the independent variable and plot the results of log (y).

x	2	4	6	8
y	0.1	1	10	100
log y	−1	0	1	2

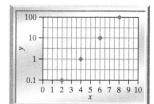

Another method of linearization is to take the logarithm (base 10) of the axis values, and plot the original y values on this altered axis.

A note about the use of logarithmic scales:

- The original data would fit an exponential model ($y = 0.01e^{1.15x}$), and when plotted on a logarithmic vertical axis, the data points appear in a straight line.
- The logarithmic axis allows us to more easily distinguish between the values of the two lowest data points, even though the data range covers three orders of magnitude. On the original graph, 0.1 and 1 were almost in the same vertical position.
- Note that you *do not* have to calculate the logarithms of the data points. You simply plot the actual values on a logarithmic scale.

Logarithm graphs are discussed in more detail in the next section. We can use logarithmic axes to help us determine an appropriate model type using the following process:

1. Plot the data using normal (linear) scales for both axes. If the data appear to lie more or less in a straight line, a linear model is likely to be a good choice.

2. Plot the data on a logarithmic vertical scale and a normal (linear) horizontal scale. If the data then appear to lie more or less in a straight line, an exponential model is likely to be a good choice.

3. Plot the data with logarithmic scales for *both* axes. If the data then appear to lie more or less in a straight line, a power law model is likely to be a good choice.

4. Although not covered in this course, you could plot the data on a logarithmic horizontal scale and a normal (linear) vertical scale. If the data then appear to lie more or less in a straight line, a logarithmic model is likely to be a good choice.

REMEMBER, this is only valid if we assume the data fits one of the three models being discussed. This process is summarized in the chart below.

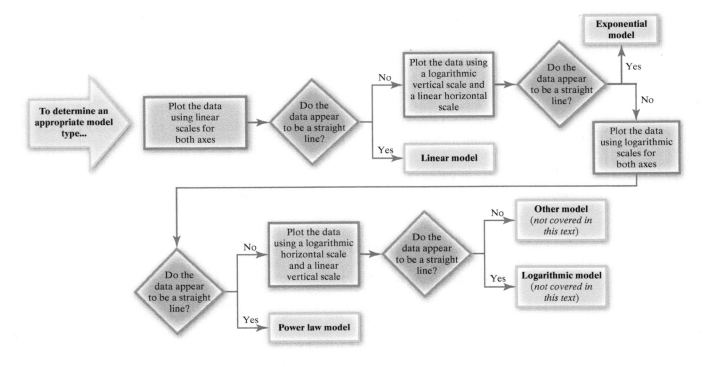

Guideline 4: Consider the R^2 Value

When a trendline is generated in Excel, the program can automatically calculate an **R^2 value**, sometimes called the **coefficient of determination**. The R^2 value is an indication of the variation of the actual data from the equation generated—in other words, it is a measure of how well the trendline fits the data. The value of R^2 varies between 0 and 1. If the value of R^2 is exactly equal to 1, a perfect correlation exists between the data and the trendline, meaning that the curve passes exactly through all data points. The farther R^2 is from 1, the less confidence we have in the accuracy of the model generated. When fitting a trendline to a data set, we always report the R^2 value to indicate how well the fit correlates with the data.

In reality, a fit of $R^2 = 1$ is rare, since experimental data are imprecise in nature. Human error, imprecision in instrumentation, fluctuations in testing conditions, and natural specimen variation are among the factors that contribute to a less-than-perfect fit. **The best R^2 value is not necessarily associated with the best model and should be used as a guide only.** Once again, making such decisions becomes easier with experience.

When displaying the equation corresponding to a trendline, you may have already noticed how to display the R^2 value.

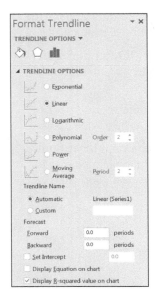

✎ *To display an R^2 value:*

- Right-click or double-click on the trendline, or select the trendline then choose **Design > Add Chart Element > Trendline > More Trendline Options . . .**
- In the **Format Trendline** palette that opens, from the **Trendline** Options tab, check the box for **Display R-squared value on chart**. Click the "X" to close.

⌘ **Mac OS:** To show the R^2 value on a Mac, double-click the trendline. In the window that opens, click **Options** and select **Display R-squared value**. Click **OK**.

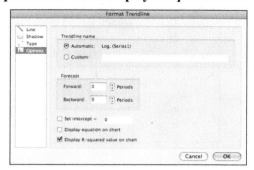

Try different models and compare the R^2 values.

- If one of the R^2 values is considerably smaller than the others, say, more than 0.2 less, then that model very likely can be eliminated.
- If one of the R^2 values is considerably larger than the others, say, more than 0.2 greater, then that model very likely is the correct one.

  In any case, you should always consider Guidelines 1 through 3 above to minimize the likelihood of error.

WARNING!

While practicing with trendlines in the preceding chapters, you may have noticed a choice for polynomial models. Only rarely would this be the proper choice, but we mention it here for one specific reason—a polynomial model can always be found that will perfectly fit any data set. In general, if there are N data points, a polynomial of order $N - 1$ can be found that goes exactly through all N points. Excel can only calculate polynomials up to sixth order. For example, a data set with five data points is plotted below. A fourth-order polynomial can be found that perfectly fits the data. Let us consider a simple spring stretching example to illustrate why a perfect fit to the data is not necessarily the correct model.

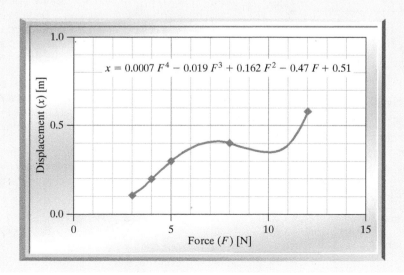

$$x = 0.0007\, F^4 - 0.019\, F^3 + 0.162\, F^2 - 0.47\, F + 0.51$$

The graph shows the five data points for spring displacement as a function of force. As force increases, displacement increases, but the points are certainly not in a straight line. Also shown is a fourth-order polynomial model that goes through every point—a perfect fit. This, however, is a terrible model.

Presumably you agree that as force increases, displacement *must* increase as well. The polynomial trendline, however, suggests that as force increases from about 7 to 10 newtons, the displacement *decreases*.

Always ask yourself if the model you have chosen is obviously incorrect, as in this case. We do not use polynomial models in this book, and so discuss them no further.

THE THEORY OF OCCAM'S RAZOR

It is vain to do with more what can be done with less.
or
Entities are not to be multiplied beyond necessity.

—William of Occam

It is probably appropriate to mention Occam's Razor at this point. Those who choose to pursue scientific and technical disciplines should keep the concept of Occam's Razor firmly in mind. **Occam's Razor refers to the concept that the simplest explanation or model to describe a given situation is usually the correct one.** It is named for William of Occam, who lived in the first half of the fourteenth century and was a theologian and philosopher.

● **EXAMPLE 13-2**

The velocity of a ball was recorded as it rolled across a floor after being released from a ramp at various heights. The velocities were then plotted versus the release heights. We want to fit a trendline to the data.

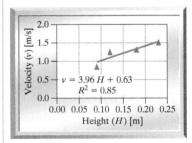

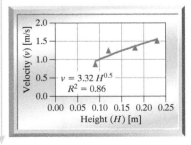

We start with the simplest form, a linear fit, shown on the left. We know that if the ramp is at a height of zero, the ball will not roll down the ramp without any external forces. The linear fit yields an intercept value of 0.6, indicating that the ball will have an initial velocity of 0.6 meter per second when the ramp is horizontal, which we know to be untrue. It seems unlikely experimental variation alone would generate an error this large, so we try another model.

We choose a power fit, shown in the center. With an R^2 value of 0.86, the equation fits the data selection well, but is there a better fit? Using the same data, we try a third-order polynomial to describe the data. The polynomial model, which gives a perfect fit, is shown on the bottom with an R^2 value of 1.

While the polynomial trendline gave the best fit, is this really the correct way to describe the data? Recall that in theory the potential energy of the ball is transformed into kinetic energy according to the conservation of energy law, written in general terms

$$PE_{initial} = KE_{final} \quad or \quad mgH = \frac{1}{2}mv^2$$

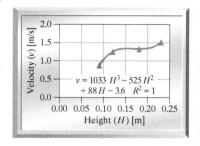

Therefore, the relationship between velocity and height is a relationship of the form

$$v = (2gH)^{1/2} = (2g)^{1/2}H^{1/2}$$

The relation between velocity and height is a power relationship; velocity varies as the square root of the height. The experimental error is responsible for the inaccurate trendline fit. In most instances, the polynomial trendline will give a precise fit but an inaccurate description of the phenomenon. **It is better to have an accurate interpretation of the experimental behavior than a perfect trendline fit!**

Guideline 5: Should We Consider Model Types Not Covered Here?

Many phenomena may be accurately characterized by a linear model, power law model, or exponential model. However, there are innumerable systems for which a different model type must be chosen. Many of these are relatively simple, but some are mind-bogglingly complicated. For example, modeling electromagnetic waves (used for television, cell phones, etc.) or a mass oscillating up and down while hanging from a spring requires the use of trigonometric functions.

You should always keep in mind that the system or phenomenon you are studying may not fit the three common models we have covered in this book.

NOTE ON ADVANCED MATH

Actually, sinusoids (sine or cosine) can be represented by exponential models through a mathematical trick first concocted by Leonhard Euler, so we now refer to it as Euler's identity. The problem is that the exponents are imaginary (some number times the square root of −1).

Euler's identity comes up in the study of calculus, and frequently in the study of electrical or computer engineering, early in the study of electric circuits. Euler's identity can be expressed in several different forms. The basic identity can be stated as the following equation, where i is the square root of −1:

$$e^{i\pi} = -1$$

Another form often used in electrical engineering is

$$\cos \theta = 0.5(e^{i\theta} + e^{-i\theta})$$

13.2   INTERPRETING LOGARITHMIC GRAPHS

Plot data using logarithmic axis to linearize the data
Interpret a graph using logarithmic scales to develop a mathematical model

A "regular" plot, shown on a graph with both axes at constant-spaced intervals, is called **rectilinear**. When a linear function is graphed on rectilinear axis, it will appear as a straight line. Often, it is convenient to use a scale on one or both axes that is not linear, where values are not equally spaced but instead "logarithmic," meaning that powers of 10 are equally spaced. Each set of 10 is called a **decade** or **cycle**. A logarithmic scale that ranges either from 10 to 1,000 would be two cycles, 10–100 and 100–1,000. Excel allows you to select a logarithmic scale for the abscissa, the ordinate, or both.

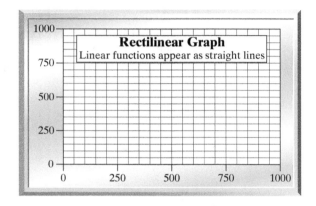

If one scale is logarithmic and the other linear, the plot is called **semilogarithmic** or **semilog**. Note in the figure below on the left that the abscissa has its values equally spaced and so is a linear scale. However, the ordinate has powers of 10 equally spaced and thus is a logarithmic scale.

If both scales are logarithmic, the plot is called **full logarithmic** or **log–log**. Note in the figure below on the right that both axes have powers of 10 equally spaced.

There are four different combinations of linear and logarithmic axes, each corresponding to one of four specific trendline types that will appear linear on that particular graph type. If the plotted data points are more or less in a straight line when plotted with a specific axis type, the corresponding trendline type is a likely candidate, as discussed earlier.

Once the data are plotted as logarithmic, how do you read data from this graph? This is perhaps best shown through examples.

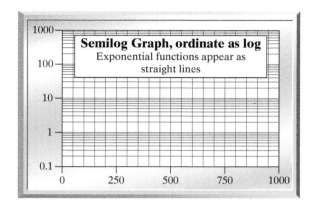

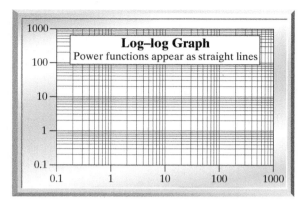

Derivation of Power Law Model

Consider a power law model:

$$y = bx^m$$

Now take the logarithm of both sides of the equation.

$$\log y = \log (bx^m) = \log b + \log x^m = \log b + m \log x$$

Using the commutative property of addition, you can write:

$$\log y = m \log x + \log b$$

Since b is a constant, $\log b$ is also a constant. Rename $\log b$ and call it b'. Since x and y are both variables, $\log x$ and $\log y$ are also variables. Call them x' and y', respectively. Using the new names for the transformed variables and the constant b:

$$y' = mx' + b'$$

This is a linear model! Thus, if the data set can be described by a power law model and you plot the logarithms of both variables (instead of the variables themselves), the transformed data points will lie on a straight line. The slope of this line is m, although "slope" has a somewhat different meaning than in a linear model. The "intercept" value, b, occurs when $x = 1$, since $\log(1) = 0$.

● EXAMPLE 13-3

When a body falls, it undergoes a constant acceleration. Using the figure, determine the mathematical equation for distance (d), in units of meters, of a falling object as a function of time (t), in units of seconds.

Since the graph appears linear on log–log paper, we can assume a power law relationship exists of the form:

$$d = bt^m$$

For illustration, a line has been sketched between the points for further clarification of function values.

To establish the power of the function (m), we estimate the number of decades of "rise" (shown as vertical arrows) divided by the decades of "run" (horizontal arrow):

$$\text{Slope} = \frac{\text{Change in decades of distance}}{\text{Change in decades of time}} = \frac{2 \text{ decade}}{1 \text{ decade}} = 2$$

To establish the constant value (b), we estimate it as the ordinate value when the abscissa value is 1, shown in the shaded circle. When the time is 1 second, the distance is 5 meters.
The resulting function:

$$d = 5t^2$$

This matches well with the established theory, which states

$$d = \frac{1}{2} g t^2$$

The value of ½ g is approximately 5 m/s².

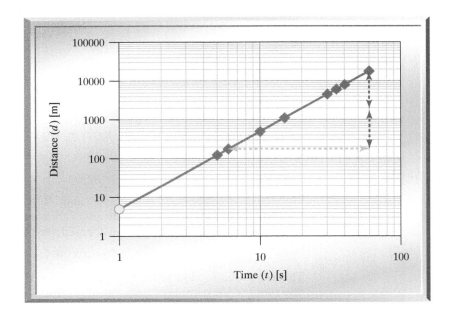

Derivation of Exponential Law Model

NOTE

For a refresher on logarithm rules, please see Appendix A online.

Consider an exponential model:

$$y = be^{mx}$$

Now take the logarithm of both sides of the equation.

$$\log y = \log(be^{mx}) = \log b + \log e^{mx} = \log b + (mx)\log e$$

Using the commutative property of addition, you can write:

$$\log y = m(\log e)x + \log b$$

Since b is a constant, $\log b$ is also a constant. Rename $\log b$ and call it b'. Since y is a variable, $\log y$ is also a variable; call it y'.

Using the new names for the transformed variable y and the constant b:

$$y' = m(\log e)x + b'$$

This is a linear model! Thus, if the data set can be described by an exponential law model, and you plot the logarithm of y (instead of y itself) versus x, the transformed data points will lie on a straight line. The slope of this line is $m(\log e)$, but again, "slope" has a somewhat different interpretation. The term $(\log e)$ is a number, approximately equal to 0.4343; the slope is 0.4343 m.

● EXAMPLE 13-4

A chemical reaction is being carried out in a reactor; the results are shown graphically in the figure. Determine the mathematical equation that describes the reactor concentration (C), in units of moles per liter, as a function of time spent in the reactor (t), in units of seconds.

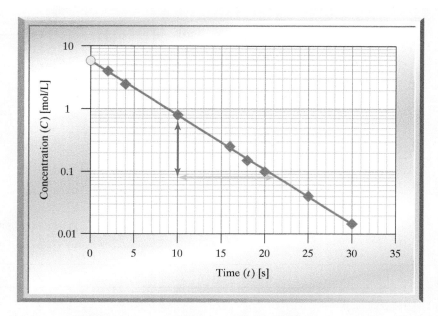

Since the graph appears linear on semilog paper where the ordinate is logarithmic, we can assume an exponential law relationship exists of the form:

$$C = be^{mt}$$

For illustration, a line has been sketched between the points for further clarification of function values.

Since this is an exponential function, to determine the value of m, we must first determine the slope:

$$\text{Slope} = \frac{\text{Change in decades of concentration}}{\text{Change in time}}$$

$$= \frac{-1 \text{ decade}}{21.5 \text{ s} - 10 \text{ s}} = -0.087 \text{ s}^{-1}$$

The value of m is then found from the relationship: slope = $m(\log e)$.

$$m = \frac{\text{slope}}{\log e} = \frac{-0.087 \text{ s}^{-1}}{0.4343} = -0.2 \text{ s}^{-1}$$

When time = 0 seconds, the constant (b) can be read directly and has a value of 6 [mol/L]. The resulting function:

$$C = 6e^{-0.2t}$$

**COMPREHENSION
CHECK 13-1**

An unknown amount of oxygen, kept in a piston type container at a constant temperature, was subjected to increasing pressure (P), in units of atmospheres; as the pressure (P) was increased, the resulting volume (V) was recorded in units of liters. We have found that a log–log plot aligns the data in a straight line. Using the figure, determine the mathematical equation for volume (V) in units of liters, and of a piston filled with an ideal gas subjected to increasing pressure (P) in units of atmospheres.

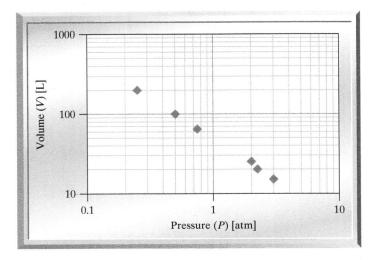

**COMPREHENSION
CHECK 13-2**

The data shown graphically in the figure describe the discharge of a capacitor through a resistor. Determine the mathematical equation that describes the voltage (V), in units of volts, as a function of time (t), in units of seconds.

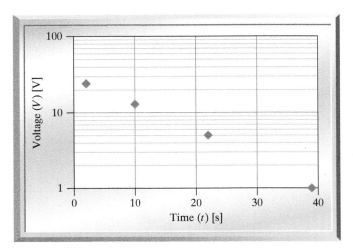

13.3 CONVERTING SCALES TO LOG IN EXCEL

LEARN TO: Use Excel to convert a graph into logarithmic axis to make a data series appear linear

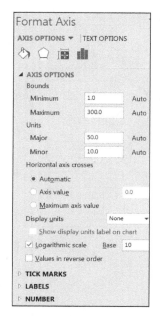

✎ *To convert axis to logarithmic:*

■ Right-click the axis > Format Axis or double-click on the axis. The **Format Axis** palette will appear.
■ Click **Axis Options**, then check the box for **Logarithmic scale**. The Base should automatically appear as 10; this default value is correct.

Alternatively:

■ Click the chart. In the toolbar, select **Design > Add Chart Element > Axis > More Axis Options**.
■ In the corresponding palette, select **Axis Options > Bar Graph Symbol**.
■ Click **Axis Options**, then check the box for **Logarithmic scale**.

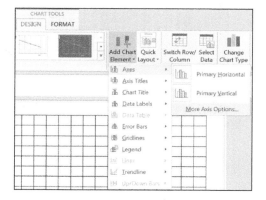

⌘ **Mac OS:** Double-click on the axis you want to convert to logarithmic. The Format Axis window will appear. Click **Scale** in the list on the left side of the window, and then click the checkbox near the bottom that says "Logarithmic scale."

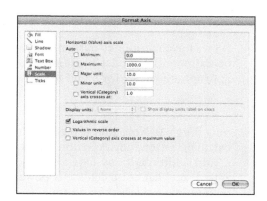

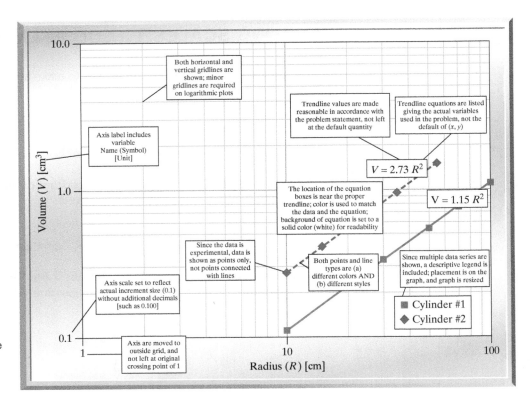

Figure 13-1 Example of a proper plot, showing multiple experimental data sets with trendlines and logarithmic axes.

Above is an example of a properly formatted graph, showing an experimental data series with power trendlines. The axes have been made logarithmic to allow the data series to appear linear.

13.4 DEALING WITH LIMITATIONS OF EXCEL

LEARN TO: Understand the limitations in using Excel to model power or exponential data containing an offset
Determine appropriate steps to alter data using Excel if an offset is present

As we have mentioned earlier, Excel will not correctly calculate a trendline for a power or exponential model containing a vertical offset. In other words, it can calculate appropriate values for b and m in the forms

$$y = bx^m + c \quad \text{or} \quad y = be^{mx} + c$$

only if $c = 0$. Note that if the data inherently has a vertical offset, Excel may actually calculate a trendline equation, but the values of b and m will not be accurate.

In addition, if any data value, dependent or independent, is less than or equal to zero, Excel cannot calculate a power law model. If one or more dependent variable data points are less than or equal to zero, exponential models are unavailable.

In the real world, there are numerous systems best modeled by either a power or an exponential model with a nonzero value of c or with negative values, so we need a method for handling such situations.

Case 1: Vertical Asymptote

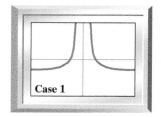

Since a vertical asymptote implies a power model with a negative exponent, there will be a horizontal asymptote as well. If the horizontal asymptote is not the horizontal axis (implying a vertical offset), Excel will calculate the model incorrectly or not at all. The object here is to artificially move the asymptote to the horizontal axis by subtracting the offset value from every data point. If you have a sufficient range of data, you may be able to extract the offset from the data.

For example, if the three data points with the largest values of x (or smallest if the asymptote goes to the left) have corresponding y values of 5.1, 5.03, and 5.01, the offset is likely to be about 5. (This assumes there are other values in the data set with considerably different y values.) You can also try to determine from the physical situation being modeled at what nonzero value the asymptote occurs. In either case, simply subtract the offset value from the vertical component of *every* data point, plot this modified data, and determine a power trendline. Once the trendline equation is displayed, edit it by adding the offset to the power term. Note that you subtract the value from the data points but add it to the final equation.

Case 2: No Horizontal Asymptote

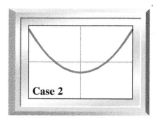

Assuming it has been established that the model should not be linear, Case 2 implies a power model with a positive exponent. If you have a data point for $x = 0$, the corresponding y value should be very close to the vertical offset. Also, you may be able to determine the offset value by considering the physical situation. In either case, proceed as in Case 1, subtracting the offset from every data point, etc.

Case 3: Horizontal Asymptote, No Vertical Asymptote

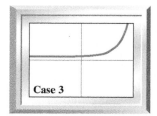

Case 3 implies an exponential model. The object, as in Case 1, is to artificially move the asymptote to the horizontal axis. Also as in Case 1, you may be able to determine the offset by considering the physical system or by looking at the data points with the largest or smallest values. Again, subtract the determined value from every data point, etc.

Case 4: A Few Values with Small Negative Value, Most Positive

In Case 4, the negative values may be a result of measurement inaccuracy. Either delete these points from the data set or change the negative values to a very small positive value.

Case 5: Many or All Data Points Negative

If the independent values are negative, try multiplying every independent value by -1. If this works, then make the calculated value of b negative after the trendline equation is calculated. You may have to apply some of the procedures in the previous cases after negating each data value.

Negative dependent values may simply be a negative offset to the data. If you can determine the asymptote value, ask if essentially all values are greater than the asymptote value. If so, it is probably just an offset. If not, then multiply every dependent data value by -1, and proceed in a manner similar to that described in the preceding paragraph.

NOTE

Sometimes, due to inaccuracy of measurement, one or more of the data points near the asymptote may be negative after the offset value is subtracted, and Excel will be unable to process the data. You can circumvent this either by deleting such data points or by making the vertical component a very small positive value.

● **EXAMPLE 13-5**

The following data were collected in an experiment. We wish to determine an appropriate model for the data.

As the independent variable gets larger, the dependent variable appears to be approaching 10. This is even more apparent when graphed. Subtracting this assumed offset from every data point gives a new column of modified dependent data.

Since we subtracted 10 from every data point, we need to correct the equation by adding 10, giving $y = 14.3e^{-0.5x} + 10$.

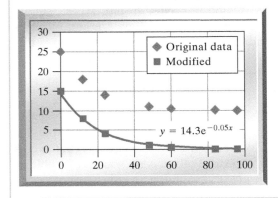

Independent	Dependent	Modified Dependent
0	25.0	15.0
12	18.0	8.0
24	14.0	4.0
48	11.0	1.0
60	10.5	0.5
84	10.2	0.2
96	10.1	0.1

If All Else Fails

If you are convinced that the model is exponential or power with an offset but you cannot determine its value, consider making further measurements for larger or smaller values of the independent variable. Particularly in data that has a horizontal asymptote, further measurements may make the value of the asymptote more obvious. In the first chart below, the value of the asymptote is not clear. By extending the measurements in the direction of the asymptote (positive in this case), it is clear that the asymptote has a value of 2. Note also that it becomes much clearer that the data are not linear.

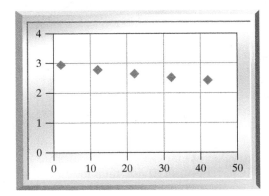

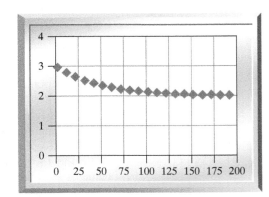

● **EXAMPLE 13-6**

The data shown describe the discharge of a capacitor through a resistor. Before the advent of microprocessors, intermittent windshield wipers in automobiles often used such circuits to create the desired time delay. We wish to determine an appropriate model for the data.

Time (t) [s]	2	10	22	39
Voltage (V) [V]	24	13	5	1

- ■ *Select the data series and create a linear trendline, being sure to display the equation and the R^2 value.*
- ■ *Without deleting the first trendline, click one of the data points again—be sure you select the points and not the trendline—and again add a trendline, but this time choose a power trend.*
- ■ *Repeat this process for an exponential trend.*

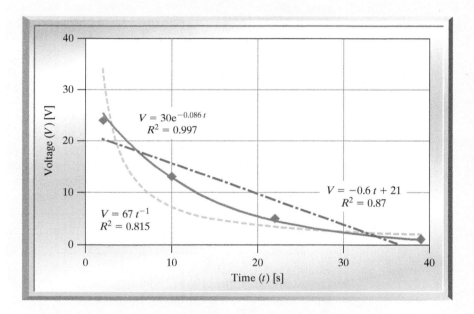

You should now have a chart with three trendlines. Things to note:

- ■ *Neither the linear nor power trendlines are very good compared to the exponential line, and both have an R^2 value less than 0.9. These are probably not the best choice.*
- ■ *The exponential model fits the data very closely and has an R^2 value greater than 0.95; thus, it is probably the best choice.*

As a model check, compare the graph by using logarithmic scales. If the model is exponential, the data should appear linear on a semilogarithmic plot with the ordinate shown as logarithmic.

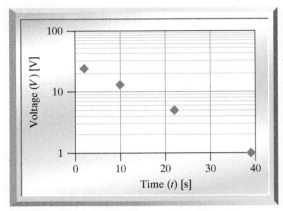
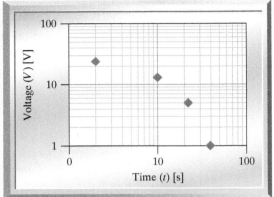

Based on this analysis, you would choose the exponential model. As it turns out, the exponential model is indeed the correct one, being the solution to a differential equation describing the capacitor's behavior. Most students learn about this in second semester physics, and some study it in much more depth in electrical and computer engineering courses.

● **EXAMPLE 13-7**   These data describe the temperature of antifreeze (ethylene glycol) in the radiator of a parked car. The temperature of the surrounding environment is −20 degrees Fahrenheit. The initial temperature (at $t = 0$) is unknown.

Time (t) [min]	10	18	25	33	41
Temperature (T) [°F]	4.5	1.0	−2.1	−4.6	−6.4

- Determine an appropriate model type for these data.
- Determine the vertical offset of the data.
- Plot the modified data and generate the correct trendline equation to describe this data.

It seems reasonable that the temperature will be asymptotic to the surrounding temperature (−20 degrees Fahrenheit) as time goes on. Also, there is no known mechanism whereby the temperature could possibly go to infinity for any finite value of time, so there is no vertical asymptote. This indicates an exponential model with a negative exponent. Since the asymptote is at −20 degrees Fahrenheit, subtract −20 (i.e., add 20) from every data point before plotting.

Time (t) [min]	10	18	25	33	41
Temperature (T) [°F]	4.5	1.0	2.1	4.6	−6.4
Offset temperature (T_O) [°F]	24.5	21.0	17.9	15.4	13.6

Since you subtracted −20 from every data point, you should add −20 to the trendline equation, giving

$$T = 29.5e^{-0.019t} - 20$$

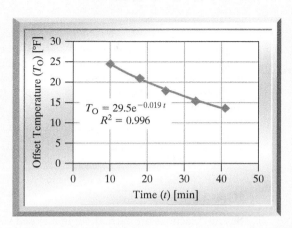

The following data were collected during an experiment. We wish to determine an appropriate model for the data.

Independent	Dependent
0	−25
10	−45
20	−85
25	−106
30	−154

Assume the car in Example 13-7 is cranked up and driven 50 feet into a garage. The temperature inside the garage is 5 degrees Fahrenheit. These data describe the temperature of antifreeze in the radiator after it is driven into the garage and the motor turned off.
- Determine an appropriate model type for these data.
- Determine the vertical offset of the data.
- Plot the modified data and generate the correct trendline equation to describe this data.

Time (t) [min]	5	13	25	34	51
Temperature (T) [°F]	−13.0	−10.0	−6.8	−4.5	−1.5

In-Class Activities

ICA 13-1

Capillary action draws liquid up a narrow tube against the force of gravity as a result of surface tension. The height the liquid will move up the tube depends on the radius of the tube. The following data were collected for water in a glass tube in air at sea level. Show the resulting data and trendline, with equation and R^2 value, on the appropriate graph type (rectilinear, semilog, or log–log) to make the data appear linear.

Radius (r) [cm]	0.01	0.05	0.10	0.20	0.40	0.50
Height (H) [cm]	14.0	3.0	1.5	0.8	0.4	0.2

ICA 13-2

Several reactions are carried out in a closed vessel. The following data are taken for the concentration (C) of compounds A, B, and C [grams per liter] as a function of time (t) [minutes], from the start of the reaction. Show the resulting data and trendlines, with equation and R^2 value, on the appropriate graph type (rectilinear, semilog, or log–log) to make the data appear linear.

Time (t) [min]	2	5	8	15	20
Concentration of A (C_A) [g/L]	0.021	0.125	0.330	1.120	2.050
Concentration of B (C_B) [g/L]	0.032	0.202	0.550	1.806	3.405
Concentration of C (C_C) [g/L]	0.012	0.080	0.200	0.650	1.305

ICA 13-3

An environmental engineer has obtained a bacteria culture from a municipal water sample and allowed the bacteria to grow. The data are shown below. Show the resulting data and trendline, with equation and R^2 value, on the appropriate graph type (rectilinear, semilog, or log–log) to make the data appear linear.

Time (t) [h]	2	3	5	6	7	9	10
Concentration (C) [ppm]	21	44	111	153	203	318	385

ICA 13-4

In a turbine, a device used for mixing, the power requirement depends on the size and shape of impeller. In the lab, you have collected the following data. Show the resulting data and trendline, with equation and R^2 value, on the appropriate graph type (xy scatter, semilog, or log–log) to make the data appear linear.

Diameter (D) [ft]	0.5	0.75	1	1.5	2	2.25	2.5	2.75
Power (P) [hp]	0.004	0.04	0.13	0.65	3	8	18	22

ICA 13-5

Being quite interested in obsolete electronics, Angus has purchased several electronic music synthesis modules dating from the early 1970s and is testing them to find out how they work. One module is a voltage-controlled amplifier (VCA) that changes the amplitude (loudness) of an audio signal by changing a control voltage into the VCA. All Angus knows is that the magnitude of the control voltage should be less than 5 volts. He sets the audio input signal to an amplitude of 1 volt, then measures the audio output amplitude for different control voltage values. The table below shows these data. Show the resulting data and trendline, with equation and R^2 value, on the appropriate graph type (*xy* scatter, semilog, or log–log) to make the data appear linear.

Control voltage (*V*) [V]	−4.0	−2.5	−1.0	0.0	1.0	2.5	4.0
Output amplitude (*A*) [V]	0.116	0.324	0.567	0.962	1.690	3.320	7.270

ICA 13-6

Referring to the previous ICA, Angus is also testing a voltage-controlled oscillator. In this case, a control voltage (also between −5 and +5 volts) changes the frequency of oscillation in order to generate different notes. The table below shows these measurements. Show the resulting data and trendline, with equation and R^2 value, on the appropriate graph type (*xy* scatter, semilog, or log–log) to make the data appear linear.

Control voltage (*V*) [V]	−4.0	−2.5	−1.0	0.0	1.0	2.5	4.0
Output frequency (*f*) [Hz]	28	99	227	539	989	3,110	8,130

The following instructions apply to ICA 13-7 to ICA 13-9. Examine the following models. Determine if the graph will appear linear on:

(A) Rectilinear axes
(B) Semi log, abscissa as logarithmic, axes
(C) Semi log, ordinate as logarithmic, axes
(D) Logarithmic (both) axes
(E) None of the above

ICA 13-7

Q	Model	Abscissa	Ordinate	Will appear linear on ...				
				A	B	C	D	E
(a)		F	L					
(b)	$L = BF^{0.5}$	L	B					
(c)		F	B					

ICA 13-8

Q	Model	Abscissa	Ordinate	Will appear linear on ...				
				A	B	C	D	E
(a)		V	R					
(b)	$R = H^{0.5}V^{-2}L$	L	R					
(c)		V	L					
(d)		V	H					

ICA 13-9

Q	Model	Abscissa	Ordinate	Will appear linear on ...				
				A	B	C	D	E
(a)		S	M					
(b)	$M = \dfrac{W}{T}S^2 e^{-\frac{R}{L}}$	W	T					
(c)		1/L	M					
(d)		R	T					

The following instructions apply to ICA 13-10 to ICA 13-21. Examine the following graph of a fictitious function. Determine the model type shown:

(A) Exponential
(B) Linear
(C) Power
(D) None of the above

Determine the value and units of m and b for the model.

ICA 13-10

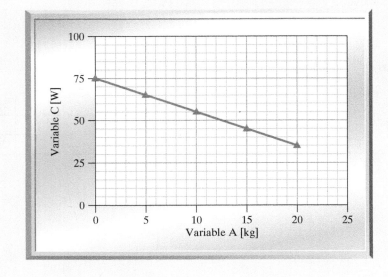

Model type ...			
A	B	C	D
Determine parameter value & units			
m		b	
value	units	value	units

ICA 13-11

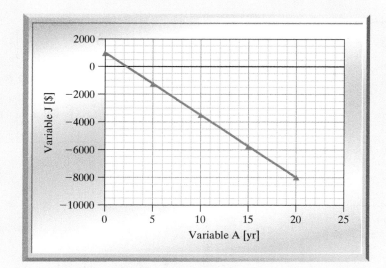

Model type ...			
A	B	C	D

Determine parameter value & units			
m		b	
value	units	value	units

ICA 13-12

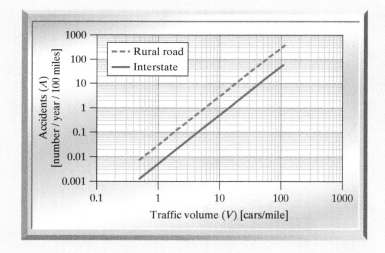

Model type ...			
A	B	C	D

Determine parameter value & units			
m		b	
value	units	value	units

ICA 13-13

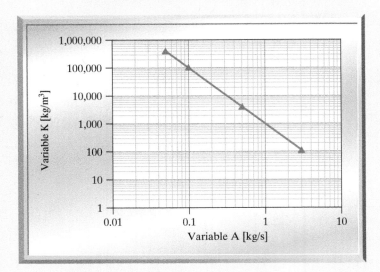

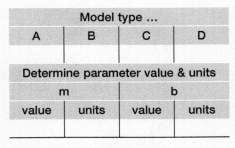

Model type ...			
A	B	C	D

Determine parameter value & units			
m		b	
value	units	value	units

ICA 13-14

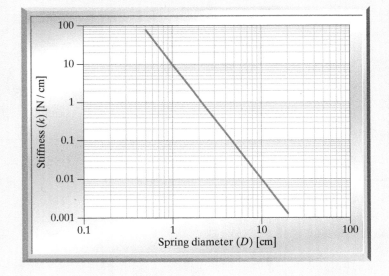

Model type ...			
A	B	C	D

Determine parameter value & units			
m		b	
value	units	value	units

ICA 13-15

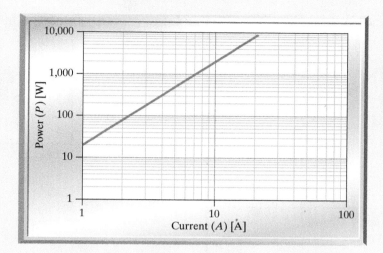

Model Type ...			
A	B	C	D
Determine parameter value & units			
m		b	
value	units	value	units

ICA 13-16

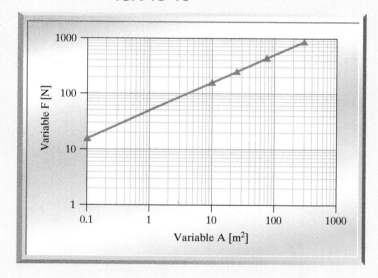

Model Type ...			
A	B	C	D
Determine parameter value & units			
m		b	
value	units	value	units

ICA 13-17

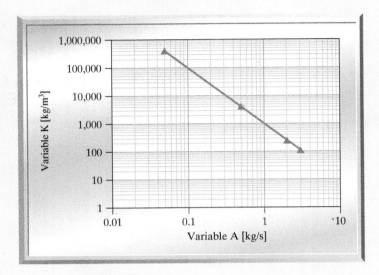

Model Type ...			
A	B	C	D
Determine parameter value & units			
m		b	
value	units	value	units

ICA 13-18

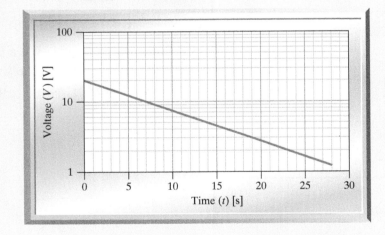

Model Type ...			
A	B	C	D
Determine parameter value & units			
m		b	
value	units	value	units

ICA 13-19

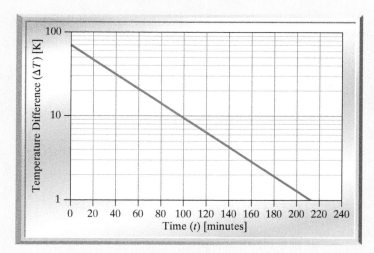

Model Type ...			
A	B	C	D

Determine parameter value & units			
m		b	
value	units	value	units

ICA 13-20

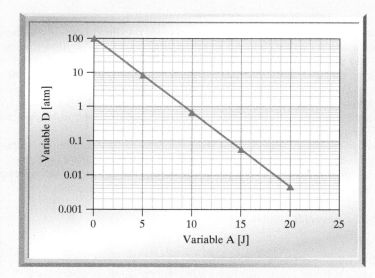

Model Type ...			
A	B	C	D

Determine parameter value & units			
m		b	
value	units	value	units

ICA 13-21

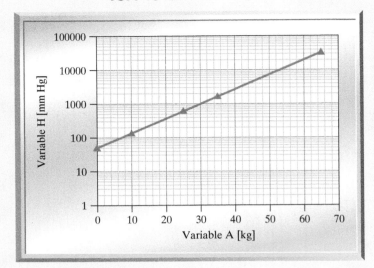

Model Type ...			
A	B	C	D

Determine parameter value & units			
m		b	
value	units	value	units

ICA 13-22

As a reminder, Reynolds Number is discussed in the chapter on Dimensionless Numbers.

When discussing the flow of a fluid through a piping system, we say that friction occurs between the fluid and the pipe wall due to viscous drag. The loss of energy due to the friction of fluid against the pipe wall is described by the friction factor. The **Darcy friction factor** (f) was developed by Henry Darcy (1803–1858), a French scientist who made several important contributions to the field of hydraulics. The friction factor depends on several other factors, including flow regime, Reynolds number, and pipe roughness. The friction factor can be determined in several ways, including from the Moody diagram (shown below).

Olive oil having a specific gravity of 0.914 and a viscosity of 100.8 centipoise is draining by gravity from the bottom of a tank. The drain line from the tank is a 4-inch diameter pipe made of commercial steel (pipe roughness, $\varepsilon = 0.045$ millimeters). The velocity is 11 meters per second. Determine the friction factor for this system, using the following process:

Step 1: Determine the Reynolds number: $Re = \dfrac{\rho v D}{\mu}$.

Step 2: Determine flow regime.

- If the flow is laminar ($Re \leq 2{,}000$), proceed to Step 4.
- If the flow is turbulent or transitional ($Re > 2{,}000$), continue with Step 3.

Step 3: Determine the relative roughness ratio: (ε/D).
Step 4: Determine the *Darcy friction factor* (f) from the diagram.

ICA 13-23

Repeat ICA 13-22 with the following conditions:

  Lactic acid, with a specific gravity of 1.249 and dynamic viscosity of 40.33 centipoise, is flowing in a 1½-inch diameter galvanized iron pipe at a velocity of 1.5 meters per second. Assume the pipe roughness (ε) of galvanized iron is 0.006 inches. Determine the friction factor for this system.

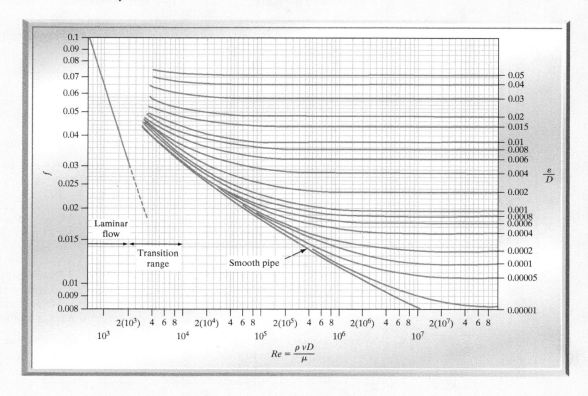

ICA 13-24

This activity requires data from ICA 8-41; the procedure is shown here for reference.

Materials

Bag of cylinders   Scale   Calipers   Ruler

Procedure

For each cylinder, record the mass, length, and diameter and / or width in an Excel workbook.

Analysis

- Using formulas in Excel, determine the volume and density for each cylinder.
- Use data from constant mass set, graph density (ordinate) versus length.
- Use data from constant volume set, graph density (ordinate) versus mass.
- Both graphs should be proper plots, with appropriate trendlines and logarithmic axes to prove your trendline choices by making the data appear linear.

Chapter 13 REVIEW QUESTIONS

1. An environmental engineer has obtained a bacteria culture from a municipal water sample and has allowed the bacteria to grow.

Time (*t*) [min]	1	2	4	6	7	9	10
Concentration (*C*) [ppm]	9	15	32	63	102	220	328

   (a) Show the resulting data and trendline, with equation and R^2 value, on the appropriate graph type (*xy* scatter, semilog, or log–log) to make the data appear linear.
   (b) Assume the value of "m" in the resulting model is the growth constant. Use the trendline determined to find the value and units of the growth constant for this bacteria.

2. An environmental engineer has obtained a bacteria culture from a municipal water sample and allowed the bacteria to grow.

Time (*t*) [min]	1	2	4	6	7	9	10
Concentration (*C*) [ppm]	11.9	17.1	27.0	37.3	42.0	52.3	56.9

   (a) Show the resulting data and trendline, with equation and R^2 value, on the appropriate graph type (*xy* scatter, semilog, or log–log) to make the data appear linear.
   (b) Assume the value of "m" in the resulting model is the growth constant. Use the trendline determined to find the value and units of the growth constant for this bacteria.

3. An environmental engineer has obtained a bacteria culture from a municipal water sample and allowed the bacteria to grow.

Time (*t*) [min]	1	2	4	6	7	9	10
Concentration (*C*) [ppm]	0.5	4.2	32.5	107.5	170.6	346.0	489.8

   (a) Show the resulting data and trendline, with equation and R^2 value, on the appropriate graph type (*xy* scatter, semilog, or log–log) to make the data appear linear.
   (b) Assume the value of "m" in the resulting model is the growth constant. Use the trendline determined to find the value and units of the growth constant for this bacteria.

4. A growing field of inquiry that poses both great promise and great risk for humans is nanotechnology, the construction of extremely small machines. Over the past couple of decades, the size that a working gear can be made has consistently gotten smaller. The table shows milestones along this path.

Years from 1967	0	5	7	16	25	31	37
Minimum gear size [mm]	0.8	0.4	0.2	0.09	0.007	2E-04	8E-06

   (a) Show the resulting data and trendline, with equation and R^2 value, on the appropriate graph type (*xy* scatter, semilog, or log–log) to make the data appear linear.

(b) According to this model, how many years does it take (from any point in time) for the minimum size to be cut in half?

(c) According to the model, during what year will the smallest gear be one-tenth the size of the smallest gear in 2009?

5. If an object is heated, the temperature of the object will increase. The thermal energy (Q) associated with a change in temperature (ΔT) is a function of the mass of the object (m) and the specific heat (C_p). Specific heat is a material property, and values are available in literature. In an experiment, heat is applied to the end of an object, and the temperature change at the other end of the object is recorded. An unknown material is tested in the lab, yielding the following results.

Heat applied (Q) [J]	2	8	10	13	18	27
Temp change (ΔT) [K]	1.5	6.0	7.0	9.0	14.0	22.0

(a) Show the resulting data and trendline, with equation and R^2 value, on the appropriate graph type (xy scatter, semilog, or log–log) to make the data appear linear.

(b) If the material was titanium, what mass of sample was tested?

(c) If a 4-gram sample was used, which of the following materials was tested?

Material	Specific Heat Capacity (C_p) [J/(g K)]
Aluminum	0.91
Copper	0.39
Iron	0.44
Lead	0.13
Molybdenum	0.30
Titanium	0.54

6. The Volcanic Explosivity Index (*VEI*) is based primarily on the amount of material ejected from a volcano, although other factors play a role as well, such as height of plume in the atmosphere. The table below shows the number of volcanic eruptions (N) over the past 10,000 years having a VEI of between 2 and 7.

There are also VEI values of 0, 1, and 8. There is a level 0 volcano erupting somewhere on the Earth essentially all the time. There are one or more level 1 volcanoes essentially every day. The last known level 8 volcano was about 26,000 years ago.

Volcanic Explosivity Index (*VEI*) [−]	Number of Eruptions (*N*) [−]
2	3,477
3	868
4	421
5	168
6	51
7	5

(a) Show the resulting data and trendline, with equation and R^2 value, on the appropriate graph type (xy scatter, semilog, or log–log) to make the data appear linear.

(b) How many level 1 volcanoes does the model predict should have occurred in the last 10,000 years?

(c) How many level 8 volcanoes does the model predict should have occurred in the last 10,000 years?

7. Biosystems engineers often need to understand how plant diseases spread in order to formulate effective control strategies. The rate of spread of some diseases is more or less linear, some increase exponentially, and some do not really fit any standard mathematical model.

   Grey leaf spot of corn is a disease (caused by a fungus with the rather imposing name of *Cercospora zeae-maydis*) that causes chlorotic (lacking chlorophyll) lesions and eventually necrotic (dead) lesions on corn leaves, thus reducing total photosynthesis and yield. In extremely severe cases, loss of the entire crop can result.

   During a study of this disease, the number of lesions per corn leaf was counted every 10 days following the initial observation of the disease, which we call day 0. At this time, there was an average of one lesion on every 20 leaves, or 0.05 lesions per leaf. The data collected during the growing season are tabulated.

   (a) Show the resulting data and trendline, with equation and R^2 value, on the appropriate graph type (*xy* scatter, semilog, or log–log) to make the data appear linear.
   (b) According to the model, how many lesions were there per leaf at the start of the survey?
   (c) How many lesions are there per leaf after 97 days?
   (d) If the model continued to be accurate, how many days would be required to reach 250 lesions per leaf?

Day	Lesions per Leaf	Day	Lesions per Leaf
0	0.05	110	4
20	0.10	120	6
30	0.20	140	17
40	0.26	150	20
60	0.60	170	40
80	1.30	190	112
90	2	200	151

8. A **pitot tube** is a device used to measure the velocity of a fluid, typically, the airspeed of an aircraft. The failure of a pitot tube is credited as the cause of Austral Líneas Aéreas flight 2553 crash in October 1997. The pitot tube had frozen, causing the instrument to give a false reading of slowing speed. As a result, the pilots thought the plane was slowing down, so they increased the speed and attempted to maintain their altitude by lowering the wing slats. Actually, they were flying at such a high speed that one of the slats ripped off, causing the plane to nosedive; the plane crashed at a speed of 745 miles per hour.

   In the pitot tube, as the fluid moves, the velocity creates a pressure difference between the ends of a small tube. The tubes are calibrated to relate the pressure measured to a specific velocity. This velocity is a function of the pressure difference (P, in units of pascals) and the density of the fluid (ρ in units of kilogram per cubic meter).

$$v = \left(\frac{2}{\rho}\right)^{0.5} P^m$$

Pressure (P) [Pa]	50,000	101,325	202,650	250,000	304,000	350,000	405,000	505,000
Velocity fluid A (v_A) [m/s]	11.25	16.00	23.00	25.00	28.00	30.00	32.00	35.75
Velocity fluid B (v_B) [m/s]	7.50	11.00	15.50	17.00	19.00	20.00	22.00	24.50

Fluid	Specific Gravity
Acetone	0.79
Citric acid	1.67
Glycerin	1.26
Mineral Oil	0.90

(a) Show the resulting data and trendline, with equation and R^2 value, on the appropriate graph type (*xy* scatter, semilog, or log–log) to make the data appear linear.
(b) Determine the value and units of the density for each data set using the trendline equations.
(c) From the chart at left, match each data set (A, B) with the correct fluid name according to the results of the density determined from the trendlines.

9. As part of an electronic music synthesizer, you need to build a gizmo to convert a linear voltage to an exponentially related current. You build three prototype circuits and make several measurements of voltage and current in each. The collected data is given in the table below.

Circuit A		Circuit B		Circuit C	
Voltage (V_A) [V]	Current (I_A) [mA]	Voltage (V_B)[V]	Current (I_B) [mA]	Voltage (V_C) [V]	Current (I_C) [mA]
−2.7	0.28	−2.7	0.11	0	0.79
−0.4	1.05	−1.5	0.36	0.5	1.59
0	1.74	0	1.34	1.4	5.41
1.2	3.17	0.8	2.37	2.3	20.28
2.9	7.74	2.6	14.53	2.9	41.44

(a) Show the resulting data and trendline, with equation and R^2 value, on the appropriate graph type (*xy* scatter, semilog, or log-log) to make the data appear linear.

(b) Which of the three circuits comes the closest to doubling the current for an increase of one volt? Note that this doubling is independent of the actual values of voltage. Example: If the current was 0.3 mA at 2.7 volts, it should be 0.6 mA at 3.7 volts, 1.2 mA at 4.7 volts, 2.4 mA at 5.7 volts, etc.

(c) Calculate the value that should appear in the exponent if the current is to double with each increase of 1 volt. Note that you should perform this calculation without referring to the data, the plots, or the trendline equations. This is a purely theoretical calculation.

10. The data below was collected during testing of an electromagnetic mass driver. The energy to energize the electromagnets was obtained from a bank of capacitors. The capacitor bank was charged to various voltages, and for each voltage, the exit velocity of the projectile was measured when the mass driver was activated.

Voltage (V) [kV]	9	13	15	18	22	25
Velocity (v_p) [m/s]	430	530	580	650	740	810

(a) Show the resulting data and trendline, with equation and R^2 value, on the appropriate graph type (*xy* scatter, semilog, or log-log) to make the data appear linear.

(b) What would the velocity be if the capacitors were charged to 1,000 volts?

(c) What voltage would be necessary to accelerate the projectile to 1,000 meters per second?

(d) Assume that the total capacitance is 5 farads. If the capacitors are initially charged to 10,000 volts and are discharged to 2,000 volts during the launch of a projectile, what is the mass of the projectile if the overall conversion of energy stored in the capacitors to kinetic energy in the projectile has an efficiency of 0.2? Recall that the energy stored in a capacitor is given by $E = 0.5\,CV^2$, where C is capacitance in farads and V is voltage in volts.

NOTE

Due to several complicated nonlinear losses in the system that are far beyond the scope of this course, this is a case of a model in which the exponent does not come out to be an integer or simple fraction, so rounding to two significant figures is appropriate. In fact, this model is only a first approximation— a really accurate model would be considerably more complicated.

11. The relationship of the power required by a propeller (shown as the power number, on the ordinate) and the Reynolds number (abscissa) is shown in the graph below. For a propeller, the Reynolds number (Re) is written slightly differently, as

$$Re = \frac{D^2 n \rho}{\mu}$$

where D is the blade diameter [meters] and n is the shaft speed [hertz]. The power number (N_p) is given by the following, where P is the power required [watts].

$$N_p = \frac{P}{\rho n^3 D^5}$$

Use the chart below to answer the following questions:

(a) If the Reynolds number is 500, what is the power number for a system described by Curve A?

(b) If the power number (N_p) is 30, what is the Reynolds number for a system described by Curve A?

(c) If the Reynolds number is 4,000, what is the power (P) required in units of watts at a shaft speed (n) of 0.03 hertz? Assume the system contains acetone, with a kinematic viscosity of 0.419 stokes. The density of acetone is 0.785 grams per cubic centimeter. Use Curve B in the graph to determine your answer. (*Hint:* Use the Reynolds number of the system to first calculate the diameter, then find the power number, and then calculate the power.)

(d) If the power number (N_p) is 5, what is the diameter (D) of the blade in units of centimeters at a shaft speed (n) of 0.02 hertz? Assume the system contains brine, with a kinematic viscosity of 0.0102 stokes. Use Curve A in the graph to determine your answer. (*Hint:* Find the Reynolds number of the system first, and then calculate the diameter.)

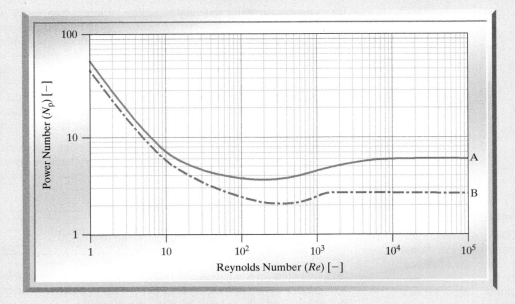

12. When a fluid flows around an object, it creates a force, called the drag force, that pulls on the object. The coefficient of drag (C_d) is a dimensionless number that describes the relationship between the force created and the fluid and object properties, given as

$$C_d = \frac{F_D}{\frac{1}{2}\rho v^2 A_p}$$

where F_D is the drag force, ρ is the fluid density, and v is the velocity of the object relative to the fluid. The area of the object the force acts upon is A_p, and for spheres is given by the area of a circle. The Reynolds number in this situation is written as

$$Re = \frac{D_p \rho v}{\mu}$$

where D_p is the diameter of the object the force acts upon. The chart below shows this relationship. The dashed lines show the predicted theories of Stokes and Newton compared to the solid line of actual results.

(a) If the Reynolds number is 500, what is the coefficient of drag?

(b) If the coefficient of drag is 2, what is the Reynolds number?

Ethylene glycol has a dynamic viscosity of 9.13 centipoise and a specific gravity of 1.109.

(c) If the fluid flows around a sphere of diameter 1 centimeter travelling at a velocity of 2.45 centimeters per second, determine the drag force on the particle in units of newtons. (*Hint:* First determine the Reynolds number.)

(d) If a coefficient of drag of 10 is produced, what is the diameter of the particle? Assume the fluid is moving at 1 centimeter per second. (*Hint:* First determine the Reynolds number.)

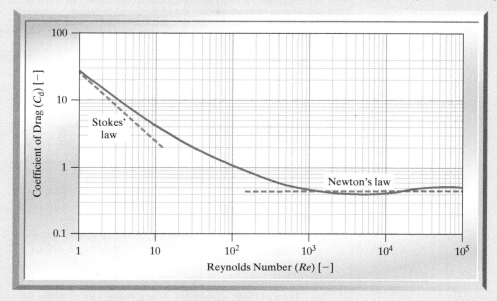

13. When discussing the flow of a fluid through a piping system, we say that friction occurs between the fluid and the pipe wall due to viscous drag. The loss of energy due to the friction of fluid against the pipe wall is described by the friction factor. The Darcy friction factor (f) was developed by Henry Darcy (1803–1858), a French scientist who made several important contributions to the field of hydraulics. The friction factor depends upon several other factors, including flow regime, Reynolds number, and pipe roughness. The friction factor can be determined in several ways, including the Moody diagram (discussed in ICA 13-22) and several mathematical approximations presented here.

In the laminar flow range, the *Darcy friction factor* can be determined by the following formula, shown as the linear line on the Moody diagram: (see ICA 13-22 for the Moody diagram)

$$f = \frac{64}{Re}$$

In the turbulent range, the friction factor is a function of the Reynolds number and the roughness of the pipe (ε). For turbulent flow smooth pipes (where the relative roughness ratio (ε/D) is very small), the *Blasius formula* can be used to calculate an approximate value for the Darcy friction factor.

$$f = 0.316(Re)^{-1/4}$$

This simple formula was developed by Paul Richard Heinrich Blasius (1883–1970), a German fluid dynamics engineer. Later, a more accurate but more complex formula was developed in 1939 by C. F. Colebrook. Unlike the Blasius formula, the Colebrook formula directly takes into account the pipe roughness.

The *Colebrook formula* is shown below. Notice that both sides of the equation contain the friction factor, requiring an iterative solution.

$$\frac{1}{\sqrt{f}} = -2\log\left(\frac{\varepsilon/D}{3.7} + \frac{2.51}{Re\sqrt{f}}\right)$$

To begin the iteration, the Colebrook calculation must have an initial value. Use the Blasius approximation as the first value for f, and determine the first iterative value of the Colebrook equation to use as your friction factor.

While this will only give us an approximation of the correct friction factor, a true solution requires using iteration. If you have covered iteration in Excel (see Appendix Materials), your instructor may provide other instructions on how to determine f.

Prepare an Excel worksheet to compute the friction factor.

Sample Data						
Fluid	Water		Pipe Type	Commercial Steel		
Density (ρ) [g/cm^3]	Viscosity (μ) [cP]	Volumetric Flowrate (Q) [gpm]	Diameter (D) [in]	Roughness (ε) [mm]	Reynolds Number (Re) [-]	Flow Regime
1	1.002	500	6	0.045	263,020	Turbulent

Darcy Friction Factor (f) [-]			Initial f Value		
Laminar	Colebrook		Blasius	Moody Value	
	0.0174		0.0140	0.0185	

Input Parameters:

▪ Fluid: should be chosen from a drop-down list using the material properties listed below. Used with the lookup function to determine:
  • Density
  • Viscosity
  • Volumetric flow rate
  • Diameter

  (ε) [grams per cubic centimeter]
  (μ) [centipoises]
  (Q) [gallons per minute]
  (D) [inches]

▪ Type of pipe: should be chosen from a drop-down list using the properties listed below. Used with the lookup function to determine:
  • Pipe roughness   (ε) [millimeters]

Output Parameters:

Be sure to include the appropriate unit conversions. You may add cells to the worksheet template to complete the necessary unit conversions.

▪ Reynolds number.
▪ Flow regime (laminar, transitional, or turbulent).
▪ Only the correct Darcy friction factor (one of these two values) should be displayed based on the flow regime.
  • For laminar flow, use the equation: $f = 64/Re$.
  • For turbulent flow determined with the Colebrook formula, use the Blasius equation as the initial f value.
▪ Determine the friction factor by hand from the Moody diagram (see ICA 13-22) and list the value found from the graph in the worksheet, as a comparison to your determined value.

Use the following parameters as a test case:

• Fluid = Acetone
• Pipe Type = Cast Iron
• Volumetric Flowrate = 50 gpm
• Pipe Diameter = 2 in

CHAPTER 14
STATISTICS

Probability is associated with assessing the likelihood that an event will or will not occur. For example:

Airplane crash	River breaching a levee	Nuclear reactor accident
Tornado	Failure of equipment	Terminal cancer
Earthquake	Microprocessor failure	Space probe data reception

Statistics are used for design-concept evaluation because they provide quantitative measures to "things" that behave in a random manner. This evaluation helps us make rational decisions about everything from natural events to manufactured products. Statistics, as well as probability, use numerical evidence to aid decision making in the face of uncertainty. Roles of statistics in engineering include the following:

- Evaluation of new or alternative designs, concepts, and procedures
- Estimation of amount to bid on projects
- Management (human uncertainty, economic uncertainty, and others)
- Determination of degree of acceptable item-to-item variation (quality control)

Often, the best way to analyze an engineering problem is to conduct an experiment. When we take this approach, we face several questions:

- How many tests do we need?
- How confident are we in the results?
- Can we extrapolate the results to other conditions?
- Can we estimate how often the result will lie within a specified range?

There are many other related issues, but addressing all of them requires a separate book. Many readers will take or have taken an entire course in probability or statistics, so for now we just touch on some of the important fundamentals.

- **Repeated tests:** When a test is conducted multiple times, we will not get the same (exact) result each time. For example, use a ruler to measure the length of a particular brand of shoe manufactured by Company X. You can produce a table of values, all of which will be nearly, but not exactly, the same. This is because you make slight errors in measurement, so even if every shoe is identical, there will always be some errors in your measurement. Moreover, every shoe is not exactly identical.
- **Differences in a population:** What is the heart rate of all students in a class? Obviously, not everyone will have the same heart rate. We do expect, however, that everyone's rate will lie between, say, 40 and 140 beats per minute. Through measurement, we can determine this variation. In fact, we may find that the average rate for females and males differs. Statistical procedures help us analyze situations such as this.

■ **Manufacturing errors:** Suppose you are manufacturing a run of widgets and a buyer wants all of them to be exactly alike. Obviously, this is impossible, but you can make them almost alike and then tell the buyer how much variation to expect. If you measure each widget as it comes off the assembly line, there will certainly be some variation.

■ **Design criteria for products:** When you build a house, you would like it to stand safely for some period of time. For example, you might specify that the house be designed to withstand a windstorm that would occur, on average, every 50 years. For that case, you must be able to calculate the wind speeds associated with such a storm. Statistical methods allow you to do this.

14.1 HISTOGRAMS

LEARN TO: Create a histogram by hand given starting data
Justify the choice of a reasonable bin size

To illustrate several common statistical concepts, we use data representing the height of several freshman engineering students. Table 14-1 shows the height, to the nearest inch, of each student in a typical class. Table 14-2 shows the same data, summarized by number of students at each height.

Table 14-1 Student height

Student ID	Height (H) [in]
A	67
B	73
C	71
D	69
E	68
F	64
G	70
H	72
I	67
J	71
K	70
L	68
M	66
N	71
O	74
P	71
Q	68
R	72
S	67
T	64
U	75
V	74
W	72

Table 14-2 Summary of height data

Height (H) [in]	Number of Students
62	0
63	0
64	2
65	0
66	1
67	3
68	3
69	1
70	2
71	4
72	3
73	1
74	2
75	1
76	0
77	0
Total	23

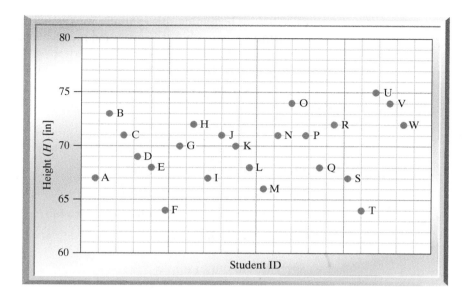

Figure 14-1 Example of student height, shown on scatter plot.

When we graph the values shown in Table 14-1, we end up with a scatter plot with data that is exactly the same: scattered, as shown in Figure 14-1.

Instead of using a scatter plot, we can group the data and plot the group values in a chart similar to a column chart, shown in Figure 14-2. Using the summarized data shown in Table 14-2, we will place two height ranges into a single column or **bin**. The first bin will contain all student-height values less than 62 inches. The next bin will contain student-height values of 62 and 63 inches. The next bin will contain student-height values of 64 and 65 inches, and so on. The abscissa of the graph is the height values; the ordinate is the number of students measured at each height range. Graphs of this nature are called **histograms**. By counting the number of blocks, we find the area under the curve represents the total number of samples taken, in this case, the total number of students (23) observed.

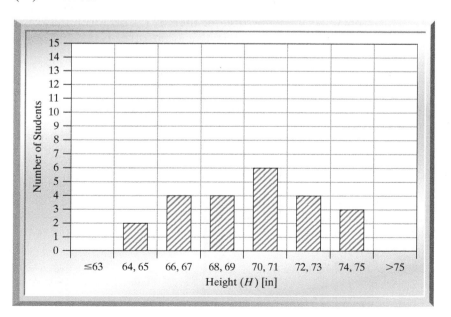

Figure 14-2 Example of student height, shown on a histogram.

Technically, before beginning this example we should have mathematically determined a bin size, rather than arbitrarily grouping the measurements in pairs (62 and 63 in one bin, 64 and 65 in the next bin, etc.). There are several ways to calculate the bin size that will best display the information; below is one method.

Determination of Bin Size

Step One: Determine the number of bins needed.

Number of Bins = Square root of number of data points, rounded to whole number

Step Two: Determine the range of the data.

Range = $X_{max} - X_{min}$

Step Three: Determine the number of items in each bin.

Bin Size = Range divided by Number of Bins, rounded to whole number

Let us apply this to our example.

Step 1: As shown, we have a class of 23 students, so we would need five bins, since the square root of 23 is about 4.8, which rounds to 5. Four would probably also work fine, as would 6. Remember this is just a rule of thumb.

Step 2: The shortest person is 64 inches tall and the tallest is 75, so the range is 11 inches.

Step 3: Dividing the range determined in Step 2 by the number of bins determined in Step 1, we get 2.2, or about 2 inches per bin. On the other hand, we might instead decide to have four bins. If we divide the range by 4, we have 2.75 or 3 inches per bin.

Depending on the number of bins, we sometimes get two different, but acceptable, bin sizes. By changing the bin size, we can change the appearance of the data spread, or the data **distribution**.

What happens to the student height data if we alter the bin size? The plot on the preceding page shows a 2-inch bin interval, and Figure 14-3(a) shows a 3-inch interval.

In Figure 14-3(b), we have used a 4-inch bin interval, and while it is not what we obtained from the "rule of thumb" (2- or 3-inch intervals), it is still mathematically correct but not as informative as the other two.

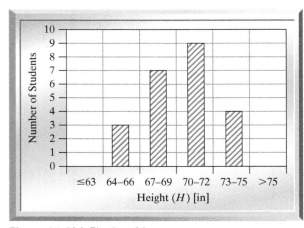

Figure 14-3(a) Bin size of 3.

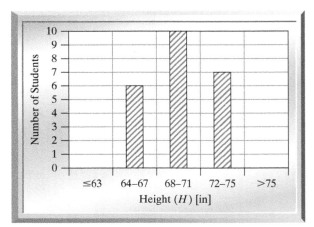

Figure 14-3(b) Bin size of 4.

COMPREHENSION CHECK 14-1

The table below lists the number of computer chips rejected for defects during random testing over the course of a week on a manufacturing line. Four samples of 20 parts are pulled each day.

Use the following data to generate a histogram by hand.

1	1	8	0	2	0
0	2	10	1	3	2
0	1	12	0	2	1
1	6	15	0	0	
3	8	1	2	5	

14.2 STATISTICAL BEHAVIOR

LEARN TO: Determine the mean, median, variance, and standard deviation by hand
Justify the choice of using mean or median in estimating central tendency
Define the relationship between variance and standard deviation

NOTE

Average or Mean = typical, expected value of the data set; sensitive to outliers.

Median = value representing the exact middle value of the list; typically unaffected by outliers. Data must be in ascending order to determine!

When we have gathered the data and plotted a distribution, the next step is to explain the outcome to others. For convenience, we identify a set of parameters to describe distributions.

One parameter of a distribution is the average value. The **average**, or **mean**, is an estimate of the value most representative of the population. This is often called the **central tendency** of the data. The computation of the mean ($\overline{X}$) of a data set containing N values is given in the equation below.

$$\text{Mean} = \overline{X} = \frac{1}{N}(X_1 + X_2 + \cdots + X_N) = \frac{1}{N}\sum_{i=1}^{N} X_i$$

In other words, the mean is the sum of all of the values divided by the total number of values.

The **median**, another measure of central tendency, is the value between the lower half and the upper half of the population. In other words, if all data points are listed in numerical order, the median is the value exactly in the middle of the list. If the number of data points is odd, the median will be the middle value of the population. If the number of data points is even, however, the median will be the average of the two values at the center. A few examples should clarify this.

Set	Data	Mean	Median
1	1, 2, 3, 4, 5, 6, 7	4	4
2	1, 50, 70, 100	55	60
3	5, 10, 20, 40, 80	31	20
4	50, 50, 50, 50, 50, 1,000	208	50

Review the data shown in set 4. It would seem logical if every data point has a value of 50 except one, the average of the data should be about 50; instead, it is 208!

This illustrates the sensitivity of the mean to **extreme values**, or **outliers**. Note that the median is unaffected or only slightly affected. It is for this reason that the mean is insufficient to describe the central tendency of all distributions.

Two other terms are useful in describing a distribution: **variance** and **standard deviation**. Both of these terms quantify how widely a set of values is scattered about the mean. To determine the variance (V_x^2), the difference between each point and the mean is determined, and each difference is squared to keep all terms positive. This sum is then divided by one less than the number of data points.

> **NOTE**
>
> Variance = measure of data scatter; has SQUARED UNITS of the original data set.
>
> Standard deviation = square root of the variance; has units of the original data set.

$$\text{Variance} = V_x^2 = \frac{1}{N-1}((\overline{X} - X_1)^2 + (\overline{X} - X_2)^2 + \cdots + (\overline{X} - X_N)^2)$$

$$= \frac{1}{N-1}\sum_i^N (\overline{X} - X_i)^2$$

The standard deviation (SD_x) is found by taking the square root of the variance:

$$\text{Standard deviation} = SD_x = \sqrt{V_x^2}$$

If we again examine the data found in Table 14-2, we can calculate the mean, median, variance, and standard deviation for our height data.

Height (H) [in]	Number of Students
62	0
63	0
64	2
65	0
66	1
67	3
68	3
69	1
70	2
71	4
72	3
73	1
74	2
75	1
76	0
77	0
Total	**23**

Calculation of the Mean:
Total number of points (N)
= 23 students

The sum of all heights
= (2 students * 64 inches/student) + (1 * 66) + (3 * 67) + (3 * 68) + (1 * 69)
+ (2 * 70) + (4 * 71) + (3 * 72) + (1 * 73) + (2 * 74) + (1 * 75)
= 1,604 inches

Mean
= 1,604 inches/23 students
= 69.7 inches/student

Calculation of the Median:
Put data in order of value, listing each entry once
    64, 64, 66, 67, 67, 67, 68, 68, 68, 69, 70, 70, 71, 71, 71, 71, 72, 72, 72, 73, 74, 74, 75
Find the center value since the total number of students is odd
    64, 64, 66, 67, 67, 67, 68, 68, 68, 69, **70**, 70, 71, 71, 71, 71, 72, 72, 72, 73, 74, 74, 75
Median = 70 inches

Calculation of Variance: Note that the variance will have the same units as the variable in question squared, in this case, "inches squared."

$$\text{Variance} = \frac{1}{23-1}((69.7 - 64)^2 + (69.7 - 64)^2 + (69.7 - 66)^2 + \cdots$$

$$+ (69.7 - 75)^2) = 9.5 \text{ in}^2$$

Calculation of Standard Deviation: The standard deviation has the same units as the variable in question, in this case, "inches."

$$\text{Standard deviation} = \sqrt{9.5} = 3.08 \text{ in}$$

● **EXAMPLE 14-1**

Consider the following velocity data, listed in units of feet per second. Determine the mean, median, variance, and standard deviation of the data.

1	28	14	32	35	25	14	28	5
16	42	35	26	5	33	35	16	14

Calculation of the Mean:

Total number of points (N) = 18

*Sum of all data   (ΣX_i) = (1) + (2 * 5) + (3 * 14) + $\cdots$ + (42) = 404*

Mean   = 404/18 = 22.4 feet per second

Calculation of the Median:

Put data in order, listing each entry once.

> *1, 5, 5, 14, 14, 14, 16, 16, 25, 26, 28, 28, 32, 33, 35, 35, 35, 42*

Find the center two values and average them, since total number of entries is even (18).

> *1, 5, 5, 14, 14, 14, 16, 16, **25**, **26**, 28, 28, 32, 33, 35, 35, 35, 42*

Median = (25 + 26)/2 = 25.5 feet per second

Calculation of Variance:

Variance = $\dfrac{1}{18-1}$ ((22.4 − 1)^2 + $\cdots$ + (22.4 − 42)^2) = 147 (ft/s)^2

Calculation of Standard Deviation:

Standard deviation = $\sqrt{147}$ = 12.1 feet per second

● **EXAMPLE 14-2**

Consider the following energy data, given in units of joules. Determine the mean, median, variance, and standard deviation of the data.

159	837	618	208	971	571	379	220	31

Calculation of the Mean:

Total number of points (N) = 9

Sum of all data   (ΣX_i) = 159 + 837 + $\cdots$ + 31 = 3,994

Mean   = 3,994/9 = 443.7 = 444 joules

Calculation of the Median:

Put data in order, listing each entry once.

> *31, 159, 208, 220, 379, 571, 618, 837, 971*

Find the center value since the total number of students is odd (9; center value at entry 5).

> *31, 159, 208, 220, **379**, 571, 618, 837, 971*

Median = 379 joules

Calculation of Variance:

Variance = $\dfrac{1}{9-1}$[(444 − 31)^2 + $\cdots$ + (444 − 971)^2] = 105,059 joules^2

Calculation of Standard Deviation:

Standard deviation = $\sqrt{105,059}$ = 324 joules

COMPREHENSION CHECK 14-2	For the following mass data given in units of kilograms, determine the mean, median, variance, and standard deviation.

8	7	9	11	16
12	2	9	10	9

COMPREHENSION CHECK 14-3	For the following temperature data given in units of degrees Celsius [°C], determine the mean, median, variance, and standard deviation.

105	120	110	100	102
103	58	110	100	118

14.3 DISTRIBUTIONS

LEARN TO: Draw the expected distribution, given an expected change in baseline
Assign a possible cause for change, given baseline distribution and new distribution
Define a "normal" distribution

From Figures 14-2 and 14-3 on the preceding pages, you can see a similarity in the histogram shape of all three plots. The values start small, increase in size, and then decrease again. In the case of student height, this means that a few people are short, most people have some "average" height, and a few people are tall. This same conclusion is true in many things we can measure. For example:

- If we weigh many standard-size watermelons (neither miniature nor giant), we will find that most weigh between 20 and 30 pounds. A few weigh less than 20 pounds, and a few weigh more than 30 pounds.
- As we look through a dictionary, we find that there are many words with between four and six letters. There are a few with one, two, or three letters and a few with more than six, but clearly most have between four and six letters.
- To improve efficiency in the office, we had an expert to monitor the length of phone calls made by the staff. The expert found that most of the time, phone calls lasted between 3 and 5 minutes, but a few were longer than 5 and some others lasted only a minute.

Normal Distributions

We wanted to know how many "flexes" it takes to cause a paper clip to fail, so we asked volunteers to test the bending performance of paper clips by doing the following:

- Unfold the paper clip at the center point so that the resulting wire forms an "S" shape.
- Bend the clip back and forth at the center point until it breaks.
- Record the number of "flexes" required to break the clip.

Using these data, we created Figure 14-4. This is the same as the earlier histogram, but the "boxes" are replaced by a smooth curve through the values.

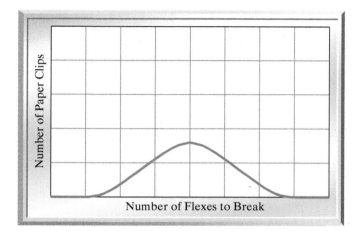

Figure 14-4 Distribution of paper clip failure.

When you are interested in the *shape* of the curve rather than the exact data values, you can replace the bars of the histogram with a smooth curve and rename the graph a **distribution**. A distribution is considered *normal* if the following rules hold true. This is known as the **68-95-99.7 rule**, shown in Figure 14-5.

- 68% of values are within one standard deviation (1σ) of the mean (μ).
- 95% of values are within two standard deviations (2σ).
- 99.7% of values are within three standard deviations (3σ).

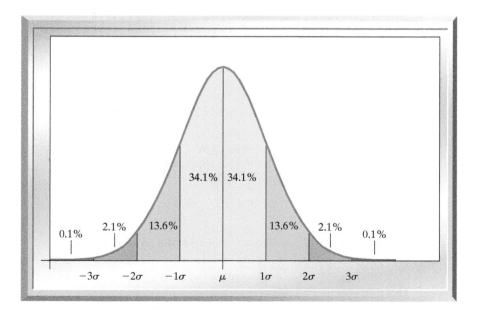

Figure 14-5 "Normal" distribution, showing the 68–95–99.7 rule.

● EXAMPLE 14-3   Suppose we ask a class of students how many states they have visited. The results might appear as shown below.

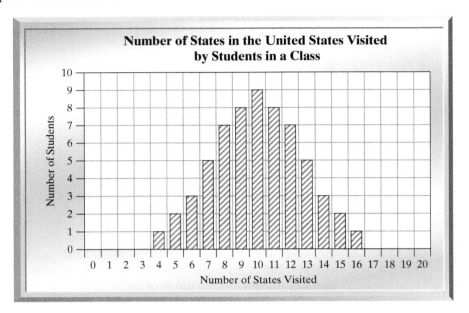

It seems that most have visited between 8 and 12, and that as many have visited more than 10 as have visited fewer than 10. A few have visited as many as 16 states, and all the students have visited at least 4. Let us calculate some values pertinent to this situation.

How many students are there in the class?

To do this we simply add the number of students represented by each bar, or

$$1 + 2 + 3 + 5 + 7 + 8 + 9 + 8 + 7 + 5 + 3 + 2 + 1 = 61 \text{ students}$$

What is the cumulative number of state visits?

*We answer this by totaling the product of the bar height with the number of states represented by the bar. For example, 5 students have visited 7 states, so those 5 students have visited a total of 5 * 7 = 35 states. Or, 8 students have visited 11 states, so those students have visited a total of 88 states. We calculate*

$$1*4 + 2*5 + 3*6 + \cdots + 2*15 + 1*16 = 610 \text{ states}$$

What is the average number of states visited by a student?

Once we have the values from our first two answers, this is straightforward division: the total number of visits divided by the total number of students.

$$610/61 = 10 \text{ states per student}$$

Notice that the value 10 is in the center of the distribution. For distributions that are symmetrical (such as this one), the average value is the one in the center, the one represented by the largest number of occurrences.

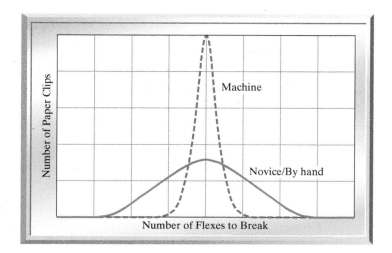

Figure 14-6 Distribution of paper clip failure after a decrease in variance.

Decrease in Variance

Let us examine the shape of the distribution of paper clip failures discussed earlier. How would the distribution change if we brought in a machine that did it "exactly" the same way each time? Both the distribution from the data class and the distribution of the machine are shown in Figure 14-6. The same number of clips was tested in each case, so the areas under each curve must be the same.

This exercise illustrates that distributions that have the same mean (and median) can look very different. In this case, the difference between these two distributions is in their "spread," or their variation about the mean. The effect of using a machine to break the paperclips was a decrease in the variance.

Shift in Mean

Redraw the paper clip distribution; then on the same plot, sketch the distribution if each volunteer tested the same number of clips that were manufactured by the same manufacturer as before with the same variance, but were stronger and typically required 10 more flexes to fail. The result is shown in Figure 14-7. The stronger material caused the distribution to shift to the right. Since the variance and number of clips remained the same, the shape and size of the curve remains the same.

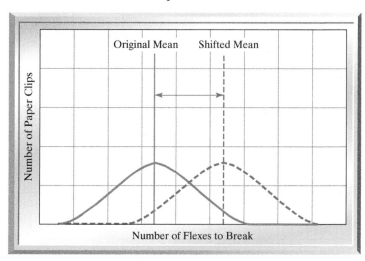

Figure 14-7 Distribution of paper clip failure with a shift.

Skewed Data

It is often easy to place an upper or lower limit on the value of the possible outcome. In these cases, the distribution is no longer symmetric—it is **skewed**. A population is **positively skewed** if the mean has been pulled higher than the median, and **negatively skewed** if the mean has been pulled lower than the median (see Figure 14-8 for an example of a positively skewed graph). You have probably heard news reports that use the median to describe a distribution of income in the United States. The median is used in this case because the distribution is positively skewed. This skew is caused by two factors, the presence of extreme values (millionaires) and the **range restriction**, the latter because income cannot be lower than $0. The extreme values causing the positive skew are not shown on the graph. Most of these would be far off the page to the right.

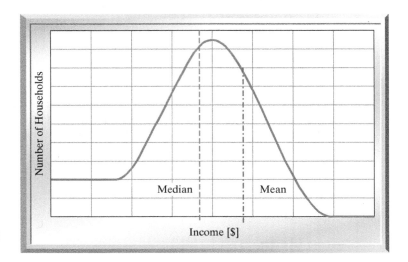

Figure 14-8 Distribution of positively skewed data.

COMPREHENSION CHECK 14-4   For each graph shown below, decide if the mean, variance, or population size has changed.

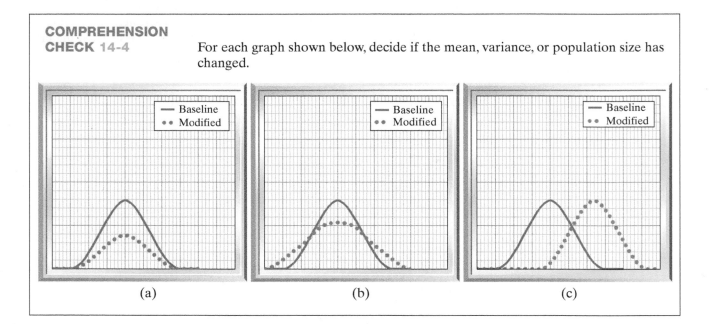

● **EXAMPLE 14-4**   For each scenario, identify one graph from the following set that best illustrates how the baseline curve would change under the conditions of that scenario. Each graph shows the usual distribution (labeled baseline) and the way the distribution would be modified from the baseline shape (labeled modified) under certain conditions.

The graphs show SAT composite (verbal + quantitative) scores, for which 400 is generally considered to be the minimum possible score and 1,600 is considered to be the maximum possible score.

(a) The designers of the SAT inadvertently made the test more difficult, while the variance of the scores remains the same.

This is shown by Curve (F): Area and variance the same; mean shifted to left.

(b) The variability of scores is reduced by switching to true/false questions, while the average remains the same.

This is shown by Curve (D): Area and mean are the same; distribution is narrower.

(c) A population boom increases the number of students seeking college admission.

This is shown by Curve (B): Area increases, distribution stays the same.

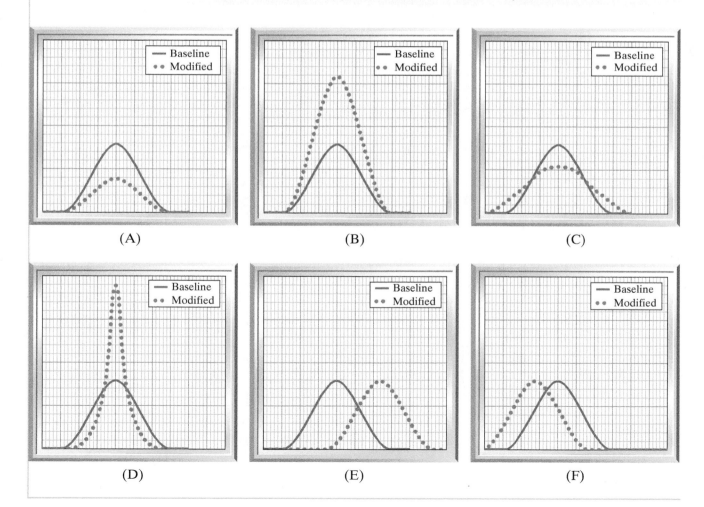

Use the scenario described in Example 14-4. For each scenario, identify one graph from the graph choices shown in Example 14-4 that best illustrates how the baseline curve would change under the conditions of that scenario.

(a) The economy declines, so more students decide to enter the workforce instead of attending college. The variance in the SAT scores remains the same.

(b) As a performance measure, all high school seniors are required to take the SAT; the variance remains the same.

(c) Due to mantory test preparation courses, the mean of the SAT increases for the same number of students taking the exam. The variance remains the same.

14.4 CUMULATIVE DISTRIBUTION FUNCTIONS

LEARN TO: Draw a CDF by hand given starting data or a histogram

For the earlier student height plot using two heights per bin, we will graph the bin data but now show the values on the ordinate as a fraction rather than a whole number. To do this, we divide the number of students in each bin of the histogram by the total number of students. If we now add the heights of all the bars in the new plot, they should equal 1. This is called a **normalized plot**, shown in Figure 14-9. We "normalized" the values by dividing by the total number of data points. This graph holds no new information; it is simply a rescaling of the histogram we drew earlier.

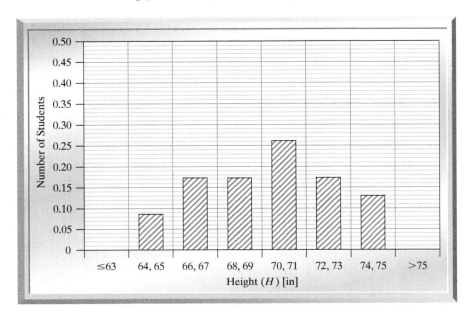

Figure 14-9 Normalized plot of student height, originally shown in Figure 14-2.

This plot can be used as an intermediate step to obtain a final plot called a **cumulative distribution function (CDF).** We derive this plot by summing the values for each bin on the normalized plot from the first bin up to each individual bin. For example, suppose the values in the first three bins were 0, 0.08, and 0.18. By adding the values, we get new "cumulative" values: bin 1 = 0; bin 2 = 0 + 0.08 = 0.08; and bin 3 = 0 + 0.08 + 0.18 = 0.26. It should be obvious that we can obtain the CDF value for each bin by adding the normalized value of that bin to the CDF value of the bin before it. The CDF values are usually shown as percentages rather than fractions, for example, 50% instead of 0.5.

As we move across the plot, the values should go from 0 to 1. Using the height data in the normalized plot below, we have produced a cumulative distribution shown in Figure 14-10. Sometimes, the CDF is shown as a continuous, curved line rather than a column chart. Both the original histogram and the cumulative distribution plot are useful tools in answering questions about the composition of a population.

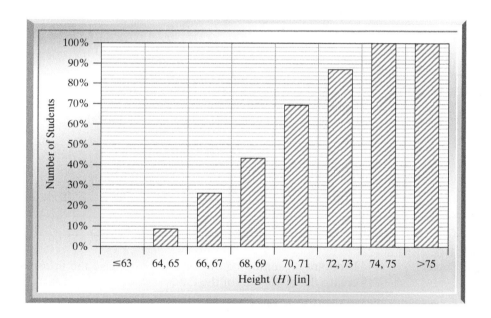

Figure 14-10 CDF of student height, originally shown in Figure 14-2.

● EXAMPLE 14-5

Consider the following pressure data, given in units of pascals. Draw the histogram and CDF of the data.

36	9	33	11	23	3
34	39	56	51	39	1
27	25	2	1	53	32
14	41	55	28	29	19
51	15	25	10	35	38

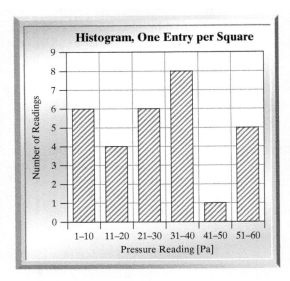

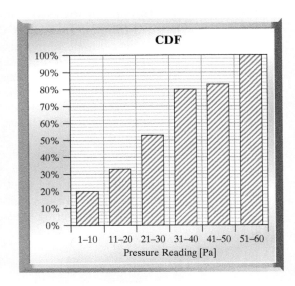

COMPREHENSION CHECK 14-6

Consider the weight of shipping boxes sent down an assembly line, given in units of newtons. Draw the histogram and CDF of the data.

38	103	20	42	16
20	74	63	90	61
114	79	61	50	64

COMPREHENSION CHECK 14-7

Data are presented below for 25 entries. Use the information from the CDF to create the histogram of the data.

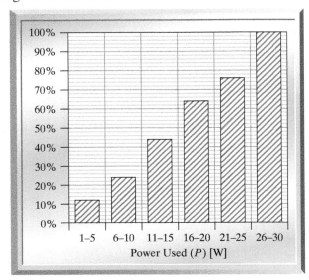

14.5 STATISTICAL PROCESS CONTROL (SPC)

We showed that a histogram such as the one shown in Figure 14-11 visually summarizes how a set of values is distributed. Sometimes, however, we are not only interested in the values themselves, but also in how the distribution changes over time.

For example, as a machine in a factory operates, it may slowly (or occasionally quickly) lose proper alignment or calibration due to wear, vibrations, and so on. If a machine was making bolts with a mean length of 1 inch and a standard deviation of 0.01 inch when it first began operating, after it had made 100,000 bolts, the alignment may have drifted so that the mean was only 0.95 inches with a standard deviation of 0.02 inch. This may be unacceptable to the customer purchasing the bolts, so the parameters of the process need to be monitored over time to make sure the machine is readjusted as necessary.

A graph called a **quality control chart** is often used to show how close to the mean the results of a process are when measured over time. The graph is usually a scatter plot, with the abscissa shown as time or another indicator that would change with time, such as batch number. Figure 14-12 shows a sample control chart, the mean, and the standard deviation.

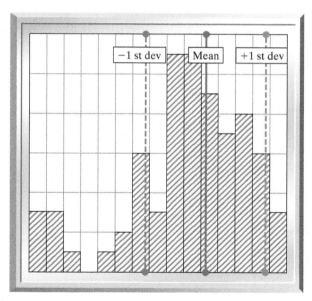

Figure 14-11 Sample histogram.

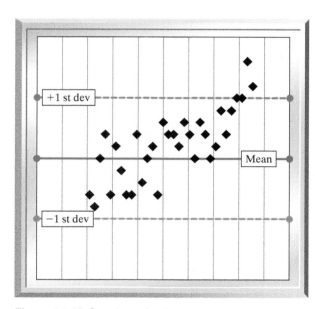

Figure 14-12 Sample quality chart.

When tracking a manufacturing process, engineers are often concerned with whether the process is "in control," or behaving as expected. **Statistical Process Control (SPC)** is a method of monitoring, controlling, and improving a manufacturing process. In some situations, the desired mean and acceptable deviation limits may be preset for a variety of reasons (chemistry, safety, etc.). Often, the upper or lower limits of control are determined by the desired end result. For example:

- The reactor temperature must not rise above 85 degrees Celsius or the reactant will vaporize.
- The injection pressure should be between 50 and 75 kilopascals to ensure that the part is molded properly.
- A bolt must be machined to ±0.02 inches to fit properly in a chair leg.

An engineer will study how the process relates to the control limits and will make adjustments to the process accordingly. To discuss whether a process is in control, we can divide a chart into zones, shown in Figure 14-13, to create a control chart. The mean is determined either by the desired end result (the iron content of the product must average 84%) or by the process itself (the reactor temperature should average 70 degrees Fahrenheit for an optimum reaction to occur). The standard deviation is most often determined by experimentation. For example:

- The purity range for this product is ±0.0005%.
- The standard deviation for the reactor temperature must not exceed 5 degrees Fahrenheit or the reaction will create unwanted by-products.
- The standard deviation of the current gain of the transistors being produced must be less than 15.

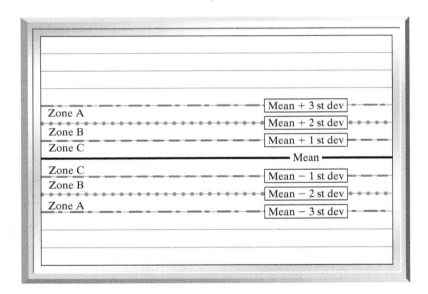

Figure 14-13 Standard deviation ranges.

Eight Ways to Be Out of Control

A variety of conditions can indicate that a process is out of control. First published by Lloyd S. Nelson in the October 1984 issue of the *Journal of Quality Technology*, the **Nelson Rules** are listed below, with examples and graphs. In the graphs, solid points indicate the rule violations. The actual conditions may vary slightly from company to company, but most take the same standard form. For example, a company may operate with Rule 3 stated as seven or eight points in a row instead of six.

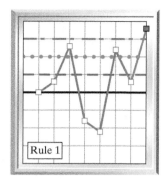

1. **A point falls anywhere beyond Zone A.** The value is more than three standard deviations away from the mean. May occur on either side of the mean.

   Example: The mean temperature of a reactor is 85 degrees Celsius with a standard deviation of 5 degrees Celsius. If the temperature exceeds 100 degrees Celsius, the reactor vessel may explode. If the temperature falls below 70 degrees Celsius, the reaction cannot proceed properly.

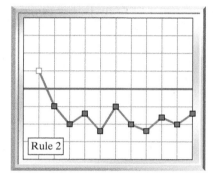

2. **Nine points in a row occur on the same side of the mean.** The actual value seems to be drifting away from the mean.

   Example: The percentage of boron in a semiconductor should be 250 parts per billion. Nine consecutive samples have boron contents less than this value. The machine incorporating the boron into the semiconductor material may need to be cleaned or recalibrated.

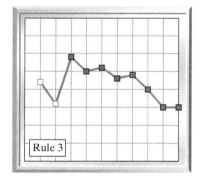

3. **Six points occur with a consistently increasing or decreasing trend.** If this pattern continues, the values will eventually become unacceptable.

   Example: The shaft length of a part is increasing with each successive sample; perhaps the grinding wheel needs to be changed.

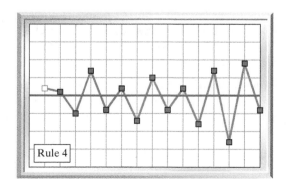

4. **Fourteen points in a row alternate from one side of the mean to the other.** The process is unstable.

   Example: The control system for a crane errs from one side to the other. This may indicate a sensor failure or the need to reprogram the controller.

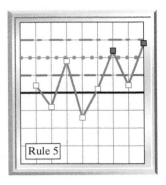

Rule 5

5. **Two out of three points in a row occur in Zone A.** The process is close to the upper limit; take preventive measures now.

   Example: A robot that is spot-welding parts in an automobile is coming close to the edge of the material being welded. It probably needs attention.

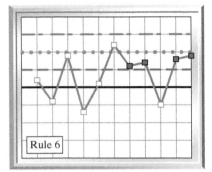

Rule 6

6. **Four out of five points in a row occur in Zone B.** The process is very close to the upper limit; take preventive measures now.

   Example: Four out of five customers in the bank teller queue have waited more than one standard deviation to be helped. Perhaps another teller is needed.

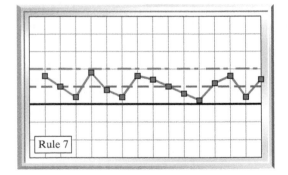

Rule 7

7. **Fifteen points in a row occur in Zone C; points can occur on either side of the mean.** The process is running too perfectly; in many applications the restrictions can be loosened to save time and money.

   Example: The thickness of all washers being manufactured for quarter-inch bolts is within 0.0005 inch of the desired mean. Very few applications require washers with such close tolerances. Perhaps the process could be set to process the washers faster.

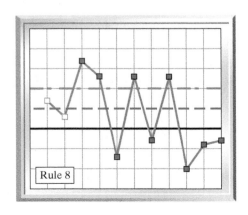

Rule 8

8. **Eight points in a row occur beyond Zone C; points can occur on either side of the mean.** The process does not run close enough to the mean; the parts are never quite on target; may indicate a need for a process adjustment.

   Example: The postmark machine in a regional postal distribution center is stamping the envelopes too high or too low; it probably needs attention.

● **EXAMPLE 14-6**   The data shown in the table were collected from a manufacturing process that makes bolts. Assume the process specifies an average bolt length of 10 inches, with a standard deviation of 0.25 inches. Is this process under statistical control?

Part	Length (L) [in]	Part	Length (L) [in]
1	10.00	11	10.25
2	10.25	12	10.65
3	10.65	13	9.50
4	9.50	14	9.36
5	9.36	15	9.25
6	9.00	16	10.50
7	10.50	17	10.20
8	10.20	18	9.80
9	9.80	19	10.45
10	10.00	20	10.10

The control chart for these data is shown below. Rule 1 is violated since a point falls outside of Zone A (part 6) and Rule 5 is violated as parts 14 and 15 fall insides Zone A. The process is not in statistical control.

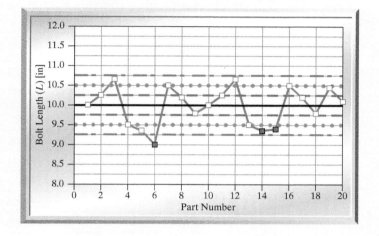

COMPREHENSION CHECK 14-8

The pressure in a water filter is monitored in a chemical plant. The filter should operate at 18 pounds-force per square inch [psi], with a standard deviation of ±2 psi. Analyze the data shown to determine if the filter is behaving as expected (the process is in control; the filter does not require any attention) or if the filter required attention (the process is out of control; the filter should be cleaned). Refer to the Nelson rules to explain your conclusion, and include the time the violations occur.

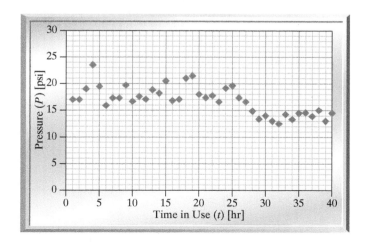

14.6 STATISTICS IN EXCEL

LEARN TO: Create a histogram and CDF given a set of data in Excel
Determine the mean, median, variance, and standard deviation using Excel

In Chapter 10, some common built-in statistical functions were introduced. Tables 10-3 is repeated here as Tables 14-3. Please review Example 10-2 for a refresher on statistical functions in Excel.

Table 14-3 Statistical functions in Excel

Function as Written in Excel	Definition
AVERAGE (cells)	Finds the mean or average value of a list of cells
MAX (cells)	Finds the maximum value in a list of cells
MEDIAN (cells)	Finds the median value of a list of cells
MIN (cells)	Finds the minimum value in a list of cells
STDEV.P (cells)	Finds the standard deviation value of a list of cells
VAR.P (cells)	Finds the variance value of a list of cells

To create **histograms** and **CDFs** with Excel, you need to first activate the Analysis ToolPak in Microsoft Excel.

- In Excel, go to the Office button and click **Options**.
- Choose the **Add-Ins** tab on the left menu of the Excel Options window to display all the active add-in applications in Excel. Notice in our list that the Analysis ToolPak is listed as inactive.

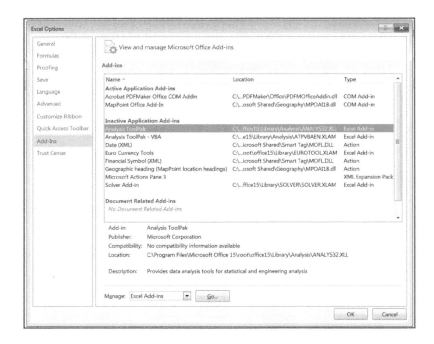

- At the bottom of the Excel Options window, select **Excel Add-Ins** in the **Manage** drop-down menu and click **Go**.
- In the Add-Ins window, check the **Analysis ToolPak** option and click **OK**.
- A prompt might pop up telling you to install the add-in—click **Yes** and finish the installation, using the Office Installer.

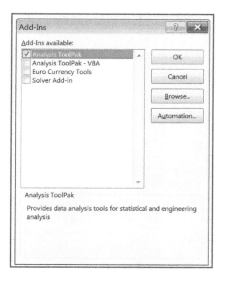

The outline below gives the steps necessary to use the data analysis tool in Excel for basic statistical analysis of a data set. This is presented with an example of the high and low temperatures during the month of October 2006.

- *If necessary, input the data; the data for this example have been provided online. Use Column A to input an identifier for the data point, in this case, the date. Columns B and C will contain the actual high and low temperatures for each day, respectively.*
- *Next, decide on the bin range. This discussion focuses on the high temperatures, but can easily be repeated with the low temperatures.*
  - *A rule of thumb is that the number of bins is approximately equal to the square root of the number of samples. While it is obvious in this example how many total samples are needed, the COUNT function is often very useful. October has 31 days, and the square root of 31 is 5.57; thus, you should choose either 5 or 6 bins.*
  - *Examine your data to determine the range of values. Using the MAX and MIN functions, you can determine that the highest high temperature during October was 86 degrees Fahrenheit and the lowest high temperature was 56 degrees Fahrenheit. Thus, your range is 86 − 56 = 30 °F.*
  - *Since 5.57 is closer to 6 than to 5, choose 6 bins. Remember, however, that you might want to try a different number of bins to see if that would result in a clearer representation of the data. With a range of 30 degrees Fahrenheit, 6 bins gives 30 °F/6 bins = 5 °F per bin.*

- Type the range of values that will appear in each bin. For example, the first bin will contain temperatures 55, 56, 57, 58, and 59; the second bin will contain temperatures 60–64, and so on.
- In the adjacent column, type the corresponding upper value of temperature for each of the bins listed.

👆 **To create histograms and CDF charts:**

- Go to **Data** > **Analysis** > **Data Analysis** and under Analysis Tools choose **Histogram**. Click **OK**.

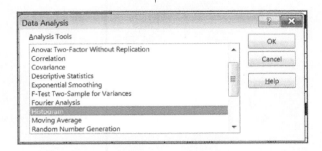

- In the **Input Range**, click the icon at the right end of the blank box. You can then highlight the range (in this case, $B$6:$B$36). Close the box by clicking the icon at the right-hand end of this small box where the range is shown.
- Repeat this procedure for the **Bin Range**, highlighting the cells that contain the upper values.
- Next, for the **Output Range**, click the circle and identify a single cell to begin the placement of the output data.
- Finally, check the boxes to activate the options of **Cumulative Percentage** calculations and **Chart Output**.
- Click **OK**.

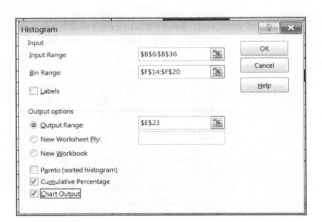

Your worksheet should now look like this:

- **Replace the values in the histogram data table for "Bin"** with the "Bin Labels" you entered earlier. This will change the axis labels to the range, rather than the upper value, for each bin.

- **Move the histogram location** to a new worksheet rather than imbedded in the original worksheet to allow the data to be seen clearly. After selecting the chart, use the **Chart Tools > Design > Location > Move Chart** option to select "As new sheet."

- **Modify the histogram to be a proper plot** just as you would with any other chart. The same rules for a "proper plot" apply to a histogram also, so make sure the background is white and alter the series colors, etc., as appropriate. The histogram generated with the directions above is shown below, properly formatted.

- **Change the vertical scale on the left axis** to be a multiple of 2, 5, or 10 to allow the cumulative percentages on the right axis to line up with the gridlines. This is important to do!

- **Change the vertical scale on the right axis** to be a maximum value of 100%. This is important to do. The resulting analysis should appear as follows.

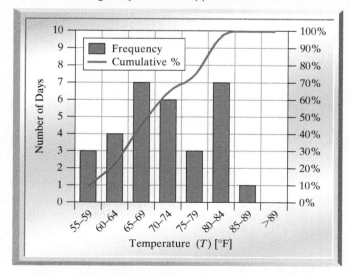

COMPREHENSION CHECK 14-9   Repeat this analysis, using the daily low temperatures during October 2006.

⌘ Statistics on the Mac OS

Unfortunately, as this book goes to press, Microsoft has chosen not to include the histogram tool in Excel 2008 or Excel 2011 for the Mac OS. You have a few options.

- If you have an Intel-based Mac, you can use Excel 2007 or 2010 for Windows. If you do not know how to activate the Windows option on your machine, ask your friendly local Mac guru at your computer center.
- You can use Excel 2004 for the Mac OS, which did include a histogram tool.
- You can create the histogram manually according to the instructions below.

To create histograms and CDF charts using Mac OS Excel 2008 or 2011:

Create columns for the data, bin ranges, and upper value in each bin as described above.

Next, determine the number of data points in each bin. After doing a few, you will find it easy. Use the advanced Excel function, known as an array function, to accomplish this determination. A detailed explanation of array functions is beyond the scope of this book, but if you follow the instructions below *carefully*, you should not have any trouble. The specific array function to use is called FREQUENCY.

1. In the cell immediately to the right of the topmost "upper bin value" cell (this would be cell G14 in the example above) enter the formula

    = FREQUENCY (DataRange, UpperBinValueRange)

   and press return. In the example above, this would be

    = FREQUENCY (B6:B36, F14:F20)

NOTE

Do not select these cells by clicking the bottom one and dragging up to the top one—it will not work correctly.

Do not use the replicate handle in the lower-right corner of the cell to drag down.

2. Click-and-hold the cell into which you entered the formula, then drag straight down to the cell in the row *following* the row containing the last "upper bin value." This would be cell G21 in the example above. Release the mouse button. At this point, you will have a vertical group of cells selected (G14:G21 in the example), the top cell will contain the number of data points in the first bin, and the rest of the selected cells *will be blank*. The formula you entered in the topmost of these cells will appear in the formula bar at the top of the window.
3. Click once in the formula in the formula bar. The top cell of the selected group will be highlighted.
4. Hold down the Command (⌘) key and press Return. The selected cells will now contain the number of data points in each bin immediately to the left. The bottommost selected cell will contain the number of data points larger than the upper bin value in the final bin. In the example, this "extra" cell should contain a 0, since no values are larger than those in the final bin. Note the formulae that appear in these cells are all identical—the cell references are exactly the same. This is normal for an array function.

Use these values to create the histogram.

1. Select the cells containing the bin ranges (E14:E20 in our example), then hold down the command (⌘) key while you select the cells containing the number of data points per bin. In our example, since the "extra" cell at the bottom contains a 0, you need

not include it. If this were nonzero, you might want to add a cell at the bottom of the cell ranges that said something like >89. You should now have the two columns for bin ranges and number per bin selected (E14:E20 and G14:G20 in our example).

2. In the toolbar, select **Gallery > Charts > Column**. A row of column chart icons should appear.

3. Click the first icon, which shows pairs of columns. The chart that appears shows the histogram. Be sure to follow all appropriate proper plot rules for completing the histogram.

Finally, generate the CDF. If you have survived this far, you should be able to do this with minimal guidance. Create another column of values next to the column containing the number of data points per bin. In the cell next to the topmost bin cell, enter the number of data points in that bin. In the next cell down, enter a formula that will add the cell above to the cell beside it containing the number of data points in that bin. Replicate this formula down to the last bin. Each cell in the new column should now contain the sum of all data points in all bins to that point.

14.7 STATISTICS IN MATLAB

LEARN TO: Create a histogram and CDF given a set of data in MATLAB
Determine the mean, median, variance and standard deviation using MATLAB

Literally hundreds of functions are built into MATLAB. A few statistical functions, similar to Table 14-3 for Excel, are shown in Table 14-4.

Table 14-4 Common MATLAB statistical functions

MATLAB Function	Definition
ceil(X)	Rounds each element of X up to the next largest integer.
fix(X)	Rounds each element of X to the neighboring integer closest to 0.
floor(X)	Rounds each element of X down to the next smallest integer.
length(X)	If X is a vector, length(X) returns the number of elements in X. If X is a matrix, length(X) returns either the number of rows in X or the number of columns in X, whichever is larger.
max(X) and min(X)	Finds the maximum or minimum value of X. If X is a matrix, returns the maximum or minimum value of the elements of each column in X.
mean(X)	Finds the mean or average of the elements of X. If X is a matrix, mean(X) returns the mean of the elements in each column of X.
median(X)	Finds the median value of X. If X is a matrix, median(X) returns the median value of the elements of each column in X.
round(X)	Rounds each element of X to the nearest integer.
size(X)	Returns a vector of the number of rows and columns of X.
std(X)	Finds the standard deviation value of the elements of X. If X is a matrix, std(X) returns the standard deviation of each column of X.
var(X)	Finds the variance value of X. If X is a matrix, var(X) returns the variance of the elements of each column of X.

● **EXAMPLE 14-8**

You are studying the number of fatal accidents that occur during different times of the day. Using MATLAB and the data shown, determine the mean, median, variance and standard deviation. The data represent the number of accidents between midnight and 6 A.M. for nine consecutive weeks.

Week	Number of Fatal Accidents
A	190
B	202
C	179
D	211
E	160
F	185
G	172
H	205
I	177

Given the accident data:

```
>> accidents=[190 202 179 211 160 185 172 205 177];
```

Mean:

```
>> mean_accidents=ceil(mean(accidents))
mean_accidents =
  187
```

Median:

```
>> median_accidents=median(accidents)
median_accidents =
  185
```

Variance:

```
>> variance_accidents=var(accidents)
variance_accidents =
  281.9444
```

Standard deviation:

```
>> stdev_accidents=std(accidents)
stdev_accidents =
  16.7912
```

● **EXAMPLE 14-9**

MATLAB examples

The outline below gives the steps necessary to use MATLAB for basic statistical analysis of a data set. This is presented as an example of the high and low temperatures during the month of October 2006. The data are given in a starting MATLAB file in the online materials. This discussion focuses on the high temperatures, but would hold for the low temperatures as well.

1. **Input the data.** *The first column is simply an identifier (in this case, the date). The second and third columns contain the actual raw data of high and low temperatures for each day, respectively. This step has already been completed in the provided file.*
2. **Decide on the bin range.** *A rule of thumb is that the number of bins needed is approximately equal to the square root of the number of samples. While it is obvious in this example how many total samples are needed, the length function is often very useful.*

```
>> number_bins=round(sqrt(length(high)))
number_bins=
     6
```

3. **Examine your data to determine the range of values.** *Using the max and min functions, you can determine the highest high z and the lowest high temperature. Use these values to determine the range and number of points in each bin.*

```
>> max_high=max(high)
max_high =
    86
```

```
>> min_high=min(high)
min_high =
    56
>> range = max_high - min_high
range =
    30
>> bin_size = range/number_bins
bin size =
    5
```

4. ***Determine the range of values that will appear in each bin.*** *For example, the first bin will contain temperatures 55 − 59; the second bin will contain temperatures 60 − 64. Create a vector by typing in the values with all of the center values of the ranges for each bin and a cell array with all of the bin range labels.*

```
>> center_value=[57 62 67 72 77 82 87];
>> bin_range={'55-59'; '60-64'; '65-69';
   '70-74'; '75-79'; '80-84'; '85-89'};
```

Below, histograms are created using three different types of data sets and the hist function.

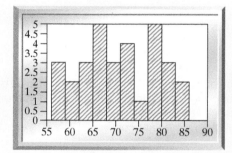
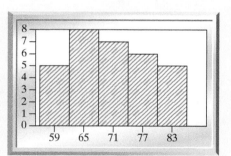

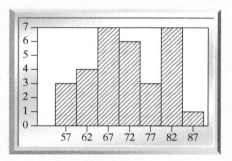

- ***One argument specified (data set):*** *By default, hist separates the data into 10 equally spaced bins and displays the histogram in a figure. Note that the image to the left is not a proper plot.*

```
>> hist(high)
```

- **Two arguments specified (data set, number of bins):** *hist separates the data into the specified number of bins and displays the histogram in a figure. MATLAB divides the range between the minimum and maximum values of the data set into the number of bins specified by the user. Note that MATLAB does not line up the bins on powers of 5, 10, 100, etc., in order to create a reasonable graphing axis. Note that the image to the left is not a proper plot.*

```
>> hist(high, 5)
```

- **Two arguments specified (data set, center value of bins):** *hist separates the data into bins specified by the center value of each bin provided in the vector passed to the function and displays the histogram in a figure. Note that the image to the left is not a proper plot. This is the preferred method, since this result matches our results in Excel.*

```
>> hist(high,center_value)
```

In our discussion of the hist function, we have not addressed what data the hist function will return if we assign it to a variable. For example, if we save the result of hist using the centers of each bin and save the result of the function call to the variable N, we see the following result.

```
>> N=hist(high,center_value)
N=
   3   4   7   6   3   7   1
```

It is clear that the data stored in N is the same information conveyed by the histogram, but instead of a graphical representation, we now have integer values of the number of temperatures contained in each bin.

The Cumulative Distribution Function (CDF) is created in MATLAB by the following procedure.

1. Create the cumulative sum of the histogram data using the `cumsum` built-in function.

```
>> HTSum=cumsum(N)
HTSum=
   3   7   14   20   23   30   31
```

2. Normalize the cumulative sum.
To normalize our data, we divide by the total number of elements represented in the histogram (in this example, we are dealing with 31 temperatures). In general, we solve this by dividing by the maximum value of the cumulative sum and multiplying the result by 100 to create a CDF within the range of 0%–100%.

```
>> CDF=HTSum/max(HTSum)*100
CDF=
   9.6774  22.5806  45.1613  64.5161  74.1935  96.7742  100.0000
```

*We will use subplots to allow both the histogram and CDF to be shown side-by-side.
To create a bar graph of our histogram, use the bar function. Be sure to make the graph
a proper plot.*

```
>> subplot(1,2,1) bar... (N)
>> set(gca,'XTickLabel',bin_range);
```

*To create a line graph of the CDF, use the plot function. Be sure to make the graph a
proper plot.*

```
>> X=1:1:number_bins; subplot(1,2,2) plot... (X, CDF)
>> set(gca,'XTickLabel',bin_range); ylim([0 100]);
```

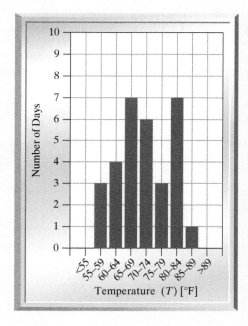

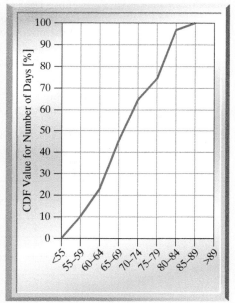

Repeat this analysis, using the daily low temperatures during October 2006.

In-Class Activities

ICA 14-1

This exercise includes the measurement of a distributed quantity and the graphical presentation of the results. You are to determine how many flexes it takes to cause a paper clip to fail.

Test the bending performance of 20 paper clips by doing the following:

- Unfold the paper clip at the center point so that the resulting wire forms an "S" shape.
- Bend the clip back and forth at the center point until it breaks.
- Record the number of flexes required to break the clip.

On a copy of the table below, record the raw data for the paper clips you break. Then, summarize the data for the team by adding up how many clips broke at each number of flexes. Each team member should contribute 20 data points unless otherwise instructed by your professor. Analyze the data using one of the methods below, as specified by your instructor. Create a histogram with an appropriate bin size and a CDF, using the data collected and creating the graphs:

(a) by hand
(b) using Excel
(c) using MATLAB

Paper clip flexing data

Paper Clip	Flexes to Break
1	
2	
3	
4	
5	
6	
7	
8	
9	
10	
11	
12	
13	
14	
15	
16	
17	
18	
19	
20	

Summary of data

No. of Flexes	No. of Clips

ICA 14-2

For the following pressure data, recorded in units of pound-force per square inch, answer the following questions.

1	14	2	15	10
6	3	1	18	

(a) What is the mean of the data?
(b) What is the median of the data?
(c) What is the variance of the data?
(d) What is the standard deviation of the data?

ICA 14-3

A technician tested two temperature probes by inserting their probes in boiling water, recording the readings, removing and drying the probes, and repeating the process. The results are shown below, giving temperature reading in degrees Celsius.

(a) What is the mean of each probe?
(b) What is the median of each probe?
(c) What is the variance of each probe?
(d) What is the standard deviation of each probe?

Probe 1	87.5	86.5	88	89.5	87	88.5	89
Probe 2	95.5	100	101.5	97.5	90.5	91.5	103.5

ICA 14-4

One of the NAE Grand Challenges for Engineeering is **Develop Carbon Sequestration Methods**. According to the NAE website: "In pre-industrial times, every million molecules of air contained about 280 molecules of carbon dioxide. Today that proportion exceeds 380 molecules per million, and it continues to climb. Evidence is mounting that carbon dioxide's heat-trapping power has already started to boost average global temperatures. If carbon dioxide levels continue up ward, further warming could have dire consequences, resulting from rising sea levels, agriculture disruptions, and stronger storms (e.g., hurricanes) striking more often."

The Mauna Loa Carbon Dioxide Record is the longest continuous record of atmospheric concentrations of carbon dioxide (CO_2), the chief greenhouse gas responsible for global climate warming. These data are modeled as the Keeling Curve, a graph showing the variation in concentration of atmospheric CO_2 based on measurements taken at the Mauna Loa Observatory in Hawaii under the supervision of Charles David Keeling. It is often called the most important geophysical record on Earth and has been instrumental in showing that mankind is changing the composition of the atmosphere through the combustion of fossil fuels.

The Keeling Curve also shows a cyclic variation in each year corresponding to the seasonal change in the uptake of CO_2 by the world's land vegetation. Most of this vegetation is in the northern hemisphere, where most of the land is located. The level decreases from northern spring onward as new plant growth takes CO_2 out of the atmosphere through photosynthesis and rises again in the northern fall as plants and leaves die off and decay to release the gas back into the atmosphere.

Data and wording for this problem set were obtained from: www.esrl.noaa.gov/gmd/ccgg/trends/. Additional information on the Mauna Loa Observatory can be found at: http://scrippsco2.ucsd.edu/.

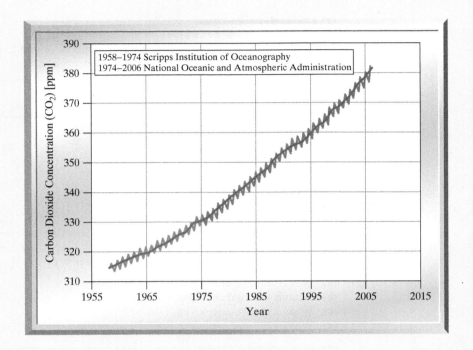

Examine the increase in monthly CO_2 emissions for 2009, taken from the Mauna Loa data set. All values given are in parts per million [ppm] CO_2 as the difference between the December 2008 and the monthly 2009 reading.

1.38	4.64	−0.77	3.23	2.20	0.45
1.87	3.89	−1.16	3.92	0.37	1.73

(a) What is the mean of these data?
(b) What is the median of these data?
(c) The variance of the data set shown here is 3.5 parts per million squared [ppm^2]. What is the standard deviation of these data?
(d) The estimated annual growth rates for Mauna Loa are close, but not identical, to the global growth rates. The standard deviation of the differences is 0.26 parts per million per year [ppm/year]. What is the variance?

ICA 14-5

You use the data from the Mauna Loa observatory in the previous question to create the following histogram and CDF. These data reflect the observed yearly increase in CO_2 emissions for the past 51 years. The annual mean rate of growth of CO_2 in a given year is the difference in concentration between the end of December and the start of January of that year. If used as an average for the globe, it would represent the sum of all CO_2 added to, and removed from, the atmosphere during the year by human activities and by natural processes.

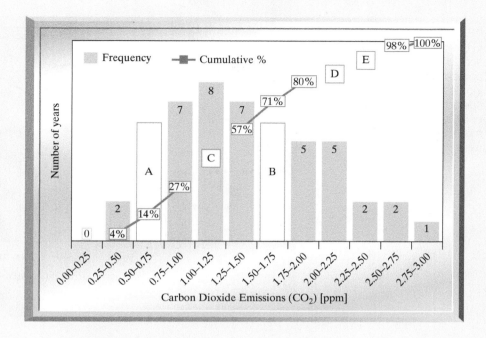

(a) What is the value of point A?
(b) What is the value of point B?
(c) What is the value of point C?
(d) What is the value of point D?
(e) What is the value of point E?

ICA 14-6

Polyetheretherketone (PEEK)™ are polymers that are resistant to both organic and aqueous environments; they are used in bearings, piston parts, and pumps. Several tests were conducted to determine the ultimate tensile strengths in units of megapascals [MPa]. The following CDF shows results from 320 points.

(a) What is the frequency value of A on the chart?
(b) What is the frequency value of B on the chart?
(c) What is the frequency value of C on the chart?
(d) What is the frequency value of D on the chart?
(e) What is the frequency value of E on the chart?

NOTE

In the graph, the locations of A–E are approximate. In other words, you cannot *guess* the value based upon the graph—you must *calculate* the value.

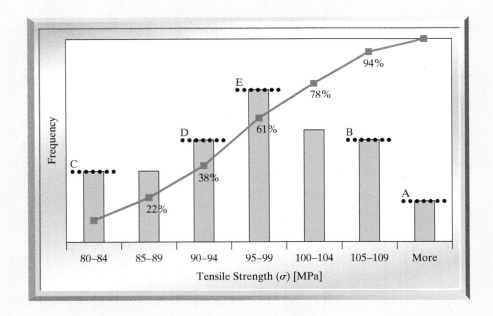

ICA 14-7

A technician tested a temperature probe by inserting it in boiling acetic acid (theoretical boiling point is 118 degrees Fahrenheit), recording the readings, removing and drying the probe, and repeating the process. The data are shown in the following table.

Temperature, Probe 1 (*T*) [°F]	120	118	105	115	105	120	125
Temperature, Probe 2 (*T*) [°F]	100	90	95	105	90	Missing Point	

(a) Determine the mean of Probe 1.
(b) Determine the median of Probe 1.
(c) A second probe was tested, yielding a mean of 95 degrees Fahrenheit and a median of 92.5 degrees Fahrenheit. If the data from Probe 2 are as shown above, determine the missing data point.
(d) If a probe has a standard deviation of 8 degrees Fahrenheit, what is the variance of the probe?

ICA 14-8

A technician tested two temperature probes by inserting them in boiling water (theoretical boiling point is 100 degrees Celsius), recording the readings, removing and drying the probe, and repeating the process. The CDF for both probes is shown below.

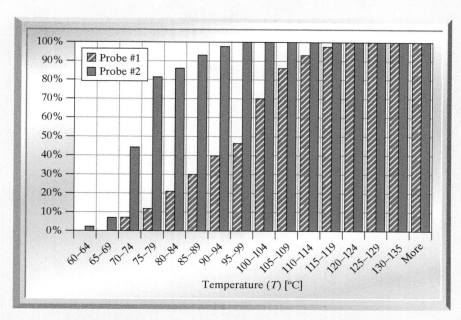

(a) Using this information, which probe would you choose to use? Explain why.
(b) How would you use the probe you chose above to ensure that you found the correct boiling point?
(c) Which probe has the higher standard deviation?

ICA 14-9

During the month of November, the heating system in your apartment appeared to be broken. To prove this, you record the following daily high temperatures in degrees Fahrenheit, taken every other day:

58	54	60	58	55	55	60	60
86	80	85	85	82	85	91	93

(a) Calculate the mean and median of the data.
(b) Draw the associated histogram and CDF for the data by hand; plot temperature on the abscissa and days on the ordinate.
(c) When you take your complaint to the apartment manager, he fails to see the problem; according to his heating bill, your apartment had an average temperature of 72 degrees Fahrenheit. Show both the mean and the median on the graph drawn for part (b). Which is a better presentation of the data, part (a) or part (b)? Justify.

ICA 14-10

You are assigned to inspect metal-composite beam trusses for a new bridge being built over a nearby lake. The manufacturer has run a prototype set of 500 beams and conducted strength tests, which you consider to be the baseline case, shown by the solid line in all graphs. Examine the graphs, and explain the changes to the baseline curve observed in the dashed line by choosing a cause from the following list. The strength of the beam is shown on the abscissa.

(a) The manufacturer tested 1,000 beams instead of 500 beams.
(b) A reinforcing coating was used on a sample of 500 beams.
(c) The manufacturer upgrades processing equipment to lower the variability of the metal-composite strength.

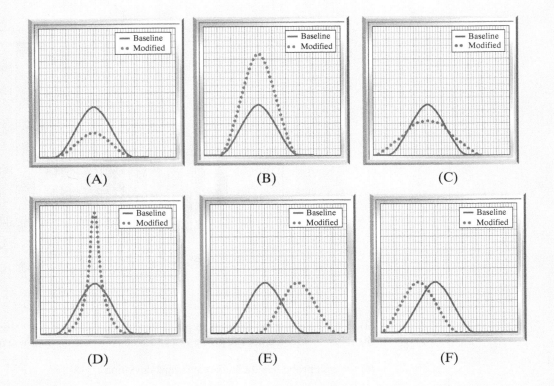

ICA 14-11

Use the scenario described above. Examine the graphs shown, and explain the changes to the baseline curve observed in the dashed line by choosing a cause from the following list. The strength of the beam is shown on the abscissa.

(a) The manufacturer tested 200 beams instead of 500 beams.

(b) An impurity, which caused the beams to weaken, was discovered in a sample of 500 beams.

(c) During a plant strike by union workers, substitute workers manufacture the beams.

ICA 14-12

You test several temperature probes by inserting them in boiling ethanol (theoretical boiling point is 78.4 degrees Celsius), recording the readings, removing and drying the probe, and repeating the process 20 times. The distribution curves for the probes are shown in the previous question. The solid line "baseline" curve in every graph is the same curve, for a previous probe tested 20 times in boiling ethanol.

(a) Which probe was tested 40 times instead of 20 times?

(b) Which probe has the highest standard deviation?

(c) During the testing of one probe, you suspect your assistant of using formic acid (which boils at 101 degrees Celsius) instead of ethanol. Which probe did your assistant incorrectly test?

ICA 14-13

Use the scenario described above. Determine the probe tested by the data shown in the graph.

(a) Which probe has the lowest standard deviation?

(b) Which probe was tested 10 times instead of 20 times?

(c) During the testing of one probe, you suspect your assistant of using chloroform (which boils at 61 degrees Celsius) instead of ethanol. Which probe did your assistant incorrectly test?

(d) If you could choose between probes C and F, which probe would you choose to use? In a single sentence, describe how you would use the probe to ensure you determine the correct boiling point.

ICA 14-14

The data below were collected from a manufacturing process for making plastic cylinders. According to the specifications, the cylinder diameter should be 100 inches (the average diameter is 100 inches) and the standard deviation is ±5 inches.

Graph the data on a control chart. A blank grid has been provided online; you may use this grid, or use graph paper as directed by your instructor. Be sure to clearly indicate the "Zones" of control.

Using the eight SPC rules, determine whether the process is in statistical control. If it is not in statistical control, indicate which rule or rules are violated and list the part numbers that violate that rule.

Part	Diameter (D) [in]	Part	Diameter (D) [in]
1	100	10	96
2	106	11	89
3	103	12	89
4	99	13	87
5	90	14	92
6	95	15	94
7	105	16	87
8	107	17	96
9	97	18	98

ICA 14-15

The data below were collected from a manufacturing process involving reactor temperature measured in degrees Celsius. The following values are desired: average = 100 degrees Celsius; standard deviation = ±10 degrees Celsius.

Graph the data on a control chart. A blank grid has been provided online; you may use this grid, or use graph paper as directed by your instructor. Be sure to clearly indicate the "Zones" of control.

Using the eight SPC rules, determine whether the process is in statistical control. If it is not in statistical control, indicate which "rule" or "rules" are violated and list the part numbers that violate that rule.

Reading No.	Temperature (T) [°C]	Reading No.	Temperature (T) [°C]
1	100	11	103
2	105	12	101
3	106	13	100
4	97	14	98
5	98	15	97
6	95	16	96
7	101	17	104
8	100	18	102
9	96	19	95
10	105	20	101

ICA 14-16

The data below were collected from a manufacturing process involving reactor temperature measured in degrees Celsius. The following values are desired: average = 100 degrees Celsius; standard deviation = ±5 degrees Celsius.

Graph the data on a control chart. A blank grid has been provided online; you may use this grid, or use graph paper as directed by your instructor. Be sure to clearly indicate the "Zones" of control.

Using the eight SPC rules, determine whether the process is in statistical control. If it is not in statistical control, indicate which "rule" or "rules" are violated and list the part numbers that violate that rule.

Reading No.	Temperature (T) [°C]	Reading No.	Temperature (T) [°C]
1	101.0	11	97.5
2	103.5	12	100.0
3	98.5	13	92.0
4	100.5	14	97.0
5	96.5	15	103.0
6	102.5	16	103.0
7	108.0	17	88.0
8	100.0	18	100.5
9	102.0	19	102.5
10	104.0	20	98.5

Chapter 14 REVIEW QUESTIONS

1. The table below lists the number of computer chips rejected for defects during random test-ing over the course of a week on a manufacturing line. Four samples of 20 parts are pulled each day. Use the following data to generate a histogram and CDF in Excel.

1	1	8	0	2	0
0	2	10	1	3	2
0	1	12	0	2	1
1	6	15	0	0	
3	8	1	2	5	

2. Repeat the analysis in Review 14-1, using MATLAB and the data available online.

3. An Excel worksheet, titled "Midterm Data," is available online. Use the data provided to determine the following:

   (a) Class mean and median.
   (b) Class standard deviation.
   (c) Often in problems such as this, the bin sizes are preset according to certain constraints. Draw a histogram and CDF, based on the letter grade ranges given below. After the histogram is created, change the bin labels to be the letter grade rather than the numerical value.

Grade	F	D	C	B	A
Minimum	0	60	70	80	90
Maximum	59	69	79	89	100

Use the chart to determine the following:

   (d) How many students received a C on the exam?
   (e) What percentage of students received an A on the exam?
   (f) What percentage of students received a passing grade (C, B, or A) on the exam?

4. Repeat the analysis in Review 14-3, using MATLAB and the data available online.

5. A company that fabricates small, custom machines has been asked to generate a machine that throws darts at a dart board as precisely and accurately as possible. To assess the preci-sion and accuracy of each proposed design, the engineers build a model and record the distance from the bullseye of the dart board to the location of each dart thrown—both the straight-line distance (A) and the horizontal (B) and vertical (C) distances are recorded separately with regard to the bullseye, as demonstrated in the figure. The engineers throw 15 darts with their prototype machine and record the three data points for each dart.

   Using the data collected for a design in the starting workbook, create a histogram and a CDF in Excel for the straight-line distance (A), as well as the horizontal (B) and vertical (C) distances and determine which graph or graphs are better for assessing the performance of the design if we were interested in (a) if the machine is throwing accurately to hit the bulls-eye or (b) if the machine needs to be calibrated (or adjusted) to correctly hit the bulls-eye. Justify your answer with a few sentences about why you selected the graph or graphs.

6. Repeat the analysis in Review 14-5, using MATLAB and the data available online.

7. This information was taken from the report of the EPA on the U.S. Greenhouse Gas Inventory (http://www.epa.gov).

"Greenhouse gas emission inventories are developed for a variety of reasons. Scientists use inventories of natural and anthropogenic emissions as tools when developing atmospheric models. Policy makers use inventories to develop strategies and policies for emission reductions and to track the progress of those policies. Regulatory agencies and corporations rely on inventories to establish compliance records with allowable emission rates.

In nature, carbon is cycled between various atmospheric, oceanic, biotic, and mineral reservoirs. In the atmosphere, carbon mainly exists in its oxidized form as CO_2. CO_2 is released into the atmosphere primarily as a result of the burning of fossil fuels (oil, natural gas, and coal) for power generation and in transportation. It is also emitted through various industrial processes, forest clearing, natural gas flaring, and biomass burning."

The EPA website provides data on emissions. The data found in the file online were taken from this website for the year 2001 for all 50 states and the District of Columbia.

(a) Use the data provided in the starting file to create a histogram with an appropriate bin size; use Excel.
(b) Determine the mean and median of the data.
(c) Which value more accurately describes the data? Indicate your choice (mean or median) and the value of your choice. Justify your answer.

8. Repeat the analysis in Review 14-7, using MATLAB and the data available online.

(a) Use the data provided in the starting file to write a program to determine an appropriate bin size. Use the bin size to continue the program and create a histogram of the data.
(b) Determine the mean and median of the data. Write a formatted output statement to the Command Window with this information.
(c) Which value more accurately describes the data? Indicate your choice (mean or median) and justify your answer using a comment statement at the end of your program file.

9. The Excel data provided online was collected by Ed Fuller of the NIST Ceramics Division in December 1993. The data represent the polished window strength, measured in units of kilopounds per square inch [ksi], and were used to predict the lifetime and confidence of airplane window design. Use the data set to generate a histogram and CDF in Excel (http://www.itl.nist.gov/div898/handbook/eda/section4/eda4291.htm).

10. Repeat the analysis in Review 14-9, using MATLAB and the data available online.

11. Choose *one* of the following options and collect the data required. For the data source you select, do the following using the analysis in Excel.

■ Construct a histogram, including justification of bin size.
■ Determine the mean, median, variance, and standard deviation values.
■ Construct a cumulative distribution function.

(a) On a campus sidewalk, mark two locations 50 feet apart. As people walk along, count how many steps they take to go the 50 feet. Do this for 125 individuals.
(b) Select 250 words at random from a book (fiction). Record the number of letters in each word. Alternatively, you can count and record the words in 250 sentences.
(c) Go to one section of the library, and record the number of pages in 125 books in that same section.
(d) Interview 125 people to determine how far their home is, in miles, from the university.

12. Repeat the analysis in Review 14-11, using MATLAB.

Part 4

PUNCTILIOUS PROGRAMMING

LEARNING OBJECTIVES

The overall learning objectives for this part include:

Chapter 15:

■ Defining the scope of a problem and creating a written or graphical algorithm to solve the problem.

Chapter 16:

■ Understand the various methods of storing information in MATLAB.
■ Performing basic matrix operations.

Chapter 17:

■ Writing MATLAB programs and / or functions to solve engineering problems.
■ Reading and interpreting MATLAB programs written by others.
■ Debugging a program to identify different types of errors.

Chapter 18:

■ Writing input statements to allow the user to interact with the MATLAB environment.
■ Write output statements to inform the user of program outcomes.
■ Create graphs and use trendlines to enhance problem solving.
■ Read data and record results between MATLAB and Microsoft Excel environments.

Chapter 19:

■ Use conditional statements and switch statements to automate decision making.
■ Use error and warning statements to aid the user in program execution.

Chapter 20:

■ Use looping structures (for and while) to write eliminate large blocks of repetitive code.
■ Use a GUI to aid the user in interacting with the MATLAB environment.

Computers are controlled by software that can be designed in a variety of programming languages. Computer programs are a translation of what you want to accomplish into something the computer can understand, so the term "programming language" is particularly appropriate. Some computer programs are installed permanently or temporarily on computer chips, and others are installed on a variety of other media, such as hard drives or removable media like CD-ROMs.

Computers relentlessly produce a particular result given a particular set of input conditions. It can be frustrating when you make a simple mistake in a computer program—the computer will do exactly what you tell it to do, even if your mistake would be obvious to a person.

The biggest difference between a computer and a person is that you can ask a person open-ended questions—questions like design questions that can have many answers. Computers can only process questions that have a single answer.

This makes the process of programming a computer a bit like trying to ask another person to solve a problem when they are on the other side of a wall and you can communicate only by passing them slips of paper asking questions that can have only one answer and waiting for the person to pass back a slip of paper with the answer on it.

If a computer always produces the same result every time given the same input conditions, then why does my computer crash sometimes when I am doing something that should work?

The computers you use are simultaneously running a large number of complicated computer programs, including the operating system, background programs, and whatever programs you have started intentionally. Sometimes these programs compete for resources, causing a conflict. Other times, programs are complicated enough that the "input conditions," including the configuration of data in memory and on the hard disk, the time on the system clock, and other factors that change all the time while the computer is running create a combination of circumstances that the programmers never anticipated and so did not include programming code to handle, and the system crashes.

SOME ADVANTAGES OF COMPUTERS

Given our description of how computers work, it may sound to some as if computers are too simple to be useful. The value of programming is linked to a few important characteristics of computers.

- *Calculation speed:* Although computers can only answer analytical questions, they can answer such questions very quickly—in small fractions of a second. Computer programs can therefore ask the computer a lot of questions in a short time, and thus find the answer to more complicated problems by breaking down the complicated question into a series of simple questions.
- *Information storage:* In "Memory: Science Achieves Important New Insights into the Mother of the Muses" (*Newsweek*, September 29, 1986), Sharon Begley estimates that the mind can store an estimated 100 trillion bits of information. The typical computer has a small amount of storage compared to that, but computers are gaining. Where computers have a bigger advantage is that new information can be incorporated in a fraction of the time it takes a human to learn it.
- *Information recall:* Computers have nearly 100% recall of information, limited only by media failures. The human brain can be challenged to recall information in exactly the same form as it was stored.

WISE WORDS: WOULD YOU CONSIDER YOUR CURRENT POSITION TO BE "PURE ENGINEERING," A "BLEND OF ENGINEERING AND ANOTHER FIELD," OR "ANOTHER FIELD?"

I always feel my work is not "pure engineering," but rather often a blend of engineering, sales, accounting, research, inspection, and maintenance.

E. Basta, Material Engineer

I would consider my career in another field from engineering, however, highly reliant on my engineering background. As a management consultant, I have to break down complex problems, develop hypotheses, collect data I believe will prove or disprove the hypotheses, and perform the analysis. My focus area is companies who develop highly engineered products.

M. Ciuca, ME

My position is mostly pure engineering.

E. D'Avignon, CpE

I work in a blend of engineering and business. I spend most of my time working on business-related activities—forecasting, variance reporting, and timing/work decisions—but I also have to work closely with our field engineers and understand our project scopes. I use both my business and engineering knowledge on a daily basis—without each, I would not be able to succeed at my job.

R. Holcomb, IE

It is definitely a blend of engineering and law with a heavy dose of technical writing. It takes the thinking of an engineer or scientist to truly comprehend the inventions and the skill of a writer to convey the inventor's ideas in written and image terms that others will understand (including juries of lay people). It takes the thinking of a lawyer to come up with creative strategies and solutions when faced with a certain set of facts.

M. Lauer, EnvE

My current position is definitely a blend of engineering and at least one other field, but more like five other fields. I definitely use my engineering background in the way I think, the way I analyze data, how I approach problems, and how I integrate seemingly unrelated information together. The project management skills that I learned in engineering are helpful, too.

B. Holloway, ME

Even though my boss calls Hydrology "Voodoo Engineering," it is pure engineering.

J. Meena, CE

A blend of mechanical/aerospace engineering and human factors engineering—and management.

R. Werneth, ME

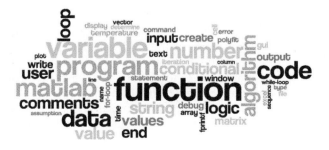

CHAPTER 15
ALGORITHMS

Learning to create effective algorithms is a crucial skill for any aspiring engineer. In general, an **algorithm** is a well-defined sequence of instructions that describe a process. Algorithms can be observed in everyday life through oral directions ("Simon says: raise your right hand"), written recipes ("Bake for 15 minutes at 350 degrees Fahrenheit"), graphical assembly instructions, or other graphical cues. As an engineer, writing any algorithm requires a complete understanding of all the necessary actions and decisions that must occur to complete a task.

When writing an algorithm, you must answer a few questions before attempting to design the process. To even begin thinking of a strategy to describe a process, you must have carefully defined the scope of the problem. The **scope** of an algorithm is the overall perspective and result that the algorithm must include in its design.

For example, if we are required to "sum all numbers between 1 and 5," before thinking about an approach to solve the problem, we must first determine if the scope is properly defined. Does the word "between" imply that 1 and 5 are included in the sum? Do "numbers" include only the integer values? What about the irrational numerical values? Clearly, we observe that we cannot properly define the scope of the charge to add all numbers between 1 and 5.

Likewise, imagine you were charged to design a device that transports people from Atlanta, Georgia, to Los Angeles, California. How many people must the device transport? Does the device need to travel on land? Should it travel by air? Should it travel by water? Does the device require any human interaction?

This section covers two methods of defining a process: with **written algorithms** and with **graphical algorithms**. Both methods require properly identifying the scope of the problem and all of the necessary input and output of the process.

15.1 SCOPE

LEARN TO: Define the scope of a problem
Define known and unknown quantities in a problem
Document any assumptions necessary to solve a problem

One of the most difficult steps in designing an algorithm is properly identifying the entire scope of the solution. Like solving a problem on paper involving unit conversions and equations, it is often necessary to state all of the known and unknown variables in order to determine a smart solution to the problem. If information is left out of the problem, it might be necessary to state an assumption in order to proceed with a solution. After all variables and assumptions about the problem have been identified, it is then possible to create a sequence of actions and decisions to solve the problem.

To clearly understand the scope of the problem, we often find it helpful to formally write out the known and unknown information, as well as state any assumptions necessary to solve the problem. In the following examples, notice that as the problem statements become more and more refined, the number of necessary assumptions decreases and eventually disappears.

● EXAMPLE 15-1

For the problem statement, list all knowns, unknowns, and assumptions.

Problem: Sum all numbers between 1 and 10.

Known:

- ■ *The minimum value in the sum will be 1.*
- ■ *The maximum value in the sum will be 10.*

Unknown:

- ■ *The sum of the sequence of numbers.*

Assumptions:

- ■ *We will only include the whole number values (e.g., 1, 2, 3, . . .) in the sum.*
- ■ *The sum will include the starting value of 1 and the ending value of 10.*

● EXAMPLE 15-2

For the problem statement, list all knowns, unknowns, and assumptions.

Problem: Sum all numbers between (and including) 1 and 10.

Known:

- ■ *The minimum value in the sum will be 1.*
- ■ *The maximum value in the sum will be 10.*

Unknown:

- ■ *The sum of the sequence of numbers.*

Assumptions:

- ■ *We will only include the whole number values (e.g., 1, 2, 3, . . .) in the sum.*

● EXAMPLE 15-3

For the problem statement, list all knowns, unknowns, and assumptions.

Problem: Sum all whole numbers between (and including) 1 and 10.

Known:

- ■ *The minimum value in the sum will be 1.*
- ■ *The maximum value in the sum will be 10.*

Unknown:

- ■ *The sum of the sequence of numbers.*

Assumptions:

- ■ *[None]*

COMPREHENSION CHECK 15-1

For the problem statement, list all knowns, unknowns, and assumptions. Problem: Sum all even numbers between (and including) 2 and 20.

COMPREHENSION CHECK 15-2

For the problem statement, list all knowns, unknowns, and assumptions. Problem: Multiply all powers of 5 between (and including) 5 and 50.

15.2 WRITTEN ALGORITHMS

LEARN TO: Create a linear written algorithm to solve an engineering problem
Create a written algorithm that implements decision pathways
Define the terms feedback loop and indefinite feedback loop

A written algorithm is a narrative set of instructions required to solve a problem. In everyday life, we encounter written algorithms in the form of oral instructions or written recipes. However, it is extremely common for humans to "fill in the blanks" on a poorly written algorithm. Imagine you are handed a strongly guarded family recipe for tacos. One of the steps in the archaic recipe is to "cook beef on low heat until done." To the veteran cook, it is apparent that this step requires cooking the prepared ground beef on a stove-top in a sauce pan for approximately 10 minutes on a burner setting of 2 to 3. To a first-time cook, the step is poorly defined and could result in potentially inedible taco meat.

Engineers and Written Algorithms

As an engineer, to write effective algorithms you must ensure that every step you include in a written algorithm must not be subject to misinterpretation. It is helpful to write an algorithm as if it were to be read by someone completely unfamiliar with the topic. Each step in the written algorithm should be written such that the stepwise scope is properly defined. The **stepwise scope** is all of the known and unknown information at that point in the procedure. If a step in an algorithm contains an assumption, you must formally declare it before proceeding with the next step. By ensuring that the stepwise scope is well defined, you ensure that your algorithm will not be subject to misinterpretation.

All written algorithms should be expressed sequentially. The most effective algorithms are written with many ordered steps, wherein each step contains one piece of information or procedure. While the author of an algorithm may consider each step in an algorithm to be "simple," it might not be trivial to an external interpreter. When writing an algorithm, it is helpful to assume that the reader of your algorithm can only perform small, simple tasks. Assume that your algorithm can be interpreted by a computer. A computer can execute small tasks efficiently and quickly, but unlike a human, a computer cannot fill in the blanks with information you intended the reader to assume.

Decision-making can be expressed in a written algorithm. Assume you are designing a process to determine if the value read from a temperature sensor in a vehicle indicates it is unsafe for operation. To express the decision in a written algorithm, phrase your decisions in questions that have a "Yes" or "No" response.

Format of Written Algorithms

The first step in writing any algorithm is defining the scope of the problem. After you define the scope of the problem, create an *ordered* or *bulleted list* of actions and decisions. Imagine taking an English class and writing a research report on the influence of 19th-century writers on modern-day fiction authors. Before writing the paper, you would create an outline to ensure that your topics have connectivity and flow. Just like the outline of an English paper, an algorithm is best expressed as a sequential list rather than as complete paragraphs of information.

   If a decision is required in the algorithm, indent the actions to indicate the action is only associated with the particular condition.

● **EXAMPLE 15-4**

Create a written algorithm to express a temperature given in relative units [°F or °C] in the corresponding absolute units [K or °R].

Known:

   ■ *Temperature in relative units (degrees Celsius or degrees Fahrenheit).*

Unknown:

   ■ *Temperature in absolute units (kelvins or degrees Rankine).*

Assumptions:

   ■ *Since the problem does not explicitly state the temperature of interest, assume that the interpreter of the algorithm will input the temperature and units.*

Algorithm:

   1. *Input the numeric value of the temperature.*
   2. *Input the units of the numeric value of the temperature.*
   3. *Ask if the input unit is degrees Fahrenheit.*
      (a) If yes, calculate the value in degrees Rankine.
      (b) If no, calculate the value in kelvins.
   4. *Display the new value and absolute unit.*
   5. *End the process.*

● **EXAMPLE 15-5**

Create a written algorithm to calculate the sum of a sequence of whole numbers, given the upper and lower bounds of the sequence.

Known:

   ■ *Upper bound of whole number sequence.*
   ■ *Lower bound of whole number sequence.*

Unknown:

   ■ *Sum of all whole numbers between the upper and lower bound.*

Assumptions:

   ■ *Since the problem does not explicitly state the upper and lower bounds, assume the interpreter will ask for the values.*
   ■ *Include the boundary values in the summation.*

Algorithm:

1. *Input the lower bound of the sequence.*
2. *Input the upper bound of the sequence.*
3. *If the lower bound is larger than the upper bound,*

    (a) *Warn the user that the input is invalid.*
    (b) *End the process.*

4. *If the upper bound is larger than the lower bound,*

    (a) *Create a variable to keep track of the sum (S).*
    (b) *Create a variable to keep track of the location in the sequence (L).*
    (c) *Set the initial value of S to be zero.*
    (d) *Set the initial value of L to be the lower bound.*
    (e) *If the value of L is less than or equal to the upper bound,*

        (i) *Add L to the current value of S.*
        (ii) *Add one to the current value of L.*
        (iii) *Return to step 4.e. and ask the question again.*

    (f) *If the value of L is greater than the upper bound,*

        (i) *Display the sum of the sequence (S).*

5. *End the process.*

In step 4.e.iii, we required that the interpreter return to an earlier step in the algorithm after changing the values of our variables. This allows us to create a **feedback loop** necessary to calculate the sequence of values. A feedback loop is a return to an earlier location in an algorithm with updated values of variables. It is important to note that if we failed to update the variables, the feedback loop will never terminate. A nonterminating feedback loop is also known as an **infinite feedback loop**.

COMPREHENSION CHECK 15-3   Create a written algorithm to multiply all integer powers of 5, 5^x, for x between (and including) 5 and 50.

15.3 GRAPHICAL ALGORITHMS

LEARN TO: Sketch a flowchart that implements a linear algorithm
Sketch a flowchart that implements decision pathways
Recognize and interpret shapes used in a graphical algorithm

To visualize a process, a graphical representation of algorithms is used instead of a written algorithm. A **flowchart** is a graphical representation of a written algorithm that describes the sequence of actions, decisions, and path of a process. Designing a flowchart forces the author of the algorithm to create small steps that can be quickly evaluated by the interpreter and enforces a sequence of all actions and decisions. Flowcharts are used by many different disciplines of engineering to describe different types of processes, so learning to create and interpret flowcharts is a critical skill for a young engineer. In fact, in the United States, any engineers who discover a new innovative algorithm can submit their concept to a patent office by representing the process in terms of a flowchart.

Three different shapes are used in the creation of flowcharts in this book; a number of other widely used operators are encountered across the world. In this book, we describe all actions with rectangles, all decisions with diamonds, and all connections between shapes with directional arrows.

Rules for Creating a Proper Flowchart

- The flowchart must contain a START rectangle to designate the beginning of a process.
- All actions must be contained within rectangles.
- All decisions must be contained within diamonds.
- All shapes must be connected by a one-way directional arrow.
- The flowchart must contain an END rectangle to designate the end of a process.

Actions

Actions are any executable steps in an algorithm that do not require a decision to be made. Based on this definition, any defined variables, calculations, and input or output commands would all be contained within action rectangles.

All simple actions are contained within a single rectangle on the flowchart. For each rectangle, two arrows are always associated with the shape, with two exceptions. The inward arrow to the rectangle represents the input to the action. It is assumed that any variables defined in the stepwise scope of an action rectangle are accessible and can be used in the action. The outward arrow from the rectangle represents the output of the action. If any new variables or calculations are performed within the rectangle, those values are passed along to the next shape's stepwise scope.

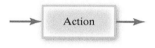

- Exception One: The START rectangle represents the beginning of the flowchart and does not contain an inward arrow. An oval shape is also commonly used to represent the start of an algorithm.
- Exception Two: The END rectangle represents the end of the flowchart and does not contain an outward output arrow. An oval shape is also commonly used to represent the end of an algorithm.

Decisions

Decisions are any executable steps in an algorithm that require the answer to a question with "Yes" or "No." All decisions in a flowchart must be represented within a diamond shape.

For each diamond on a flowchart, at least three arrows are always associated with the shape. The inward arrow to the diamond represents the input to the decision. It is assumed that any variables defined in the stepwise scope of a decision diamond are accessible and can be used in the decision. The two outward arrows that exit decision diamonds represent the conditional branch based on the outcome of the question asked within the diamond. If the outcome of the decision is true, the flow of the process will follow the "Yes" branch; otherwise, it will follow the "No" branch. Since no new variables are created in a decision diamond, the stepwise scope that enters the decision diamond is passed on to the next shape of each conditional branch.

● **EXAMPLE 15-6**   Create a flowchart to express a temperature given in relative units [°F or °C] in the corresponding absolute units [K or °R].

Known:

■ *Temperature in relative units (degrees Celsius or degrees Fahrenheit).*

Unknown:

■ *Temperature in absolute units (kelvins or degrees Rankine).*

Assumptions:

■ *Since the problem does not explicitly state the temperature to be determined, the interpreter of the algorithm will ask for the temperature and units.*

Flowchart:

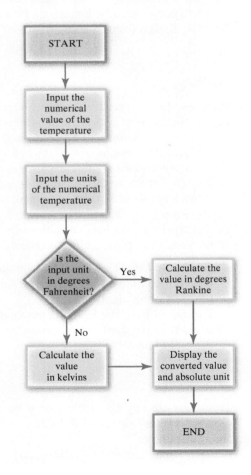

● **EXAMPLE 15-7**   Create a flowchart to calculate the sum of a sequence of whole numbers, given the upper and lower bounds of the sequence.

Known:

■ *Upper bound of whole number sequence.*
■ *Lower bound of whole number sequence.*

Unknown:

■ *Sum of all whole numbers between the upper and lower bound.*

Assumptions:

■ *Since the problem does not explicitly state the upper and lower bounds, the interpreter will ask for the values. Include the boundary values in the summation.*

Flowchart:

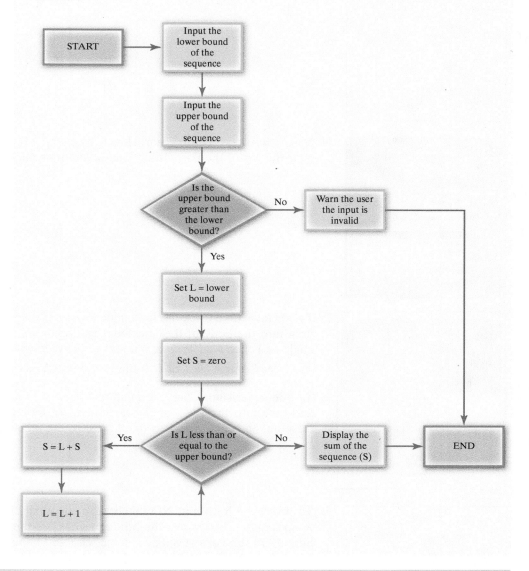

COMPREHENSION CHECK 15-4

Create a graphical algorithm to multiply all integer powers of 5, 5^x, for x between (and including) 5 and 50.

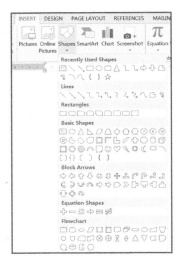

Flowchart Creation in Microsoft Word

Open a new Microsoft Word document. Click the **Insert** ribbon at the top of the Microsoft Word editor window. Click the **Illustrations > Shapes** drop-down menu. You will need to use the rectangle and diamond shapes under the Flowchart section as well as the directional arrows under the Lines section.

⌘ **Mac OS:** Access the flowchart shapes by clicking the Object Palette button near the top of the Formatting Palette and then clicking the Shapes button.

↬ **To add an action:** Click the Rectangle tool from the Shapes menu and click-and-drag into the body of the document to draw a rectangle. Right-click the rectangle and click Add Text to add text to the rectangle.

⌘ **Mac OS:** Control-click or two-finger tap to access the **Add Text** menu item.

↬ **To add a decision:** Click the Diamond tool from the Shapes menu and click-and-drag into the body of the document to draw a diamond. Right-click the diamond and click Add Text to add text to the rectangle.

↬ **To insert the YES and NO labels:** Use the Text Box option under the Basic Shapes menu. To remove the border, right-click the text box and click Format Shape. On the Format Shape sidebar, choose **Shape Options > Paint Bucket > Line**, click "No line". Click the "X" to close the sidebar.

⌘ **Mac OS:** In the main menu, click **Insert > Text Box**. The default is probably "no border," but the border can be modified in the formatting palette.

↬ **To add an arrow:** Click the single direction arrow from the Shapes menu and starting from the source click-and-drag to the destination.

15.4 ALGORITHM BEST PRACTICES

LEARN TO:	Design algorithms that prevent unwanted results
	Utilize iteration to repeat a process a set number of times
	Generate appropriate test cases for algorithms

If you have never composed a written or graphical algorithm before, the remaining part of this section details specifics on how to begin planning and writing algorithms from scratch. This section does not intend to be a definitive resource on algorithm development, but it may provide guidance if you are struggling to break down a process into small, achievable steps.

Actions

In every action within an algorithm, there must be a key verb that defines the purpose of that step within an algorithm. The remaining subsections discuss different types of actions and list some of the common verbs associated with that category of action.

Establishing Variables and Constants

After defining the scope of a problem, it might become obvious that there are intermediate calculations or assumed constants that must be contained throughout the process. Along with the explicitly defined known values, these intermediate and constant values are referred to as variables. Algorithmic variables are different from the mathematic definition of a variable because algorithmic variables are treated more like containers to store known values and results of calculations rather than being some unknown entity in a mathematical expression. They are called variables because the stored value can be written, overwritten, and used by other actions or decisions in the algorithm.

Example	Action
We assume the acceleration due to gravity is 9.8 meters per second squared.	**Set** variable g to be 9.8.

Other Verbs					
Set	Define	Assign	Write	Store	Designate
Label	Name	Cast	Insert	Save	Initialize

User Interaction

It is often necessary to write algorithms that can be executed with prompts for input from the person using the algorithm, provide feedback on results, or display any error messages generated in the algorithm.

User Input:

Example	Action
We want the user of the algorithm to provide the amount of water in gallons.	**Input** the amount of water in gallons, save in variable W.
Other Verbs	

Input	Ask	Load	Request	Query	Prompt

User Output:

Example	Action
We want the algorithm to inform the user that the amount of water can't be negative.	**Display** error message to user "Warning: amount of water can't be negative!"
Other Verbs	

Output	Display	Reveal	Write	Warn

Calculations and Conversions

When algorithms involve calculating a value using an equation, it is helpful to write out the full equation and identify which variables in the algorithm correspond to the variables in the expression. For unit conversions, it is not necessary to write out the conversion factors since those are published standards that are readily available to anyone executing your algorithm. When using conversions, it is best to list them individually so they are easily recognizable to the user. For example, when converting from feet to centimeters, the expression $L = L/3.28 * 100$ is easily recognized as the conversion from feet to meters, and then from meters to centimeters. It is harder to recognize the conversion of $L = L * 30.48$. Furthermore, it is easy to make a calculation error; it is easier to allow the program to calculate for you. When dealing with unit conversions, it is ideal to save the converted value back into the original variable to reduce the number of variables you need to keep track of in your algorithm. We will discuss MATLAB's capabilities to handle this type of equation in later chapters.

Calculations:

Example	Action
We want to calculate the thermal energy of a substance using the expression $Q = m\,C_p\,\Delta T$, where m is the mass, C_p is the specific heat, and ΔT is the change in temperature.	**Compute** the thermal energy: $Q = m\,C_p\,\Delta T$ All variables should appear in the variable list.
Other Verbs	

Calculate	Adjust	Count	Measure	Add	Multiply
Subtract	Divide	Compute	Increment	Decrement	

Conversions:

Example	Action
We want to convert a variable t from minutes to seconds and save the result back in the variable t.	**Convert** t from minutes to seconds, save in t.
Other Verbs	

Convert	Change	Alter	Revise	Switch

Referencing Other Algorithms

When developing a large program, it is sometimes helpful to break that program into several smaller programs, and then reference the smaller programs within the large program. In MATLAB, these are called **functions**. As a rule of thumb, each custom function you create should have its own separate algorithm. If you have separate algorithms for a program and the different functions referenced in the code, it makes the algorithms simpler to understand and easier to debug. When calling a function within an algorithm, it is critical to list the variables passed to the function and variables captured by the function. In general, the most common verb used with functions is "call." If you know the name you plan to use for your function, list it; otherwise, this can be set later.

Example	Action
We want to use a function named *Poltocar* that converts coordinates from polar to Cartesian. We will pass in the variable Z as the radius and the variable T as the angle. We will capture the x-coordinate in the variable X and the y-coordinate in the variable Y.	**Call** *Poltocar* In: Z, T Out: X, Y

Decisions

All decisions made in algorithms must be constructed as binary decisions. Typical decisions in algorithms involve comparing variables, examining the contents of a variable, or examining the dimensionality of a variable. Any decisions that require some amount of computation in the decision should be split so that the calculations occur in actions before reaching the decision block.

Error Checking

Including error checking in an algorithm allows for the creation of robust solutions to problems that will not lead to incorrect or unstable answers. In general, a check for an error will either terminate the algorithm or lead to some action that will allow the algorithm to continue; the program should notify the user that an error has occurred (see Figure 15-1). If you want your algorithm to re-prompt the user for input to assure that proper data are contained in a variable before proceeding into the remainder of the algorithm, see section on "Error Prevention." The remainder of this section discusses three different types of errors that may occur in an algorithm, but this is only a starting point. The amount and type of errors that can occur in an algorithm are infinite, so it is up to the designer of the algorithm to decide how and when error checking should occur.

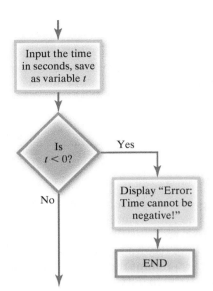

Figure 15-1 An example of error checking embedded in a flowchart.

Division by Zero and Infinite Values

If your algorithm contains a calculation where a combination of one or more variables in the computed expression could lead to a division by zero, it is smart to include a check to see if the result is zero. Some languages like MATLAB will happily compute an expression with a zero divisor and return the result as "INF"—a special MATLAB reserved word representing infinity.

Invalid Dimensions of Variables

When an algorithm assumes that one or more variables contain matrices or vectors, any calculations on those variables must follow the same mathematical rules associated with the matrix operation. For example, if an algorithm requires two matrices to be added together, it would be wise to include a check to see if the two matrices have the same number of rows and columns before attempting to add them together. This will prevent algorithms from crashing due to an invalid computation. In addition, this will prevent issues related to accessing elements of a matrix that do not exist.

Invalid Range of Values

Since variables typically represent some measured or computed value, restrictions on those variables that apply in real life may not be directly enforced in your algorithm. For example, if your algorithm prompts a user to input a quantity that cannot be negative (length, volume, time, etc.), it is smart to check if the value in the variable is reasonable. Likewise, if your algorithm should not generate complex values (e.g., $3 + 2i$), your algorithm will need to check to see if the result of a computation would generate a complex value instead of the desired real value.

Error Prevention

Error prevention looks for the same type of errors that are detected in error checking, but error prevention will allow your algorithm to prompt or re-prompt the user to

> **NOTE**
>
> For more information on Matrix Operations, refer to Appendix A.6 online.

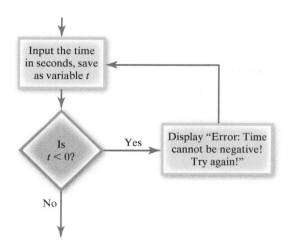

Figure 15-2 An example of error prevention embedded in a flowchart.

correct the erroneous variables. For example, if your algorithm asks the user to type in a time and the user erroneously types a negative value, your algorithm could detect the incorrect value and go back to the input statement to force the user to type the value again (and again, and again . . .) until the user types a value within the acceptable range (see Figure 15-2). In most programming languages, the structure that enables error prevention is the `while` loop.

Iteration

Some algorithms require repeated calculations that typically involve the use of a sequence of values or some operation on a vector or matrix stored in a variable. Such algorithms are considered to be iterative because they require a counter variable to keep track of when to terminate. For example, assume we have a vector, **V**, which contains positive and negative values in random order. If we want to create two new vectors, **VN** and **VP**, that contain the negative and positive values of **V** respectively, we will need to iterate through each element of the vector **V**, make a decision about each value, and store it in the corresponding vector. To do this, we would need to create a **counter variable**, or sometimes called an **index variable**, that will keep track of the number of times we have repeated a calculation or decision. If we create a counter variable, X, and initialize it to be the number 1, X will actually serve two purposes. In addition to keeping track of the number of times we have repeatedly made decisions and stored new values into **VN** and **VP**, it will also serve as the index variable into the **V** vector so that we can access element V(1), V(2), and so on until we reach the last element in **V**. Figure 15-3 demonstrates this scenario as a flowchart, including the iterated counter variable X.

Algorithms that will require iteration typically have a scenario where you have to repeat some decision or calculation "for each" or "for every" element or value within a sequence or vector. Since there is no "for each" or "for every" building block within an algorithm, this type of structure must be constructed out of the following steps:

- Initialization of a counter variable (e.g., Set X to be 1)
- A decision that involves the value of a counter variable (e.g., if X is less than or equal to the number of elements in **V**)
- Some action block that increments the counter variable (e.g., Set X equal to the current value of X plus 1)

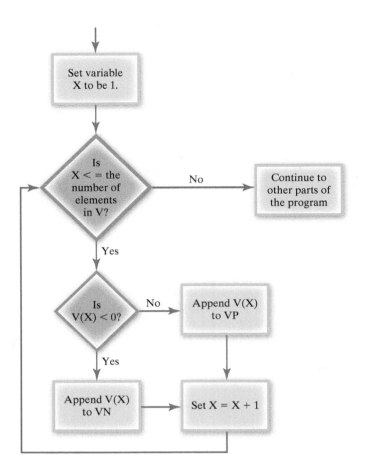

Figure 15-3 An example of iteration embedded in a flowchart.

After the counter increment action block, the algorithm can loop or refer back to the decision made on the increment variable. In most programming languages, the structure that enables iteration in an algorithm is the for loop.

Testing Your Algorithm

The last step in writing an algorithm is developing test cases that will reveal whether or not your algorithm behaves as expected. The key to writing test cases is figuring out how many test cases are necessary to confirm whether or not your code works. In general, there should be at least one or two test cases that will demonstrate the proper behavior of the algorithm given good input values. Not only should a test case include a list of all of the inputs used to generate the output, but you should also compute the expected output of the algorithm by hand in order to verify that the algorithm works. In addition, there should be test cases that verify all of the error checking/prevention built in to the algorithm works properly. Any decisions that lead to different states within your algorithm should have a test case to verify that the logic you designed is arranged properly in order to generate the desired output.

For example, assume we have designed an algorithm that will calculate power given energy and time. In our algorithm, we included two error checks—the first check to see if energy is greater than 50 joules and the second check to see if time is greater than 0 seconds. If either of these conditions are not true, the algorithm will display an error message "Error: Incorrect input value" and terminate. In addition, we added logic to check to see if the energy in the system is greater than 500 joules and if that is true, added 5 seconds to the time variable; otherwise, if the energy is less than or equal to 500 joules we left the time variable alone.

A test case for this scenario would look like this:

Input	Output
$E = 0$ J, $T = 30$ seconds	Error: Incorrect input value
$E = 55$ J, $T = -3$ seconds	Error: Incorrect input value
$E = 400$ J, $T = 5$ seconds	$P = 80$ W
$E = 550$ J, $T = 10$ seconds	$P = 36.7$ W

To help you develop good algorithms, we have included an algorithm template online to help you document all of the variables, procedures, and test cases necessary to create correct and verifiable algorithms. Examples of how this template can be used are provided below and on select problems in the remaining chapters.

● **EXAMPLE 15-8**   Create an algorithm to determine the volume of a cylinder, given the radius and height.

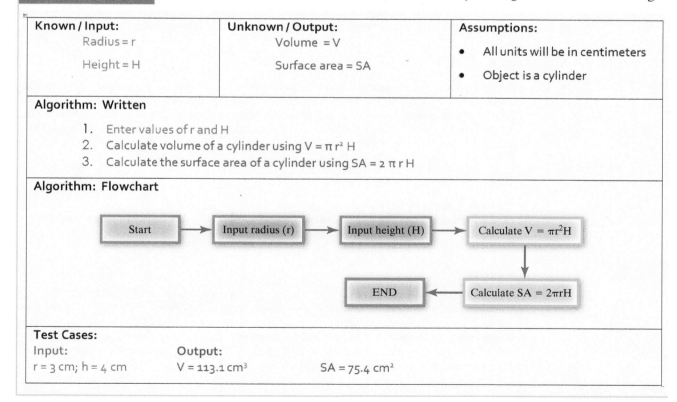

Known / Input:
  Radius = r

  Height = H

Unknown / Output:
  Volume = V

  Surface area = SA

Assumptions:
- All units will be in centimeters
- Object is a cylinder

Algorithm: Written

1. Enter values of r and H
2. Calculate volume of a cylinder using $V = \pi r^2 H$
3. Calculate the surface area of a cylinder using $SA = 2 \pi r H$

Algorithm: Flowchart

Start → Input radius (r) → Input height (H) → Calculate $V = \pi r^2 H$ → Calculate $SA = 2\pi r H$ → END

Test Cases:

Input:
r = 3 cm; h = 4 cm

Output:
$V = 113.1$ cm^3 $SA = 75.4$ cm^2

In-Class Activities

For ICA 15-1 to 15-7, create an algorithm (written and/or flowchart as specified by your instructor) to solve the following problems.

ICA 15-1

Your instructor will provide you with a picture of a structure created using K'Nex™ pieces. Describe the steps necessary to create the structure in the picture. When you are finished, hand your algorithm to the instructor and wait for further instruction.

ICA 15-2

Describe the steps necessary to create a paper airplane. You may assume that you are starting with a single sheet of 8½ × 11 inch paper. When you are finished, hand your algorithm to the instructor and wait for further instruction.

ICA 15-3

Describe the steps necessary to create a jelly sandwich. You may assume that you are starting with a loaf of bread, jar of jelly, a knife, and a plate on the table in front of you. When you are finished, hand your algorithm to the instructor and wait for further instruction.

ICA 15-4

An unmanned X-43A scramjet test vehicle has achieved a maximum speed of Mach number X.XX in a test flight over the Pacific Ocean, where X.XX is a positive value entered by the user. Mach number is defined as the speed of an object divided by the speed of sound. Assume the speed of sound is 343 meters per second. Determine the speed in units of miles per hour. For a test case, you may assume that the user provides the value of 9.68 for the Mach number.

ICA 15-5

Calculate a temperature provided by the user in units of Fahrenheit in units of kelvin. As a test case, you may assume the user provides the temperature of −129 degrees Fahrenheit, which is the world's lowest recorded temperature.

ICA 15-6

Determine the mass of oxygen gas (formula: O_2, molecular weight = 32 grams per mole) in a container, in units of grams. You may assume that the user will provide the volume of the container in units of gallons, the temperature in the container in degrees Celsius, and the pressure in the container in units of atmospheres. For your test case, you may assume that the user provides 1.25 gallons for the volume of the container, 125 degrees Celsius for the temperature, and 2.5 atmospheres for the pressure in the container.

ICA 15-7

Determine the length of one side of cube of solid gold, in units of inches. You may assume that the specific gravity of gold is 19.3 and that the user will provide the mass of the cube in units of kilograms. As a test case, you can assume that the user has a 0.4 kilogram cube.

ICA 15-8

The Occupational Safety & Health Administration (OSHA) defines safety regulations on working environments to protect workers from unsafe conditions. The flowchart below shows how OSHA categorizes the safety level of the working temperature given the environment temperature in degrees Fahrenheit. Given the flowchart, for what range of heat index (in degrees Fahrenheit) will the risk level be Lower (Caution), Moderate, High, or Very High to Extreme?

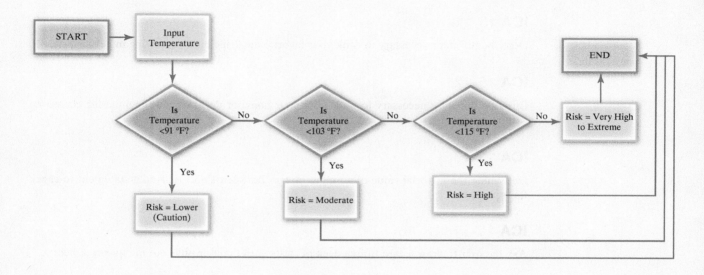

ICA 15-9

Given the flowchart below, for what range of values of pressure (in atmospheres) will the light be each of the colors Yellow, Blue, and Violet?

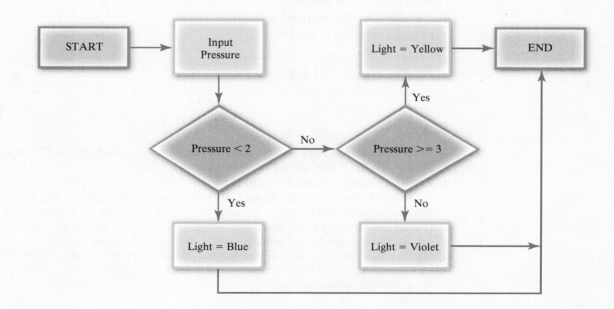

For ICA 15-10 to 15-14, create an algorithm (written and/or flowchart as specified by your instructor) to solve the following problems.

ICA 15-10

Model the decision of a driver after looking at the color of a traffic light. You may assume that the traffic light contains three bulbs (red, yellow, green) to represent stop, slow down, and go.

ICA 15-11

Describe the steps necessary to cook your favorite meal, including a starting materials list.

ICA 15-12

Describe the steps necessary to walk from your home or dorm to your engineering classroom without using any street names.

ICA 15-13

Determine the factorial value of an input integer between 1 and 10. Add a statement to check for input range.

ICA 15-14

Ask the user to draw a card from a deck of cards until the user pulls out the queen of hearts.

ICA 15-15

Create a flowchart that represents the following written algorithm.
- Input the height of person 1 [in units of feet] as P1
- Input the height of person 2 [in units of feet] as P2
- If person 1 is taller than person 2

  • Display "Person 1 is taller"

- Otherwise, if person 2 is taller than person 1

  • Display "Person 2 is taller"
  • Otherwise, display "They are the same height"

ICA 15-16

A reaction vessel is equipped with both temperature and pressure sensors. Create a flowchart that represents the following written algorithm.
- Read the values of temperature and pressure.
- If the temperature exceeds the maximum safe temperature (TMax), the status should be listed as "unsafe," and a variable T should be set to 1. Otherwise, T should equal 0.
- If the pressure exceeds the maximum safe pressure (PMax), the status should be listed as "unsafe," and a variable P should be set to 1. Otherwise, P should equal 0.
- If both temperature and pressure are less than their corresponding maxima, the status should be listed as "safe" and both variables T and P should be set to 0.
- Repeat the entire procedure.

1. Create an algorithm to determine the weight of a rod in units of pound-force on the surface of Callisto, Jupiter's moon. You may assume that the user of the algorithm will provide the volume of the rode in units of cubic meters. Your algorithm may assume that the specific gravity is 4.7 and the gravitational acceleration on Callisto is 1.25 meters per second squared. As a test case, you can assume the user has a rod with a volume of 0.3 cubic meters.

2. The Eco-Marathon is an annual competition sponsored by Shell Oil, in which participants build special vehicles to achieve the highest possible fuel efficiency. The Eco-Marathon is held around the world with events in the United Kingdom, Finland, France, Holland, Japan, and the United States.

   A world record was set in the Eco-Marathon by a French team in 2003 called Microjoule with a performance of 10,705 miles per gallon. The Microjoule runs on ethanol. Create an algorithm to determine how far the Microjoule will travel in kilometers given a user-specified amount of ethanol, provided in units of grams. For your test case, you may assume that the user provides 100 grams of ethanol.

3. Create an algorithm to determine the density of tribromoethylene in units of kilograms per cubic meter in a cylindrical tank. Your algorithm should be written in such a way that the user provides the height measured in units of feet of the tribromoethylene in the tank, the surface pressure in units of atmospheres, and the total pressure at the bottom of the tank, also measured in atmospheres. For your test case, you may assume that the user provides a height of 25 feet for the tank, tank surface pressurization of 3 atmospheres, and a total pressure at the bottom of the tank of 5 atmospheres.

4. Create an algorithm to determine how long, in units of seconds, it will take a motor to raise a load into the air. Assume the user will specify the power of the motor in units of watts, the rated efficiency as a percentage (in whole number form—for example, 50 for 50%), the mass of the load in kilograms, and the height the load is raised in the air in units of meters. As a test case, you may assume the user provides the 100 watts for the power of the motor, 60% for the efficiency of the motor, 100 kilograms for the mass of the load, and 5 meters for the height the load is raised.

5. Create an algorithm to determine how long it will take to boil acetone using a hot plate, assuming acetone has a boiling point of 56 degrees Celsius. You may assume that the user of your algorithm will need to ask for the amount of time (split into the number of minutes and seconds) it takes to boil a user provided volume of water, measured in milliliters, as well as the temperature of the lab in degrees Fahrenheit, which is also the initial temperature of the water before boiling. In addition, the user will provide the power rating of the hot plate in units of watts and the volume of acetone to be boiled in the experiment in milliliters. Note that your algorithm must determine the efficiency of the hot plate. As a test case, the hot plate takes an average of 8 minutes and 55 seconds to boil 100 milliliters of water in a 75 degree Fahrenheit laboratory with a 283 watt hot plate and it is desired to boil 100 milliliters of acetone.

6. The Apple TV™ is a personal video device created by Apple, Inc that attaches to high-definition televisions to present streaming content to a viewer on demand, in contrast to a standard source (cable/satellite) set-top box or digital video recorder (DVR) that presents recorded or live broadcast signals on a television. According to a study conducted by the Natural Resources Defense Council in June 2011, if consumers were to move from set-top boxes to smaller "thin" devices like the Apple TV, there would be an overall 70% reduction in annual energy costs resulting from use of set-top boxes if they were replaced by smaller energy efficient devices like the Apple TV.

   Below is a data table that shows the typical power consumption of the Apple TV in different power states (standby/off, idle—not playing any video content, playing via Ethernet, and playing via Wifi). Create an algorithm that allows a user to provide the power currently being used by their Apple TV in units of watts and determine the state of the device. If the user provides value for the power outside of the range in the table below, your algorithm should report that the state of the device is unknown.

Power Consumption of the Apple TV

State	Power Consumption [W]
Off/Standby	less than 0.5
Idle	0.5 to 1.5
Streaming via Ethernet	1.5 to 1.6
Streaming via Wifi	1.6 to 2

7. Humans can see electromagnetic radiation when the wavelength is within the spectrum of visible light. Create an algorithm to determine if a given wavelength [nanometer, nm] is one of the six spectral colors listed in the chart below. Your algorithm should ask the user to enter a wavelength, then indicate in which spectral color the given wavelength falls or provide a warning if it is not within the visible spectrum.

Color	Wavelength Interval [nm]
Red	~ 700–635
Orange	~ 635–590
Yellow	~ 590–560
Green	~ 560–490
Blue	~ 490–450
Violet	~ 450–400

8. Create an algorithm to display the letter grade in a course. A course grade is typically reported as a real number with values from 0 to 100. Your algorithm should ask the user to provide a grade in numerical form and display the letter grade corresponding to a numerical grade if the entered value is between 0 and 100 inclusive. If the value is outside this range, ask the user to enter the value again.

Typical range of grades:

A: $90 <= grade$
B: $80 <= grade < 90$
C: $70 <= grade < 80$
D: $60 <= grade < 70$
F: $grade < 60$

9. Create an algorithm to determine whether a given altitude [meters] is in the troposphere, lower stratosphere, or the upper stratosphere. The algorithm should include a check to ensure the user entered a positive value. If a non-positive value is entered, the program should warn the user and terminate. In addition, your algorithm should calculate and report the resulting temperature in units of degrees Celsius [°C] and pressure in units of kilopascals [kPa]. Refer to atmosphere model provided by NASA: http://www.grc.nasa.gov/WWW/K-12/airplane/atmosmet.html.

10. Create an algorithm to determine whether a given Mach number is subsonic, transonic, supersonic, or hyper sonic. Assume the user will enter the speed of the object in meters per second, and the program will calculate the Mach number and determine the appropriate Mach category. As output, the program will display the Mach catagory. The algorithm should include a check to ensure the user entered a positive value. If a non-positive value is entered, the program should warn the user and terminate. Refer to the NASA page on Mach number: http://www.grc.nasa.gov/WWW/K-12/airplane/mach.html.

11. Construct an algorithm to determine the class rank (freshman, sophomore, junior, or senior) of students enrolled in this course. You may assume the user will enter the total number of students in the course, and the program will ask the user to enter the total number credit hours earned by each student. The program will count the number of students in each class rank. The program will produce as output the total number of students in the class and the percentage of students who are in each class rank.

    In this algorithm, you may assume that a freshman has earned less than 30 credit hours, a sophomore between 30 and 59, a junior is between 60 and 89, and a senior has earned 90 or more credit hours.

12. Create an algorithm to ask the user to enter the number of Internet-enabled devices they own. If the user enters a negative number or a number greater than 50, the message "This is not reasonable. Try again." should appear to the user and they should be asked to enter another value. The error message should continue to appear each time they enter an invalid value. When the user provides an acceptable value, the message "Thank you" should be displayed and the algorithm should terminate.

13. Create an algorithm to first ask the user to enter a positive number. After checking that the value entered is positive, determine all of the even numbers between 0 and that value that are also evenly divisible by the number three. If the user enters a non-positive value, ask the user to enter a new value. At the end of your algorithm, your algorithm should display the total number of values that meet the specified criteria.

    HINT: The mathematical operator modulus (%) will return the remainder after division by a specific number. For example, 5% 4 is 1 because 5 can be evenly divisible by 4 once, with a remainder of one—the modulus. Likewise, 10% 4 is 2 because 10 can be evenly divisible by 4 twice, with a remainder of two—the modulus.

14. Create an algorithm to ask the user to enter a positive value. You may assume the user enters a positive number and you do not need to check if the value is indeed positive. Determine which is greater: the sum of the whole-even numbers between 0 and the entered value or the sum of the whole-odd numbers between 0 and the entered value. At the end of your algorithm, your algorithm should display "The sum of the odd numbers is greater" or "The sum of the even numbers is greater", depending on the outcome of the algorithm.

15. You want to calculate your grade point ratio (GPR). Create an algorithm to input your courses for this semester, the semester hours for each course, the letter grade you expect to earn, and number of grade points earned for each course (such as A = 4). At the end of the algorithm, your algorithm should display the average GPR for the semester using the following formula: summation of the product of the semester hours and number of points earned divided by the summation of semester hours.

CHAPTER 16
MATLAB VARIABLES AND DATA TYPES

A variable in MATLAB is not like a variable in mathematics. In math, a variable is typically an unknown for which you wish to determine a value. In MATLAB, on the other hand, a variable is simply a label for a container (or location) in which information is stored. Variables can be classified according to the type of information they hold. In the workspace, the data type of each variable is represented by an icon shown in the leftmost column of the workspace by the variable name. Table 16-1 below illustrates the different variable classifications in MATLAB.

Table 16-1 Variable Classifications in MATLAB

ICON	Data Type	Description
	Numeric Array	Scalars, vectors, and matrices containing numbers
abc	Character Array	Text strings. Each character occupies one element
✓	Logical Array	0 means false; 1 means true Discussed in Chapter 19
{ }	Cell Array	Contains mixed data types. Indexed numerically.
⊟	Structure Array	Contains mixed data types. Data organized into named fields.
⁒	Sparse Array	Saves memory by storing only non-zero elements
⬚	Symbolic Array	Allows symbolic mathematics within MATLAB Not covered in this text

16.1 VARIABLE BASICS

LEARN TO: Remember the naming rules for variables
Understand the use of = as the assignment operator

Every variable in MATLAB must have a name. This allows us to keep track of large amounts of information and gives a means whereby our code can use the stored information relatively easily. MATLAB names must follow certain rules to avoid unintended side-effects.

Naming Rules

- All names must consist only of letters, numbers, and the underscore character (displayed by holding "Shift" and typing a hyphen).

- Names can *only* begin with alphabetic letters (no numbers or special characters).

- Names cannot be longer than 63 characters.

- Names in MATLAB are case sensitive: `Frog` and `frog` are different.

- Names cannot have the same name as any other identifier (program name, function name, built-in function, built-in constant, reserved word, etc.), because MATLAB's order of execution will prevent the program from finding the correct item.

These rules apply to ANY named item in MATLAB, not just variables. We will give further detail in the next chapter.

Always choose names that have meaning within the context of the program, not just random letters. We cannot overemphasize the importance of well-chosen variable names in creating self-documenting code: code that explains itself. For example, if a variable contained the diameter of a bolt, the name `BoltDiam` is immediately recognizable for what it contains; a randomly chosen variable such as `X1` or `Q` has no meaning in the context of the program.

COMPREHENSION CHECK 16-1

Which of the following are valid MATLAB variable names? For those that are not valid, explain why they are invalid.

(a) `m`	**(c)** `4mass`	**(e)** `MyFile-docx`
(b) `mass6`	**(d)** `m&m©`	**(f)** `ReactorYield`

The Assignment Operator

Before beginning our discussion of data types in MATLAB, we need to introduce the concept of the **assignment operator**. The purpose of an assignment operator is to tell the computer to put a value into a variable. Perhaps unfortunately, the most commonly used assignment operator in modern programming languages is =, or the "equal" sign. We say unfortunately, because this notation often confuses novices. In mathematics, a statement such as A = A + 1 is an equation and has exactly two solutions for A: infinity and negative infinity. However, in programming this means "add one to whatever is in variable A, then place the result back in A".

It is important to note in MATLAB the = symbol should be read as "is assigned the value of". Thus, the programming statement V2 = V2 + 4 is read "V2 is assigned the value of (the original value of) V2 plus four". Note that the original value of V2 is lost in this process.

It is also VERY important to note that the transfer of data in an assignment statement is ALWAYS from right to left.

Consider the programming statement Ex1 = V3 − V4^P1.

When the computer executes this statement, it first recognizes that it is an assignment statement. Therefore it first looks at the expression to the right of the equals and determines its value: Raise the value in V4 to the value in P1 and subtract that from the value in V3. Next, it looks to the left of the equal sign to find the destination, thus placing the calculated result into the variable Ex1.

It is also important to understand that whatever appears to the left of the assignment operator MUST be a variable, or as we will see later, a group of variables. For example, you will get an error if you type A + 1 = A since you cannot have a computation on the left of the equal sign. Also, any variables that appear on the right must already be defined before the statement is executed.

> To avoid the dual problem of mistaking = for "equals" and to explicitly indicate the direction of the movement of information, some languages use a left pointing arrow (or other symbols) for the assignment operator.

COMPREHENSION CHECK 16-2

Which of the following assignment statements are valid? For those that are not valid, explain why. For those that are valid, show what value is placed into which variable. Assume the following variables (and no others) have already been defined: A = 2 B = −1 C = 3 D = 2.5

Note that the priority of operators is the same as in Microsoft Excel.

(a) X = A	**(e)** V = D − Q^2	**(i)** D = D^B
(b) B = Y	**(f)** U + 13 = 65	**(j)** A = 9999
(c) Z = A + 55	**(g)** T^2 = 4	**(k)** A + B = C − 5
(d) W = A^B + C	**(h)** Part#3 = C	**(l)** QPDoll = C^C

16.2 NUMERIC TYPES AND SCALARS: ⊞

Numeric data is exactly that—information consisting of one or more numbers. In MATLAB, as in most computer languages, there are actually several different types of numeric data. As an example, numbers can be classified as integers and non-integers (floating point numbers), and the two types are encoded differently using binary digits (1s and 0s) inside the computer. The major numeric types are listed in Tables 16-2 and 16-3, but a complete discussion is beyond the scope of this introductory material. For the moment, it is sufficient to note that the default numeric type in MATLAB is double precision, even if the value being stored has no fractional part.

Since the default numeric type in MATLAB is double precision, and doubles have the greatest range and, except for int64 and uint64, also the greatest precision of all of the standard numeric types, why would you ever want to change to another format with less precision and/or range? Occasionally, when your application is processing gargantuan quantities of data, switching to either single precision or one of the integer formats will save memory space and/or increase execution speed. Since memory is cheap and processors are amazingly fast, this is seldom a significant factor in most engineering applications, and is not worth dealing with the possible problems of increased round-off error, results beyond the range of the selected format, etc.

In addition to numeric types, variables containing numbers can also be categorized based on how many values are stored in that variable, and how they are arranged. MATLAB variables containing only numeric data are considered to be matrices, hence the name MATrix LABoratory. We will separate these into three broad categories: scalars, vectors, and matrices. We will discuss vectors and matrices further in Sections 16-3 and 16-4.

Table 16-2 Floating Point Formats

Name	Bytes	Approximate Precision	Non-zero Minimum	Non-infinite Maximum
Double	8	16 decimal digits	$\pm 2.2251 \times 10^{-308}$	$\pm 1.7977 \times 10^{308}$
Single	4	7 decimal digits	$\pm 1.1755 \times 10^{-38}$	$\pm 3.4028 \times 10^{38}$

Table 16-3 Integer Formats

Bytes	Signed			Unsigned		
	Name	Minimum	Maximum	Name	Minimum	Maximum
1	int8	−128	127	uint8	0	255
2	int16	−32,768	32,767	uint16	0	65,535
4	int32	−2,147,483,648	2,147,483,647	uint32	0	4,294,967,295
8	int64	-9.2234×10^{18}	9.2234×10^{18}	uint64	0	1.8447×10^{19}

Scalars

In this section we will discuss scalars and a variety of issues relating to scalars, although many of the concepts will carry over to our discussion of vectors and matrices.

A **scalar** is simply a single numeric value, such as $7, -35.12, 2.778 \times 10^{15}$, or $2.4 + 3.92i$. **In MATLAB, a scalar is actually considered a 1×1 matrix.**

To define a scalar, you simply use the assignment operator ($=$) to place the desired value into a variable. Remember that the location into which a value is being place is ALWAYS to the left of the equal sign.

Examples of scalars include:

```
Num=34
Age=62
Root1=15.67-14.65i
BigNum=3.5E246
TinyNum=5.7E-105
```

Predefined Constants

The following names are already defined as special constants in MATLAB. You should avoid using them for other purposes.

$$\begin{aligned}\mathbf{pi} &= \text{the constant pi}(\pi) \text{ to 15 decimal places} \\ \mathbf{i} &= \sqrt{-1} \\ \mathbf{j} &= \sqrt{-1}\end{aligned}$$

COMPLEX NUMBERS

```
Q=sqrt(-9);
```
Q will contain $0 + 3i$
where $i = \sqrt{-1}$

NOTE: j is used by electrical engineers to avoid confusion with electric current which usually uses i as the variable.

COMPREHENSION CHECK 16-3

Write MATLAB code to complete the following commands.

(a) Place the number 8 into the variable `Int2`.
(b) Place the number thirty five point seven into the variable `Real2`.
(c) Place the number 47.98×10^{56} into the variable `Big2`.
(d) Place the number 3×10^{-15} into the variable `Small2`.

Calculations with Scalars

For the most part, the mathematical operators used in Microsoft Excel work the same way in MATLAB, including parentheses and priority of operators.

● **EXAMPLE 16-1**

Recall variable names should have meaning in the context of their use. Here, DPM refers to Divide Plus Multiply, RTP refers to Raise To Power, and RTPP refers to Raise to Power with multiple elements in the Power.

What is stored in the variable when each line of MATLAB code below is exectuted?

```
DPM= 38/19 + 5*3;
```
   DPM *contains 17*

```
RTP= 3^2 + 1;
```
   RTP *contains 10*

```
RTPP= 3^(2 + 1);
```
   RTPP *contains 27*

Numeric Functions

There are hundreds of functions built into MATLAB for performing a wide variety of operations with numeric data. These are similar to the functions you learned about in your study of Excel, and in many cases even have the same name, such as sin, sqrt, or round. We will introduce quite a few functions throughout the subsequent sections. A sample of functions used with numeric values is shown in Table 16-4.

Table 16-4 **Selected Numeric Functions**

Function	Description	Function	Description
single	Convert to single precision	round	Round to nearest integer
double	Convert to double precision	ceil	Round toward positive infinity
int8	Convert to 8 bit integer	floor	Round toward negative infinity
int32	Convert to 32 bit integer	fix	Round toward zero
uint64	Convert to unsigned 64 bit integer	sqrt	Determine the square root
inf	Infinity	nthroot	Determine the Nth root
NaN	Not a Number	sin	Sine of angle in radians
intmax	Maximum for specified integer type	sind	Sine of angle in degrees
intmin	Minimum for specified integer type	acos	Inverse cosine in radians
realmax	Maximum for specified floating-point type	acosd	Inverse cosine in degrees
realmin	Minimum for specified floating-point type	exp	Exponential function
real	Real part of a complex number	log	Natural logarithm
imag	Imaginary part of a complex number	log10	Base 10 logarithm

Functions to Help You Learn Other Functions

The two functions help and doc can be invaluable in learning what various MATLAB functions do and how they are used (their syntax). They can also help you explore the often labyrinthine sets of built-in functions to discover new and useful features of the language.

To illustrate the use of the help function, at the prompt in the command window type help log. A short explanation of log appears, along with the syntax used. Near the end of the information is a section that says "See also" followed by a list of hyperlinks to related functions.

To illustrate the use of the doc function, at the prompt in the Command Window type doc weekday. This launches the documentation browser. The documentation browser makes it relatively easy to explore MATLAB. In the figure below, note the following features:

doc and help in general should only be used as single line commands in the Command Window, not included in an m-file. M-files will be discussed in the next chapter.

- The **Contents** outline on the left. This shows an outline of the organization of MATLAB functions into related groups, and includes drop-down menus for Examples, Concepts, Troubleshooting, etc. If the Contents outline is not visible, click the little outline icon near the top left to expand it.
- Hyperlinks to examples on the left of many subtopics within the main informational window.
- The search box at the top of the main information window. Here, you can type keywords to search for functions that do particular types of tasks.

■ Scrolling down to the bottom of the main information window will list related functions under **See Also**, similar to the help function.

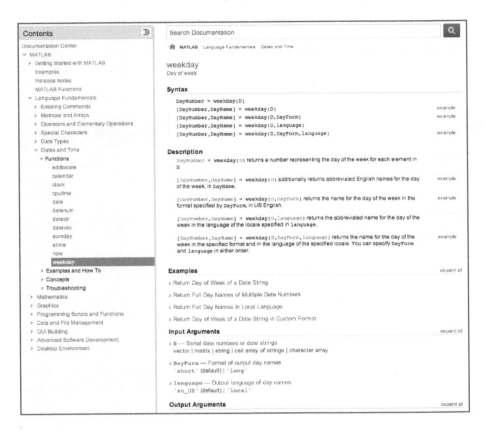

Displaying Numbers

The default numeric display format in MATLAB is to show four decimal places unless the value has no fractional part. For numbers with fractional parts and a magnitude less than 10,000 but greater than 0.001, MATLAB will display up to three digits to the left of the decimal point and four decimal places. For values outside of this range, MATLAB will display the value in scientific notation, with the most significant digit to the left of the decimal point and four decimal places.

`100*pi`	will display as 314.1593
`1000*pi`	will display as 3.1416e+03
`pi/1000`	will display as 0.0031
`pi/10000`	will display as 3.1416e−04

Values with no fractional part and a magnitude less than 10^{10} will display as an integer. Larger values will display with five significant figures in scientific notation as above.

`123123123`	will display as 123123123
`1231231231`	will display as 1.2312e+09

NOTE

Even if a number has no fractional part, it will be stored as a double precision floating point number. If you want a value to be stored in one of the integer formats, you must specifically tell MATLAB to do so.

You may change the default display format with the `format` function. For example `format long` will change the default display format to show 15 digits instead of only 5. More information about the format function can be found by typing `help format` or `doc format` in the Command Window.

COMPREHENSION CHECK 16-4

(a) Calculate the two roots of the quadratic equation $2x^2 + 2x + 1 = 0$ using the quadratic formula and place them in `R1` and `R2`. Note that MATLAB should do this calculation—do not calculate by hand and enter the resulting values.

(b) Calculate the tangent of 75 degrees and place the result in `Trig2`.

16.3 VECTORS

LEARN TO: Define numeric vectors in MATLAB's workspace
Perform basic vector operations
Write mathematic expressions using functions on an entire vector

A **vector** consists of numeric values organized into a single row or a single column. Examples include $[3.5 \ -38 \ 0 \ -1]$ and $\begin{bmatrix} -1 \\ 0 \\ 3.2 \end{bmatrix}$. **A vector is either an N × 1 matrix (column vector) or 1 × N (row vector), where N is an integer greater than 1.**

Defining Vectors

As with scalars, the usual method for defining a vector is to use the assignment operator (=). There are a few immediate questions, however, since vectors have more than one value and may be organized as either a row or column.

1. How do we tell MATLAB we are defining a vector and not a scalar?
2. How do we tell MATLAB whether we are creating a row or a column vector?
3. How do we distinguish the individual values from each other?

First, when we wish to define a vector, the first character following the equal sign is [(open square bracket). Once we have entered all of the numbers, we end with] (close square bracket). It is also possible to define vectors using indexing, which is discussed later in this section.

The solution to the second question also solves the third: we separate the numbers by **delimiters**—either a space, a comma, or a semicolon. If we separate the individual values with spaces or commas, a row vector will be created. If we separate the values with semicolons, they will be placed in a column vector.

NOTE

A **space** or **comma** delimiter creates a row

A **semicolon** delimiter creates a column

● **EXAMPLE 16-2**

What is stored in the variable when each line of MATLAB code below is exectued?

```
Pair = [23 4.3];
```
    Pair *contains the row vector* [23 4.3]
```
Trio = [1, 4, 79857];
```
    Trio *contains the row vector* [1 4 79857]
```
CTrio = [0;0;97];
```

    CTrio *contains the column vector* $\begin{bmatrix} 0 \\ 0 \\ 97 \end{bmatrix}$

The Transpose (') Operator

If you need to convert a row vector to a column vector, or vice versa, use the apostrophe or single quote to transpose it.
    Consider the following two lines of code:

```
V = [6,-9, 3];              VT = V';
```

V will contain [6 −9 3]   VT will contain $\begin{bmatrix} 6 \\ -9 \\ 3 \end{bmatrix}$

Special Case: Linear Sequences

It is fairly common to need a vector containing a set of equally spaced values, so MATLAB includes a short-cut method for creating such sequences.
    If you wish to create a sequence of values in a row vector incrementing by one, such as 1, 2, 3, 4, 5, you can use the **colon operator** to separate the first and last value of the sequence.

NOTE

A **colon** delimiter creates a sequence

● **EXAMPLE 16-3**

What is stored in the variable when each line of MATLAB code below is exectued?

```
LSeq=1:5;
```
LSeq *contains* [1 2 3 4 5]

Note that the brackets are optional in this case. You could also enter LSeq=[1:5];

If you wish a sequence that increments by a value other than 1, you may place the increment value between the first and last value, separated by colons.

● **EXAMPLE 16-4**

What is stored in the variable when each line of MATLAB code below is exectued?

```
LseqA=5:15:80;
```
LSeqA *contains* [5 20 35 50 65 80].

Frac=0.7:0.03:0.88;

Frac *contains* [0.7 0.73 0.76 0.79 0.82 0.85 0.88]. *Fractional values are allowed*

Rev=4:-3:-2;

Rev *contains* [4 1 −2]. *Negative values are allowed.*

Miss=1:5:20;

Miss *contains* [1 6 11 16]. *Note that the increment did not land on the final value (20). In cases like this, the sequence will stop on the last value BEFORE it exceeds the stated end value.*

COMPREHENSION CHECK 16-5

Each problem should be done with a single MATLAB statement:

(a) Create a column vector named N4 containing the values 17, 34, −94, 16, and 0.

(b) Create a row vector named Tiny containing the values 3.4×10^{-14}, 9.02×10^{-23}, and 1.32×10^{-9}

(c) Create a row vector named Ev containing all even integers from 2 to 250.

(d) Create a column vector name Tenths containing the decreasing sequence 10, 9.9, . . . 0.2, 0.1, 0

Calculations with Vectors

Basic calculations with vectors are somewhat more complicated than the same calculations with scalars.

Addition and Subtraction

When addition or subtraction involves a vector, there are two cases:

1. A scalar and a vector: the scalar is added or subtracted to each element of the vector.

2. Two equal size vectors: corresponding elements of the two vectors are added or subtracted.

If you attempt to add two vectors that are not the same size, you will get angry red letters, indicating an error.

● EXAMPLE 16-5

What is stored in the variable when each line of MATLAB code below is executed?

Assume V1=[2 5 9];   V2=[3 0];   V3=[4 -7 0];

D1=V1-4;

D1 *contains* [−2 1 5].

S1=V1+V3;

S1 *contains* [6 −2 9].

E1=V1+V2;

Will return the message: Error using + Matrix dimensions must agree.

Multiplication and Division

A complete discussion of vector multiplication will be deferred to the next section on matrices. For now, we will only consider cases similar to the two mentioned for addition and subtraction:

1. A vector multiplied or divided by a scalar: each element of the vector is multiplied or divided by the scalar. NOTE: if you attempt to divide a scalar by a vector, you will get angry red letters.
2. A vector multiplied or divided by an equal length vector: corresponding elements of the two vectors are multiplied or divided. NOTE: This requires the use of the **element-wise operator**, sometimes referred to as the "**dot operator**" since the actual operator is preceded by a period (or "dot") symbol, as shown below.

NOTE

The **dot operator** indicates an element-wise operation

If you attempt an element-wise multiplication or division of two vectors that are not the same size, you will get angry red letters.

● **EXAMPLE 16-6**

What is stored in the variable when each line of MATLAB code below is exectuted?

Assume V1=[2 5 9]; V2=[3 0]; V3=[4 -7 0];

    Q1=V1/5;

Q1 *contains* [0.4 1 1.8].

    P1=V2*300;

P1 *contains* [900 0].

    P2=V1.*V3;

P2 *contains* [8 −35 0]. *Note the dot before the asterisk (.* instead of *). This tells MATLAB that the multiplication is to be done on an element-wise basis.*

    Q2=V3./V1;

Q2 *contains* [2 −1.4 0]. *Note the dot before the slash (./ instead of /). This tells MATLAB that the division is to be done on an element-wise basis.*

    Q3=5/V1;

Will return the message: Error using / Matrix dimensions must agree.

    P3=V1*V3;

Will return the message: Error using * Matrix dimensions must agree.

The reasons for these errors will become clear when we discuss matrices in the next section.

    Q4=V3/V1;

Q4 *contains* −0.2445. *For an explanation of this seemingly mysterious result, refer to any general reference on matrix operations. For the moment just take note that vector division without the dot probably does not do what you expected.*

Powers

We will consider three cases here, all of which are element-wise operations.

1. A vector raised to a scalar.
2. A scalar raised to a vector.
3. A vector raised to a vector of equal size.

In all three cases, we will use .^ (not simply ^) to inform MATLAB to do an element-wise operation.

● **EXAMPLE 16-7**

What is stored in the variable when each line of MATLAB code below is exectuted?

Assume V1=[2 5 9]; V2=[3 0]; V3=[4 −7 0];
 R1=V1.^3;

R1 *contains* [8 125 729]   *Each element of* V1 *is cubed*
 R2=2.^V3;

R2 *contains* [16 0.0078 1]   *The number 2 is raised to each element of* V3
 R3=V3.^V1;

R3 *contains* [16 −16807 0] *Raise each element of* V3 *to the*
             corresponding element of V1.

 R4=V2.^V1;

Will return the message:

Error using .^ Matrix dimensions must agree.

Combined Operations

All of the standard rules concerning priority of operators, use of parentheses, etc. apply to computations with vectors, the only difference being that both intermediate and final results may be vectors instead of scalars.

● **EXAMPLE 16-8**

What is stored in the variable when each line of MATLAB code below is exectuted?

Assume V4= [2 1 −2]; V5=[3 −2 1.5];
 R=(10-V4./V5).^2*3;

R *contains* [261.33 330.75 385.33]

 Sequence of operations:

1. V4 *is divided element-wise by* V5 [0.6667 −0.5 −1.3333]
2. *Each of these values is subtracted from 10* [9.3333 10.5 11.3333]
3. *Each of those values is squared* [87.1111 110.25 128.4444]
4. *Each of those values is multiplied by 3* [261.33 330.75 385.33]

COMPREHENSION CHECK 16-6

Assume a row vector named Vals has already been defined. Write a single MATLAB statement that will perform the following calculation using each element of Vals and leave the results in a vector named Comps: $C = (3V + 5)^4 − 16$ where V represents the individual values in Vals, and C represents the individual results in Comps. Example: if Vals= [2 0 −1], Comps=[14625 609 0]

Functions Used with Vectors

Most of the functions listed in Table 16-4 also work with vectors. In most cases, such as `sqrt`, `sin`, or `round`, these automatically perform the stated operation on each element individually. There are quite a few MATLAB functions that would seldom if ever be used with scalars, but are very helpful in dealing with vectors. A few of these are listed in Table 16-5. You can obtain more information by typing either `help` or `doc` followed by the function name.

Table 16-5 Selected Functions Used with Vectors

Function	Description
min	Find smallest value. Can also find location of smallest value in the vector.
max	Find largest value. Can also find location of largest value in the vector.
sort	Sort elements in ascending or descending order.
zeros	Create a vector of all zeros.
ones	Create a vector of all ones.
rand	Create a vector of random numbers.
length	Find the number of elements in a vector. VERY useful!
unique	List all values in a vector with no repetitions in result.
intersect	Find all values in both of two vectors, no repetitions in result
union	Find all values in either of two vectors, no repetitions in result
setdiff	Find all values in one vector that are not in another vector, no repetitions in result.
setxor	Find all values in each of two vectors that are not in the other, no repetitions.

All of the functions in Table 16-5 are actually matrix functions. Matrices will be covered in the next section.

The last five functions, as well as functions like `min` and `max`, can also find the locations of the desired values in the vector.

Other Notes on Creating Vectors

You can include calculations, functions, etc. inside the brackets when defining vectors.

Examples:

NOTE

To **concatenate** means to combine

1. Vectors can be combined (concatenated) by simply listing them in the desired order inside of square brackets. For row vectors, the individual items should be separated by spaces or commas; for column vectors they should be separated by semicolons. Use the single quote as needed to transpose a row to column before combining.

   V4 = [2 1 −2];   V6 = [3; −2; 1.5];
   CV = [V4, V6'];
   CV contains [2 1 −2 3 −2 1.5]

2. You wish to create a two element vector named MM containing the maximum and minimum values in vector V100. This can be done using

   MM = [max(V100), min(V100)];

3. You wish to create a vector OddMM consisting of the odd integers from 1 to 50 followed by three times the square root of each element in MM from the previous example.

   OddMM = [1:2:50, 3*sqrt(MM)];

(a) Assume you have four row vectors containing data on traffic flow named T1, T2, T3, and T4. Using a single MATLAB statement, combine these four, in that order, into a single column vector named TFC. Example:

$$T1=[2 \ 6 \ 4]; \ T2=[0 \ -1]; \ T3=[9 \ -1 \ 0];$$
$$T4=[7 \ 7]; \ TFC=[2;6;4;0;-1;9;-1;0;7;7]$$

(b) Using a single MATLAB statement, create a row vector named Rev that contains all even integers from 10 to 10,000 in ascending order followed by all integer multiples of 7 from 700 to 7 in descending order.

(c) Assume you have a row vector named RV5. Using a single MATLAB statement, create a new row vector named Pow that contains, in this order,

1. The elements of RV5.
2. The square roots of each element of RV5.
3. The square of each element of RV5.

Vector Indexing

Frequently you will need to change a single element or group of elements within a vector, or perform some operation on only some of the elements within a vector. **Indexing** or **addressing** allows you to accomplish this. To access a specific element or elements within a vector, we place the numeric positions of the elements we wish to use in parentheses after the vector name. For example, in the vector V1 = [2   5   9], the statement V1(2) indicated the second element in V1, or the value 5.

Creating Vectors Using Indexing

We have already seen that we can place a list of values in brackets to create a vector. We can also create vectors using indexing. As an example, assume the vector AVec containing the values 2, 0, and 5 could be created by

```
AVec=[2 0 5];
```

This could also be accomplished using

```
AVec(1)=2; % Define Element 1
AVec(2)=0; % Define Element 2
AVec(3)=5; % Define Element 3
```

Although this may look like a lot more work at first, as we will see later, this is the best way to define vectors in some situations.

What happens if you wish to specify some element of an undefined vector other than the first element?

In the command window, type this to be sure try3 does not already exist:

```
clear try3
```

Now type

```
try3(3)=9
```

Do not place a semicolon at the end of the line so that try3 will be echoed to the screen. What can you say about the first two elements, try3(1) and try3(2), that were not defined?

Changing Individual Values of Vectors

You can change elements individually without modifying the others using vector indexing.

● **EXAMPLE 16-9**

Note that vector indexing works fine with column vectors. It is just the <u>creation</u> of new vectors where row is the default format.

What is stored in the variable when each line of MATLAB code below is exectuted?

$$\text{Assume } V7 = \begin{bmatrix} 3 \\ -7 \\ 34 \\ 0 \\ 18 \end{bmatrix}$$

V7(3) = -1;

$$V7 \text{ will then contain } \begin{bmatrix} 3 \\ -7 \\ -1 \\ 0 \\ 18 \end{bmatrix}$$

Deleting Values from Vectors

Sometimes you need to simply delete elements from a vector—not replace them with zeros, but actually delete them making the vector shorter. This can be done by specifying the elements to be deleted to be the **empty element**, indicated by [].

● **EXAMPLE 16-10**

What is stored in the variable when each line of MATLAB code below is exectuted?

Assume V8 contains [2 1 5 8 6 3].

V8(3)=[];

This will delete the third element, so V8 now contains [2 1 8 6 3].

Specifying More Than One Element Using Indexing

If you wish two or more elements of a vector to have the same value, you can list the indexes of those values in the parentheses separated by commas.

● **EXAMPLE 16-11**

What is stored in the variable when each line of MATLAB code below is exectuted?

Assume V9 contains [3 −2 5 0 −7].

V9(2,4,5)=99;

This will replace the 2nd, 4th and 5th elements with the number 99, so V9 now contains [3 99 5 99 99].

Using Linear Sequences as Indexes

You can use the colon operator to create a linear sequence of values to use as indices inside the parentheses.

● EXAMPLE 16-12

What is stored in the variable when each line of MATLAB code below is exectuted?

$$\text{Assume CV1} = \begin{bmatrix} 3 \\ -7 \\ 34 \\ 0 \\ 18 \end{bmatrix}$$

```
CV1(2:4)=99;
```

This will replace the 2nd, 3rd and 4th elements with the number 99, so CV1 now contains

$$\begin{bmatrix} 3 \\ 99 \\ 99 \\ 99 \\ 18 \end{bmatrix}$$

● EXAMPLE 16-13

What is stored in the variable when each line of MATLAB code below is exectuted?

Assume RV1 contains [3 6 −2 7 0 0 −4 −6 9 13].

```
RV1(2:3:10)=0;
```

This will replace the every third element, starting with the 2nd element (replacing the 2nd, 5th and 8th . . .) up to the 10th element, so RV1 now contains [3 0 −2 7 0 0 −4 0 9 13].

Calculations with Part of a Vector

● EXAMPLE 16-14

Determine the sine of the fifth element of vector T20, assuming the values in T20 are angles given in radians. Place the result in S5.

```
S5=sin(T20(5));
```

● EXAMPLE 16-15

Assume you have a 100-element vector D1 containing data. Create a new vector RD1 containing 50 elements comprising the square roots of the even numbered elements of D1.

```
RD1=sqrt(D1(2:2:100));
```

● EXAMPLE 16-16

Assume you have a 1000-element vector D2 containing data. Create a new vector ZRD2 containing 1000 elements in which the odd numbered elements are zero and the even numbered elements are the squares of the corresponding even numbered elements of D2.

```
ZRD2(2:2:1000)= D2(2:2:1000).^2;
```

● **EXAMPLE 16-17**

Assume you have a vector D3 containing an unknown number of elements. Modify D3 so that all odd numbered elements are replaced by the cosines of the odd numbered values. All even numbered values should be unchanged. Assume the odd numbered elements contain angles in degrees.

```
D3(1:2:length(D3)) = cosd(D3(1:2:length(D3)));
```

WARNING

If you try to do a calculation on a vector element that does not exist, such as the sixth element of a five element vector, you will get an error. The length function can prove very useful if you do not know how many elements a vector has, or if the number of elements might change during execution of the program.

COMPREHENSION CHECK 16-8

(a) Write a single MATLAB command that will create a 50,000-element vector named Biggie in which every tenth element equals −9999 and all other elements equal 0.

(b) Assume a vector LV has already been defined. Write a single MATLAB command that will delete all of the even numbered elements, leaving LV with half as many elements.

(c) Assume a vector named D has an even number of elements. Write a single MATLAB command that will create a new vector named DS with half as many elements, in which each element is the sum of adjacent odd-even pairs in D.

Example:

If D= [2 5 4 -7 3 0], then DS will equal [7 -3 3], found by the vector:

$$[D(1) + D(2) \quad D(3) + D(4) \quad D(5) + D(6)]$$

16.4 MATRICES

LEARN TO: Define numeric matrices in MATLAB's workspace
Perform basic matrix operations
Write mathematic expressions using functions on an entire matrix

A **matrix** or **array** consists of numbers organized into rows and columns. The size of a matrix is given as R × C, where R is the number of rows and C is the number of columns.

Examples include $\begin{bmatrix} 0.2 & 3 & 0 \\ -7 & 0.05 & 99 \end{bmatrix}$ which is a 2 × 3 matrix, and $\begin{bmatrix} 1 & 0 & 0 & 0 \\ 1 & 1 & 0 & 1 \\ 1 & 0 & 1 & 0 \\ 0 & 1 & 1 & 1 \end{bmatrix}$ which

is a 4 × 4 matrix. All numeric data in MATLAB, including scalars and vectors, are matrices. MATLAB is, after all, derived from the words **MAT**rix **LAB**oratory. A scalar is simply a 1 × 1 matrix, whereas a vector is either 1 × C (row) or R × 1 (column). Note that all numeric data, whether scalar, vector, or matrix, is represented in the workspace by a square icon divided into four smaller squares used to symbolize a matrix.

Defining Matrices

The basic way to define a matrix is to combine the methods used to create row and column vectors, but matrices are created row by row, not column by column—you specify the first row with elements separated by commas or spaces, then use a semicolon to move to the next row.

● **EXAMPLE 16-18**

What matrix is formed by the following commands?

```
M1=[0 -4 3;-2 6 0.2];
```

Creates the 2 × 3 matrix M1 $=\begin{bmatrix} 0 & -4 & 3 \\ -2 & 6 & 0.2 \end{bmatrix}$

```
M2=[0,-4;3,-2;6 0.2];
```

Creates the 3 × 2 matrix M2 $=\begin{bmatrix} 0 & -4 \\ 3 & -2 \\ 6 & 0.2 \end{bmatrix}$

Creating Matrices Using Indexing

When using indexing with matrices, we need to specify both the row and column of the element in question. Instead of a single number, place two integers separated by a comma in the parentheses following the matrix name. The first value is the row number, and the second value is the column number.

● **EXAMPLE 16-19**

What matrix is formed by the following commands?

Note that when using indexing to create a matrix, the order in which the matrix is defined is not predefined. In the M3 example, the matrix was defined column by column, not row by row.

```
M3(1,1)=5;
M3(2,1)=0;
M3(1,2)=1;
M3(2,2)=8;
```

Creates the 2 × 2 matrix M3 $=\begin{bmatrix} 5 & 1 \\ 0 & 8 \end{bmatrix}$

If you create an element of a matrix in such a way that for the row and column specified there are elements of the matrix that are unspecified, MATLAB will automatically make them zero.

● **EXAMPLE 16-20**

What matrix is formed by the following commands?

```
M4(2,3) = 77;
```

Creates the 2 × 3 matrix M4 $=\begin{bmatrix} 0 & 0 & 0 \\ 0 & 0 & 77 \end{bmatrix}$

```
M5(2,3)=55;
M5(3,2)=88;
```

Creates the 3 × 3 matrix M5 $=\begin{bmatrix} 0 & 0 & 0 \\ 0 & 0 & 55 \\ 0 & 88 & 0 \end{bmatrix}$

Using the Colon Operator to Create Linear Sequences for Indexing Matrices

● EXAMPLE 16-21

What matrix is formed by the following commands?

Assume M5 has already been defined as in the previous example.

    M5(1,2:3) = -1;

This command states that Row 1, Columns 2 through 3 are set to −1.

M5 *now contains* M5 $= \begin{bmatrix} 0 & -1 & -1 \\ 0 & 0 & 55 \\ 0 & 88 & 0 \end{bmatrix}$

Defining a Matrix from Another Matrix

● EXAMPLE 16-22

What matrix is formed by the following commands?

Assume M5 has been defined as in the previous example.

    M6=M5(1:2,2:3);

This command states the variable M6 *equals Rows 1 and 2, Columns 2 and 3 of* M5.

This creates M6 $= \begin{bmatrix} -1 & -1 \\ 0 & 55 \end{bmatrix}$

NOTE

A **colon** used as an index indicated to use all rows or all columns in the matrix.

Accessing Entire Rows or Columns

Often you wish to specify an entire row or entire column or a matrix. MATLAB provides a shortcut notation for this situation. Instead of placing a 1 for the first row (or column) before the colon and the total number of rows (or columns) after the colon, simply type a colon by itself.

● EXAMPLE 16-23

What matrix is formed by the following commands?

Assume M5 has been defined as above.

    M7=M5(:,2);

This command states the variable M7 *equals all rows, Column 2 of* M5.

This creates the 3 × 1 matrix (or column vector) M7 $= \begin{bmatrix} -1 \\ 0 \\ 88 \end{bmatrix}$

    M8=M5(1:2:3,:);

This command states the variable M8 *equals Rows 1 and 3, all columns of* M5.

This creates the 2 × 3 matrix M8 $= \begin{bmatrix} 0 & -1 & -1 \\ 0 & 88 & 0 \end{bmatrix}$

Creating a Column Vector (or a R × 1 Matrix)

You can use the colon to force a vector definition to be a column instead of the default row.

● **EXAMPLE 16-24**

What matrix is formed by the following commands?

```
CV2(:,1)=[1 4 3 7];
```

This command states the variable CV2 *equals all rows, one column of values. This creates*

$$CV2 = \begin{bmatrix} 1 \\ 4 \\ 3 \\ 7 \end{bmatrix}$$

Deleting Rows or Columns from a Matrix

The colon operator in combination with the empty element [] can be used to delete entire rows or columns from a matrix.

● **EXAMPLE 16-25**

What matrix is formed by the following commands?

$$\text{Assume } M9 = \begin{bmatrix} 3 & -9 & 14 \\ 6 & 0.5 & -4 \\ 44 & 5 & 1 \end{bmatrix}$$

```
M9(2,:)=[];
```

This command replaces Row 2, all columns with an empty matrix, deleting Row 2 from the matrix. Now,

$$M9 = \begin{bmatrix} 3 & -9 & 14 \\ 44 & 5 & 1 \end{bmatrix}$$

Deleting Individual Elements from a Matrix

● **EXAMPLE 16-26**

What matrix is formed by the following commands?

$$\text{Assume } M10 = \begin{bmatrix} -1 & -2 \\ 3 & 5 \end{bmatrix}$$

```
M10(2,1)=[];
```

This command replaces Row 2, the first column with an empty matrix. This will result in the error:

```
Subscripted assignment dimension mismatch.
```

The error occurs because in a matrix, all rows must have the same number of columns and all columns must have the same number of rows. Deleting a single element from a row or column would violate this rule. You can, however, replace elements with zeros.

```
M10(2,1)=0;
```

This command replaces the element in Row 2, Column 1 with a zero, so

$$M10 = \begin{bmatrix} -1 & -2 \\ 0 & 5 \end{bmatrix}$$

Matrix Transpose

In the section on vectors, we saw that the single quote (') operator changes a row vector to a column vector, or vice versa. This is actually just a special case of a matrix transpose. The transpose of a matrix swaps rows and columns—the first row of the original matrix becomes the first column of the transposed matrix, the second row becomes the second column, etc.

● EXAMPLE 16-27   What matrix is formed by the following commands?

$$\text{Assume M1} = \begin{bmatrix} 0 & -4 & 3 \\ -2 & 6 & 0.2 \end{bmatrix}$$

```
T1 = M1';
```

This will transpose the M1 matrix, and store it in T1: $T1 = \begin{bmatrix} 0 & -2 \\ -4 & 6 \\ 3 & 0.2 \end{bmatrix}$

COMPREHENSION CHECK 16-9

(a) Create the matrix $CCM1 = \begin{bmatrix} 18 & 0.3 \\ -4.1 & -1 \\ 0 & 17 \end{bmatrix}$ using a single MATLAB command.

(b) Create the matrix $CCM2 = \begin{bmatrix} 0 & 0 & 0 \\ 0 & 0 & 1 \times 10^{15} \\ 0 & 0 & 1 \times 10^{15} \end{bmatrix}$ using a single MATLAB command.

(c) Assume the 3×3 matrix CCM3 has already been defined as

$$CCM3 = \begin{bmatrix} 3 & 9 & 14 \\ 6 & 0.5 & 4 \times 10^{-2} \\ 44 & 0 & 1 \times 10^3 \end{bmatrix}$$

Using a single MATLAB command, define a new 2×2 matrix named Corners that contains the corner elements of CCM3. Your code should still work correctly if the contents of CCM3 changes but remains a 3×3; in other words, DO NOT hard-code the four values.

Calculations with Matrices

For the basics of matrix operations, please refer to Appendix A.6 online. The following discussion assumes that you already understand things like a matrix transpose or matrix multiplication.

Addition and Subtraction

When addition or subtraction involves a matrix, there are two cases:

1. A scalar and a matrix: the scalar is added or subtracted to each element of the matrix.
2. Two equal size matrices: corresponding elements of the two matrices are added or subtracted. If you attempt to add two matrices (both non-scalar) that are not the same size, you will get angry red letters.

● **EXAMPLE 16-28**   What matrix is formed by the following commands?

Assume $ExM1 = \begin{bmatrix} 3 & 0.5 & 0 \\ 5 & -7 & 2 \end{bmatrix}$; $ExM2 = \begin{bmatrix} 9 & -4 \\ 8 & 3.7 \end{bmatrix}$; $ExM3 = \begin{bmatrix} 19 & 2 & 3.4 \\ -6 & 1 & -3 \end{bmatrix}$;

D1=7−ExM1;

D1 *contains* $\begin{bmatrix} 4 & 6.5 & 7 \\ 2 & 14 & 5 \end{bmatrix}$

S1=ExM1 + ExM3;

S1 *contains* $\begin{bmatrix} 22 & 2.5 & 3.4 \\ -1 & -6 & -1 \end{bmatrix}$

E1=ExM1 + ExM2;

Will return the message:
Error using + Matrix dimensions must agree.

Multiplication and Powers

We will consider four cases of matrices involved in multiplication and powers.

1. A scalar and a matrix: The scalar is multiplied by each element of the matrix.
2. Two equal size matrices multiplied on an element-by-element basis. Note that the two matrices MUST have the same dimensions. NOTE: This requires the use of the element-wise operator as shown below.
3. A true matrix multiplication (refer to Appendix A.6 online): In this case, the number of columns of the first matrix MUST equal the number of rows of the second matrix or the matrix multiplication is not defined.
4. A matrix raised to a scalar. Until you understand considerably more about matrix arithmetic, it would be wise to avoid fractional or negative powers when using ^ (full matrix power). Negative and fractional powers are fine with element-by-element powers (.^)—they work just as you would expect.

● EXAMPLE 16-29   What matrix is formed by the following commands?

Assume $\text{ExM1} = \begin{bmatrix} 3 & 0.5 & 0 \\ 5 & -7 & 2 \end{bmatrix}$; $\text{ExM2} = \begin{bmatrix} 9 & -4 \\ 8 & 3.7 \end{bmatrix}$; $\text{ExM3} = \begin{bmatrix} 19 & 2 & 3.4 \\ -6 & 1 & -3 \end{bmatrix}$

$\text{RV} = [2 \ 5 \ 9]$; $\text{CV} = \begin{bmatrix} 3 \\ -1 \\ 5 \end{bmatrix}$

```
P1=3*ExM1;
```

P1 contains $\begin{bmatrix} 9 & 1.5 & 0 \\ 15 & -21 & 6 \end{bmatrix}$

```
P2=ExM1.*ExM3;
```

P2 contains $\begin{bmatrix} 57 & 1 & 0 \\ -30 & -7 & -6 \end{bmatrix}$ Recall the symbol .* means element-wise multiplication

P3=ExM1*ExM3;
Error using * Inner matrix dimensions must agree.

P4=RV*CV;

P4 contains 46

P5=CV*RV;

P5 contains $\begin{bmatrix} 6 & 15 & 27 \\ -2 & -5 & -9 \\ 10 & 25 & 45 \end{bmatrix}$

P4 and P5 show that matrix multiplication is NOT commutative!

P6=ExM2*ExM1;

P6 contains $\begin{bmatrix} 7 & 32.5 & -8 \\ 42.5 & -21.9 & 7.4 \end{bmatrix}$

P7=ExM1*ExM2;
Error using * Inner matrix dimensions must agree.
P6 and P7 show that commuted matrix multiplication is not necessarily even defined!

P8=ExM2^2;

P8 contains $\begin{bmatrix} 49 & -50.8 \\ 101.6 & -18.31 \end{bmatrix}$

P9=ExM1^2;
Error using ^ Inputs must be a scalar and a square matrix.
To compute elementwise POWER, use POWER (.^) instead.

P10=ExM1.^2;

P10 contains $\begin{bmatrix} 9 & 0.25 & 0 \\ 25 & 49 & 4 \end{bmatrix}$ Recall using symbol .^ means element-wise power

Division

The only case we will consider in this text is division of a matrix by a scalar. In this case each element of the matrix is divided by the scalar. Division by a matrix is beyond the scope of this text. Refer to any general reference on matrix algebra for more information.

● **EXAMPLE 16-30**

What matrix is formed by the following commands?

Assume $\text{ExM2} = \begin{bmatrix} 9 & -4 \\ 8 & 3.7 \end{bmatrix}$

Q1=ExM2/4;

Q1 *contains* $\begin{bmatrix} 2.25 & -1 \\ 2 & 0.925 \end{bmatrix}$

Functions Used with Matrices

NOTE

All of the functions used with vectors in Table 16-5 can be used with matrices, but some do NOT do what you might expect. For example, length does **not** find the total number of elements in a matrix and max does **not** find the single largest element in the matrix.

Most of the functions listed in Table 16-4 and 16-5 also work with matrices. In most cases, such as sqrt, sin, or round, these automatically perform the stated operation on each element individually. There are quite a few MATLAB functions that would seldom if ever be used with scalars and/or vectors, but are very helpful in dealing with matrices. A few of these are listed in Table 16-6. You can obtain more information by typing either help or doc followed by the function name.

Table 16-6 Selected Functions Used with Matrices

Function	Description
size	Find the number of rows and columns in a matrix. VERY useful!
eye	Create identity matrix with R rows and C columns, where all elements are zero except the diagonal
inv	Find the inverse of a matrix.
reshape	Create matrix containing the same elements but different dimensions
ndims	Determines the number of dimensions of a matrix
diag	Specify or extract diagonals of matrix
trace	Sum of elements on the diagonal
flipud	Flip matrix in up/down direction
fliplr	Flip matrix in left/right direction
rot90	Rotate matrix 90 degrees counterclockwise
sparse	Create sparse matrix; removes all zero elements from a matrix
find	Find indices of all non-zero elements in a matrix
full	Convert sparse matrix to full matrix

● **EXAMPLE 16-31**   What matrix is formed by the following commands?

Assume ExM1 $= \begin{bmatrix} 3 & 0.5 & 0 \\ 5 & -7 & 2 \end{bmatrix}$

```
[R,C]=size(ExM1);
```

R *contains 2 and* C *contains 3*

```
Ident=eye(3);
```

Ident *contains* $\begin{bmatrix} 1 & 0 & 0 \\ 0 & 1 & 0 \\ 0 & 0 & 1 \end{bmatrix}$

```
Mod1=reshape(ExM1,3,2);
```

Mod1 *contains* $\begin{bmatrix} 3 & -7 \\ 5 & 0 \\ 0.5 & 2 \end{bmatrix}$

```
Mod2=fliplr(ExM1);
```

Mod2 *contains* $\begin{bmatrix} 0 & 0.5 & 3 \\ 2 & -7 & 5 \end{bmatrix}$

**COMPREHENSION
CHECK 16-10**

(a) Create a matrix CC1 defined as the square root of half of each element in matrix QPD.
(b) Create a matrix CC2 defined as 17 plus the sum of corresponding elements in matrices X1 and X2. Assume X1 and X2 are the same size.

16.5 CHARACTER STRINGS

LEARN TO: Define text strings in MATLAB's workspace
Combine existing text strings
Write expressions using special functions to modify character strings

Character Strings abc

A variety of data, such as names, part identification, or week days, requires alphabetic or alphanumeric data. Such information is stored in a **character string**, also called a text string or simply text, and is denoted in the workspace with a square icon containing the letters abc.

A character string is in one sense like a numeric vector, in that each character of the string is in a separate element of the variable where it is stored. For example, if the variable Z contains the text string 'Cat', the second element of Z contains the character 'a'. Examples of text strings include 'Ignatius J. Reilly', 'Part # 23B', and 'Wednesday'.

Note that punctuation marks and spaces each require a separate element within the variable. For example, `'Part # 23B'` is a ten element character string; elements 5 and 7 are the blank character, and element 6 is the number symbol #. Also, numerals in a text string each require a separate element, and are encoded in binary very differently from the corresponding numeric value; in this example, elements 8 and 9 are the numerals 2 and 3 encoded as characters.

Defining Character Strings

When creating a character string using the assignment operator (=), simply enter the desired text enclosed in single quotes.

```
TS1='American Bison';
TS2='Tuesday, May 11, 868';
TS3='42';
```

Note that `TS3` is a text string, not a numeric value, and consists of two characters, `'4'` and `'2'`.

Including an Apostrophe in a Text String

If you wish to create a text string including an apostrophe, there is a minor problem since MATLAB will think the apostrophe is the end of the text string, not a character to be included in the text string. However, MATLAB also knows that if it is processing a text string and finds TWO single quotes in a row (2 single quotes, NOT one double quotation mark) it knows to place a single apostrophe in the text string, not terminate the string. Thus, if you want to place the text "Willy's brain" into variable `WB`, you would type `WB='Willy''s brain';`

Combining Text Strings

Just like you can combine vectors by concatenation in square brackets, you can combine text strings.

```
W1='Willy''s';
W2='Brain';
TS=[W1,' Weird ',W2];
```

TS contains `Willy's Weird Brain`. Note the spaces in the single quotes before and after `Weird`.

Using Indexing with Character Strings

Character strings can be created or modified using indexing, and indexing can also be used to extract portions of a text string.

```
TS='Willy''s Weird Brain';
Word1=TS(1:7)
```
Word1 contains `Willy's`. Note the apostrophe is ONE character.
```
W2=TS(length(TS)-3:length(TS));
```
Word2 contains `rain`.
```
TS(9:14)=[];
```
TS now contains `Willy's Brain`

TEXT CREATION

We saw earlier that the single quote is used as the transpose operator. Single quotes are also used to define character strings. MATLAB is clever enough to understand the meaning of the quote from context: if a single quote immediately follows a matrix, it is the transpose operator; if two single quotes surround characters, they are being used to indicate that those characters are simply text, not variables or calculations or MATLAB commands.

Functions Used with Character Strings

Some of these functions (e.g., `isletter`) return a logical array. Logical arrays will be covered in a later chapter.

Although many of the standard mathematical operators and functions will actually process character strings without errors, you may not get the results you expect, and you need to be certain that you understand what actually happens before trying to use these with text.

There are, however, numerous functions specifically for manipulating text, several of which are included in Table 16-7 below.

Table 16-7 **Selected Functions Used with Character Strings**

Function	Description
blanks	Create a string of blanks (compare the zeros function used with matrices)
char	Convert ASCII codes into characters
ischar	Determines if a variable is a character string
strcat	Concatenate strings
isletter	Finds alphabetic characters in a string
isspace	Finds space characters in string
isstrprop	Finds elements in string meeting certain criteria, such as lowercase or punctuation
strfind	Find a string within another string
strrep	Replace substring within a string
strcmp	Compare two strings
strcmpi	Compare two strings ignoring case
lower	Convert string to all lowercase
upper	Convert string to all uppercase
num2str	Convert number to string
str2num	Convert string to number

COMPREHENSION CHECK 16-11

(a) Create a variable named MTS containing the text: My hero's hat

(b) Create a variable named B containing 17 blanks followed by your name followed by 691 more blanks.

(c) Assume Avian='A wet bird never flies at night';
Modify Avian so that the word "wet" is replaced with the word "crepuscular" and the word "never" is replaced by "seldom". Note that you should actually modify ONLY the two words in question, not simply type in the complete new sentence.

(d) Assume Ultimate='The answer is 42';
Convert the substring "42" in Ultimate into its corresponding numeric value and place it in UltAns. Your solution should work as long as the "number" at the end of the string is exactly two digits.

16.6 CELL ARRAYS {}

LEARN TO: Define cell arrays in MATLAB's workspace
Perform basic operations on cell arrays
Write expressions using special functions to modify cell arrays

So far in our discussion of data types in MATLAB, all elements stored in a specific variable are the same type of thing: either all numeric or all text. Sometimes, however, it would be convenient to be able to store different types of information in a single variable. MATLAB provides two data types that allow us to store both numeric values and non-numeric values such as text within a single structure stored in a variable. The first of these structures is called a **cell array** or **cell matrix**.

Cell Arrays

The basic idea of the cell array is that each element in a cell array contains another MATLAB data structure. An element in a cell array might be a numeric matrix, whether a scalar, a vector or a matrix; it might be a text string; or it might even be another cell array.

Defining Cell Arrays

Recall that when we define numeric variables, scalars are defined using a simple assignment statement such as $S1 = 57.43$, whereas vectors and matrices are defined by enclosing the multiple values in square brackets, e.g., $M1 = [3.5, -9;13, -4.2]$. Text strings are defined using single quotes: $TS = 'ARF'$. We also saw that we could define individual elements of matrices or text strings using indexing. For example $M2(2,4) = 42$ places the value 42 into the second row, fourth column element of $M2$ and $TS1(5:9) = 'BOOF!'$ places the text string BOOF! into elements 5 through 9 of $TS1$.

Cell arrays are defined in a similar manner, with one key difference: the use of curly braces { }.

● **EXAMPLE 16-32**   What is stored in the variable by following commands?

Assume $M3 = [3, 5; 1 9]$ and $TS3 = 'GRRR'$
$CA1 = \{TS3, 42, M3, 'REOWR'\}$
$CA1$ *now contains four elements in a single row:*
$CA1\{1\}$ *The text string* GRRR
$CA1\{2\}$ *The number* 42
$CA1\{3\}$ *A 2x2 numeric matrix with the same elements as* M3
$CA1\{4\}$ *The text string* REOWR
  Note that the individual elements are different types of things: a scalar, a matrix, and two text strings.
  Note the use of curly braces to index into the cell array.

We could also use indexing to define one or more elements of a cell array separately instead of all at once. The cell array CA1 above could also be created with the following code:

```
CA1(1) = {'GRRR'}; % braces tell MATLAB CA1 is a cell array
CA1(2:2:4) = {42,'REOWR'}; % CA1(3) will be created empty
CA1(3) = {[3,5;1,9]}; % Go back to specify CA1(3)
```

Note that the cell array indices are in parentheses, whereas the contents to be placed in the indexed values are in curly braces. This might be confusing at first since we used parentheses here and referred to using curly braces to indexing cell arrays above. We will clarify the difference in the use of the two notations in the next section.

COMPREHENSION CHECK 16-12

(a) Create a cell array named Cabinet with one row and three columns. The first cell should contain the number 77, the second cell should contain the text "Dr. Caligari", and the third cell should contain a 25 × 100 matrix filled with ones.

(b) Create a 2 × 2 cell array named Cyls containing the following:
   a. First row: "Diameter", "Length"
   b. Second row: 1.5, a column vector containing all integers from 1 to 25

Extracting Data from Cell Arrays

When we use indexing with parentheses to get information out of a numeric matrix, the result is another numeric matrix. If M4=[1 3 5;6 8 0] and we create another variable as M5=M4(:,2:3), then M5 is a 2 × 2 numeric matrix containing [3 5; 8 0].

When we use indexing with parentheses to get information out of a text string, the result is another text string. If TS4='Dogs vs Cats' and we create another variable as TS5=TS4(4:9), then TS5 is a text string containing s vs C.

In general, when we access some of the elements of a variable using index values in **parentheses**, the result is the same **variable type** as the original variable.

But what about cell arrays, since they often contain different variable types in the various elements?

This is perhaps best illustrated live at the computer, so we suggest that you fire up MATLAB and type the following simple commands in the Command Window.

First, we will set up three variables. Do not include a semicolon so each echoes to the screen.

Type:

```
S6=777  % define a scalar
```

The following appears on the screen:

```
S6=
   777
```

Next, type:

```
M6=[9 7 8; 3 5 4]  % define a 2 × 3 matrix
```

The following appears on the screen:

```
M6=
   9   7   8
   3   5   4
```

Finally, type:

```
TS6='apricot'   % Define a text string
```

The following appears on the screen:

```
TS6  =
apricot
```

As you will see in a moment, it is important that you note exactly how these values are echoed to the screen.

Next, we will create a cell array containing the scalar, the matrix, and the text string created above. Add a semicolon to suppress the output in this case, however.

```
CA6={S6,M6,TS6};   % Create cell array with three elements
```

If you look at CA6 in the workspace, it will say <1×3 cell>.

Now we will attempt to extract each of these three elements from the cell array using parentheses to get the original contents back. First, extract the scalar in element 1.

```
CA7=CA6(1)   % Extract first element
```

Echoed to the screen is

```
CA7 =
    [777]
```

Comparing this to the echoed value from the original scalar S6 above, we see there is a slight difference: there are brackets around the value!

Now do the same with the matrix in the second element of the cell array.

```
CA8=CA6(2)   % Extract second element
```

Echoed to the screen is

```
CA8 =
    [2×3 double]
```

This is even stranger. The original matrix echoed the individual values to the screen, but when we attempted to extract it from the cell array, it just gave us the matrix dimensions in brackets.

Finally, extract the third element, the text string.

```
CA9=CA6(3)   % Extract third element
```

The echo to the screen is

```
CA9=
    'apricot'
```

Comparing this to the echo of the original text string, we see that the text is enclosed in single quotes, whereas in the original echo of TS6, there were no quotes.

Obviously something is different here, and in fact, if you were to try to use these extracted values functions or computations that expected a scalar, a matrix, or a text string respectively, you would get an error message. For example, type

```
SUM=CA7+111
```

This seems perfectly reasonable, and should give an answer of 888. However, you get the error message

```
Undefined function 'plus' for input arguments of type 'cell'.
```

The point is that when parentheses are used to extract values from a numeric matrix, the result is a numeric matrix, from a text string the result is a text string, and **values extracted from a cell array are a cell array**, thus they cannot be used where MATLAB is expecting numbers or text.

Obviously there must be a way to overcome this problem or cell arrays would be extremely limited in their utility. The answer is embodied in the well-known alliterative mnemonic: **Curly for Contents**.

With the cell array CA6 still in your workspace, try extracting the **contents** using curly braces instead of parentheses:

Type:

```
S7=CA6{1}  % Extract contents first element
```

Echo:

```
S7 =
    777
```

Type:

```
M7=CA6{2}  % Extract contents second element
```

Echo:

```
M7 =
     9     7     8
     3     5     4
```

Type:

```
TS7=CA6{3}  % Extract contents third element
```

Echo:

```
TS7 =
apricot
```

Note that the echoes to the screen are exactly the same as when we originally defined them. You may now use S7, M7, and TS7 anywhere you can use a scalar, a matrix, or a text string respectively.

We can also extract parts of these variables using indexing, just like we could with the original variables.

For example:

```
V=M7(2,3) places the value 4 into V
T=TS7(5:7) places the text string cot into T
```

What if we wanted to place the second column of the second element of the cell array CA6 into CV1?

We could use

```
CV1=CA6{2};
CV1=CV1(:,2);
```

or we can use a shortcut method, directly indexing into the extracted matrix:

```
CV1=CA6{2}(:,2);
```

Although all of the above examples have used a cell array with a single row thus we used a single index value in the curly braces, cell arrays can have 2 dimensions thus two index values.

Now let us look at a slightly more complicated example. Again it is recommended that you type this in on the computer.

We will set up a cell array CA12 containing two other cell arrays.

```
CA10={[8 6 4;3 7 0],'Occurrence'};
CA11={[2 3 4;7 6 5],'Then'};
CA12={CA10,CA11};
```

What if we wanted to add the two 2×3 matrices found in the two cell arrays of CA12? Try

```
Result=CA12{1}(1) + CA12{2}(1);
```

You might think that this will pull out the first elements of each of the two cell arrays in CA12 (the two 2×3 matrices), but instead, we get the error

Undefined function 'plus' for input arguments of type 'cell'.

The reason is that since CA12{1} refers to CA10, which is itself a cell array, when we use parentheses to index, we get another cell array, NOT the original matrix. In this case we have to extract the contents of the contents, so both indices must have curly braces.

```
Result=CA12{1}{1} + CA12{2}{1};
```

This will give us the correct sum of the two matrices.

A similar situation exists if we wanted to extract part of the text strings. To get characters 2, 3, and 4 from Then, we would use

```
T=CA12{2}{2}(2:4);
```

T now contains hen.

- The first {2} pulls out the contents of the second element in CA12: a cell array.
- The second {2} pulls out the contents of the second element of that inner cell array: Then.
- The final (2:4) pulls the 2nd through 4th elements from that text string, placing hen into T.

COMPREHENSION CHECK 16-13

Assume a cell array named CA has three cells in a single row.

- The first cell contains a name in the format X.Y.Family. For example: M.V.Smith.
- The second cell contains a 2×3 matrix. For example: [1 3 5;9 6 3]
- The third cell contains a 3×2 matrix. For example: [4 7;−2 −6;0 1]

(a) Extract the family name (Smith in the example above) from the first cell and place it in column one of a newly created second row of CA. Your solution should work for family names of any length. Note that the first six characters of the name in the first cell will always be the two initials, each followed by a dot and a space.

    (b) Multiply the matrix in the second cell of row 1 by the matrix in the third cell of row 1 and place the result in the second row, second column of CA.

    (c) Calculate the element-wise product of the matrix in row 1, column 2 by the transpose of the matrix in row 1, column 3. Place the result in the third column of the second row of CA.

Functions Used with Cell Arrays

Some helpful functions for cell arrays are listed in Table 16-8. You can obtain more information by typing either `help` or `doc` followed by the function name.

Table 16-8 **Selected Functions Used with Cell Arrays**

Function	Description
iscell	Determines if a variable is a cell array
cell	Create a cell array filled with empty matrices
num2cell	Converts a numeric matrix into a cell array
mat2cell	Split matrix into sub-matrices and store as cell array
cell2mat	Convert cell array to matrix. All cells must be same type: numeric or text
cellfun	Apply a function to a cell array
celldisp	Display contents of cell array in command window

● **EXAMPLE 16-33**

What is stored in the variable by following commands?

$$M1 = \begin{bmatrix} 1 & 4 & -8 & 0 \\ 9 & 3 & 12 & 6 \\ 0 & 1 & -5 & 2 \end{bmatrix}$$

```
T1 = 'Zero'
S1 = 42
CA1 = {M1,T1,S1}

IC1 = iscell(CA1);
```
IC1 *contains 1 (true) since the variable* CA1 *is a cell array*
```
IC2 = iscell(M1);
```
IC1 *contains 0 (false) since the variable* M1 *is a matrix, not a cell array*
```
CA2 = cell(4);
```
CA2 *is a 4 × 4 cell array of empty matrices*
```
CA3 = cell(2,5);
```
CA3 *is a 2 × 5 cell array of empty matrices*
```
CA4 = mat2cell(M1, [2 1], [3 1])
```

iscell returns a logical variable. Logical variables will be covered in a later chapter.

Unsuppressed, the following appears on screen

```
CA4 =
    [2×3 double]        [2×1 double]
    [1×3 double]        [          2]
```

The command mat2cell will split the matrix M1 *into the following combinations, starting in the upper, left corner of the matrix:*

$$\begin{bmatrix} 1 & 4 & -8 \\ 9 & 3 & 12 \end{bmatrix}$$

$$\begin{bmatrix} 0 \\ 6 \end{bmatrix}$$

$$\begin{bmatrix} 0 & 1 & 5 \end{bmatrix}$$

$$\begin{bmatrix} 2 \end{bmatrix}$$

```
celldisp(CA4)
```

The following appears on screen

```
CA4{1,1} =
       1      4     -8
       9      3     12
CA4{2,1} =
       0      1     -5
CA4{1,2} =
       0
       6
CA4{2,2} =
       2
```

```
[rows,cols]=cellfun(@size,CA4)
```

The following appears on screen

```
rows =
       2      2
       1      1
cols =
       3      1
       3      1
```

NOTE: This gives us the sizes of the four matrices in CA4.

CA4{1,1} *is 2 × 1*
CA4{1,2} *is 2 × 1*
CA4{2,1} *is 1 × 3*
CA4{2,2} *is 1 × 1*

cellfun uses a handle (sort of like a pointer) to the function desired. The @ symbol before the function name creates the appropriate handle, telling MATLAB to use that function on the cell array.

COMPREHENSION CHECK 16-14

NOTE: You may want to use help or doc to investigate the operation of some of the functions in Table 16-7 to solve these problems.

(a) Convert an M × N matrix BigMat to an M × N cell array BigCell consisting of the scalar values from each corresponding element of BigMat.

Example: If BigMat is defined by BigMat = [2 6;5 8], your code would produce the same cell array as BigCell = {[2] [6];[5] [8]}. Your solution must, of course, work for any matrix, whether or not you know its contents.

(b) Assume a cell array VCell contains only numeric vectors. Create a matrix VCellMax with the same dimensions as the cell array containing the maximum value of each vector in the corresponding location of the cell array.

Example:
If VCell = {[1 5 2] [−3 −5 −6 −1]}, then VCellMax = [5 −1]

16.7   STRUCTURE ARRAYS 🔲

As we saw in the previous section, we can use cell arrays to store different types of things in one variable: matrices, text, other cell arrays, etc. To access the different elements of a cell array, we use standard indexing, usually with curly braces, to extract the content of a specific cell or cells.

Sometimes it would be convenient if we could refer to different cells or groups of cell using a descriptive name instead of a number. We could assign specific index values to named variables and use these variable names instead of the numbers they hold to access elements from a cell array. However, there is a more direct method of using names to access specific elements within a mixed-content variable. Such a variable is called a **structure array,** and it inherently uses names instead of numbers to access different parts of the structure.

Structure Arrays

A structure array consists of one or more **structures**, each containing the same **fields**. Each field contains a value or values relating to a specific aspect of the structure.

As an example, we might have a structure array named MetalData containing information about metals. MetalData might contain the fields Type (Steel, Brass, Zinc, etc.), SpecificGravity, ThermalConductivity, and Resistivity.

Defining Structure Arrays

First, a quick review of defining the other data types we have considered.

When defining numeric variables, scalars are defined using a simple assignment statement such as S1=−699, whereas vectors and matrices are defined by enclosing the multiple values in square brackets, such as M1=[3.5, −9; 13,−4.2]. Indexing can be used to define individual elements or groups of elements. For example, M2(4,3:5)=[9 6 3] places the three values 9, 6, and 3 into the third, fourth, and fifth columns of the fourth row of M2.

Text strings are defined using single quotes: TS1='Neon'. Individual elements or substrings of text variables can be defined using indexing. For example TS2(6:10)= 'Argon' places the text string Argon into elements 6 through 10 of TS2.

Cell arrays are defined in a similar manner, except curly braces are used to enclose the elements composing the cell array. These elements might themselves be scalars, matrices (using brackets), text (using single quotes), or even other cell arrays.

Structure arrays, on the other hand, use a somewhat different scheme, perhaps best explained by way of an example. Type the following lines into the command window:

```
MetalData.Type='Zinc';
MetalData.SpecGrav=7.14;
MetalData.ThermCond=116;
MetalData.Resistivity=59E-9;
```

It may appear that these variables violate the naming rules (no periods allowed), but in the case of structure arrays, the period is not part of a name, but a separator between two names: the structure name and the field name.

Now the structure array `MetalData` contains a single structure comprising 4 fields. We can add another similar structure to the `MetalData` structure array as follows:

```
MetalData(2).Type='Copper';
MetalData(2).SpecGrav=8.96;
MetalData(2).ThermCond=401;
MetalData(2).Resistivity=16.78E-9;
```

Now `MetalData` is a 1×2 structure array containing information about the two metals, tin and copper.

We can add fields to the two structures within the MetalData in a similar manner.

We can create multiple rows in a structure array by using double index notation, such as `MetalData(2,1)`.

```
MetalData(1).Symbol='Zn';
MetalData(1).Isotopes=[66 67 68];
MetalData(2).Symbol='Cu';
MetalData(2).Isotopes=[63 65];
```

Note that we had to use an index value of 1 to add fields to the first structure (Zinc), since there are now two structures in `MetalData`. When we first defined this single structure (for Zinc) there was no ambiguity, so an index was not needed, although it could have been used.

NOTE: We have used the field `Isotopes` to list only the stable isotopes. There are other isotopes of these metals with varying half-lives.

If we type `MetalData` in the command window, it will print the following to the screen:

```
MetalData =
1×2 struct array with fields:
    Type
    SpecGrav
    ThermCond
    Resistivity
    Symbol
    Isotopes
```

This tells us how many structures there are in `MetalData` and how they are organized (one row and two columns) as well as the names of the fields within the structures.

If we wish to know the contents of one of the structures within `MetalData`, we can type `MetalData(N)`, where N is the number of the structure for which we wish to see the contents. For example, typing `MetalData(2)` prints the following to the screen:

```
        Type:  'Copper'
    SpecGrav:  8.9600
   ThermCond:  401
 Resistivity:  1.6780e-08
      Symbol:  'Cu'
    Isotopes:  [63    65]
```

COMPREHENSION CHECK 16-15

Create a structure array named `Resistors` containing data on three resistors, including fields for Value, Power, Composition, and Tolerance. The three resistors should have the following specifications (enter numeric values only for Value, Power, and Tolerance, not the units):

- 100,000 ohms, ¼ watt, Metal Film, 0.1%
- 2,200,000 ohms, ½ watt, Carbon, 5%
- 15 ohms, 50 watts, Wire Wound, 10%

Extracting Data from Structure Arrays

Accessing the contents of a structure array is very straightforward. We do not have to worry about "contents" as we did with cell arrays since each field has its own data type.

Using the `MetalData` example above, if we wanted the type of the first metal, we would type

```
MetalData(1).Type
```

This returns the text string `Zinc`.

If we wanted the first two characters of the type of metal number 1, we would type

```
MetalData(1).Type(1:2)
```

This returns the text string `Zi`.

We can use calculations and functions directly with values extracted from structure arrays.

```
min(MetalData.Resistivity)
```

finds the minimum resistivity of all of the metals `MetalData`.

```
max(MetalData(1).Isotopes)
```

This returns 68, the mass number (number of protons and neutrons) of the heaviest stable isotope of the first metal, Zinc.

COMPREHENSION CHECK 16-16

Use the data stored in `MetalData` above to answer the following questions:

(a) Write a single line of code that will determine the mass in kilograms of one cubic meter of zinc and place the result in `MZn`.

(b) Assume the number of one of the structures in `MetalData` is stored in a variable `MNum`. Write a single line of code that will place the mass number of the lightest isotope of the corresponding metal in the variable `LtIso`.

Functions Used with Structure Arrays

Table 16-9 lists several functions specifically designed to use with structure arrays.

Table 16-9 Selected Functions Used with Structure Arrays

Function	Description
isstruct	Determines if a variable is a structure array
isfield	Determines if a name is a field within a specific structure
struct	Another way to create structures
orderfields	Sorts field names in specified order
setfield	Another way to specify the content of fields
rmfield	Remove a field from a structure array
cell2struct	Convert cell array to structure array
struct2cell	Convert structure array to cell array

● EXAMPLE 16-34

isfield returns a logical variable. Logical variables will be covered in a later chapter.

What is stored in the variable by following commands?

Assume `MetalData` has already been defined as above.

```
IsF1=isfield (MetalData, 'Density');
```
`IsF1` *contains 0 (false), since density is not a field defined in* `MetalData`

```
IsF2=isfield (MetalData, 'SpecGrav');
```
`IsF2` *contains 1 (true), since specific gravity is not a field defined in* `MetalData`

To create a structure array named `MetalSort` with the same data but with the field names sorted in alphabetical order,

```
MetalSort = orderfields(MetalData);
```

If you now type **MetalSort** in the command window, the following will appear:

```
1×2 struct array with fields:
        Isotopes
        Resistivity
        SpecGrav
        Symbol
        ThermCond
        Type
```

Note that this is an ASCII sort. In ASCII, capital letters have a "lower" value than lowercase values. If the field containing the element symbol had been lowercase – "symbol" – it would have appeared last in the list.

Note that the original structure array `MetalData` remains unchanged. A sorted copy was created and placed in `MetalSort`. Fields do not have to be sorted in ASCII order; other types of sorts, including custom sorts, are possible.

16.8 SAVING AND RESTORING VARIABLES

For a variety of reasons, we sometimes would like to be able to save all or some of the variables in the workspace and then restore them later. For example, we might wish to archive results, we might want to use the same data in another program, or we might need to share a set of variables with colleagues. Some of the online files associated with this text were created using the following method.

Variables can also be saved as .txt files in ASCII format, but this is beyond the scope of this textbook. See the MATLAB documentation files for more information.

To save all variables in the workspace, type

save ('filename')

In this case, the filename must have an extension of .mat on the end. If you do not include .mat, MATLAB will add it for you.

As an example, the command

```
save('TestVar.mat')
```

will save all of the variables currently in the workspace in a file named `TestVar.mat` placed in the current directory.

To place a set of stored variables into the workspace, type

load ('filename')

Again, the filename must have an extension of .mat on the end. For example,

```
load('TestVar.mat')
```

will place all of the variables stored in `TestVar.mat` into the current directory.

To save only selected variables in a .mat file, use the format

save ('filename', 'Var1', 'Var2', . . .)

As an example:

```
save('TV2.mat','Dens','Temp','Vol')
```

will store the three workspace variables `Dens`, `Temp`, and `Vol` in the file `TV2.mat`.

You can also load only selected variables from a .mat file. The format is similar to the save format. For example, assume `TV2.mat` was created as in the previous example.

```
load('TV2.mat','Dens','Vol')
```

will place the two variables `Dens` and `Vol` from the file `TV2.mat` into the workspace.

The commands `save` and `load` also support "wild card" variable names using the asterisk (*) symbol.

For example,

```
save('WC1.mat','Q*')
```

will save all workspace variables beginning with Q in the file `WC1.mat`.

```
load('WC2.mat','*3')
```

will load all variables stored in the file `WC2.mat` that end with 3.

```
save('WC3.mat','*_*')
```

will save all workspace variables containing an underscore character in the file `WC3.mat`.

WARNING

If your workspace already has variables with the same names as any of the variables being loaded, they will be replaced, thus losing the contents in those variables prior to the load. No warning will be generated.

COMPREHENSION CHECK 16-17

(a) Store all workspace variables in the file `TempData.mat`.
(b) Load all variables stored in `PressData` into the workspace.
(c) Save the workspace variables `Pr1`, `Pr2`, and `Tmp3` in the file `PTData.mat`.
(d) Store all variables whose names end with "a1" in the file `a1Var.mat`.
(e) Load all variables stored in `VelData` whose names contain "XS" into the workspace.

In-Class Activities

ICA 16-1

Which of the following are not valid MATLAB variable names? Circle all that apply. For those that are invalid, state why.

(a) `BigNum.docx`
(b) `Two_Nums`
(c) `This is a very long MATLAB variable name`
(d) `2BRO2B`
(e) `Is_This_Valid?`
(f) `Var = V + 1;`
(g) `Mult2`
(h) `exp`
(i) `GClefSign`
(j) `AbcDEFGHijKLmnopqrstuvWXyz_Has_Lots_of_Characters`
(k) `DoNotPassGo_DoNotCollect$200`

ICA 16-2

Do the following scripted exercise. The **>>** prompt indicates what you should type into the MATLAB Command Window. Note that some of these commands may result in error messages.

`>> m=[10,20]*30`	% Multiply a row vector containing 10 and 20 by 30, store in variable m
`>> m1=[10;20]*30`	% Multiply a column vector containing 10 and 20 by 30, store in variable m1
`>> n=m+1`	% Add 1 to every element in variable m, store in variable n
`>> r=m+n`	% Add row vector in variable m to column vector in variable n, store in r. Note that even though this is dimensionally inconsistent, this works in MATLAB because it will allow any vectors (row or column) to be added together as long as they contain the same number of elements
`>> v=[2:2:6]`	% Create a row vector of numbers between 2 and 6, increasing by 2, store in v
`>> u=[1:0.5:3]`	% Create a row vector of numbers between 1 and 3, increasing by 0.5, store in u
`>> j=u+v`	% Add vector v to vector u Why will this not work?
`>> a=sin(u)`	% Take the sine of each element in the vector u
`>> b=sqrt(u)`	% Take the square root of each element in the vector u
`>> c=u^2`	% Square vector u Why will this not work?
`>> d=u.^2`	% Square each element of vector u
`>> e=[10,20;30,40]`	% Create a matrix of numbers 10 and 20 in the first row, 30 and 40 in the second row, store in the variable e
`>> f=[1,2,3;4,5]`	% Create a matrix of numbers 1, 2, and 3 in the first row, 4 and 5 in the second row, store in the variable f. Why will this not work?

ICA 16-3

Writing the MATLAB code necessary to create the following variables (parts (a)—(d)) or calculate the following matrix computations (parts (e)—(m)). If a calculation is not possible, explain why. You may assume that the variables created in parts (a) through (d) are available for the remaining computations in parts (e) through (m). For parts (e)—(m) that is possible, determine the expected result of each computation by hand.

(a) Save matrix $\begin{bmatrix} 3 & 8 \\ 5 & 7 \end{bmatrix}$ in variable W

(b) Save matrix $\begin{bmatrix} 4 & 8 & 1 \\ 5 & 1 & 6 \end{bmatrix}$ in variable X

(c) Save matrix $\begin{bmatrix} 3 \\ 5 \end{bmatrix}$ in variable Y

(d) Save matrix $\begin{bmatrix} 4 & 2 \\ 2 & 9 \end{bmatrix}$ in variable Z

(e) Add W + Z, save in variable A

(f) Subtract Y − Z, save in variable B

(g) Multiply W * X, save in variable C

(h) Multiply X * Z save in variable D

(i) Transpose X, save in variable E

(j) Multiply W * Z term-by-term, save in variable F

(k) Square Z, save in variable G

(l) Square X, save in variable H

(m) Add 20 to each element in X, save in variable I

ICA 16-4

Assuming t = [9 10;11 12] and v = [2 4;6 8;10 12] are currently stored in MATLAB's workspace, what is the output of each of the following statements? If an error will occur, explain why.

(a) A = t(1,1) + v(1,1)
(b) B = t[1,1] + v[1,1]
(c) C = t * v
(d) D = v * t
(e) E = v(:,2) + t(:,2)
(f) F = v(2,:) + t(2,:)
(g) G = t(1,1) * v(3,:)
(h) H = t(1,:) * v(1,:)
(i) J = t(1,:) .* v(1,:)

ICA 16-5

For each of the following problems, write a single MATLAB statement that will accomplish the stated purpose.

(a) Assume four scalars S1, S2, S3, and S4 have already been defined. Place the smallest of these four values into SmallS.

(b) Assume that a vector V1 has already been defined. Place the largest value in V1 into BigVal.

(c) Assume three vectors Va, Vb, and Vc have already been defined. Find the length of the vector with the most elements and place the result in MaxL.

(d) Create a 500-element column vector P17M11 containing two hundred number seventeens followed by three hundred number negative elevens.

(e) Create a vector UV that contains one of each value that is stored in another vector V, eliminating duplicates. Example: V = [1 3 5 3 4 1]; UV = [1 3 4 5]

(f) Create a vector r100 that contains 100 random values between −5 and 5.

ICA 16-6

For each of the following problems, write a single MATLAB statement that will accomplish the stated purpose.

(a) Create a 150 × 150 matrix N9999 that contains all zeros except for the major diagonal (upper left to lower right). All elements on the major diagonal should contain the value −9999.

(b) Create a 1200 × 1200 matrix p75 that contains all zeros except for the minor diagonal (lower left to upper right). All elements on the minor diagonal should contain the value 75.

(c) Place the number of rows of matrix Ma into MaRows and the number of columns of matrix Ma into MaCols.

(d) Assume matrix Mx contains a single non-zero value. Place the row number containing this non-zero value into NZR and the column value in NZC.

(e) Assume matrix Mz has already been defined. Place the row numbers of all elements in Mz that are negative into vector MzRN and the corresponding column numbers into MzCN.

(f) Assume that matrix MS has already been defined. Place the elements on the major diagonal into row vector MSD.

ICA 16-7

For each of the following problems, write a single MATLAB statement that will accomplish the stated purpose. Assume a text string TS1 has already been defined.

(a) Create a vector LetLoc with the same number of elements as TS1. For each element of TS1 that is alphabetic, the corresponding element of LetLoc should equal 1. All other elements of LetLoc should be 0. Example: TS1='%@3Gb6' returns LetLoc=[0 0 0 1 1 0]

(b) Create a vector Alphas that has the numeric positions of all alphabetic characters in TS1. Example: TS1='%@3Gb6' returns Alphas=[4 5]

(c) Place the numeric index of the first alphabetic character in TS1 into Alpha1. Example: TS1='%@3Gb6' returns Alpha1=4

(d) Place the last alphabetic character in TS1 into LastLetter. Example: TS1='%@3Gb6' LastLetter=b

(e) Find all occurrences of the string @3G in string TS1 and place the locations of the first character of each such substring (@) into Str3G. Example: TS1='%@3Gb6kl@3G9@33G' returns Str3G=[2 9]

ICA 16-8

Assume a structure array SA1 has already been defined.

    For each of the following problems, write a single MATLAB statement that will accomplish the stated purpose. You may use variables created in any problem to help solve problems farther down the list.

(a) Place the number of characters in the text string into LenTex.
(b) Place the number of alphabetic characters in the text string into NumChar.
(c) Place the number of non-alphabetic characters in the text string into NumNon.
(d) Place the number of values in the vector into LenVec.
(e) Place the sum of all elements in the vector except the last two into SumM2.
(f) Place the number of rows of the matrix into MR and the number of columns of the matrix into MC.
(g) Create a new 2 × 2 cell array CA1SubM from the matrix that contains the same contents as the matrix in CA1 but divided into four sections:
- A scalar equal to the top left element from CA1
- A row vector equal to the remainder of the first row
- A column vector equal to the remainder of the first column
- A matrix with all remaining elements.

ICA 16-9

You wish to design a structure array to maintain a list of small hardware needed for a variety of different products. The structure should include the following information:

- An alphanumeric product code for each product being produced
- For each product, the general types of hardware needed, such as bolt, screw, washer, nut, etc.
- For each specific hardware type, the specifications, including (as appropriate) length, diameter, material, subtype, thread type, etc. Note that there may be more than one specification for a given type of hardware, such as bolts with two different lengths and diameters.
- For each specific hardware item, the quantity required for the product in question.

Create a structure array containing the parts lists for the two products below.

Product 1: Product code WP42

- 4 – steel hex-head bolts, 3/4 inch long, 1/8 inch diameter
- 8 – steel nuts 1/8 inch diameter

Product 2: Product code ES65

- 16 – steel torx-head bolts, 1 inch long, 5/16 inch diameter
- 8 – steel lock washers 5/16 inch diameter
- 16 – steel nuts 5/16 inch diameter

Chapter 16 REVIEW QUESTIONS

1. Assume four row vectors named `Prod10`, `Prod11`, `Prod12`, and `Prod13` contain data on production of various electronic devices at your company during the four years 2010, 2011, 2012, and 2013, respectively. The corresponding elements in each represent the number of a specific part manufactured during that year. For example, the first element might contain the number of 2N3904 transistors produced during each year, whereas the fifth column might contain the number of IC555 timer chips produced. You may assume all four vectors contain the same number of elements, corresponding to the same produced items.

   Write a single line of code to answer each of the following questions. You may use the results of any question to answer subsequent questions if desired. Note that your solutions should work regardless of the number of elements in the four vectors.

   (a) Create a new vector `TotalProd` that contains the total number of each item produced during the four-year period. Note that `TotalProd` will have the same number of elements as the original four vectors.

   (b) Create a new vector `AvgProd` that contains the average number produced per year of each item during the four-year period. Note that `AvgProd` will have the same number of elements as the original four vectors.

   (c) Create a four element column vector `YearProd` that contains the total number of all units produced during each year. 2010 production should be in the first (top) element.

   (d) Determine the maximum number of any type of device produced during each year and place the results in a four element column vector `MaxProd`.

   (e) Determine the maximum number of any device produced during any year and place the result in the scalar `OverallMax`.

   (f) If your company makes a profit of one-fifth of one cent on each device produced, regardless of type, determine the total profit made during this four year period and place the result in `Profit`. Your result should be in dollars.

2. Assume a matrix named `Prod` contains data on production of various electronic devices at your company during several years. Each row of the matrix contains production data for a single year. The first element in each row contains the year, e.g., 2007 or 10012. The remaining elements in each represent the number of a specific part manufactured during that year. For example, the second element might contain the number of 2N3904 transistors produced during each year, whereas the fifth column might contain the number of IC555 timer chips produced. You may assume that corresponding elements in each row contain production numbers for the same type of device.

   Write a single line of code to answer each of the following questions. You may use the results of any question to answer subsequent questions if desired.

   A sample `Prod` matrix is provided online. Note that your solution must work for any properly formatted matrix `Prod`.

   (a) Create a row vector `TotalProd` that contains the total number of years in the first element and the total number of each item produced during all listed years in the remaining elements. Note that `TotalProd` will have the same number of elements as the number of columns in the `Prod` matrix.

   (b) Create a row vector `AvgProd` that contains the total number of years in the first element and the average number of each item produced during all listed years in the remaining elements. Note that `TotalProd` will have the same number of elements as the number of columns in the `Prod` matrix.

   (c) Create a two-column matrix `YearProd`. The first column should contain the same years as those in the first column of `Prod`, and the second column should contain the total number of all units produced during each year.

(d) Create a two-column matrix `MaxProd`. Determine the maximum number of any type of device produced during each year and place the results in the second column of the corresponding row in `MaxProd`.

(e) Determine the maximum number of any device produced during any year and place the result in the scalar `OverallMax`.

(f) If your company makes a profit of one-fifth of one cent on each device produced, regardless of type, determine the total profit made during all listed years and place the result in `Profit`. Your result should be in dollars.

(g) The solution to this problem is considerably more complicated than the corresponding problem using vectors (Review Question 1). What is the major advantage gained by this extra complexity?

MATLAB
examples

3. Assume that a cell array `PrCA` already exists, and contains a single item: the matrix `Prod` from Review Question 2. None of the other results required by that problem have been determined, however.

Augment `PrCA` so that it contains the original matrix `Prod` as well as all of the results required by Review Question 2. You may choose any organization of the cell array that seems logical to you. The information stored in each variable in Review Question 2 should be added to the cell array with a single line of code. You may NOT simply use the `struct2cell` function with the result from Review Question 4.

A sample `PrCA` cell matrix is provided online. Note that your solution must work for any properly formatted initial matrix in `PrCA`.

The sample matrix provided has data for five different devices (columns 2 through 6). Add a five element cell array to `PrCA` that contains the following part designations, corresponding to the five devices listed: `2N3904, 2N3906, 2N2222, IC555, IC741`. This should be the first element (first row, first column) of `PrCA`, thus the other entries will be shifted to other locations. Note that this is specific to the sample matrix provided. Other matrices would, of course, have different part designations.

MATLAB
examples

4. Assume that the matrix `Prod` from Review Question 2 already exists, but none of the other results required by that problem have been determined.

Create a single structure array named `PrStr` that contains the original matrix `Prod` as well as all of the results required by that problem. You may choose any organization of the structure array that seems logical to you as well as any field names that seem reasonable to you. You may NOT simply use the `cell2struct` function with the result from Review Question 3.

The sample matrix provided has data for five different devices (columns 2 through 6). Add a five element cell array to `PrStr` that contains the following part designations, corresponding to the five devices listed: `2N3904, 2N3906, 2N2222, IC555, IC741`. You may choose any field name you deem appropriate. Note that this is specific to the sample matrix provided. Other matrices would, of course, have different part designations.

5. (a) Create a cell array named `Cylinder` containing one row with the following elements:
   - The text string Height(cm)   The value 12
   - The text string Diameter(cm)   The value 1.5
   - The text string Specific Gravity The value 3.5

(b) Create a cell array named `Pipe` containing the following elements:
   - The text string Height(cm)   The value 20
   - The text string OD/ID(cm)   A row vector containing the values 2.5 and 2.2

(c) Create a 2 × 3 cell array named `Parts` containing the following elements:
   - The first row should contain the text string "Quantity", the value 100 and the cell array `Cylinder`
   - The second row should contain the text string "Quantity", the value 15 and the cell array `Pipe`

(d) Using the `Parts` cell array, create the following variables. Note that your code should work if the contents of `Parts` changes—DO NOT hard code any values.

- `NumCyl`, containing the number of cylinders (1st row, 2nd column of `Parts`)
- `VolCyl`, containing the volume (cm^3) of one cylinder ($V = \pi r^2 H$), where the diameter is in the 4th element of the cell array in the 1st row, 3rd column of `Parts` and Height is in the 2nd element of that same cell array in `Parts`.
- `MassCyl`, containing the mass in grams of one cylinder. (You should be able to figure out where the specific gravity is by now.)
- `NumPipe`, containing the number of pipes (2nd row, 2nd column of `Parts`)
- `IVolPipe`, containing the internal volume (cm^3) of one cylinder ($V = \pi r^2 H$). You will have to determine where the values needed are stored using the explanations for `NumCyl` and `VolCyl` as a guide. Note that OD/ID means Outside Diameter/ Inside Diameter.
- Add two columns to the cell array `Parts`. The 4th column of `Parts` should contain the text Total Mass(g) in the 1st row and Total Volume(cm^3) in the 2nd row. The 5th column of `Parts` should contain the corresponding TOTAL mass of all of the cylinders and the TOTAL internal volume of all of the pipes.

6. Refer to the specifications for Review Question 16-5.

Create a structure array to contain the same information given in parts (a) through (c) in Review Question 16-5. Note that it may be appropriate to incorporate the text values into the structure array as field names instead of data. You may use any organizational structure and field names that seem logical to you—there are various possibilities.

Add entries to the structure array corresponding to the calculated volumes and masses listed in part (d) of Review Question 16-5. Again, you may use any organizational structure or field names that seem logical to you.

CHAPTER 17
PROGRAMS AND FUNCTIONS

Programming is the process of expressing an algorithm in a language that a computer can interpret. To correctly automate a process on a computer, a programmer must be able to correctly speak the language both grammatically and semantically. In this text, we communicate with a computer by using the MATLAB programming language. In the previous sections, the idea of creating algorithms to represent a process and creating variables in a programming language like MATLAB has been established, so this section intends to combine the two ideas to create programs and functions.

17.1 PROGRAMS

LEARN TO: Understand how to navigate the MATLAB interface
Remember the naming rules for programs, functions, and variables
Create, execute, and modify programs in MATLAB

Certain principles apply to programming, regardless of what language is being used. Entire textbooks have been written on this subject, but a few important concepts are addressed here.

Notes About Programming in General

- **Programming style:** Just like technical reports should follow a particular format to ensure they can be understood by someone reading them, all programs should have a few common elements of programming style, particularly the inclusion of comments that help identify the source of the program and what it does. For any program, a proper header should be written describing the scope of the problem, including a problem statement and definition of all input and output variables used in the program. Properly commenting the source code is also critical for ensuring that someone else can follow your work on the program.
  As a rule of thumb, for each rectangle and diamond in a flowchart, there should be a few comments in the source code where that action occurs.

- **Program testing:** When you write a program, testing it is a critical step in making sure that it does what you expect. Lots of things can go wrong.
  - *Syntax errors:* These violate the spelling and grammar rules of the programming language. Compilers (programs that interpret your computer program) generally identify their location and nature.

- *Runtime errors*: These occur when an inappropriate expression is evaluated during program execution. Such errors may occur only under certain circumstances. Examples of runtime errors are division by zero, the logarithm of zero, or the wrong kind of input, such as a user's entering letters when numbers are expected. Computer programs should anticipate runtime errors and alert users to the error (rather than having the program unexpectedly terminate).
- *Formula coding errors*: It is not uncommon to enter a formula incorrectly in a form that does not create either a syntax or a runtime error. Evaluating even a few simple calculations by hand and comparing them to the values calculated by the program will usually reveal this kind of error.
- *Formula derivation errors*: This difficult error to discover in programming occurs when the computer is programmed correctly but the programming is based on a faulty conceptualization. This kind of error is difficult to figure out because programmers generally assume that a program that executes without generating any errors is correctly written. This situation underscores the importance of checking a solution strategy before starting to write a computer program.

■ **Keeping track of units:** Some computer programs can be designed to have the user keep track of units as long as they use consistent units. Other computer programs require input data to be in a particular set of units. Regardless of which approach you use, the way in which units are managed must be clear to the user of the program and in the program's comments.

■ **Documentation:** In any programming language, there is usually a special character or pair of characters that tell the program interpreter to ignore everything to the right of the special character to allow the programmer to write human readable notes within the code of the program. These notes are commonly referred to as "comments" within the code. A great deal of controversy surrounds how much documentation is necessary in any program, but this text proposes and follows the following guideline to properly document a program:

For every numbered item in a written algorithm, you should include that item as a comment in your code.

In addition, at the top of each program, it is extremely helpful to at least write a problem statement and document any variables used within the program. It is helpful to cluster your description of variables into three groups: input variables, output variables, and function variables.

Notes Particular to MATLAB

Before proceeding with the material on MATLAB, it would be wise to review the material on matrices in the appendix materials. Since variables in MATLAB are inherently matrices, it is critical that you understand not only some basic matrix concepts, but also the specific notation used in this text (as well as MATLAB) when referring to matrices. Certain details specific to MATLAB are important to note early on.

■ **The MATLAB interface:** The MATLAB program window, shown below, has a number of subwindows. The two main windows we are concerned with for now are the Command Window and the Editor Window.

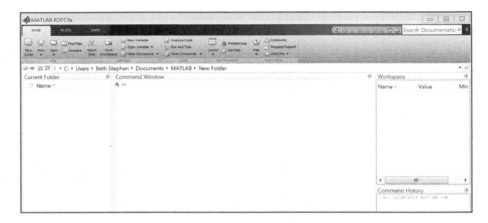

• The *Command Window* can be used as a powerful but awkward calculator. The  button at the top-right side of the Command Window menu bar will display a menu for common layout commands, including the ability to close or "undock" the Command Window from the MATLAB program window.

To restore the appearance of MATLAB to the default layout, select the **Layout** menu from the **Home** ribbon and click **Default**.

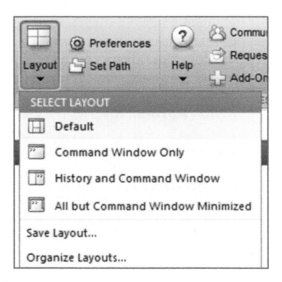

NOTE

clc = clear the
    Command Window

To clear any text from the Command Window, enter the special reserved MATLAB expression clc in the Command Window.

FILE TYPES

Word = .docx

Excel = .xlsx

Powerpoint = .pptx

MATLAB = .m

- Although you can enter MATLAB statements in the Command Window, the *Editor/Debugger window* is the interface of choice for developing MATLAB programs. The editor stores your commands in M-files. This permanent record of your commands allows you to make small changes to either the program or the inputs and to re-execute a complicated set of commands. The editor also assists in the formatting of MATLAB programs, using both indentation and color to distinguish program elements. To launch the editor window, press the **New Script** button on the **Home** ribbon or use CTRL+N. The Editor interface will launch in a new window.

- **Naming programs, functions, and variables in MATLAB:** In MATLAB, program names, function names, and variable names must all follow certain rules to prevent unintended side effects:

Naming Rules

- All names must consist only of letters, numbers, and the underscore character (displayed by holding "Shift" and typing a hyphen).
- Names can *only* begin with alphabetic letters (no numbers or special characters).
- Names cannot be longer than 63 characters.
- Names in MATLAB are case sensitive: `Frog` and `frog` are different.
- Names cannot have the same name as any other identifier (program name, function name, built-in function, built-in constant, reserved word, etc.), because MATLAB's order of execution will prevent the program from running in the intended order.

COMPREHENSION CHECK 17-1

Which of the following are valid MATLAB variable names?

(a) `my name`	**(d)** `m`	**(g)** `my_var`	**(j)** `for`
(b) `length`	**(e)** `m6`	**(h)** `@clemson`	**(k)** `HELLO[]`
(c) `MyLength`	**(f)** `4m`	**(i)** `my.variable`	

NOTE

Order of Search:

- Variable
- Built-in function
- Program or function in current directory
- Program or function in current path

- **Order of Search:** Order of search is the sequence MATLAB goes through when you type a name in either the Command Window or in a program or function. If you type `Frog` in the Command Window:

1. MATLAB checks if `Frog` is a variable, and displays its value if it is.

2. MATLAB checks if `Frog` is one of MATLAB's built-in functions, and executes that function if it is.

3. MATLAB checks if `Frog` is a program or function in its current directory, and executes the program or function if it is.

4. MATLAB checks if `Frog` is a program anywhere in its path, and executes the program or function if it is. The location where you store your MATLAB programs or functions must be included in MATLAB's path. You can check where MATLAB is looking for programs and functions by typing `path` in the Command Window. Any M-files in the directories listed will be visible to MATLAB. If you

try to execute an M-file outside any of the directories listed, MATLAB will ask if you want to switch current directories or add that directory to the list of paths MATLAB can see.

- **what and who:** To display a list of all MATLAB programs in the current directory, type what into the Command window. To display all variables currently in MATLAB's workspace, type who in the Command Window. Remember that all variables automatically clear after you exit MATLAB.
- **Comments:** For documenting or commenting any code in MATLAB, a special character is used to "comment" out text: the percent symbol (%). The comment character can appear anywhere in a MATLAB program or function, but preferably either at the beginning of a line or at the middle of a line of MATLAB code. Everything after the percent sign to the end of the line is ignored by MATLAB, so you as a programmer can "comment out" any broken lines of code during code testing in addition to providing comments. Program or function file headers will usually have 6–10 lines of comments at the top of every program and more throughout the rest of the program or function.

```
% This is an example of a comment line.
% Comment lines are shown in the Editor Window in green.
```

A **block comment** is a block of non-executed text between the special block characters %{ and %} that allow the user to type full length paragraphs as a comment without needing to type the % symbol before each sentence. For example:

```
%{
This is an example of using
a block of comments in a code
%}
```

Program Structure and Use

Programs are a set of instructions given to a computer to perform a specific task. In this section, we create MATLAB program files, or **M-Files**, to automate our processes. To create a program in MATLAB, launch the MATLAB editor. By default, the editor will create a new, blank document named Untitled, or Untitled2, or Untitled3, and so on, depending on how many unsaved programs are open in the editor at once. The following example provides a walkthrough for creating a basic program, as well as screenshots of the actions described in the text to help you to follow along while recreating these steps on your own computer running MATLAB.

● **EXAMPLE 17-1**

We want to create a MATLAB program to convert Cartesian coordinates (x, y) to polar coordinates (r, θ). Before we can even attempt to write the program, we need to recall some information about the coordinate systems.

We know the following:

- In the Cartesian coordinate system, the coordinates (x, y) represent how "far away" a particular data point is from the origin $(0, 0)$ by discussing the horizontal and vertical distance with respect to the origin. The x-value represents the horizontal distance and the y-value represents the vertical distance.

■ In the polar coordinate system, the coordinates (r, θ) represent the exact distance from the point to the origin (r) as well as the angle of elevation (θ) with respect to the origin $(0, 0)$ in units of radians.

- The conversion from polar coordinates to Cartesian coordinates is

$$x = r \cos \theta$$
$$y = r \sin \theta$$

where θ the angle of elevation in radians.
- The conversion from Cartesian coordinates to polar coordinates is

$$r = \sqrt{x^2 + y^2} \qquad \theta = \tan^{-1}\left(\frac{y}{x}\right)$$

We have the equations necessary to write a program to convert Cartesian coordinates to polar coordinates, and vice versa.

First, we need to ask MATLAB for more information on doing things like calculating a square root and calculating an inverse tangent of a value.

In MATLAB's Command Window, we search for the built-in functions to calculate a square root and an inverse tangent. The `lookfor` *function allows you to search MATLAB help documentation for certain key words. Note that if you type* `lookfor square root` *into the Command Window, MATLAB displays an error message. The* `lookfor` *command is expecting only one keyword following the command "lookfor", so we decide to try our search again, this time including only the word "square."*

Because MATLAB is searching through every built-in function, we need a way to tell MATLAB to stop, because when the function `sqrt` *appears, it seems to be the exact function we need. To terminate a MATLAB command early, we press* **CTRL + C** *(i.e., the CTRL key and the "C" key at the same time) on our keyboard, and the prompt will return to the Command Window.* `CTRL + C` *can also be used to stop a program caught in an infinite loop or that otherwise wandered away and got lost.*

To ask for more information on the function `sqrt`, *we type* `help sqrt` *to double-check that the function is going to perform our intended calculation as well as details of how to use it.*

NOTE

CTRL + C = stops MATLAB from executing.

Repeating this process to find the inverse tangent function, we determine that atan *is the correct function necessary to calculate the inverse tangent. We note, from the help documentation, that the* atan *function will return the inverse tangent in radians.*

*To create a program, we click the **New Script** button on MATLAB's Home tab. After creating a new blank M-file, we need to write out our problem statement as code comments. Comments are any non-interpreted text that you would like to include in your code file. All comments start with the percent symbol (%) and everything to the right of the symbol will be ignored on a per-line basis. Comments can follow any executable statements in our code, but for now, we will add the first couple of lines in our MATLAB program by writing out a short problem statement with the % symbol before any text we write.*

*Next, we start writing our code. In a MATLAB program, it is good practice to start the program by clearing all of the variables from the workspace (*clear*) and clearing the Command Window (*clc*). That way, we guarantee that if we run our program on a different computer or run it after restarting MATLAB, our program will create all the variables we need to solve the problem and not rely on the workspace having variables predefined before code execution.*

Now we are ready to start our program. Let us look at the step-by-step written algorithm necessary to solve this problem:

1. *Create a variable to contain the x-coordinate as a variable named "x."*
2. *Create a variable to contain the y-coordinate as a variable named "y."*
3. *Calculate the radius by taking the square root of the sum of the squares of x and y and store the result in a new variable called "r."*
4. *Calculate the angle by taking the inverse tangent of the result of dividing y by x and store the result in a new variable called "Theta."*

In the written algorithm, the first thing we have to do is to manually assign the values of x and y. For this example, we assign x to contain the value of 5 and y to contain the value of 10, but in later chapters, we show how the user of a program can enter values. Note that in addition to creating the variables x and y, we have also added additional comments in the header of our program documenting what these variables represent.

Note that MATLAB highlights the = symbol in the editor. When we move the cursor over the assignment operator (=), a pop-up message tells us that we can suppress the output of the assignment expression by using a semicolon. For now, we omit the semicolon and observe MATLAB's behavior when we leave the code unsuppressed.

Next, we type the equations to calculate the radius and the angle, using the built-in MATLAB functions we discovered with `lookup` and `help`. In addition, we've added extra comments about the new variables representing the radius and angle of the polar coordinate.

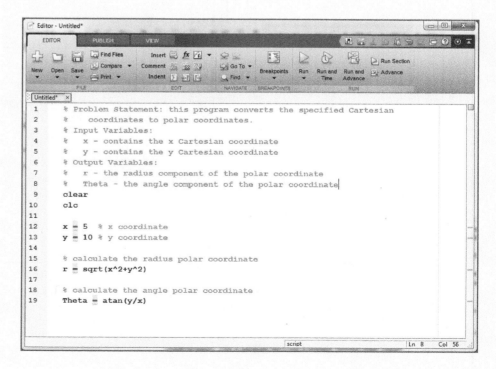

Next, we save the program in MATLAB's path with a file name that follows the program-naming convention. We choose the name "CartesianToPolar" since that name nicely describes the purpose of the program.

*To save a program, we click the **Save** icon in the Editor window.*

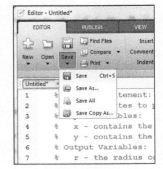

⌘ ***Mac OS:*** *MATLAB is one of the few programs that does not modify the main menu at the top of the screen. Instead, its main menu is at the top of the MATLAB window, just as in the Windows implementation. This is because MATLAB is actually running under an X Windowing System, similar to Linux or UNIX®.*

Running the Program

There are a number of different ways to run a MATLAB program located within MATLAB's path.

Method 1: *In the main MATLAB window (not the Editor), type the name of the program in the Command Window and press **Enter.***

Method 2: *In the main MATLAB window (not the Editor), right-click the program you want to run while in the Current Directory box and select **Run.***

Method 3: *With the program loaded in the Editor window, click the **Save and Run** button in the toolbar.*

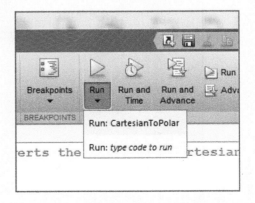

We see that MATLAB spits out the results of every assignment and calculation performed in the program. Let us assume we want to show only the output from the calculations of r and Theta, and not the output of the assignment of x and y. To do this, we add a semicolon (;) at the end of each line of code we do not want showing up in the output of the program.

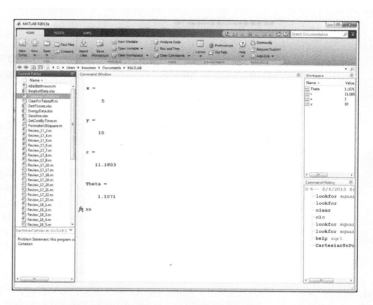

Now when we save and run our modified program, we will see only the output from the calculations of r and Theta.

Programming Features in Our Coverage of MATLAB

MATLAB has many advanced programming features that make sophisticated numerical analysis, including simulation, possible. In this text, you will learn basic programming structures to solve engineering analysis problems.

- **Data types:** Covered in the previous chapter, there are different data types that can be stored and manipulated by MATLAB. Some of the more common data types used by programs include numeric and string variables, but many applications also use vector and matrix variables for advanced calculations, as well as special types like cell arrays for storing a combination of different types within a single structure.

- **Input and output:** By gathering input, the program can solve a different problem each time the program is executed. Output statements allow you to produce formatted text to communicate with the user. Likewise, being able to read and write Microsoft Excel files using MATLAB code allows your program to perform calculations without needing to type in a bunch of data and permanently save results to special MATLAB data files (called .mat files.)

- **Conditional statements:** These allow a program to take different paths for various user input, intermediate calculations, or final results. Conditional statements allow the programmer to ask questions in order to make decisions.

- **Looping:** Repetition is critical in breaking down complicated problems into many simple calculations.

- **Plotting:** Graphs communicate data relationships in a variety of forms.

17.2 FUNCTIONS

LEARN TO: Create, execute, and modify functions in MATLAB
Understand the difference between local and global variables

Functional programming allows the designer of an algorithm to recycle a segment of code to reduce the amount of redundant code. Decreasing code redundancy allows for cleaner source code that is easier to read. **Functions** are a special class of programs that require the user to pass in input variables and capture output variables.

User-defined functions are similar to programs in that they contain a series of executable MATLAB statements in M-files that exist independently of any program we create in MATLAB. To allow any MATLAB program to call a user-defined function, we must follow a few guidelines to ensure that our function will run properly.

LAW OF ARGUMENTS

In computer programming, and often in math as well, the word "argument" does *not* refer to an altercation or vehement disagreement. In this context, it means the information that is given to a function as input to be processed. If you use the function sqrt to find the square root of 49, you would write sqrt(49) : 49 is the argument of sqrt—the value upon which the sqrt function performs its calculations. Functions may have zero arguments (e.g., rand will calculate a single random number between 0 and 1—no input is required), one argument (e.g., sqrt(4)), or two or more arguments (e.g., power(a,b) raises a to the power b).

Function Creation Guidelines

■ The first line in a function must be a function definition line:

```
function [output_variables] = function_name(input_variables)
```

- *output_variables:* A comma-separated list of output variables in square brackets.
- *input_variables:* A comma-separated list of input variables in parentheses. The list of input variables to a function are commonly referred to as **arguments**.
- *function_name:* Function names cannot be the same as a built-in function, user-created variables, or any reserved word in MATLAB. Avoid creating variables with the same name as a user-defined function because you will not be able to call your function.

■ **The name of the function must be the same as the file name**. For example, if the function name is sphereVolume, the function must be saved in an M-file named sphereVolume.m, where .m is just the extension of the M-file. In addition to the aforementioned function-naming rules, the name of the function must also follow all program-naming rules, including omitting spaces in the file name.

■ To execute a function, you must call it from MATLAB's Command Window or from a different program or function by passing in input variables and saving the resulting output into different variables.

■ Do *not* use the built-in function clc within one of your own functions. The functions you are writing are intended to be general purpose and can be called from other programs (or functions), so if text is written to the screen prior to calling a function that contains the `clc` command, it will wipe the Command Window clean—losing all of the previous output on the screen. For a different reason, the `clear` command should not be used within a function since functions usually contain input arguments, so calling the `clear` command would delete any input variables and their values. In general, the `clear` and `clc` commands should only appear at the top of programs, not functions!

Function Structure and Use

The following examples demonstrate the structure of different functions and how MATLAB programs can use the functions to reduce code redundancy.

● **EXAMPLE 17-2**

Assume we are required to create a function, `areaCircle`, to calculate the area of a circle given the radius. The function should accept one input (radius) and return one output (area). Furthermore, we are told to suppress all calculations within the function.

Source Code

```
% Problem Statement: This function calculates the area of a
% circle
% Input:
%   r—Radius [any length unit]
% Output:
%   A—Area [units of input^2]
function [A]=areaCircle(r)
% Calculation of the area of a circle
A=pi*r^2;
```

Typical Usage (typed in Command Window or a separate program):

You can call the function by typing the name of the function and passing in a value for the radius. Note that the result is stored in a variable called "ans" when you do not specify a variable to capture the output.

```
>> areaCircle(3)
ans=
    28.2743
```

You can call the function by typing the name of the function and passing in a variable.

```
>> Rad=4;
>> CircleA=areaCircle(Rad)
CircleA=
  50.2655
```

COMPREHENSION CHECK 17-2

What is the output when you "pass in" the value 10 to the function in Example 17-2?

Assume that you want to store the result of the previous function call in a variable called `Dogs`. What is the command you would type in MATLAB?

COMPREHENSION CHECK 17-3

Write a function named RAC that will accept two parameters, N and A. The function should return a single value R calculated as R = 3 sin(N^A). For this example, you do not need to include any comments with this code.

Testing Functions

MATLAB's Editor contains functionality to allow you to efficiently test functions that you write by allowing you to create different test scenarios and providing a shortcut to run those test cases you can create directly in the editor window. Assume we have created and saved the following function in MATLAB:

```
function [out1,out2,out3]=myFunctionInTheEditor(in1,in2)
out1 = in1 * 2;
out2 = out1 + in2;
out3 = [out1, out2]*3;
```

This function named myFunctionInTheEditor accepts two input arguments (in1, in2) and returns three output variables: out1 and out2 are both numbers and out3 is a vector. Assume we want to test to see what the resulting output variables will contain when the value of 5 is used for in1 and 10 is used for in2. To do this, we can use the same Run button we used for programs. The first time you press the Run button, an error message will appear in the screen indicating that the input variables are missing:

```
>> myFunctionInTheEditor
Error using myFunctionInTheEditor (line 2)
Not enough input arguments.
```

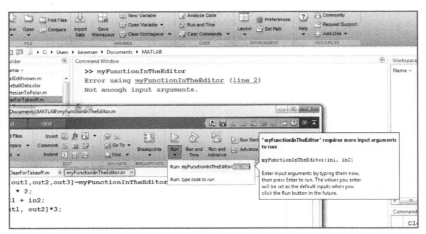

However, a little pop-up dialog appears in MATLAB's Editor Window that actually allows you type in values for the test case. Type in **5, 10** within the parenthesis on the dialog, representing the values of in1 and in2 respectively and press the Enter key. You'll notice that output has appeared in the Command Window:

```
>> myFunctionInTheEditor(5,10)
ans =
    10
```

This output shows that the function was successfully executed with the value of 5 for in1 and 10 for in2, but since this function didn't save any output variables, the value 10 is stored in the default variable ans. By default, MATLAB requires you to provide values for all of the input variables, but it does not require you to capture all of the output variables with each call. The value stored in ans, 10, is actually the value of the out1 variable calculated in the function. However, the Editor Window is smart enough to be to set up test cases where all of the output variables are assigned to variables when the function is called. Consider the test case with the value 3 for in1 and 10 for in2. To save all three output variables (for testing, we will save out1 into variable a, out2 into variable b, and out3 into variable c), select the Run drop down menu on the Editor Window again and this time type the following in the "type code to run" box: [a,b,c] = myFunctionInTheEditor(3,10)

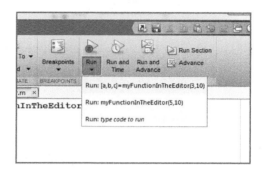

After executing the function with our new test case, the output variables are displayed properly in the Command Window:

```
>> [a,b,c]=myFunctionInTheEditor(3,10)
a =
     6
b =
    16
c =
    18  48
```

● **EXAMPLE 17-3**

Assume we are required to create a function, volumeCylinder, to calculate the volume of a cylinder given the radius. The function should accept two inputs (radius, height) and return one output (volume). For this example, you may assume that the user will input the radius and height in the same units. Any calculations in the functions must be suppressed.

Algorithm

Known/input:	Unknown/output:	Assumptions:
r = radius [cm] H = height [cm]	V = volume [cm^3]	

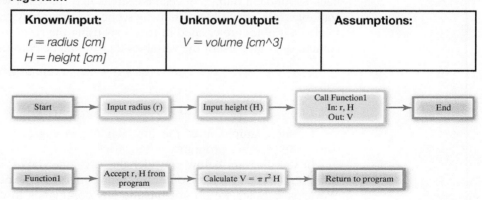

Source Code

```
% Problem Statement: Calculate the volume of a cylinder.
% Input:
%   r—Radius [any length unit]
%   H—Height [same length unit as radius]
% Output:
%   V—Volume [units of input^3]
function [V] = volumeCylinder(r, H)
% Calculation of the volume of a cylinder
V=pi*H*r^2;
```

Typical Usage

```
>> Vol1 = volumeCylinder(1,2)
Vol1=
   6.2832

>> Vol2 = volumeCylinder(2,1)
Vol2=
   12.5664
```

Note that the order of arguments passed into the function matters. The order of variables expected by the function is based on the order they are listed in the function header. Therefore, the first input argument is the radius, followed by the height.

Local and Global Variables

One important fact to note about variables is that the variables in the workspace are only available within MATLAB's Command Window and to any running program. Functions create a private workspace and cannot access any of the variables available in MATLAB's main workspace. The only way to access any variables in MATLAB's main workspace is to "pass" the variable to the program as function input. The phenomenon of having "main workspace" variables inaccessible by functions is because functions exist within a different scope from the programs. The variables created within the "private workspace" of a function are commonly referred to as **local variables**, since they are destroyed after the function executes and do not appear in the "main workspace" unless they are passed back as function output. Special constants like "pi" exist within the scope of programs. Variables that are visible within any scope are commonly referred to as **global variables**. Global variables are created in functions using the reserved word **global** followed by a comma separated list of the variables that should be considered global variables.

```
function [x] = functionName(y)
global z
z=30;
```

In this example, after the function functionName is called, the value of z is accessible by other programs or functions.

In the diagram below, consider the two inner boxes to be programs (Prgm1) or functions (Func1) and the outer box represents all of the other variables in MATLAB's Workspace. Since we do not include any commands to clear the variables from the workspace at the top of the program Prgm1, the program is able to "see" and use all of the variables within MATLAB's workspace. In addition, it will create a new variable in MATLAB's workspace (c) after we execute program Prgm1.

In contrast, the function cannot "see" or use any of the variables in MATLAB's Workspace and creates its own separate workspace to execute the code inside the function. In order to run the function, the programmer must provide the values of variables e and g by "passing" the variables into the function, the code calculates the value of d, and returns d as function output. Assume that we store the output of the function in the variable h when the function returns to the MATLAB workspace. After the function has executed, the separate workspace is destroyed, along with variables d and k, which were never stored in MATLAB's main workspace.

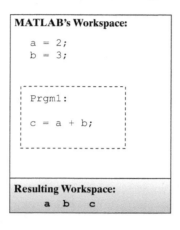

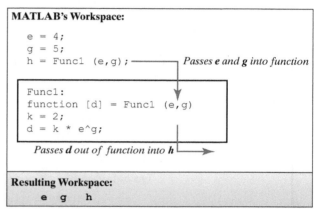

● **EXAMPLE 17-4**

Assume we are required to create a function, `circleCalculations`, to calculate the area and perimeter of a circle given the radius. The function should accept one input (radius) and return two outputs (area, perimeter). Any calculations in the functions must be suppressed.

Source Code

```
% Problem Statement: This function calculates the area and
% perimeter of a circle.
% Input:
%    r—Radius [any length unit]
% Output:
%    A—Area [units of input^2]
%    P—Perimeter [units of input]
function [A,P]=circleCalculations(r)
% Calculation of the area of a circle
A=pi*r^2;
% Calculation of the perimeter of a circle
P=2*pi*r;
```

Typical Usage

```
>> [Area,Perimeter]=circleCalculations(5)
Area=
   78.5398
Perimeter=
   31.4159
```

● EXAMPLE 17-5

Assume we are required to create a function, `cylinderCalculations`, to calculate the volume and lateral surface area of a cylinder given the radius and height. The function should accept two inputs (radius, height) and return two outputs (volume, surface area). For this example, you may assume that the user will input the radius and height in the same units. Any calculations in the functions must be suppressed.

Source Code

```
% Problem: Function calculates volume and surface area of
% cylinder.
% Input:
%   r—Radius [any length unit]
%   H—Height [same length unit as radius]
% Output:
%   V—Volume [units of input^3]
%   SA—Surface area [units of input^2]
function [V,SA] = cylinderCalculations(r,H)
% Calculation of the volume of cylinder
V=pi*H*r^2;
% Calculation of the surface area of a cylinder
SA=2*pi*r*H;
```

Typical Usage

```
>> [Volume,Surface] = cylinderCalculations(3,2)
Volume=
   56.5487
Surface=
   37.6991
```

17.3 DEBUGGING MATLAB CODE

LEARN TO: Utilize the Debugger tool in MATLAB to eliminate errors
Examine the variable values during execution of a program or function

If a program has syntax errors, MATLAB (and other compilers) will give you useful feedback regarding the type and location of the error to help you fix, or **debug**, your program. If this information is not sufficient for you to understand the problem, check with others who might have seen this error previously—some errors are particularly common. If you still cannot identify the error, you might need to use a more formal process to study the error. For other kinds of errors, this formal process is essential for diagnosing the problems. When you first write a program, you must test the output of the program with a set of inputs for which you know result. Such test cases would include:

■ Simple cases for which you can quickly compute the expected output;
■ Cases provided by an instructor or textbook with a published solution;
■ Cases for which results have already been produced by a previously tested program that does the same thing;
■ Test cases that are customarily used to test programs.

When the output of a program is different from what you expect, the debugging process begins. It is common to debug shorter programs simply by reading them and writing a few notes. Longer programs may require the use of the MATLAB Debugger, which is available as part of the MATLAB Editor. Whether you are using the MATLAB Debugger or are debugging "by hand" or in the Command Window, the same techniques apply.

Preparing for Debugging

When using the Editor/Debugger, open the program for debugging. If it is open, make sure changes are saved—MATLAB will run the saved version without including recent changes. If you are debugging from a printed program and output, make sure that the printed output came from the version you are reading. In preparing to debug a program, it is critical to be able to reproduce the conditions that caused the bug in the first place. If the bug occurs in processing data from a large data set, you may have to split the data set to find the specific data that triggered the bug.

Setting Breakpoints

When using the Editor/Debugger, establish **breakpoints** that allow you to check your agreement with the program at various stages. A breakpoint stops the program at the specified location to allow you to examine the contents of variables, etc., before the program continues. This will help you find the specific location when the program does something you were not expecting. When debugging shorter programs, write down everything the program does or make all program results display in the Command Window by removing semicolons that were used to suppress output to the Command Window.

MATLAB has two main types of breakpoints: standard (set by location in the program) and conditional (triggered at a specified location by specified conditions). We focus on standard breakpoints in this section. Standard breakpoints are normally shown as little red dots next to the line of code where the executing should pause and conditional breakpoints will appear as little yellow dots. If the breakpoint dot displays gray, either the file has not been saved since changes were made to it or there is a syntax error on the line or somewhere in the file. All breakpoints remain in a file until you clear (remove) them or until they are automatically cleared.

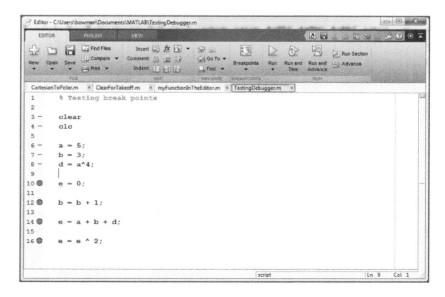

Stepping Through a Program

When using the Editor/Debugger, you must start by running the program or function. You can choose to step through the program one line at a time or have it continue until a breakpoint is encountered. Typically, you will set a breakpoint and execute the program and the Editor will automatically stop before the line the breakpoint is set on is executed. A green arrow will point to the program line when execution is paused. The controls in the Editor window will allow you to "step in" to functions you've written, or "step out" of functions you're currently in. Likewise, pressing the Continue button will resume execution — to completion or until the debugger encounters the next breakpoint.

Examining Values

When the program is paused at a breakpoint or when you are stepping through the program a line at a time, you can view the value of any variable by hovering your mouse over the variable to see whether a line of code has produced the expected result. If the result is as expected, continue running or step to the next line. If the result is not as expected, then that line, or a previous line, contains an error. You can also examine the value of a variable in the Workspace window in the main MATLAB program window.

```
1        % Testing break points
2
3 -      clear
4 -      clc
5
6 -      a = 5;
7 -      b = 3;
8 -      d = a^4;
9
10       e
         d: 1x1 double =
11
12       b = b + 1;          625
13
14       e = a + b + d;
```

Correcting Problems and Ending Debugging

If a problem is difficult to diagnose, one method to help define or correct problems is to change the value of a variable in a paused program to see if continuing with the new value produces expected results. A new value can be assigned through the Command Window, Workspace browser, or Array Editor. Do not make changes to an M-file while MATLAB is in debug mode — it is best to exit debug mode before editing an M-file. If you edit an M-file while in debug mode, you can get unexpected results when you run the file.

In-Class Activities

ICA 17-1

Which of the following are not valid program/function filenames? Circle all that apply.

(A) `2b_solved.m`
(B) `calc_circum.m`
(C) `graph-data.m`
(D) `help4me.m`
(E) `MATLAB is fun.m`
(F) `matrix*matrix.m`
(G) `Mult2#s.m`
(H) `pi.m`
(I) `ReadFile.m`
(J) `SuperCaliFragiListicExpiAliDocious.m`

ICA 17-2

Without running these code segments in MATLAB, what will be the value stored in the specified variable after executing each program?

(a) What is stored in **Dogs**?

```
clear
clc
Greyhounds = 30;
G_Cost = 250;
Dalmations = 10;
D_Cost = 150;
Dogs = Greyhounds * G_Cost + Dalmations * D_Cost;
```

(b) What is stored in **W**?

```
clear
clc
X = 2;
Y = 4;
Z = 2;
W = (Y + Z/X + Z^1/2)
```

ICA 17-3

Without running these code segments in MATLAB, what will be the value stored in the specified variable after executing each program?

(a) What is stored in **X**?

```
clear
clc
A = 0;
B = 5;
X = A^B + B^A;
```

(b) What is stored in **Ramones**?

```
clear
clc
Joey = 1;
Johnny = 2;
DeeDee = 3;
Marky = 4;
Ramones = Joey * 2 + Johnny/2 + max([DeeDee, Marky]);
```

ICA 17-4

Write a program to store the following matrices into MATLAB and perform the following calculations. All variable assignments should be suppressed, but you should leave the calculations unsuppressed. If the variable assignment or calculation is not possible or causes an error message on the screen, write MATLAB comments explaining the problem.

Input variables:

$$A = \begin{bmatrix} 4 & 6 \\ -3 & 8 \end{bmatrix} \quad B = \begin{bmatrix} 3 & 5 \\ 5 & 5 \end{bmatrix} \quad C = [0 \ 1] \quad D = \begin{bmatrix} 1 \\ 1 \end{bmatrix} \quad E = \begin{bmatrix} 3 & 6 & 5 \\ 7 & 1 & 5 \end{bmatrix} \quad F = \begin{bmatrix} 2 & 8 \\ 4 & 3 \\ 1 & 5 \end{bmatrix}$$

$$G = \begin{bmatrix} 7 & 8 & 3 \\ 4 & 8 & 2 \\ 5 & 9 & 5 \end{bmatrix} \quad H = [1 \ 2 \ \dots \ 299 \ 300] \quad I = \begin{bmatrix} 200 \\ 198 \\ \vdots \\ -298 \\ -300 \end{bmatrix}$$

$$J = \begin{bmatrix} 20 & 40 & \dots & 180 & 200 \\ 10 & 20 & \dots & 90 & 100 \end{bmatrix} \quad K = \begin{bmatrix} 5 & 50 \\ 10 & 45 \\ \vdots & \vdots \\ 45 & -45 \\ 50 & -50 \end{bmatrix}$$

Calculations:

The result of the following calculations should each be stored into variable names of your choosing. Each calculation should be stored in a different variable. Here, note the "T" indicated the matrix should be transposed.

(a) $A * B$

(b) $A + B$

(c) $A + C$

(d) $C - E$

(d) $E * F$

(f) $F * E$

(g) G^2

(h) F^T

(i) $C * D$

(j) $H + 15$

(k) $I * 30$

(l) $E^T + 30$

(m) $E^2 * 50$

(n) $B^2 * 50$

ICA 17-5

Write a MATLAB program to evaluate the following mathematical expression. The equation should utilize variables for a, b, and c. Test the program with $a = 1$, $b = 2$, and $c = 3$.

$$x = \frac{b + \sqrt{b - 4a}}{c^7}$$

ICA 17-6

Write a MATLAB program to evaluate the following mathematical expression. The equation should utilize a variable for x. Test the program with $x = 30$.

$$A = \frac{x^2 \cos (2x + 1)}{(6x) \log (x)}$$

ICA 17-7

Write a MATLAB program to evaluate the following mathematical expression. The equation should utilize variables for x, μ, and σ. Test the program with $x = 0$, $\mu = 0$, and $\sigma = 1$.

$$P = \frac{1}{\sigma \sqrt{2\pi}} e^{-(x-\mu)^2/(2\sigma^2)}$$

This program calculates a *Gaussian normal distribution*.

ICA 17-8

Write a program that, given any two 2×2 arrays (A and B) as arguments, returns the sum of the two matrices. The program is not expected to work properly for any other matrix dimensions. You must calculate each term in C individually from terms in A and B—you may not use MATLAB's ability to add matrices directly. Use the following values to test the program: A = [1 3; −2 2] and B = [−3 0; 4 −1].

ICA 17-9

Write a program that, given any two 2×2 arrays (A and B) as arguments, returns the matrix product. The program is not expected to work properly for any other matrix dimensions. You must calculate each term in C individually from terms in A and B—you may not use MATLAB's ability to multiply matrices directly. Use the following values to test the program: A = [1 3; −2 2] and B = [−3 0; 4 −1].

ICA 17-10

The Shockley diode equation gives the relationship between the voltage (V) across a semiconductor junction and the current (I) through it.

$$I = I_0(e^{\left(\frac{V}{nV_T}\right)} - 1)$$

Assume V is a vector containing several voltage values. Write a MATLAB program that will calculate a vector I of the same length containing the current corresponding to each value in V.

Test your program with $I_0 = 2 \times 10^{-11}$, n = 1, $V_T = 25.85 \times 10^{-3}$, and V = [0.4, 0.55, 0.65, −5,0].

ICA 17-11

For each MATLAB code segment shown, write the function header necessary to convert the code segment into a function. Use the guidelines specified with each problem.

(a) Assume there only needs to be one function output, the variable **X** and that the function will be stored in a file named **CandyCrush.m**.

```
X = (A + B + B^A)*pi;
```

(b) Assume the function should have five output variables: the paintable area of each wall (all 4 walls) and the total paintable area. You may assume this function will be stored in a file named **FullHouse.m**.

```
P1 = Wall1 * RoomHeight;
P2 = Wall2 * RoomHeight;
P3 = Wall3 * RoomHeight;
P4 = Wall4 * RoomHeight;

PaintableArea = P1 + P2 + P3 + P4;
```

(c) Assume the function should have 3 output variables: the minimum value, the maximum value, and the average value. You may assume this function will be stored in a file named **MinMaxMean.m**.

```
MyMin = min([D,D^2,D*10]);
MyMax = max([D^3,D*3,D + 3000]);
MyMean = mean([D/2,D/3,D/4]);
```

ICA 17-12

Assume you are given the following function:

```
function [status] = ClearForTakeoff(T)
status = [T +2, T −4; T*6, T/8];
```

(a) What is stored in the variable Z after executing the following lines of MATLAB code?

```
A = 2;
Z = ClearForTakeoff(A);
```

(b) What is stored in the variable E after executing the following lines of MATLAB code?

```
D = 0;
E = ClearForTakeoff (D);
```

ICA 17-13

A member of your team gives you the following MATLAB program. Your job is to create the functions used in the program.

```
A = 10; % area [cm^2]
H = 30; % height [cm]
V = 50; % volume [cm^3]
% calculates the radius [cm] of the circle
R1 = RadiusCircle(A);
% calculates the radius [cm] of a cone
R2 = RadiusCone(H,V);
```

ICA 17-14

Assume you are given the following function:

```
function [M_NEW,N] = SimpleCalculations(Wii)
M_NEW = Wii + 30;
N = M_NEW/2;
Wii = 35;
```

What is stored in the variables *P, C*, and *r* after executing the following lines of MATLAB code?

```
r = 5;
[P,C] = SimpleCalculations(r);
```

ICA 17-15

A novice programmer has attempted to write a program and two functions using global variables. These three files are provided for you with the online materials.

The purpose of the code is to determine the total pressure at the bottom of a cylindrical container filled with a liquid on an arbitrary planet, and to determine the potential energy of that cylinder at a given height above the planet's surface.

(a) Without running the code, determine what the values of the following variables will be following execution of the code: `g, atm, Radius, Depth, CylMass, rho, Height, H, Pressure, P, CylVol, ContentsMass, TotalMass, PE`

(b) Which of the variables in part (a) DO NOT appear in the main program workspace?

(c) For the values specified in the program, the correct answers are `Pressure` = 26,150 [Pa] and `PE` = 19,987 [J]. The program and associated functions calculate the pressure correctly, but the potential energy is wrong. Explain what went wrong and how to repair the problem.

ICA 17-16

Debug the MATLAB programs/functions provided for you with the online materials.

```
atm to Pa.m
ft to m.m
ICA #7.m
```

These files must be corrected to eliminate any syntax, runtime, formula coding, and formula derivation errors. You may assume that the header comments at the top of the program and functions are correct. In addition to the corrected files, you must submit an algorithm template, showing the main program and both functions.

ICA 17-17

Debug the MATLAB programs/functions provided for you with the online materials.

```
SG to rho.m
N_2_lbf.m
ICA S-D.m
```

These files must be corrected to eliminate any syntax, runtime, formula coding, and formula derivation errors. You may assume that the header comments at the top of the program and functions are correct. In addition to the corrected files, you must submit an algorithm template, showing the main program and both functions.

ICA 17-18

Consider the following MATLAB program and function, stored in MATLAB's Current Directory:

MyRadFunction.m

```
clear clc
function [Out] = RadF (In1, In2, In3)
Out = (In1+In2)/2 + (In2+In3)/4;
```

MyRadProgram.m

```
clear clc
InVar1=1; InVar2=3; InVar3=-1;
M=MyRadFunction(invar1), MyRadFunction(invar2),
myradfunction(invar3);
```

Fix the program and function to eliminate all of the error messages. Note that for the variables provided in the program as `InVar1`, `InVar2`, and `InVar3`, the numerical result stored in M should be 2.5.

ICA 17-19

A novice MATLAB user created the following code with poor choice of variable names. Correct the errors and fill in the blanks provided to comment this code to determine the purpose of the code.

Main Program	Comments
`T = [30, 45, 120, 150];`	**(a)** `% T =`
`Z = 2;`	**(b)** `% Z =`
	`% The purpose of the function DTOR is ...`
`[W] = DTOR(T)`	**(c)** `%`
	(d) `% W =`
	`% The purpose of the function PCAR is ...`
	(e) `%`
`[X,Y] = PCAR(Z,W)`	**(f)** `% X =`
	(g) `% Y =`

```
function [A] = DTOR(T)
A = T*2*pi/360;
```

```
function (P,Q) = PCAR(M,N)
P = M * cos(N);
Q = M * sin(N);
```

(h) The output of this code, when run, is _____

Chapter 17 REVIEW QUESTIONS

1. The specific gravity of gold is 19.3. Write a MATLAB program that will determine the length of one side of a 0.4 kilogram cube of solid gold, in units of inches.

2. An unmanned X-43A scramjet test vehicle has achieved a maximum speed of Mach number 9.68 in a test flight over the Pacific Ocean. Mach number is defined as the speed of an object divided by the speed of sound. Assuming the speed of sound is 343 meters per second, write a MATLAB program to determine the record speed in units of miles per hour.

3. A rod on the surface of Jupiter's moon Callisto has a volume of 0.3 cubic meters. Write a MATLAB program that will determine the weight of the rod in units of pounds-force. The specific gravity is 4.7. Gravitational acceleration on Callisto is 1.25 meters per second squared.

4. The Eco-Marathon is an annual competition sponsored by Shell Oil, in which participants build special vehicles to achieve the highest possible fuel efficiency. The Eco-Marathon is held around the world with events in the United Kingdom, Finland, France, Holland, Japan, and the United States.
   A world record was set in the Eco-Marathon by a French team in 2003 called Microjoule with a performance of 10,705 miles per gallon. The Microjoule runs on ethanol. Write a MATLAB program to determine how far the Microjoule will travel in kilometers given a user-specified amount of ethanol, provided in units of grams. For your test case, you may assume that the user provides 100 grams of ethanol.

5. Write a program to determine the mass of oxygen gas (formula: O_2, molecular weight = 32 grams per mole) in units of grams in a container. You may assume that the user will provide the volume of the container in units of gallons, the temperature in the container in degrees Celsius, and the pressure in the container in units of atmospheres. For your test case, you may assume that the user provides 1.25 gallons for the volume of the container, 125 degrees Celsius for the temperature, and 2.5 atmospheres for the pressure in the container.

6. Write a program to calculate a temperature provided by the user in units of Fahrenheit to units of kelvins. As a test case, you may assume the user provides the temperature of −129 degrees Fahrenheit, which is the world's lowest recorded temperature.

7. Write a program to determine how long, in units of seconds, it will take a motor to raise a load into the air. Assume the user will specify the power of the motor in units of watts, the rated efficiency as a percentage (in whole number form—for example, 50 for 50%), the mass of the load in kilograms, and the height the load is raised in the air in units of meters. As a test case, you may assume the user provides the 100 watts for the power of the motor, 60% for the efficiency of the motor, 100 kilograms for the mass of the load, and 5 meters for the height the load is raised.

8. A cylindrical tank filled to a height of 25 feet with tribromoethylene has been pressurized to 3 atmospheres ($P_{surface}$ = 3 atmospheres). The total pressure in at the bottom of the tank is 5 atmospheres. Write a MATLAB program to determine the density of tribromoethylene in units of kilograms per cubic meter.

9. Write a MATLAB program that implements the quadratic equation. Recall the quadratic equation:

$$r = \frac{-b \pm \sqrt{b^2 - 4ac}}{2a}$$

10. Write a MATLAB program that implements the Pythagorean theorem. Recall that the theorem states that the length of the hypotenuse (z) can be calculated by the sum of the squares of the adjacent sides (x and y), or

$$z = \sqrt{x^2 + y^2}$$

11. The specific gravity of gold is 19.3. Write a MATLAB function that will determine the length of one side of a cube of solid gold, in units of inches, provided the mass of the cube in kilograms.

12. An unmanned X-43A scramjet test vehicle has achieved a maximum speed of Mach number 9.68 in a test flight over the Pacific Ocean. Mach number is defined as the speed of an object divided by the speed of sound. Assuming the speed of sound is 343 meters per second, write a MATLAB function that will calculate the speed in units of miles per hour given the Mach number.

13. A rod on the surface of Jupiter's moon Callisto has a volume of 0.3 cubic meters. Write a MATLAB function that will determine the weight of the rod in units of pounds-force given the rod volume in cubic meters. The specific gravity is 4.7. Gravitational acceleration on Callisto is 1.25 meters per second squared.

14. A cylindrical tank filled to a height of 25 feet with tribromoethylene has been pressurized to 3 atmospheres ($P_{surface}$ = 3 atmospheres). The total pressure in at the bottom of the tank is 5 atmospheres. Write a MATLAB function that will determine the density of tribromoethylene in units of kilograms per cubic meter given the height in units of feet and the surface and total pressures in units of atmospheres.

15. Write a function that implements the quadratic equation. Given three inputs (a, b, and c), calculate the roots (r1 and r2) of the quadratic formula. Recall the quadratic equation:

$$r = \frac{-b \pm \sqrt{b^2 - 4ac}}{2a}$$

16. Write a function that implements the Pythagorean theorem. Recall that the theorem states that the length of the hypotenuse (z) can be calculated by the sum of the squares of the adjacent sides (x and y), or

$$z = \sqrt{x^2 + y^2}$$

17. In the starting file provided on online, there are data sets from two different data collection sessions. In the first data collection session, a lab technician collected three different measurements and recorded mass in grams, height in feet, and time in minutes. However, in data collection session two, a different lab technician collected four different measurements and recorded mass in pounds-mass, height in centimeters, and time in hours.

Your job is to write a function that will calculate the potential energy in joules and power in watts for each data condition (7 total). In addition, you will need to write a program to call the function using the datasets provided in the starting file. Your function should only consider variables in SI units, so you will need to convert the vectors in the program before passing them in to your function. Note that all conversions must be done in MATLAB code—you may not hard code any values you calculate by hand.

18. As part of a team investigating the effect of mass on the oscillation frequency of a spring, you obtain data from three different lab technicians, provided for you in the starter file online.

The data consists of frequency data on three different springs recording the amount of time it takes each spring with different masses attached to oscillate a certain number of times. In this experiment, each technician recorded the time it took for the spring to oscillate 25 times, stored in the variable *N* in the starter file.

As part of the analysis, you need to write a program containing the experimental data provided. The data should be converted to make all units consistent. The data should then be passed into a function.

The function should accept three inputs: a vector containing mass measurements (grams), a vector containing time measurements (seconds), and a variable containing the number of oscillations observed in the experiment.

The function should return two matrices. The first matrix should contain the mass measurements (kilograms) in the first column and the period (seconds), or the length of time required for one oscillation for each mass in the second column. The second matrix should contain a calculation of the force applied (newtons) by each mass in the first column and the frequency, the number of oscillations per second, or the inverse of the period (hertz) for each mass measured in the second column.

19. We have made many measurements of coffee cooling in a ceramic coffee cup. We realize that as the coffee cools, it gradually reaches room temperature. Consequently, we report the value of the coffee temperature in degrees above room temperature (so after a long time, the temperature rise will be equal to 0). Also, we realize that the hotter the coffee is initially (above room temperature), the longer it will take to cool. The values presented here are in degrees Fahrenheit.

Temperature Rise (T) [°F]						
Initial Temp Rise (T_0) [°F]	Cooling Time Elapsed (t) [min]					
	0	10	20	30	40	50
20	20	13	9	6	4	3
40	40	27	18	12	8	5
60	60	40	27	18	12	8
80	80	54	36	24	16	11

Write a MATLAB function that will perform a single interpolation given five numbers as input arguments and return the interpolated value as the only function output.

Write a MATLAB program that will calculate the following scenarios. Store each part in a different variable (e.g., part **(a)** should be stored in a variable named `PartA`, part **(b)** should be stored in a variable named `PartB`, etc.).

(a) What is the temperature (rise) of the cup of coffee after 37 minutes if the initial rise of temperature is 40 degrees Fahrenheit?

(b) If the coffee cools for 30 minutes and has risen 14 degrees Fahrenheit at that time, what was the initial temperature rise?

(c) Find the temperature rise of the coffee at 17 minutes if the initial rise is 53 degrees Fahrenheit.

20. In a factory, various metal pieces are forged and then plunged into a cool liquid to quickly cool the metal. The types of metals produced, as well as their specific heat capacity, are listed in the table below.

Material	Specific Heat [J/(g °C)]
Aluminum	0.897
Cadmium	0.231
Iron	0.450
Tungsten	0.134

The metal pieces vary in mass, and are produced at a temperature of 300 degrees Celsius. The ideal process lowers the temperature of the material to 50 degrees Celsius. The liquid used to cool the metal is glycerol. The properties of glycerol are listed below.

Material Property	Value [Units]
Specific heat	2.4 J/(g °C)
Specific gravity	1.261
Initial temperature	25 °C

There are data sets from four different data collection sessions. In the first data collection session, a lab technician collected seven different measurements and recorded mass in grams of aluminum rods. The second data set contains cadmium rods; the third data set contains iron rods, and the fourth data set contains tungsten rods.

Mass of Object [g]			
Aluminum	Cadmium	Iron	Tungsten
2,000	3,000	2,500	4,800
2,500	4,000	3,500	6,400
3,000	6,500	4,500	10,400
4,000	8,000	5,000	12,800
5,500	10,000	5,500	16,000
7,500	11,000	7,500	17,600
8,000	15,000	9,000	24,000

Your job is to write two functions: (1) to calculate the thermal energy in joules that must be removed for each rod to cool it from 300 to 50 degrees Celsius for each mass and (2) to determine the volume of fluid needed in gallons to properly cool the rod for each mass. The result from the second function should be a matrix with the first column being the mass of the rod, and the second column the volume of fluid needed.

In addition, you will need to write a program to call the functions using the datasets provided in the final table. You will call each function four times, once for each material. Your function should only consider variables in SI units, so you will need to convert the vectors in the program before passing them to your function as necessary. Note that all conversions must be done in MATLAB code—you may not hard code any values you calculate by hand.

21. Assume you are sent a file name VolumeOfBox.m, which is a function that calculates the volume of a box, given the length (L), width (W), and height (H) in non-specific units. The assumption of the function provided to you is that the length, width, and height variables you provide the function are all measured in the same unit. When you attempt to call the MATLAB function, you notice that it crashes with the following error message:

```
Error using VolumeOfBox
Too many input arguments.
```

The contents of the VolumeOfBox.m file are shown below:

```
function [L,W,H] = VolumeOfBox(V)
% Calculate the volume of a box
V = L * W * H;
```

(a) In your debugging, you have discovered that the error message on the screen means that the function header is incorrect. Write the correct function header.

(b) Write a line of MATLAB code that will call the VolumeOfBox function with the value 3 for the length, 5 for the width, and 7 for the height variables and store the volume calculation in a variable named BoxVol.

22. Assume you are sent a file named GetCostByTime.m, which is a function that calculates two different cost calculations given a time variable (t, non-unit specific) and a scaling factor, S. In the source code, the cost calculations are stored in two variables, M and N. When you attempt to call the MATLAB function, you notice that it crashes with the following error message:

```
Attempt to execute SCRIPT GetCostByTime as a function
```

The contents of the GetCostByTime.m file are shown below:

```
t = t/s;
% Calculate the total cost
M = t^2 + 3*t + 10;
N = t^2 - 2*t + 30;
```

(a) In your debugging, you have discovered that the function header is missing from this file. Write the correct function header for the `GetCostByTime.m` file.

(b) Write a line of MATLAB code that will call the `GetCostByTime` function with the value 360 for the time variable and 60 as the scaling factor and store the two different cost calculations in variables `C1` and `C2`.

23. You have been assigned to a new project at work. The previous engineer had created the following file, which your new boss claims does not work. Debug the program to correct all errors. This file must be corrected to eliminate any syntax, runtime, formula coding, and formula derivation errors. You may assume that the header comments at the top of the program and all comments throughout the program are correct.

```
% Problem Statement: A ball is thrown vertically into the air with an
% initial kinetic energy of 2,500 joules. As the ball rises, it gradually
% loses kinetic energy as its potential energy increases. At the top of
% its flight, when its vertical speed goes to zero, all of the kinetic
% energy has been converted into potential energy. Assume that no energy
% is lost to frictional drag, etc. How high does the ball rise in units of
% meters if it has a mass of 5 kilograms?
% Input Variables
% KE - Kinetic Energy [J]
% m - Mass of ball [kg]
% Output Variables
% H - Max height of ball [m]
% Other Variables
% g - Acceleration due to gravity [m/s^2]
% Assumptions
% No energy losses due to friction
% g = 9.8 m/s^2

clearscreen
clearworkspace

% Set initial variables
2500 = KE;
m = 5 kg;
gravity = 9.8;

% Calculate height, assuming Kinetic Energy = height * mass * gravity
KE(2500) = H * m * g
```

24. You have been assigned to a new project at work. The previous engineer had created the following files, which your new boss claims do not work. Debug the program to correct all errors. These files must be corrected to eliminate any syntax, runtime, formula coding, and formula derivation errors. You may assume that the header comments at the top of the program and all comments throughout the program are correct.

```
% Problem Statement: A cylindrical tank filled to a height of 25 feet with
% tribromoethylene has been pressurized to 3 atmospheres (P_s = 3 atm).
% The total pressure (P_t) at the bottom of the tank is 5 atmospheres.
%
% This program will determine the density of the tribromoethylene
% in units of kilograms per cubic meter.
%
% Inputs:
%      Height              H    25   ft
%      Surface Pressure    P_s  3    atm
%      Total Pressure      P_t  5    atm
% Outputs:
%      Density             rho  ?    kg/m^3
```

```
% Assumptions:
%       Gravity              g      9.8 m/s^2
% Define input variables
25 ft = H;
3 atm = P_s;
5 atm = P_t;
9.8 m/s^2 = g;

% Convert total and surface pressure from atm to Pa
Psurf = P*1,211,458;
P_t = P_t*14.7;

% Convert height from ft to m
H*3.28;

% Calculate density, knowing the calculation of total pressure using equation
% P_t = P_s + (rho)(g)(H)
P_t = P_s + (rho)(g)(H)
```

25. You have been assigned to a new project at work. The previous engineer had created the following files, which your new boss claims do not work. Debug the program to correct all errors.

    These files must be corrected to eliminate any syntax, runtime, formula coding, and formula derivation errors. You may assume that the header comments at the top of the program and all comments throughout the program are correct.

```
% Problem Statement: A rod on the surface of Jupiter's moon Callisto has a volume of
% 0.3 cubic meters and specific gravity of 4.7. The gravitational constant is 1.25
% meters per second squared. Determine the weight of the rod in units of
% pounds-force.
%
% Inputs:
%       Specific Gravity     SG     4.7 [-]
%       Volume               V      0.3 m^3
% Outputs:
%       Weight               w      ??? lbf
% Other variables:
%       Density              rho    ??? kg/m^3
% Assumptions:
%       Gravity              g      1.25 m/s^2
%       Density of water     r_w    1000 kg/m^3

% Define input variables
25 = SG;
g = 1.25 m/s^2;
RHO_water = 1;
VOL = 0.3 m^3;

% Calculate rod density [kg/m^3] using specific gravity
SG=Rho*r_w/1000*62.4;

% Calculate weight of rod
w = (Rho / V) (g);
```

CHAPTER 18
INPUT/OUTPUT IN MATLAB

When writing a program, it is wise to make the program understandable and interactive. This chapter describes the mechanisms in MATLAB that allow the user of a program to input values during runtime. In addition, this chapter describes a few different mechanisms for displaying clean, formatted output to the user so that the results can be read and interpreted.

18.1 INPUT

If all programs required the programmer to enter the input quantities at the beginning of the program, everyone would need to be a computer programmer to use the program. Instead, MATLAB and other programming languages have ways of collecting input from the program's user at runtime. This section focuses on program-directed user input, using three different approaches.

Numerical Input Typed by the User

The **input** function allows the user to input numerical data into MATLAB's Command Window. The user is prompted to input values at the point the input statement occurs in the code.

> Variable = input ('String')

- **Variable:** The variable where the input value will be stored
- **'String':** The text that will prompt the user to type a value

It is important to note the difference between user input and functional input. User input prompts the user in runtime to type in a value. Functional input are values passed in as arguments to a function before a function is executed. Normally, all user input occurs in programs instead of functions.

● **EXAMPLE 18-1**

Imagine you are writing a program to calculate the speed of a traveling rocket. Prompt the user to input the distance the rocket has traveled.

Before writing an input statement, it is critical to remember that MATLAB cannot handle units, so it is up to the programmer to perform any unit conversions necessary in the algorithm. Imagine that the user wants to report the speed of the rocket in miles per hour. It would be wise to have the user input the distance traveled in miles and the travel time in hours.

```
Distance = input('How far has the rocket traveled [miles]?')
Time = input('How long has the rocket been in the air? [hours]')
Speed = Distance/Time
```

In the preceding code segment, the functions were executed without a semicolon being at the end of the input call. If you insert a semicolon at the end of the input call, output of the stored variables to the screen is suppressed, which allows for cleaner display on the Command Window.

```
% Variable output suppressed
Distance = input('How far has the rocket traveled [miles]?');
Time = input('How long has the rocket been in the air [hours]?');
```

NOTE

The use of a semicolon (;) suppresses output to the Command Window.

COMPREHENSION CHECK 18-1

(a) Write an input statement to ask for the user's height in inches.
(b) Write an input statement to ask the user to enter the temperature in degrees Fahrenheit.

Text Input Typed by the User

The input function also allows the user to input text data into MATLAB's Command Window. The programmer must include an additional argument (`'s'`) to the input function to tell MATLAB to interpret the user input as text. The term `'s'` is used to indicate a string.

Variable = input ('String','s')

- *Variable:* The variable where the input value will be stored
- *'String':* The text that will prompt the user to type a value
- *'s':* Input type is text, not numeric

● **EXAMPLE 18-2**

Imagine you are required to ask for the user's name and for the name of the month he/she was born. Suppress all extraneous output.

```
Name = input('Type your full name and press enter: ','s');
DataMonth = input('What month were you born? ','s');
```

COMPREHENSION CHECK 18-2

(a) Write an input statement to ask the user for the color of his/her eyes.
(b) Write an input statement to ask the user to type the current month.

Debugging Input Statements

In the next chapter, you will learn how you can use conditional statements to prevent errors from occuring on the screen due to improper input from the user, but there are some errors that may appear during execution that will impact the flow of your program or function. Consider a simple line of MATLAB code that expects the user to type in a number:

```
M = input ('Type a number:')
```

The correct user behavior when this line of code is executed is to type a number and press enter, however, this is not always the case. Sometimes the user will accidentally include a typo in their input, or in nastier situations, the code might be facing a malicious user attempting to break the code for a variety of reasons. Assume you type the input statement in a program. If the user types the number 4 and presses the Enter key, the variable M contains the number 4, as expected.

```
Type a number: 4
M =

    4
```

However, what happens when the user types in a word or phrase? There are a few different error messages that may appear on the screen when improper text is provided to the input function. Consider the following error message sequence:

```
Type a number: there are four cats outside
Error: Unexpected MATLAB expression.

   Type a number: 4cats
    4cats
      |
   |
 Error: Unexpected MATLAB expression.
   ≫
```

On the user's first attempt, MATLAB simply did not recognize the sequence of non-numeric characters, issued the error message, and redisplayed the prompt for the user to try again. On the second attempt, the user began with a digit, making MATLAB think that the input was valid. However, when the MATLAB input interpreter saw an alphabetic character next, MATLAB became completely confused, issued the error message, terminated the program, and returned to the command prompt. Consider this error message and program termination as MATLAB's way of saying "I have no idea what's going on." If MATLAB has some idea where the error occurs, it will repeat the user provided expression and display the pipe (|) character below the character where it thinks the first invalid character appears.

Consider the following error message sequence:

```
Type a number: four
Error using input
Undefined function or variable 'four'.

Type a number: four+cats
Error using input
Undefined function or variable 'four'.
```

```
Type a number: [4; cats]
Error using input
Undefined function or variable 'cats'.

Type a number: Cats(4)
Error using input
Undefined function 'Cats' for input arguments of type 'double'.
```

In these error messages, the "**Undefined function or variable**" error message indicates that MATLAB is attempting to use the user input as a MATLAB expression and treat some values as variables or function names. In the error messages above, the word in single quotes is the value MATLAB is attempting to interpret as either a function or variable name. None of these input attempts results in program termination, and the user is prompted again for input.

Additionally, the `input` function will attempt to evaluate an expression typed by the user if there are valid variables referenced in the user input value. Assume the variable `rats` is defined in MATLAB's workspace and contains the value 10:

```
Type a number: rats+5
M =

    15
```

This expression did not result in an error message because the `rats` variable existed in MATLAB's workspace, so MATLAB evaluated the expression and stored the result in the variable M.

```
Type a number: Cats = four
Error: The expression to the left of the equals sign is not a valid
target for an assignment.
```

In some error messages, MATLAB may report one problem, but fail to report other issues. In the error message above, MATLAB is complaining about the expression to the left of the equals sign not being a valid target for an assignment. However, this error message fails to point out that the "Cats" and "four" are not variables in MATLAB's workspace. As soon as MATLAB discovers the first problem, it quits looking for additional issues and displays the error on the screen. Removing the equals sign from the input will result in a different error message.

While some values typed as input into MATLAB when the interpreter is expecting numeric input will result in a nasty error message, sometimes no error or warning messages are generated and the program will continue as if it has valid data. Consider the following scenario, using the same `input` expression, where MATLAB is expecting a number, but the user types a word as a string (enclosed by single quotes):

```
Type a number: 'cats'
M =

cats
```

Note that the result of this action is the string `'cats'` being successfully stored in the variable M. This is equivalent to using the `input` function with the extra argument denoting that MATLAB should expect character input, but that method does not require the user to type the input enclosed by single quotes. In the next chapter, you will see how functions like `isnumeric` or `ischar` can be used to determine if a variable is of a particular type, which will be necessary for assuring your program uses valid input of the correct data type.

In addition to allowing the user to type numeric input or a string, MATLAB will also allow the user to provide no input at all. Consider the following scenario, where the user only presses the `Enter` key without typing any other text after the input statement:

```
Type a number:        (no text, the user only pressed Enter)
M =

    []
```

In this situation, the value stored in the variable M is an empty vector, which is different from an empty string or the number zero. The empty vector in MATLAB is an absence of any data and is similar in nature to the concept of having a null value, which is common in other programming languages like C.

Note that all of the scenarios presented here discussed the input statement when it was expecting numeric input. The string input statement will not produce as many errors because the input provided by the user is written to a variable as a sequence of characters verbatim. Even in the scenario where the user presses the `Enter` key without typing any information, the result is an empty string.

```
M = input ('Type a number:','s')
Type any word: cats
M =
cats

Type any word:        (no text, the user only pressed Enter)
M =

    ''

Type any word: 4
M =

4
```

In this final situation, the value 4 is stored in the variable M as a number, even though the input requested a text string. The numerical value could be used in a calculation without an error occurring, or it can be used as a text string.

Menu-Driven Input

In the preceding example, the user was required to type the name of the month he/she were born, but there is no good way to predict the way the user will actually type the name of the month into MATLAB. For example, the user may abbreviate, represent the number numerically, or misspell the name of the month completely. MATLAB has a built-in input function (**menu**) that allows the programmer to specify a list of options for user selection. The menu function will display a graphical prompt of a question and responses.

Variable = menu ('String', 'opt1','opt2',...)

- ■ ***Variable:*** The variable where the ordinal value will be stored
- ■ ***'String':*** The text that will prompt the user to select an item in the menu
- ■ ***'optN':*** The options that appear as buttons in the menu

The first argument of the menu function is always the question to display (`'String'`), and the following arguments are the possible responses. The menu function does not store the actual text response, but rather the ordinal number of the response in the list. An example will help clarify this idea.

● **EXAMPLE 18-3**

Suppose we want to ask the user to input a favorite color. However, we want to force the user to choose from red, green, or blue. Suppress all extraneous output.

```
Color = menu('Favorite Color','Red','Green','Blue');
```

This command will create the menu shown. The value returned upon selection is an integer. For example, if the user were to select "Red" in the menu, the value stored in Color *would be 1 since "Red" is the first option available in the list.*

COMPREHENSION CHECK 18-3

(a) Create a menu to ask the user to select the current month.
(b) Given the menu statement below, what is stored in variable C when the user clicks "Red"?

```
C = menu('My favorite color:','Green','Blue','Yellow',
'Black','Red')
```

In addition to the menu function, the **questdlg** function will allow you to create a pop up dialog that allows the user to respond by clicking one of up to three different options for answers. The default buttons are yes, no, and cancel, although these can be customized by the programmer. The questdlg function returns the text shown on the button clicked, not the ordinal value.

> Variable = questdlg ('qstring', 'title', 'opt1', 'opt2', 'opt3')

- ■ ***Variable:*** The variable where the ordinal value will be stored
- ■ ***'qstring':*** The question being asked
- ■ ***'title':*** Creates a title in the dialog box title bar
- ■ ***'optN':*** The options that appear as buttons. If nothing is listed, the options will be yes, no, and cancel.

Consider the following example:

```
A = questdlg ('My favorite color is green', 'Color')
```

If the user chooses the No button, then the word "No" will be stored in the variable A.

In the example below, the dialog box shown is created.

```
A = questdlg ('My favorite season is…', 'Season','Winter',
    'Summer','Other')
```

Similarly, the **inputdlg** function will display a graphical input box to the user to allow them to type a string into boxes rather than typing their responses into the Command Window. Consider the following example:

```
K = inputdlg('Enter your name')
```

For more information on these functions, refer to MATLAB's documentation on the questdlg and inputdlg functions.

18.2 OUTPUT

LEARN TO: Display the contents of a variable using `disp`
Create formatted display (in sentences) using `fprintf`
Save formatted output to a string using `sprintf`

As critical as input is to enhancing the versatility of a program, output is equally important—this is how the user gets feedback on the computer's solution. Furthermore, as discussed earlier, program output of intermediate calculations is an important diagnostic tool. Once a program is working correctly, you should eliminate superfluous program output by using the semicolon, as demonstrated earlier. The program user will also find it helpful if the remaining output is neatly formatted.

Using `disp` for User Output

One of the basic methods for displaying the contents of any variable is through the use of the **disp** function.

> disp (Variable)

- *Variable:* The variable to be displayed on the screen

Given some variable x defined in MATLAB's Workspace, `disp(x)` displays the value of x to the screen. However, the `disp` command cannot display a value and text on the same line. Furthermore, `disp` relies on using MATLAB's default numerical display format for displaying any numbers, so it does not provide a capability for changing the form in which the number is displayed.

Formatting Output with `fprintf`

The formatted print command, **fprintf**, gives extensive control over the output format, including spacing.

> fprintf ('String', Var1, Var2, …)

- *'String':* The formatted output string
- *VarN:* The variables or values to be inserted into the formatted output string

The `fprintf` command can intersperse precisely formatted numbers within text, guarantee table alignment, align the decimal points of a column of numbers, etc. The `fprintf` command uses control and format codes to achieve this level of precision, as shown in Tables 18-1 and 18-2.

Table 18-1 Output control with `fprintf`

Control Character	Use	Example
\n	Inserts a new line	`fprintf('Hello\n');`
\t	Inserts a tab	`fprintf('A\tB\tC\n');`
\\	Inserts a backslash	`fprintf('Hello\\World\n');`
'' (two single quotes)	Inserts a single quote mark	`fprintf('Bob''s car\n');`
%%	Inserts a percent symbol	`fprintf('25%%');`

The biggest benefit of using `fprintf` is the ability to plug values contained in variables into formatted sentences. In addition to the formatting controls shown above, MATLAB contains a number of special controls to represent different types of variables that might be displayed within a sentence. Inserting a variable control character within a string tells MATLAB to plug in a variable at that location in the string. Note that MATLAB's documentation on `fprintf` contains additional control characters not covered in this textbook that you may find useful in your programming.

Table 18-2 Variable (numeric) and TextVariable (text) control with `fprintf`

Control Character	Use	Example: Variable = 13/15;
%f	Inserts a value shown to 6 decimal places	`fprintf('%f', Variable)` 0.866667 is displayed
%0.Mf	Inserts a fixed point value with M decimal places	`fprintf('%0.1f',Variable);` 0.9 is displayed
%N.Mf	Inserts a value with a field width of N (left padded with spaces), containing M decimal places	`fprintf('%7.2f',Variable)` _ _ _ 0.87 is displayed, where _ indicates a blank space
%0N.Mf	Inserts a value with a field width of N (left padded with zeros), containing M decimal places	`fprintf('%07.2f',Variable)` 0000.87 is displayed
%e or %E	Inserts a number in exponential notation	`fprintf('%e',Variable);` 8.66667e-01 is displayed `fprintf('%0.3E',Variable);` 8.667E-01 will display
%s	Inserts text	`fprintf('%s',TextVariable);`

● **EXAMPLE 18-4**   Assume that the following variables are defined in MATLAB's Workspace:

```
Age=20;
Average=79.939;
Food='pizza';
Postal=515;
```

Display the variables in formatted `fprintf` statements. At the end of each formatted output statement, insert a new line.

Since age is a decimal value, it is best to use the `%0.0f` *control character:*

```
fprintf('My age is %0.0f.\n',Age);
```

To display the average with two decimal places:

```
fprintf('The average is %0.2f.\n',Average);
```

Note that MATLAB rounds values when using `%f`*.*

To display a string within a sentence:

```
fprintf('My favorite food is %s.',Food);
```

To display a postal code, the field width of a postal code is typically five numbers long:

```
fprintf('My postal code is %05.0f.\n',Postal);
```

● **EXAMPLE 18-5**   Assume the variables in Example 18-4 are still defined in the workspace. Create a single formatted output statement that displays each sentence with a line break between each sentence.

```
fprintf('My age is %0.0f.\n The average is %0.2f.\n
My favorite food is %s.\n My postal code is %05.0f.\n',
Age,Average,Food,Postal);
```

In MATLAB, the previous line would be typed on a single line. Note that the order of the arguments to the function corresponds to the order of the variables in the string.

COMPREHENSION CHECK 18-4

Assume that the variable M is stored in the workspace with the value 0.3539.

(a) What would be the control code used to display M with two decimal places?
(b) What would be the control code used to display M with three decimal places in scientific notation?
(c) What would be the output of M if a control code is used to display it to two decimal places?
(d) What would be the output of M if a control code is used to display it to three decimal places in scientific notation?
(e) What would be the output of M if a control code is used to pad the field width to 10 characters, using zero padding, and showing 3 decimal places?

COMPREHENSION CHECK 18-5

Consider the following segment of code. What appears in the Command Window if this is executed?

```
clear
clc
S=[2012,27,17;2011,34,13;2010,29,7];
fprintf('Clemson-USC Football Rivalry:\n\n');
fprintf('Year\tUSC\t\tClemson\n');
fprintf('%0.0f\t%0.0f\t\t%0.0f\n',S(1,1),S(1,2),S(1,3));
fprintf('%0.0f\t%0.0f\t\t%0.0f\n',S(2,1),S(2,2),S(2,3));
fprintf('%0.0f\t%0.0f\t\t%0.0f\n',S(3,1),S(3,2),S(3,3));
```

Saving formatted output in a string: `sprintf`

The `fprintf` function is clearly the best tool available for displaying textual information on the screen, complete with handling the appropriate number of decimal places and plugging in values of different types of variables so the information can be read and interpreted by the user. In certain scenarios, it may be desired to create a formatted string, saved in MATLAB's workspace, similar to the way MATLAB can format a sentence for output to the screen. The **sprintf** function uses the same syntax as the `fprintf` function to create formatted text, complete with formatting codes and variables, but the result of the `sprintf` function is stored into a variable that will contain the formatted text as a string variable.

● EXAMPLE 18-6

Assume that the following variables are defined in MATLAB's workspace:

```
Age = 20;
Average = 79.939;
Food = 'pizza';
Postal = 515;
```

To create strings of the formatted text displayed in the previous example, the `sprintf` function can be used instead of the `fprintf` function. Assume that it is desired to store the formatted strings into variables `Str1`, `Str2`, `Str3`, and `Str4`.

Since age is a decimal value, it is best to use the `%0.0f` *control character:*

```
Str1 = sprintf ('My age is %0.0f\n',Age);
```

To display the average with two decimal places:

```
Str2 = sprintf ('The average is %0.2f\n',Average);
```

To display a string within a sentence:

```
Str3 = sprintf ('My favorite food is %s\n',Food);
```

To display a postal code, the field width of a postal code is typically five numbers long:

```
Str4 = sprintf ('My postal code is %05.0f\n',Postal);
```

18.3 PLOTTING

LEARN TO: Create proper plots using `plot` and `fplot`
Create logarithmic plots with `loglog`, `semilogx`, and `semilogy`
Create multiple plots in a figure with `subplot`

MATLAB has many plotting options, not all of which concern us in this book. The simplest way to create in MATLAB is the **plot** command.

Plotting Variables

If the vectors `time` and `distance` contain paired data, `plot(time,distance)` will plot the time data on the abscissa and the distance data on the ordinate.

In addition to time and distance, assume a second distance vector, `distance2`, contains additional distance recordings at the same time values in `time`. To plot both `distance` and `distance2` on the same graph, the plot command will contain both the `distance` and `distance2` vectors: `plot(time,distance,time,distance2)`.

---

plot (A,B,C,...)

- *A:* The horizontal axis values
- *B:* The vertical axis values
- *C:* (Optional) Specification of the line/symbol type/color
- *A,B,C:* Can be repeated for multiple data series (`plot (A1,B1,C1,A2,B2,C2)`)

Creating Proper Plots

A number of other functions allow the programmer to automatically insert information onto a graph generated in MATLAB. Many plot options are defined by separate commands, discussed below. These can be applied when the plot is created or afterwards, as long as the plot is unchanged.

- **close all:** A command to close all currently open figures. This is especially helpful when developing the code to generate your plot.
    ```
    close all
    ```
- **xlabel:** Insert a label on the abscissa.
    ```
    xlabel('Time (t) [s]')
    ```
- **ylabel:** Insert a label on the ordinate.
    ```
    ylabel('Height (H) [m]')
    ```
- **title:** Insert a title. This is optional, and should not be used if the graph will be used in another presentation format (such as a report) and a caption will accompany the graph.
    ```
    title('Flight Across The United States')
    ```
- **legend:** Insert a legend on the graph if more than one data series is present. The order of elements provided in the legend is based on the order they are passed into the plot function.
    ```
    legend('Airplane 1','Airplane 2')
    ```
- **grid:** Allows the grid to be turned on or off.
    ```
    grid on
    ```

■ **axis:** Allows the setting of the minimum and maximum values on the abscissa and ordinate, in that order.

```
axis([0 50000 0 90000])
```

Alternately, the functions `xlim` and `ylim` can be used to define the [minimum, maximum] limits on the abscissa and ordinate, respectively.

The following examples use several special graphing commands. For more information on graphing properties, refer to the MATLAB Graphing Properties, Linespec, and Special Character reference tables contained in the endpages of your textbook.

● **EXAMPLE 18-7**   Create a graph of multiple experimental data series for the following data:

H1 = [10, 15, 25, 35, 55];   H2 = [10, 30, 50, 70, 100];
P1 = [0.27, 0.41, 0.68, 0.95, 1.5];   P2 = [0.11, 0.33, 0.54, 0.76, 1.09];

```
clear
clc
H1=[10, 15, 25, 35, 55];    H2=[10, 30, 50, 70, 100];
P1=[0.27,0.41,0.68,0.95,1.5];
P2=[0.11,0.33,0.54,0.76,1.09];
plot(H1,P1,'o',H2,P2,'+');
axis([0 120 0 1.75]);
title('Experimental Data, Multiple Data Series Plot');
legend('Mass = 100 kg','Mass = 250 kg');
xlabel('Height (H) [m]');
ylabel('Power (P) [hp]');
grid on
```

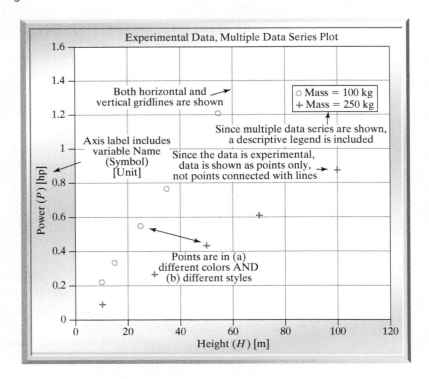

Figure 18-1 Example of a proper plot, showing multiple experimental data sets

Plotting Theoretical Expressions

Another way MATLAB can plot a function is by using **fplot**.

The way the function fplot works is to create a function of the variable (*x*), which takes the range [*a b*] in the following format:

fplot ('function(x)', [a b])

- ***function(x)*** is the function to be plotted, in terms of variable *x*.
- ***[a b]*** are the limits on the variable *x*.

It can only use a SINGLE VARIABLE for the function variable, such as an **x** or a **t** or an **m**. So, for example, try to run this plot:

```
fplot ('100*x + 52 / x + 11', [10 30])
```

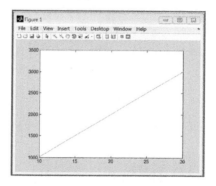

Then try this:

```
fplot ('[100*m + 52, 300*m + 100]', [10 30])
```

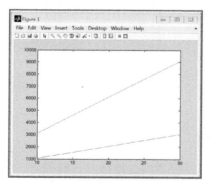

This, however, will result in an error:

```
t = 25;
x = 10;
fplot ('x*m + t', [10 30])
```

Since fplot is unable to use variables defined in the program, it has limited usefulness.

● **EXAMPLE 18-8**   Create a graph of a single theoretical data series using `fplot` of the following function, from $x = 0$ to 60: $y = 0.0273\,x + 0.05$:

```
clear
clc
fplot('0.0273*x+0.05',[0 60]);
title('Theoretical Data, Single Data Series Plot');
xlabel('Mass (m) [g]');
ylabel('Density (\rho) [g/cm^3]');
grid on
```

The same graph can be created using the `plot` *function. If no marker style is specified, the program will draw a line.*

```
clear
clc
x = [0 60];
plot(x,0.0273*x+0.05);
title('Theoretical Data, Single Data Series Plot');
xlabel('Mass(m)[g]');
ylabel('Density(\rho)[g/cm^3]');
grid on
```

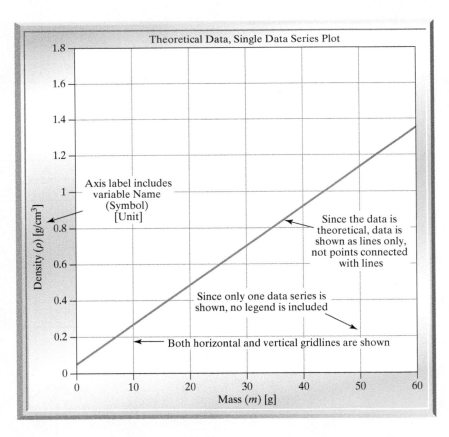

Figure 18-2 Example of a proper plot, showing a single theoretical data set.

● **EXAMPLE 18-9**

Create a graph of multiple experimental data series on logarithmic axes for the following data:

R1 = [10, 30, 50, 70, 100];   R2 = [10, 15, 25, 35, 55];
V1 = [0.11, 0.33, 0.54, 0.76, 1.09];   V2 = [0.27, 0.41, 0.68, 0.95, 1.5];

```
clear
clc
R1=[10,30,50,70,100];
V1=[0.11,0.33,0.54,0.76,1.09];
R2=[10,15,25,35,55];
V2=[0.27,0.41,0.68,0.95,1.5];
loglog(R1,V1,'s',R2,V2,'o');
grid on
xlim([1 100]);
ylim([0.1 10]);
title('Logarithmic, Experimental, Multiple Data Series Plot');
xlabel('Radius (R) [cm]');
ylabel('Volume (V) [cm^3]');
legend('Cylinder #1','Cylinder #2')
```

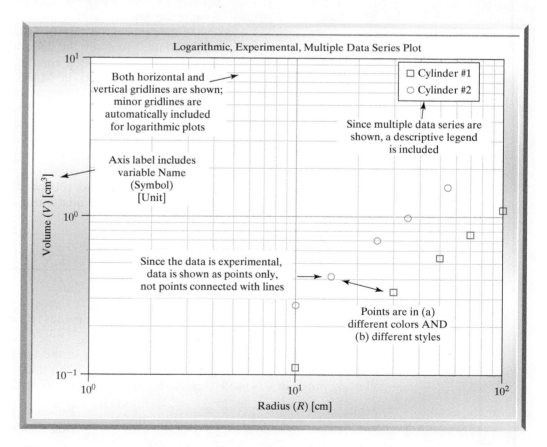

Figure 18-3 Example of a proper plot, showing multiple experimental data sets and logarithmic axes.

Creating Figures in MATLAB

NOTE

`figure` = Creates a new drawing window

When MATLAB creates a new plot, it automatically draws the plot to a "Figure" window. If a Figure window is already open, MATLAB will replace the current plot with the new plot within this window. To create multiple plot windows, type the command `figure` to create a new window before drawing your next plot. Add all titles, *x*- and *y*-axis labels, etc., before you initiate the `figure` command, because those functions execute to the newest figure. If you need to reference a previous figure, you can type `figure(N)`, where N is the number of the figure. By default, MATLAB names the first figure created Figure 1 and increases figure number by 1 as new figures are created.

It is also possible to control the background color of the figure window using the `figure` command. This may be desirable if the figure will appear in another type of publication, such as a report or presentation.

```
figure('color','white')
```

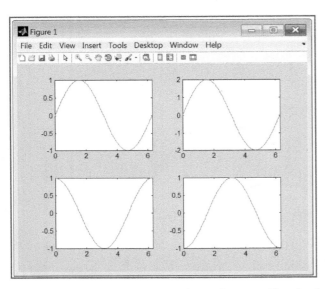

Using Subplots in MATLAB

In addition to generating single plots, MATLAB can generate multiple plots, called subplots, in a single window. This can make it easier to compare the results of different cases or to study a process from a variety of perspectives simultaneously.

In the figure shown to the left, the `fplot` command has been used to study the effect of changing the input parameters to the general sine function $A \sin(Bx + C)$. Notice that even plots in MATLAB are arranged in matrices. The command to generate the grouping of plots is shown below. Note that parameter A is amplitude, B is frequency, and C represents a phase shift.

The **subplot** command is a void function that accepts three inputs, but generates no output on the screen. As soon as the `subplot` command is executed, the next plotting command and related plotting functions will apply to that specific plot in the `subplot` until the next `subplot` command appears in the code.

---

subplot (R,C,N)

- **R:** The number of rows of plots to appear in the figure.
- **C:** The number of columns of plots to appear in the figure.
- **N:** The position in the subplot where the plot commands following the subplot command will apply.

The graph positions, N, are numbered starting in the top-left corner and going across each row, starting with the number 1 and ending with the value of R × C. The following program was used to create the subplot figure shown:

```
subplot(2,2,1),fplot('sin(x)',[0 2*pi])        plots sin(x) in top left
subplot(2,2,2),fplot('2*sin(x)',[0 2*pi])      plots 2 sin(x) in top right
subplot(2,2,3),fplot('sin(x+pi/2)',[0 2*pi])   plots sin(x + π/2) in bottom left
subplot(2,2,4),fplot('sin(x-pi/2)',[0 2*pi])   plots sin(x − π/2) in bottom right
```

● **EXAMPLE 18-10**   Create a graph from the previous two examples on the same figure with 2 rows in a single column.

```
clear
clc
figure('color', 'white')
subplot(2,1,1);
fplot('0.0273*x+0.05',[0 60];
title('Theoretical Data, Single Data Series Plot');
xlabel('Mass (m) [g]');
ylabel('Density (\rho) [g/cm^3]');
grid on
R1=[10,30,50,70,100];
V1=[0.11,0.33,0.54,0.76,1.09];
R2=[10,15,25,35,55];
V2=[0.27,0.41,0.68,0.95,1.5];
subplot(2,1,2);
loglog(R1,V1,'s',R2,V2,'o');
grid on
xlim([1 100]);
ylim([0.1 10]);
title('Logarithmic, Experimental, Multiple Data Plot');
xlabel('Radius (R) [cm]');
ylabel('Volume (V) [cm^3]');
legend('Cylinder #1', 'Cylinder #2')
```

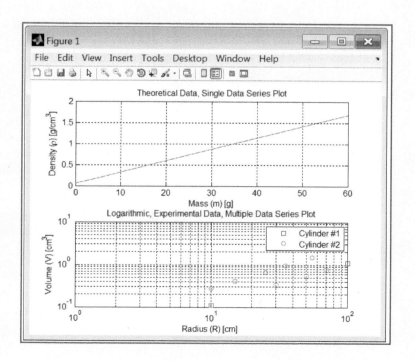

Figure 18-4 Example of a proper plot using subplots of the form 2 rows, 1 column.

18.4 POLYFIT

In the chapters on Models and Systems, three general models of importance to engineers were discussed in detail: **linear**, **power**, and **exponential**. In software programs like Microsoft Excel, built-in trendline tools will allow you to add lines representing a "best-fit" mathematical model to data sets on graphs. In MATLAB, the **polyfit** function will allow a programmer to pass in two equally sized vectors and determine the polynomial of order n that best fits the data. Consider the generic form of a polynomial:

$$p(x) = C_n X^n + C_{n-1} X^{n-1} + \cdots + C_1 X + C_0$$

In the equation above, the coefficients $(C_n, C_{n-1}, \ldots, C_1, C_0)$ are returned by the `polyfit` function, given the order of the polynomial (n) in the input.

The syntax of `polyfit` is:

> C = polyfit (X, Y, n)

- **C:** Vector of the resulting coefficients. Note that $C(1)$, the first element of the vector C, contains the coefficient by the highest power of the variable listed in the equation, C_n.
- **X:** Vector of values that correspond to the abscissa
- **Y:** Vector (of equal length to X) of values that correspond to the ordinate
- **n:** is the order of the polynomial. For a linear relationship, n = 1.

Graphing a Trendline in MATLAB

1. Create a proper plot of the data.
2. Determine if the form of the relationship is linear, power, or exponential.
3. Use the appropriate `polyfit` command based on Step 2 to determine the parameters "m" and "b" for the trendline equation.
4. Create a theoretical data set to form the trendline. Use a reasonable range based on the experimental range for the "x" values. Use the parameters from Step 3 and the theoretical "x" values. For example: x = [1:1:10] ; y = m*x + b;
5. Add the theoretical data set (x,y) to the graph created in Step 1.
6. Add the proper plot elements, such as the trendline equation, to complete the graph.

MATLAB examples

Linear Relationships

Linear relationship takes the form $y = mx + b$, where m is the slope of the line and b is the y-intercept. Linear relationships are discussed in detail in the Models and Systems chapter. The syntax of `polyfit` for a linear relationship is:

```
C = polyfit (X, Y, 1)
m = C(1)
b = C(2)
```

● **EXAMPLE 18-11**

You are part of a firm designing nanoscale speedometers to measure speeds of small moving creatures like centipedes. To test your sensor, you place a centipede on a surface marked with a grid calibrated in millimeters and measure the following data, given in MATLAB notation. Use the data to create a graph and a mathematical model.

```
T=[0, 20, 40, 60, 80, 100, 120];      % time (t) [s]
D=[0, 105, 197, 310, 390, 502, 599];  % distance (d) [mm]
```

Step 1. *Write the code to create a graph of the experimental data set [T, D]. To save space, most proper plot commands are not included here; see Example 18-7 above.*

```
plot(T,D,'dr')
```

Step 2. *This is a linear relationship.*

Step 3. *To determine the trendline parameters using the* `polyfit` *function:*

```
C=polyfit(T,D,1)
```

Note the resulting elements in `C([4.9714, 2.1429])` *are the parameters "m" and "b" of the linear equation.*

Step 4. *Create a theoretical data set in MATLAB:*

```
T2=[0:5:120];
D2=m*T2+b;
```

Step 5. *To plot the trendline as a straight, red solid line, use the* `hold` *on function to add the trendline to the original graph:*

```
hold on
plot(T2,D2,'-r');
```

Step 6. *To add a trendline equation, use the* `sprintf` *function to convert the numbers stored in variables m and b into strings and concatenate all of the strings into a single string variable:*

```
TE=sprintf('d = %0.0f t + %0.0f',m,b);
```

To add this expression on your graph near the trendline, you will need to provide coordinates where the equation should be shown using the `text` *function. The coordinates are*

NOTE

The values for x- and
y-coordinates use
the actual coordinate
values on the plot.
The center-left end of
the text string will be
located at those
coordinates.

*determined by examining the resulting graph, and choosing a location that does not interfere
with the data. Sometimes, it is easiest to create the graph, run the code, then alter the code
to include the text location.*

```
text(45,450,TE)
```

which take the form **text(x coordinate, y coordinate, variable).**

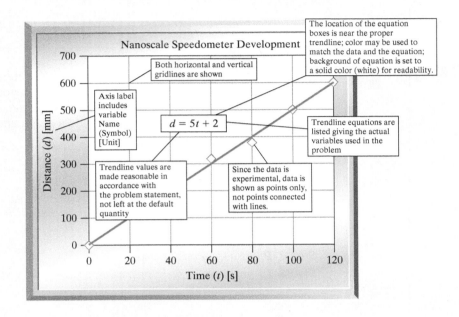

Figure 18-5 Example of a
proper plot, showing single
experimental data set with
a linear trendline.

Power Relationships

A power relationship takes the form: $y = bx^m$. Unfortunately, MATLAB does not have a
nice, clean function like `polyfit` for power functions, so some simple math must be performed in order to use the `polyfit` function with a power relationship. If we take the log
of both sides of the general power relationship equation, we get:

$$\log(y) = m \log(x) + \log(b)$$

NOTE

Many computer appli-
cations and calculators
use `log` for the base
10 logarithm and `ln`
for the natural loga-
rithm. It is easy to for-
get that MATLAB is
different, so be careful!

Power law relationships, including this derivation, are discussed in detail in the Models
and Systems chapter. This expression is similar to an order-1 polynomial, so we can use
`polyfit` to create a linear fit between log(x) and log(y) to calculate the value of m
and log(b). Note that this calculation requires the use of the common (base 10) logarithm, not the natural logarithm. **In MATLAB, the base-10 logarithm function is `log10`
and the natural logarithm function is `log`.**

Assuming abscissa and ordinate values are stored in variables X and Y respectively:

```
C = polyfit (log10 (X), log10 (Y),1)
m = C(1)
b = 10^C(2)
```

For power relationships, it is possible to use the natural logarithm instead of the common logarithm. The difference is how you calculate the values of b.

```
C = polyfit(log(X),log(Y),1)

m = C(1)

b = exp(C(2))
```

Using either the common log or natural log for performing these calculations is correct as long as the calculation of b is handled appropriately.

● **EXAMPLE 18-12**

Joule's first law, also known as the Joule effect, relates the heat generated to current flowing in a conductor. It is named for James Prescott Joule, the same person for whom the unit of Joule is named. The Joule effect states that the electric power (P) can be calculated as $P = I^2R$, where R is the resistance in ohms and I is the electrical current in amperes. The following data are collected in MATLAB notation. Use the data to create a graph and a mathematical model.

```
I=[0.50,1.25,1.50,2.05,2.25,3.00,3.20,3.50];    % Current (I) [A]
P=[1.2,7.5,11.25,20,25,45,50,65];               % Power (P) [W]
```

Step 1. Write the code to create a graph of the experimental data set [I, P]. To save space, most proper plot commands are not included here; see Example 18-7 above.

```
plot(I,P,'sb')
```

Step 2. This is a power relationship.

Step 3. To determine the trendline parameters:

```
C=polyfit(log10(I),log10(P),1)
m=C(1);
b=10^C(2);
```

Step 4. Create a theoretical data set in MATLAB:

```
I2=[0.5:0.5:3.5];
P2=b*I2^m;
```

Step 5. To plot the trendline as a straight, blue solid line, use the hold on function:

```
hold on
plot(I2,P2,'-b');
```

Step 6. To add a trendline equation to your graph, use the sprintf function to convert the numbers stored in variables n and b into a single string variable:

```
TE = sprintf('P = %3.1f I^%1.0f',b,m);
text(1,55,TE)
```

NOTE

When placing a text string on a figure, the caret (^) says to subscript the next single character or subscript the contents of braces { } immediately following.

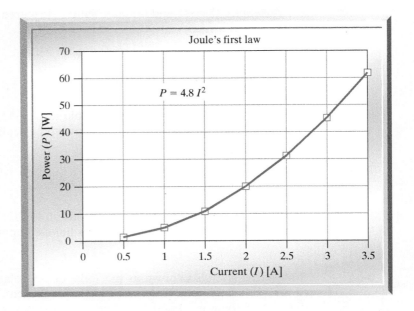

Exponential Relationships

An exponential relationship takes the form: $y = be^{mx}$. Once again, MATLAB does not have a nice, clean function like `polyfit` for exponential functions, so some math must be performed again in order to use the `polyfit` function with an exponential relationship. If we take the natural log of both sides of the general exponential relationship equation, we get:

$$\ln(y) = mx + \ln(b)$$

Experimental relationships, including this derivation, are discussed in detail in the Models and Systems chapter. This expression is similar to an order-1 polynomial, so we can use `polyfit` to create a linear fit between x and $\ln(y)$ to calculate the value of m and $\ln(b)$. Recall that the natural logarithm function in MATLAB is `log`. Assuming our abscissa and ordinate values are stored in variables X and Y, respectively:

```
C = polyfit (X, log(Y), 1)
m = C(1)
b = exp(C(2))
```

● EXAMPLE 18-13   A reaction is carried out in a closed vessel. The following data are taken for the concentration of the organic material as a function of time from the start of the reaction. A proposed mechanism to predict the concentration at any given time is $C = C_0\, e^{-kt}$, where k is the reaction rate constant and C_0 is the initial concentration of the species at time zero. The following data are collected in MATLAB notation. Use the data to create a graph and a mathematical model.

```
T=[36,65,100,160];            % Time (t) [min]
C=[0.145,0.120,0.100,0.080];  % Concentration (C) [g / L]
```

Step 1. *Write the code to create a graph of the experimental data set [T, C]. To save space, most proper plot commands are not included here; see Example 18-7 above.*

```
plot(T,C,'*g')
```

Step 2. *This is an exponential relationship.*

Step 3. *To determine the trendline parameters:*

```
P=polyfit(T,log(C),1)
m=P(1);
b=exp(P(2));
```

Step 4. *Create a theoretical data set in MATLAB:*

```
T2=[20:10:160];
C2=b*exp(m*T2);
```

NOTE

When placing a text string on a figure, the caret (^) says to subscript the next single character or subscript the contents of braces { } immediately following.

Step 5. *Plot the trendline*

```
hold on
plot(T2,C2,'-.g');
```

Step 6. *Add a trendline equation to the graph.*

```
TE=sprintf('C = %3.2f e^{%4.3ft}',b,m);
text(43,0.085,TE);
```

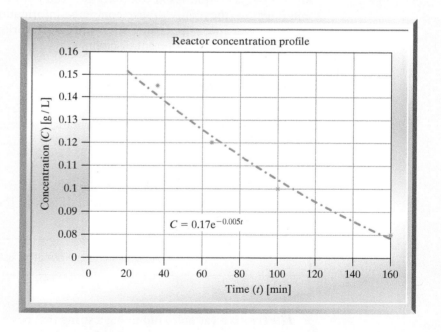

18.5 MICROSOFT EXCEL I/O

LEARN TO: Read basic Microsoft Excel workbook info with `xlsfinfo`
Read Microsoft Excel workbooks with `xlsread`
Write to Microsoft Excel workbooks with `xlswrite`

WARNING FOR MAC USERS!

Due to incompatibilities between Microsoft Excel and the Mac OS version of MATLAB 2012 and earlier, you must run at least MATLAB version 2012 in Microsoft Windows in order to use the built-in Excel I/O (input/output) functions discussed in this document. MATLAB 2013 handles Excel I/O on both platforms. In any case, Microsoft Office must be installed on the matching Operating System to use the Excel I/O functions.

In this section, you will learn to read data from Microsoft Excel workbooks into MATLAB and write information from MATLAB to an Excel workbook. File input and output is ubiquitous in computer programming if you want to give your programs and functions the ability to save computed information for use at a later time. We discuss file input and output using Microsoft Excel workbooks because it is a common file format used in many different disciplines.

Reading Microsoft Excel Workbooks

For importing data from Excel files, there are two built-in functions in MATLAB that will allow us to read in all of the information we need from our Excel files; they are `xlsfinfo` and `xlsread`.

xlsfinfo

The **xlsfinfo** function in MATLAB allows us to extract information about Microsoft Excel files stored in MATLAB's current directory. The `xlsfinfo` function will return three outputs:

[FileType, Sheets, ExcelFormat] = xlsfinfo (filename)

where

- **FileType** is a variable containing a string that describes the type of the file. If we call `xlsfinfo` on a file that is not a Microsoft Excel workbook, this string will be empty (' '); otherwise, 'Microsoft Excel Spreadsheet' will be saved in the `FileType` variable. This is not particularly helpful information, but does give us a mechanism for determining whether or not the file we are trying to open is a valid Microsoft Excel workbook.
- **Sheets** is a cell array variable containing the names of each worksheet within the Excel workbook. Each sheet name is stored as text within the cell array.
- **ExcelFormat** is a variable containing a string that describes the version of the Microsoft Excel workbook. In general, this information is not useful, but if the string is blank, it is an indicator that Microsoft Excel is not installed on your computer.

- *fileName* is the name of the Microsoft Excel file in which we are interested. The file name must be passed into `xlsfinfo` as a string and must contain the file extension of the Microsoft Excel workbook as part of the file name. The file extension of Microsoft Excel workbooks is usually .xls or .xlsx.

The following examples will use the starter file titled "ClemsonWeather.xlsx" found in the online materials. If you open the file, you will notice that there are three worksheets within the workbook, each containing day-by-day weather information for Clemson, SC, in 2008 to 2010.

For each day, we have the following values recorded the high-, average-, and low-temperature readings measured in degrees Fahrenheit (`TempHighF`, `TempAvgF`, `TempLowF`).

xlsread

The **xlsread** function allows us to read in data from Microsoft Excel workbooks.

There are a number of different variations on how `xlsread` can be used, but we will only learn about a few of the variants involving different combinations of arguments and returned values.

If we want to tell `xlsread` to import values from a particular worksheet, we can use the following syntax:

```
D = xlsread (filename, Sheet)
```

where

- *fileName* is the name of the Excel workbook including the file extension, as a string.
- *Sheet* is a string containing the name of the Excel worksheet we want to import into our variable D.

● EXAMPLE 18-14

Use `xlsread` to import all of the weather data from 2008 from ClemsonWeather.xlsx.

```
WD08 = xlsread('ClemsonWeather.xlsx','2008');
```

If we open `WD08` in MATLAB's Variable Editor, we can verify that our matrix contains all of the numeric values in the "2008" worksheet, beginning at cell B2. Notice that the dimension of `WD08` is 366 × 15, which is what we expected since 2008 was a leap year.

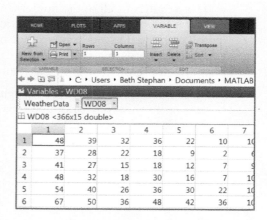

If we only want to import a particular range of an Excel file, we can add in another argument into `xlsread` that will allow us to type in ranges of values. For example, if we only wanted to import all of the cells between B2 and B5, we could provide a range B2:B5 just like we would type into Microsoft Excel.

D = xlsread (filename, Sheet, Range)

---

where

- ***fileName*** is the name of the Excel workbook including the file extension, as a string.
- ***Sheet*** is a string containing the name of the Excel worksheet we want to import into our variable D.
- ***Range*** is a string containing the cell range written in Microsoft Excel notation.

● **EXAMPLE 18-15**   Use `xlsread` to import the first 10 high temperatures from 2009 from file ClemsonWeather.xlsx. If we open ClemsonWeather.xlsx in Microsoft Excel, we notice that the first 10 values occur between B2 and B11.

```
WD09 = xlsread('ClemsonWeather.xlsx','2009','B2:B11');
```

MATLAB creates a 10×1 matrix *containing a column of values representing the first 10 high temperatures recorded in 2009.*

If we need to extract any of the text information from the Excel Workbook, we need to modify our syntax to capture two outputs from `xlsread`. To extract nonnumeric values from an Excel Workbook:

[D, T] = xlsread (filename, Sheet)

---

where

- ***fileName*** is the name of the Excel workbook including the file extension, as a string.
- ***Sheet*** is a string containing the name of the Excel worksheet we want to import.
- ***D*** is a matrix of all of the numeric values in Sheet.
- ***T*** is a cell matrix of all nonnumeric (text, dates, etc.) values in the worksheet. If a cell contains a numeric value, that value will be stored as an empty string (' ') in T. In other words, matrix D and T will not necessarily have the same dimensions. For more information, refer to the examples below.

It is worth noting that even though we are using the syntax requiring a sheet name to save text values, any of the previously covered notations will allow you to capture text values in an Excel worksheet.

● EXAMPLE 18-16

Use `xlsread` to import the first 10 high temperatures and the corresponding text values for the dates from 2009 from ClemsonWeather.xlsx. In the worksheet, the first 10 values occur between B2 and B11 and the dates are listed between A2 and A11, so the range we need to import is A2:B11.

```
[WD09,WT09] = xlsread('ClemsonWeather.xlsx','2009','A2:B11');
```

MATLAB creates two 10 × 1 matrices containing a column of values representing the first 10 high temperatures recorded in 2009 in WD09 and the corresponding text dates in a cell matrix WT09. In this special case, since the entire second column in WT09 was blank (all values were numeric), MATLAB automatically removed the second column so that WT09 is a 10 × 1 matrix.

● EXAMPLE 18-17

Use `xlsread` to import the numeric and nonnumeric values in the 2009 sheet in ClemsonWeather.xlsx.

```
[D09,T09] = xlsread('ClemsonWeather.xlsx','2009');
```

If we look at the dimensions of D09 and T09, we note that D09 is a 365 × 15 matrix, but T09 is a 366 × 16 cell matrix. This is due to the fact that T09 contains the header row with all of the column labels, as well as the entire first column containing the corresponding dates. If we examine T09 in the Variable Editor, we see that the only values in the cell matrix are the first row and first column and all of the other values in the cell matrix are empty strings (''). In light of these phenomena, special care must be taken when attempting to write MATLAB code that attempts to relate cell matrices and numeric data matrices imported using `xlsread`.

Writing Microsoft Excel Workbooks

MATLAB provides a built-in function, **xlswrite**, that enables MATLAB to export data to writing Microsoft Excel workbooks.

xlswrite

Just like with xlsread, xlswrite accepts different syntax for different writing scenarios. For the sake of brevity, we will only cover the standard use of xlswrite, but refer to MATLAB's help and doc documentation for more information. The function Xlswrite returns no output and only requires input arguments:

xlswrite (fileName, Matrix, Sheet, Cell)

where

- *fileName* is a string containing the file name you want to write to. If the Excel file does not exist, MATLAB will create a blank workbook with three blank worksheets ('Sheet1,' 'Sheet2,' and 'Sheet3') and display a warning "Warning: Added specified worksheet." This is common and is not considered an error message.
- *Matrix* is either a numeric or cell matrix containing the data you want to write to Excel file.
- *Sheet* is a string that contains the sheet name where you want to write your data.
- *Cell* is a string that designates the top-left corner of where MATLAB should start writing the data in Matrix in the Excel workbook. If Cell is not specified, MATLAB will default to writing with the top-corner set to cell A1.

● **EXAMPLE 18-18**   Use xlsread to import the numeric and nonnumeric values in the 2009 sheet in ClemsonWeather.xlsx, calculate all of the average high temperatures in units of degrees Celsius, and write the output to a new Excel file called newWeather.xlsx.

```
[D09,T09] = xlsread('ClemsonWeather.xlsx','2009');
T09{1,2} = 'TempHighC';
D09(:,1) = (D09(:,1) − 32)/1.8;
xlswrite('newWeather.xlsx',T09,'2009');
xlswrite('newWeather.xlsx',D09,'2009','B2');
```

Note that we are able to use the xlswrite *function twice: first to write the headers and dates to the Excel file, followed by writing the matrix containing the new temperatures.*

In-Class Activities

ICA 18-1

Write a MATLAB statement that results in the input request shown in bold. The >> shows where your statement is typed, and the | shows where the cursor waits for input. The display must be correctly positioned. Each has a space before the cursor (shown as |). The input variable name and the variable type are shown at the right.

(a) >>
   Enter the length of the bolt in inches: | (bolt, a number)

(b) >>
   Enter the company's name: | (Company, text)

(c) >>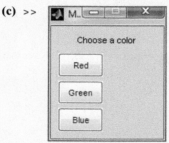

(In this statement, the window displayed will appear for the user to choose a color, and the result will be stored in the variable LineColor.)

ICA 18-2

You are writing code that is part of a purchasing system. For each item below, write a MATLAB statement to accomplish the task.

(a) Generate a menu that asks the user what they wish to buy and gives them a choice of three items: Flange, Bracket, or Hinge. The user's choice should be placed in a variable named **PartType**.

(b) Ask the user how many parts they wish to buy. Store their response in a variable named **NumParts**.

(c) Ask the user to enter their name. Store their response in a variable named **BuyerName**.

ICA 18-3

For the following questions, $z = 100/810$. Write the MATLAB output that would result from each statement.

(a) >> disp(z)
(b) >> fprintf('%f',z)
(c) >> fprintf('%e',z)
(d) >> fprintf('%0.4f',z)

ICA 18-4

For the following questions, $z = 100/810$. Write the MATLAB output statement that displays z in the format shown in bold. DO NOT hard code the values, use the value stored in z to print each one. In each case, the >> by the letter in parentheses shows where your statement is typed.

(a) >>
0.1

(b) >>
0.123

(c) >>
1.235e-001

(d) >>
The value of z is 0.123.

(e) >>
z is 0.123, so 10 z is 1.235.

ICA 18-5

Assume the following variables are stored in MATLAB's workspace:

```
MCost = 450;            % machine cost in dollars/day
WRate = 40;             % widgets produced/day
OCost = 1150;           % operating cost in dollars/day
WPrice = 47.87;         % sales price in dollars/widget
Days = 71;              % number of days the machine operates
WName = 'Sonic Pliers'; % name of the widget produced
```

Determine the output displayed on the screen by the following code:

```
TCost=MCost+OCost;
fprintf('Total Cost per Day:$%0.2f\n',TCost)
NumW=WRate*Days;
fprintf('A total of %0.0f %s was produced in %0.0f days.\n',NumW,...
...WName,Days)
Income=NumW*WPrice;
fprintf('These will sell at $%0.2f each for a total of $%0.0f.\n', WPrice,...
...Income)
fprintf('This will make a profit of $%0.2f.\n',Income-TCost*Days)
```

ICA 18-6

Assume that a three-element row vector V already exists. Write a single MATLAB statement that will print the contents of V diagonally from top left to bottom right. Display each value with three decimal places.

> Example: V = [42, −17.9626, 0.03654]
> Sample Output:
> 42.000
>   −17.963
>   0.037

ICA 18-7

The tiles on the space shuttle are constructed to withstand a temperature of 1,950 kelvin. Write a MATLAB program that will display the temperature in the four temperature units [kelvins, degrees Celsius, degrees Fahrenheit, and degrees Rankine]. Each value should be incorporated into a sentence with appropriate text, and each sentence should appear on a new line. Format all values as integers.

ICA 18-8

The specific gravity of acetic acid (vinegar) is 1.049. Write a MATLAB program to display the density of acetic acid in units of pounds-mass per cubic foot, grams per cubic centimeter, kilograms per cubic meter, and slugs per liter. Incorporate each value into a sentence with appropriate text, each sentence on a new line. All numeric values should be given to two decimal places.

ICA 18-9

Write a MATLAB program that will allow a user to type the specific heat of a value in calories per gram degree Celsius. Display the converted value in units of British thermal units per pound-mass degree Fahrenheit in the Command Window the following format using one decimal place: "The specific heat is ____ BTU / (lb_m*deg F)."

ICA 18-10

Write a program that will allow the user to type a liquid evaporation rate in units of kilograms per minute and display the value in units of pounds-mass per second, slugs per hour, and grams per second. Display the result in the Command Window using one decimal place: "The evaporation rate is _____ pounds-mass per second, ____ slugs per hour, or ____ grams per second."

ICA 18-11

In order to calculate the pressure in a flask, write a program that allows the user to type the volume of the flask in liters, the amount of an ideal gas in units of moles, and the temperature of the gas in kelvins. Display the result in the Command Window in the following format, using one decimal place: "The pressure is ___ atmospheres."

ICA 18-12

Write a program that will allow the user to type the input power of the motor in watts, the mass of the object in kilograms, the height the object will be raised in meters, and the time it took to raise the object in seconds. Display the calculated value in the Command Window in the following format, using one decimal place: "The motor is ____% efficient."

ICA 18-13

Write a MATLAB program that will ask the user to enter their age, then ask them to enter the name of their best friend, and then ask them to enter their friend's age. Determine the difference in the ages, and express this value as a positive integer. Finally, a statement in the following format should be displayed in the command window:

```
My age is _____ years.
_____ is my best friend. My friend's age is _____ years.
The difference is our age is _____ years.
```

ICA 18-14

Write a program that asks a user to enter, one at a time, the four numbers to fill a 2 × 2 matrix. For each number entered, make sure the user knows the location in the matrix of the number being entered. When the function begins, the following information should display for the user:

```
Function asks the user for a 2 × 2 matrix and display the result.
Please enter only integers, between −99,999 and 99,999.
```

Display the matrix in the Command Window as two rows and two columns, with the integers in the columns evenly spaced apart, using field width to control the column spacing.

ICA 18-15

Joule's first law, also known as the **Joule effect**, relates the heat generated to current flowing in a conductor. It is named for James Prescott Joule, the same person for whom the unit of joule is named. Create a proper plot of the experimental data.

Current (*I*) [A]	0.50	1.25	1.50	2.25	3.00	3.20	3.50
Power (*P*) [W]	1.20	7.50	11.25	25.00	45.00	50.00	65.00

ICA 18-16

Create a proper plot of the following set of experimental data collected during the charging of a capacitor. In this plot, time should be on the abscissa.

Time (*t*) [s]	0.2	0.4	0.6	0.8	1.0
Voltage (*V*) [V]	75.9	103.8	114.0	117.8	119.2

ICA 18-17

The lumen [lm] is the SI unit of luminous flux, a measure of the perceived power of light. To test the power usage, you run an experiment and measure the following data. Create a proper plot of these data, with electrical consumption (EC) on the ordinate.

	Electrical Consumption [W]	
Luminous Flux [lm]	Incandescent 120 Volt	Compact Fluorescent
80	16	
200		4
400	38	8
600	55	
750	68	13
1,250		18
1,400	105	19

ICA 18-18

You want to create a graph showing the theoretical relationship of an ideal gas between pressure (*P*) and temperature (*T*). Assume the tank has a volume of 12 liters and is filled with nitrogen (formula, N_2; molecular weight, 28 grams per mole). Allow the initial temperature to be 270 kelvin at a pressure of 2.5 atmospheres. Create a proper plot, showing the temperature on the abscissa from 270 to 350 kelvin.

ICA 18-19

The decay of a radioactive isotope can be theoretically modeled with the following equation, where C_0 is the initial amount of the element at time zero and k is the decay rate of the isotope. Create a proper plot of the decay of Isotope A [$k = 1.48$ hours]. Allow time to vary on the abscissa from 0 to 5 hours with an initial concentration of 10 grams of Isotope A.

$$C = C_0 e^{-t/k}$$

ICA 18-20

Create a proper plot of the theoretical voltage decay of a resistor-capacitor circuit:

$$V(t) = V_0\, e^{-\frac{t}{RC}}$$

You may assume that you have a capacitance (C) of 500 microfarads [μF], a resistance (R) of 0.5 ohms [Ω], and an initial voltage (V_0) of 10 volts [V]. The plot should start at time 0 seconds and increase by intervals of 1 second to 600 seconds.

ICA 18-21

Plot the following functions as assigned by your instructor using subplots, choosing an appropriate layout for the number of functions displayed. The independent variable (angle) should vary from 0 to 360 degrees.

(a) $\sin(u)$
(b) $3\sin(u)$
(c) $\sin(3u)$
(d) $\sin(u) - 3$
(e) $\sin(u + 90)$
(f) $3\sin(2u) - 2$

ICA 18-22

Plot the following functions as assigned by your instructor using subplots, choosing an appropriate layout for the number of functions displayed. The independent variable (angle) should vary from 0 to 360 degrees.

(a) $\cos(u)$
(b) $-2\cos(u)$
(c) $\cos(2u)$
(d) $\cos(u) + 2$
(e) $\cos(u - 45)$
(f) $3\cos(2u) - 2$

ICA 18-23

If an object is heated, the temperature of the body will increase. The energy (Q) associated with a change in temperature (ΔT) is a function of the mass of the object (m) and the specific heat (C_p). In an experiment, heat is applied to the end of an object, and the temperature change at the other end of the object is recorded. This leads to the equation shown below.

$$\Delta T = \frac{Q}{mC_p}$$

An unknown material with a mass of 5 kilograms is tested in the lab, yielding the following results. Use the `polyfit` function to determine the specific heat of this material and store the final result in the variable C_p.

Create a proper plot of the data. Add a linear trendline, showing the resulting trendline equation, on the graph for a change in temperature over a range of energy from 5 joules to 70 joules.

Heat Energy Applied (Q) [J]	17	40	58
Temperature Change (ΔT) [K]	2	5	7

ICA 18-24

The resistance of a typical carbon film resistor will decrease by about 0.05% of its stated value for each degree Celsius increase in temperature. Silicon is very sensitive to temperature, decreasing its resistance by about 7% for each degree Celsius increase in temperature. This can be a serious problem in modern electronics and computers since silicon is the primary material from which many electronic devices are fabricated.

Create a proper plot to compare a carbon film resistor with a resistor fabricated from specially doped silicon ("doped" means impurities such as phosphorus or boron have been added to the silicon).

For relatively small temperature differences from the reference temperature, this process is essentially linear. Use polyfit to determine linear models for each data set. For each model, add the trendline and the associated trendline equation to the graph. Use an appropriate location for the equations to clearly associate them with the correct trendline.

Temperature (T)[°C]	Resistance (R) [Ω]	
	Carbon Film	Doped Silicon
15	10.050	10.15
20	10.048	9.85
25	10.045	9.48

ICA 18-25

Today, most traffic lights have a delayed green, meaning there is a short time delay between one light turning red and the light on the cross-street turning green. An industrial engineer has noticed that more people seem to run red lights that use delayed green. She conducts a study to determine the effect of delayed green on driver behavior. The following data were collected at several test intersections with different green delay times. These data represent only those drivers who continue through the intersection when the light turns red *before* they reach the limit line, defined as the line behind which a driver is supposed to stop. The data show the "violation time," defined as the average time between the light turning red and the vehicle crossing the limit line, as a function of how long the delayed green has been installed at that intersection.

Create a proper plot of the violation time (V, on the ordinate) and the time after installation (t, on the abscissa) for all three intersections on a single graph.

Use polyfit to determine linear models for each data set. For each model, add the trendline and the associated trendline equation to the graph. Use an appropriate location for the equations to clearly associate them with the correct trendline.

Time After Installation (t) [months]	Violation Time (V) [s]		
	Intersection 1 1-Second Delay	Intersection 2 2-Second Delay	Intersection 3 4-Second Delay
2	0.05	0.1	0.5
5	0.1	0.5	1.5
8	0.3	1	2.5
11	0.4	1.3	3.1

ICA 18-26

Cadmium sulfide (CdS) is a semiconducting material with a pronounced sensitivity to light—as more light strikes it, its resistance goes down. In real devices, the resistance of a given device may vary over four orders of magnitude or more. An experiment was set up with a single light source in an otherwise dark room. The resistance of three different CdS photoresistors was measured when they were at various distances from the light source. The farther they were from the source, the dimmer the illumination on the photoresistor.

Create a proper plot of the data. Use `polyfit` to determine power model for each data set. For each model, add the trendline and the associated trendline equation to the graph. Use an appropriate location for the equations to clearly associate them with the correct trendline.

Distance from Light	Resistance (R) [Ω]		
(d) [m]	A	B	C
1	79	150	460
3	400	840	2,500
6	1,100	2,500	6,900
10	2,500	4,900	15,000

ICA 18-27

Your supervisor has assigned you the task of designing a set of measuring spoons with a "futuristic" shape. After considerable effort, you have come up with two geometric shapes that you believe are really interesting.

You make prototypes of five spoons for each shape with different depths and measure the volume each will hold. The table below shows the data you collected.

	Volume of Shape	
Depth (d) [cm]	A (VA) [mL]	B (VB) [mL]
0.5	1	1.2
0.9	2.5	3.3
1.3	4	6.4
1.4	5	7.7
1.7	7	11

Create a proper plot of the data. Use `polyfit` to determine power models for each data set. For each model, add the trendline and the associated trendline equation to the graph. Use an appropriate location for the equations to clearly associate them with the correct trendline.

Use your models to determine the depths of a set of measuring spoons comprising the following volumes for each of the two designs. Use your models to determine the depths of a set of measuring spoons comprising the following volumes for each of the two designs. V = [¼ tsp, ½ tsp, ¾ tsp, 1 tsp, 1 Tbsp]. NOTE: 1 Tbsp = 3 tsp

Print the results to the Command Window in a table similar to the format shown below.

```
Volume Needed (V) [tsp]          0.25   0.5   0.75   1    3
Depth of Design A (dA) [cm]
Depth of Design B (dB) [cm]
```

ICA 18-28

Three different diodes were tested: a constant voltage (0.65 volts) was held across each diode while the current through each was measured at various temperatures. The following data were obtained.

Create a proper plot of the data. Use `polyfit` to determine exponential models for each data set. For each model, add the trendline and the associated trendline equation to the graph.

Temperature	Current (I_D) [mA]		
(T) [K]	Diode A	Diode B	Diode C
275	852	2,086	264
281	523	1,506	179
294	194	779	81
309	69	390	35
315	47	301	26

ICA 18-29

If a hot liquid in a container is left to cool, its temperature (T) [°C] will gradually approach room temperature. This model will have the form $T = A + B\,e^{mt}$. In this case, m will always be negative and its dimension will be inverse time. If it is not clear how to determine A and B, consider that $T = A + B$ when $t = 0$, and $T = A$ as t approaches infinity.

You are to write a FUNCTION named `Cooling` that will accept two parameters:

- `Tr`: Room temperature in °C
- `TData`: A two row matrix containing measurements of a cooling liquid at various times. The first row contains the times of the measurements in minutes, and the second row contains the corresponding temperature measurements in °C

The function must perform the following operations:

- Plot the measured points
- Determine an exponential model to fit the data
- Add the exponential trendline to the graph
- Add the trendline equation for the exponential model to the graph

Example:

Room Temperature: `Tr = 30`

Temperature Data: `TData = [0.5 3 7 11; 85 48 35 33]`

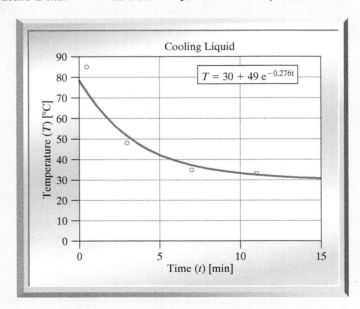

ICA 18-30

You are an engineer working for M & M / Mars™ Corporation in the M&M plant. For Halloween, M&Ms are produced in "fun size". To help with quality control, you create the worksheet below. The factory workers will examine sample bags of M&Ms, and enter the weight of the bag and the individual count of M&Ms contained in the bag.

Online, you have been given the following data in a Microsoft Excel workbook called **CandyCount.xlsx** with the data stored on a sheet named "M and M data". Only a portion of the actual data is shown.

	A	B	C	D	E	F	G	H
1	Bag Number	Mass of Bag (m) [g]	Red	Orange	Yellow	Green	Blue	Brown
2	1	15.0	3	1	5	4	4	1
3	2	13.9	3	2	3	5	1	2
4	3	14.7	1	1	9	2	3	1
5	4	14.3	2	5	4	2	1	3
6	5	14.7	2	2	6	2	2	2

Write a MATLAB program to read in the Excel data, calculate the data required as shown in the output table below, and write the results to a new Microsoft Excel file. Your output should appear as follows, where the highlighted portion is replaced by the values you calculate in your solution. Your program should also use formatted `fprintf` statements to display the table in the command window, filling in the missing information (highlighted) and displaying the data using a reasonable number of decimal places.

The program should assume the user could could enter more data to the original worksheet or modify the color names on the worksheet and the program should still run correctly.

	A	B	C	D	E	F	G
1	M and M Analysis by Color						
2		Red	Orange	Yellow	Green	Blue	Brown
3	Average per bag:						
4	Average mass per bag:						
5	Average total per bag:						
6	Color that appears the most:						
7	Color that appears the least:						

1. The specific gravity of gold is 19.3. Write a MATLAB program that will ask the user to input the mass of a cube of solid gold in units of kilograms and display the length of a single side of the cube in units of inches. The output should display a sentence like the one shown below, with the length formatted to 2 decimal places.

Sample Input/Output:
```
Enter the mass of the cube [kilograms]: 0.4
The length of one side of the cube is 1.08 inches.
```

2. An unmanned X-43 A scramjet test vehicle has achieved a maximum speed of Mach number 9.68 in a test flight over the Pacific Ocean. Mach number is defined as the speed of an object divided by the speed of sound. Assuming the speed of sound is 343 meters per second, write a MATLAB program to determine speed in units of miles per hour. Your program should ask the user to provide the speed as Mach number and return the speed in miles per hour in a formatted sentence, displayed as an integer value, as shown in the sample output below.

Sample Input/Output:
```
Enter the speed as a Mach number: 9.68
The speed of the plane is 7425 mph.
```

3. A rod on the surface of Jupiter's moon Callisto has a volume measured in cubic meters. Write a MATLAB program that will ask the user to type in the volume in cubic meters in order to determine the weight of the rod in units of pounds-force. The specific gravity is 4.7. Gravitational acceleration on Callisto is 1.25 meters per second squared. The input and output of the program should look similar to the output below. Be sure to report the weight as an integer value.

Sample Input/Output:
```
Enter the volume of the rod [cubic meters]: 0.3
The weight of the rod is 397 pounds-force.
```

4. The Eco-Marathon is an annual competition sponsored by Shell Oil, in which participants build special vehicles to achieve the highest possible fuel efficiency. The Eco-Marathon is held around the world with events in the United Kingdom, Finland, France, Holland, Japan, and the United States.

   A world record was set in the Eco-Marathon by a French team in 2003 called Microjoule with a performance of 10,705 miles per gallon. The Microjoule runs on ethanol. Write a MATLAB program to determine how far the Microjoule will travel in kilometers given a user-specified amount of ethanol, provided in units of grams. Your program should ask for the mass using an input statement and display the distance in a formatted sentence similar to the output shown below.

Sample Input/Output:
```
Enter mass of ethanol [grams]: 100
The distance the Microjoule traveled is 577 kilometers.
```

5. Write a function and program to determine the mass of oxygen gas (formula: O_2, (molecular weight = 32 grams per mole) in a container in units of grams. The function accept from the program input arguments representing the volume of the container in units of gallons, the temperature in the container in degrees Celsius, and the pressure in the container in units of atmospheres in the Command Window. The function output should be a single formatted string that contains the mass of the oxygen gas formatted to 1 decimal place followed by the units. For example the strings '10.0 grams' or '13.3 grams' would be samples of the expected output of your function. Note that this function should not generate any output on the screen.

The program should prompt the user to input the volume in gallons, the temperature in degrees Celsius, and the pressure in atmospheres, and then call the function to create the formatted string containing the mass. Finally, your program should contain an output statement to display the mass of the oxygen gas in the container. For your test case, you may assume that the user provides 1.25 gallons for the volume of the container, 125 degrees Celsius for the temperature, and 2.5 atmospheres for the pressure in the container.

Sample Input/Output:
```
Enter the volume [gallons]: 1.25
Enter the temperature [deg C]: 125
Enter the pressure [atm]: 2.5
The mass of the oxygen gas in the container is 11.6 grams.
```

6. Write a program and function to calculate a temperature provided by the user in units of Fahrenheit to units of kelvin. Your function should contain a single input argument, the temperature in degrees Fahrenheit, and return a single string as output. The string should be a formatted string containing the temperature followed by the units (K), where the value of the temperature is formatted to contain 0 decimal values. As an example, valid outputs of this function would be strings like '100 K' or '273 K'.

The program should allow the user to type in the temperature in degrees Fahrenheit, then pass that value into the aforementioned function, and display the output in a sentence formatted as shown below. As a test case, you may assume the user provides the temperature of −129 degrees Fahrenheit, which is the world's lowest recorded temperature.

Sample Input/Output:
```
Enter the temperature [deg F]: -129
The equivalent temperature is 184 K.
```

7. You are part of an engineering firm on contract by the U.S. Department of Energy's Energy Efficiency and Renewable Energy task force to develop a program to help consumers measure the efficiency of their home appliances. Your job is to write a program that measures the efficiency of stove-top burners. Before using your program, the consumer will place a pan of room temperature water on their stove (with 1 gallon of water), record the initial room temperature in units of degrees Fahrenheit, turn on the burner, and wait for it to boil. When the water begins to boil, they will record the time in units of minutes it takes for the water to boil. Finally, they will look up the power for the burner provided by the manufacturer.

The output of your program should look like the output displayed below; where the highlighted values are example responses typed by the user into your program. Note that your code should line up the energy and power calculations, as shown below. In addition, your code must display the efficiency as a percentage with one decimal place and must include a percent symbol.

```
Household Appliance Efficiency Calculator: Stove

Type the initial room temperature of the water [deg F]: 68
Type the time it takes the water to boil [min]: 21
Type the brand name and model of your stove: Krispy 32-Z
Type the power of the stove-top burner [W]: 1200

Energy required:       1267909 J
Power used by burner:  1006 W

Burner efficiency for a Krispy 32-Z stove: 83.9%
```

Sample Input/Output:

Stove Model	Room Temp [°F]	Time to Boil [min]	Rated Burner Power [W]
Krispy 32-Z	68	21	1,200
MegaCook 3000	71	25	1,300
SmolderChef 20F	72	21	1,500
Blaze 1400-T	68	26	1,400
CharBake 5	69	18	1,350

8. We want to conduct a breakeven analysis for a wooden baseball bat manufacturer who is interested in diversifying their product line. As a reminder breakeven analysis was discussed previously in the Graphing Solutions chapter, specifically in Example 11-9. Currently, the manufacturer produces white ash bats; they are interested in purchasing a second machine line to produce either maple or bamboo baseball bats.

To help the manufacturer look at the different scenarios, write a program that asks the user of the program to input the following variables IN THIS SPECIFIC ORDER:

■ Selling price of a maple bat (in dollars)
■ Selling price of a bamboo bat (in dollars)
■ The total number of bats the manufacturer can produce per week; this value is the same for either type of bat
■ The number of weeks the manufacturer plans to run their bat production machinery in a year

The manufacturing process can only make a single type of bat each week, and will produce the same number of bats in a week regardless of the material used.

Revenue is determined as the selling price of an object times the number of objects. Your program should display the total revenue generated for the scenario, as shown below:

```
Producing ## bats a week for ## weeks in a year will generate:
    Maple bat revenue: $####.##
    Bamboo bat revenue: $####.##

Total number of bats produced: #.###e+##
```

The revenue should be displayed with two decimal places and the total number of bats produced should be displayed in exponential notation with three decimal places.

In addition, each revenue line should display with a single tab at the front of each sentence, as shown above. The "#" character in the output displayed above will be actual numbers in the program you create.

Sample Input/Output. The highlighted values are entered by the user:

```
Type the selling price of a maple bat (in dollars): 16
Type the selling price of a bamboo bat (in dollars): 24
Type total number of bats manufacturer can produce per week: 50
Type number of weeks manufacturer plans to run production: 50

Producing 50 bats a week for 50 weeks will generate:
    Maple bat revenue: $40000.00
    Bamboo bat revenue: $60000.00
Total number of bats produced: 2.500e+03
```

9. We want to conduct a breakeven analysis for a wooden baseball bat manufacturer who is interested in diversifying their product line. As a reminder breakeven analysis was discussed previously in the Graphing Solutions chapter, specifically in Example 11-9. Currently, the manufacturer produces white ash bats; they are interested in purchasing a second machine line to produce hickory baseball bats.

To help the manufacturer look at the different scenarios, write a program that asks the user of the program to input the following variables IN THIS SPECIFIC ORDER:

- The number of weeks the manufacturer plans to run their bat production machinery in a year
- The total number of bats manufacturer can produce per week; value is same for either type of bat produced
- Material cost to produce a single white ash bat (in dollars)
- Material cost to produce a single hickory bat (in dollars)
- Selling price of a white ash bat (in dollars)
- Selling price of a single hickory bat (in dollars)

The cost for energy and labor for white ash bats is $2.75 per bat; however, due to difficulties associated with producing hickory bats, the cost for energy and labor is $4.25 per hickory bat. In your program, the cost of energy and labor should appear as variables.

Since the equipment already exists, there is no fixed cost for the white ash bats; the fixed cost for the hickory bats is $5,000 to purchase the new equipment. In your program, both fixed costs should appear as variables. Even though the fixed cost for the white ash is zero, you should still include it as a variable to allow the user to alter the program easily if, for instance, the manufacturer would want to examine upgrading the equipment.

The manufacturing process can only make a single type of bat each week, and will produce the same number of bats in a week regardless of the material used.

Your program should display the total profit generated for the scenario, as shown below:

```
Producing ## bats a week for ## weeks in a year will generate:
    White Ash bat profit: $####
    Hickory bat profit: $####
Total number of bats produced: #.#e+###
```

The profit should be displayed with no decimal places and the total number of bats produced should be displayed in exponential notation with one decimal places. Each profit line should display with a single tab at the front of each sentence. The "#" character in the output displayed above will be actual numbers in the program you create.

The program should generate two proper plots with the number of bats produced on the abscissa and the revenue and total cost on the ordinate for each material type. These two graphs should appear on the same figure using a subplot.

Finally, the program should generate a third plot that displays only the profit of each bat type with respect to the number of bats produced.

Sample Input / Output. The highlighted values are entered by the user:
```
Type number of weeks manufacturer plans to run production: 50
Type total number of bats manufacturer can produce per week: 50
Type a Material cost, white ash bat (in dollars): 8
Type a Material cost, hickory bat (in dollars): 12
Type selling price, white ash bat (in dollars): 16
Type selling price, hickory bat (in dollars): 24

Producing 50 bats a week for 50 weeks will in a year will generate:
White ash bat profit: $40000
Hickory bat profit: $60000

Total number of bats produced: 2.5e+03
```

Sample Figures of Cost and Revenue Curves:

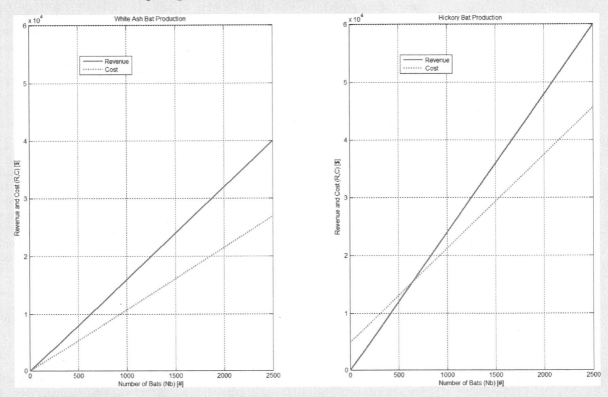

10. When one attempts to stop a car, both the reaction time of the driver and the braking time must be considered. Create a proper plot the following data.

Vehicle Speed	Distance (d) [m]	
(v) [mph]	Reaction (d_r)	Braking (d_b)
20	6	6
30	9	14
40	12	24
50	15	38
60	18	55
70	21	75

If an object is heated, the temperature of the body will increase. The energy (Q) associated with a change in temperature (ΔT) is a function of the mass of the object (m) and the specific heat (C_p). In an experiment, heat is applied to the end of an object, and the temperature change at the other end of the object is recorded. This leads to the theoretical relationship shown. An unknown material is tested in the lab, yielding the following results:

$$\Delta T = \frac{Q}{mC_p}$$

Heat applied (Q) [J]	12	17	25	40	50	58
Temp change (ΔT) [K]	1.50	2.00	3.25	5.00	6.25	7.00

11. Create a proper plot of the experimental temperature change (ΔT, ordinate) versus the heat applied (Q, abscissa).

12. Use `polyfit` to determine a linear relationship for the data set and graph the resulting trendline along with the experimental data.

13. Create a proper plot of the theoretical model that represents the temperature change (ΔT, ordinate) versus the heat applied (Q, abscissa) using `fplot`. Consider the mass (m) to be 5 kilograms and the specific heat (C_p) to be copper at 0.39 joules per gram kelvin.

Capillary action draws liquid up a narrow tube against the force of gravity as a result of surface tension. The height the liquid moves up the tube depends on the radius of the tube. The following data were collected for water in a glass tube in air at sea level.

Radius (r) [cm]	0.01	0.05	0.10	0.20	0.40	0.50
Height (H) [cm]	14.0	3.0	1.5	0.8	0.4	0.2

14. Create a proper plot of the height (H, ordinate) versus the radius (r) assuming the data are experimental.

15. Use `polyfit` to determine a power relationship for the data set and graph the resulting trendline along with the experimental data.

16. In a different experiment with different data, you determine the relationship to be $H = 0.25 \, r^{-1}$. Create a proper plot of this expression using the `fplot` command, assuming the units for both the radius and height are centimeters.

17. Use `polyfit` to determine a power relationship for the data set and plot the resulting relationship on a graph with the experimental data. This plot should be a proper plot with a logarithmic axis.

In a turbine, a device used for mixing, the power required depends on the size and shape of the impeller. In the lab, we have collected the following data:

Diameter (D) [ft]	0.5	0.75	1	1.5	2	2.25	2.5	2.75
Power (P) [hp]	0.004	0.04	0.13	0.65	3	8	18	22

18. Create a proper plot of the power (P, ordinate) versus the diameter (D) assuming the data are experimental.

19. Use `polyfit` to determine a power relationship for the data set and graph the resulting trendline along with the experimental data.

20. In a different experiment with different data, you determine the relationship to be $P = 0.25 \, D^5$. Create a proper plot of this expression using the `fplot` command, assuming the units for both the diameter and power are the same as shown in the table.

21. Use `polyfit` to determine a power relationship for the data set and plot the resulting relationship on a graph with the experimental data. This plot should be a proper plot with a logarithmic axis.

A pitot tube is a device that measures the velocity of a fluid, typically the airspeed of an aircraft. The failure of the pitot tube was credited as the cause of Austral Lineas Aéreas flight 2553's crash in October 1997. The pitot tube had frozen, causing the instrument to give a false reading of slowing speed. As a result, the pilots thought the plane was slowing down, so they increased the speed and attempted to maintain their altitude by lowering the wing slats. Actually, they were flying at such a high speed that one of the slats ripped off, causing the plane to nosedive; the plane crashed at a speed of 745 miles per hour [mph].

In the pitot tube, as the fluid moves, the velocity creates a pressure difference between the ends of a small tube. The tubes are calibrated to relate the pressure measured to a specific velocity, using the speed as function of the pressure difference (P, in units of pascals) and the density of the fluid (ρ, in units of kilograms per cubic meter).

$$v = \left(\frac{2}{\rho}\right)^{0.5} P^m$$

22. Create a proper plot of the velocity (v, ordinate) versus the pressure (P) assuming the data are experimental.

23. Use `polyfit` to determine the power relationships for the data sets and graph the resulting trendlines along with the experimental data.

24. Use `polyfit` to determine a power relationship for the data set and plot the resulting relationship on a graph with the experimental data. This plot should be a proper plot with a logarithmic axis.

Pressure (P) [Pa]	50,000	101,325	202,650	250,000	304,000	350,000	405,000	505,000
Velocity fluid A (v) [m/s]	11.25	16.00	23.00	25.00	28.00	30.00	32.00	35.75
Velocity fluid B (v) [m/s]	9.00	12.50	18.00	20.00	22.00	24.00	25.00	28.00
Velocity fluid C (v) [m/s]	7.50	11.00	15.50	17.00	19.00	20.00	22.00	24.50

A growing field of inquiry that both holds great promise and poses great risk for humans is nanotechnology, the construction of extremely small machines. Over the past couple of decades, the size that a working gear can be made has consistently gotten smaller. The table shows milestones along this path.

Years from 1967	0	5	7	16	25	31	37
Minimum gear size [mm]	0.8	0.4	0.2	0.09	0.007	2E-04	8E-06

25. Create a proper plot of the gear size (ordinate) versus the number of years from 1967 assuming the data are experimental.

26. Use `polyfit` to determine the exponential relationship for the data set and graph the resulting trendline along with the experimental data.

27. In a different experiment with different data, you determine the relationship to be MGS = $2.5\,e^{-0.5t}$. Create a proper plot of this expression using the `fplot` command, assuming the units for both the time and gear size are the same between the two data sets.

28. Use `polyfit` to determine an exponential relationship for the data set and plot the resulting relationship on a graph with the experimental data. This plot should be a proper plot using a logarithmic axis.

29. Download the weekly retail gasoline and diesel prices Excel workbook associated with this review question and place it in your main MATLAB Current Directory. This data set is based on the data set available from the U.S. Energy Information Administration: http://www.eia.gov/dnav/pet/pet_pri_gnd_dcus_nus_w.htm.
    (a) Calculate the average, minimum, and maximum retail fuel prices for each of the different types of fuel (regular, midgrade, premium, diesel) over the duration of the entire sample set. Your output should work in such a way that if the original Excel file were modified to include more weeks (rows), you would not need to change your MATLAB

code. Your output should appear similar to the format below, where the blanks are replaced by the actual calculated values:

Average Weekly Retail Gasoline and Diesel Prices

	Regular	Midgrade	Premium	Diesel
Min:				
Max:				
Average:				

Your code should calculate the values shown in the output—you should not hard code the values in the output. Each value you display should appear with two decimal values. You may use any built-in MATLAB function, including functions that find the minimum, maximum, or average values.

(b) We have decided that we want to modify our previous analysis in part **(a)** to export the computed max, min, and average values to a new Microsoft Excel workbook. The data itself should be exported to a sheet named "Fuel Price Analysis." Your data should appear similar to the worksheet below. Much like part **(a)**, your code should be written in such a way that if the original Excel file were modified to include more weeks (rows), you would not need to change your MATLAB code.

	A	B	C	D	E	F
1	Average Weekly Retail Gasoline and Diesel Prices					
2		Regular	Midgrade	Premium	Diesel	
3	Min					
4	Max					
5	Average					
6						

30. A sample of the data provided in the Microsoft Excel file online is shown below. The file contains energy consumption data by energy source per year in the United States, measured in petaBTUs.

Year	Fossil Fuels	Elec. Net Imports	Nuclear	Renewable
2007	101.605	0.106	8.415	6.830
2006	99.861	0.063	8.214	6.922

(a) Write the MATLAB code necessary to read the Microsoft Excel file and store each column of data into different variables. Create the following:

- `Yr`: A vector of all of the years in the worksheet.
- `FF`: A vector of all of the fossil fuels for each year in Yr.
- `ENI`: A vector of all electric imports for each year in Yr.
- `Nuc`: A vector of all nuclear energy consumption for each year in Yr.
- `Ren`: A vector of all renewable energy consumption for each year in Yr.
- `Hdr`: A cell array of all of the headers in row 1.

You may not hard code these variables—they should be imported from the Excel file.

(b) Create a new variable, **TotalConsumption**, which contains the sum of the four columns of energy consumption data for each year. In other words, since all five of the vectors (**Yr, FF, ENI, Nuc,** and **Ren**) we created in part **(a)** have the same length, the new variable, **TotalConsumption**, should have the same length. You may assume that you have correctly defined the variables in part **(a)**.

(c) Calculate the average fossil fuel consumption in the entire data set. For this code, you may assume that you have correctly defined **FF**, the variable containing the fossil fuel consumption data, in part **(a)**. Display the result of the calculation in the format shown below, where the number is shown to two decimal places:

```
The average fossil fuel consumption is _____
petaBTU.
```

31. An Excel file named Dart Tosses.xlsx, saved in a worksheet named "Darts" contains the measurements in this data set contain the horizontal and vertical distance from the bullseye of a dart board from 20 different tosses of a dart. A portion of the data is shown below. Write the MATLAB code necessary to determine the darts that were the closest and the furthest from the bullseye. The program should tell the user in the command window, using formatted output, the darts that are closest and farthest from the bullseye.

Dart	X	Y
Dart 1	4.04	0.55
Dart 2	2.63	0.35
Dart 3	1.10	2.97
Dart 4	4.89	5.60

CHAPTER 19
LOGIC AND CONDITIONALS

Outside the realm of computing, logic exists as a driving force for decision making. Logic transforms a list of arguments into outcomes based on a decision. Some examples of everyday decision making are as follows:

- If the traffic light is red, stop. If the traffic light is yellow, slow down. If the traffic light is green, go.

   Argument: three traffic bulbs

   Decision: is bulb lit?

   Outcomes: stop, go, slow

- If the milk has passed the expiration date, throw it out; otherwise, keep the milk.

   Argument: expiration date

   Decision: before or after?

   Outcomes: garbage, keep

To bring decision making into our perspective on problem solving, we need to first understand how computers make decisions. **Boolean logic** exists to assist in the decision-making process, where each argument has a binary result and the overall outcome exhibits binary behavior. **Binary behavior**, depending on the application, is any sort of behavior that results in two possible outcomes. Boolean logic, Boolean algebra, and related terms are named for George Boole (1815–1864), the English mathematician whose writings formed the basis of modern computer science.

19.1 RELATIONAL AND LOGICAL OPERATORS

LEARN TO: Create decisions using relational operators
Create decisions connected by logic operators
Explain the difference between short-circuit and element-wise operators

Operator	Meaning
>	Greater than
<	Less than
>=	Greater than or equal to
<=	Less than or equal to
==	Equal to
~=	Not equal to

In order to determine the relationship between two values (numbers, variables, etc.), we have a few operators with which we can compare two variables to determine whether or not the comparison is true or false.

These **relational operators** are usually placed between two different variables or mathematical expressions to determine the relationship between the two values. This expression of variable–operator–variable is typically called a **relational expression**, the result of which is always either true or false. We will refer to such results – values that can only be true or false – as **Boolean arguments**.

Sometimes all we care about is a simple relationship between two things, for example, is A greater than B? In other cases, we need to ask more complicated questions; for example is A both greater than B and less than C? Simple relational expressions can be combined by **logical operators** to create a **logical expression**. If no logical operator is required in a particular decision, then the single relational expression can be the logical expression.

To connect all of the Boolean arguments to make a logical decision, we turn to a few operators with which we can relate our arguments to determine a final outcome.

NOTE
And = &&
Or = ||
Not = ~

- **And:** The AND logical operator connects two Boolean arguments and returns the result as true if and only if *both* Boolean arguments have the value of TRUE. In MATLAB, we use the two ampersands (&&) symbol (SHIFT+7 on a keyboard) to represent the AND logical operator.
- **Or:** The OR logical operator connects two Boolean arguments and returns the result as true if *either one* (or both) of the Boolean arguments has the value of TRUE. In MATLAB, we use two pipes (||) symbol (SHIFT+\ on a keyboard) to represent the OR logical operator.
- **Not:** The NOT logical operator inverts the value of a single Boolean argument or the result of another Boolean operation. In MATLAB, we use the tilde (~) symbol (SHIFT+ ' on a keyboard) to represent the NOT logical operator. In other words, NOT True equals False, and vice versa.

● **EXAMPLE 19-1** Express the mathematical inequality in MATLAB code.

Mathematical Inequality	Expression
$4 \leq X < 5$	4 < = X && X < 5
$10 < X \leq 20$	10 < X && X < = 20
$30 \leq X \leq 100$	30 < = X && X < = 100

In this example and others, MATLAB cannot operate with multiple relational operators in a single expression—a common situation in mathematical inequalities. Instead, we must separate out the two relations and combine the expressions with the "and" symbol.

COMPREHENSION CHECK 19-1

What are the relational expressions for the following mathematical inequalities?
(a) $5 \leq t < 10$
(b) $-30 < M \leq 20$
(c) $Y \neq 100$

&&, &, and + ||, |, or: Say What?

By design, MATLAB contains a couple of different operators and functions for performing the "and" and "or" operations. The following set of guidelines will help you choose which operator will be the most appropriate choice for your code. In all of the following, assume the variable x contains the string 'tigers'.

AND

- **&&:** The double-ampersand operator is often referred to in MATLAB documentation as a short-circuit AND operator because it will terminate the evaluation of a logical expression as soon as it encounters the first "false" in a logical expression. This is particularly useful when checking to see if a certain condition is false before continuing with a special computation that is part of the logical expression.

  Sample: `isnumeric(x) && x + 10 > 5`

In the sample above, the overall result will be false because the first computation (`isnumeric(x)`) was false, so the remainder of the expression was not evaluated.

- **&:** Single-ampersand operator is often referred to in MATLAB documentation as an element-wise AND operator because it will evaluate every element in a logical expression.

  Sample: `isnumeric (x) & x + 10 > 5`

In the sample above, the overall result will be an array of six false values. The reason the result is an array is because the first computation (`isnumeric(x)`) was false, so the expression will always be false, because FALSE & ANYTHING = FALSE. In this particular case, the value of x is a string, so the logical expression is computing the ASCII value of the letters t, i, g, e, r, and s, adding 10, checking to see if the result is greater than 5, and then using the AND result, which will be false, all six times.

- **and():** The and function is a function that behaves similarly to the AND function in Microsoft Excel. This function behaves in the same fashion as the single-ampersand element-wise operator.

  Sample: `and(isnumeric (x), x + 10 > 5)`

In the sample above, the overall result will be an array of six false values since the AND function behaves identically to the element-wise operator.

OR

- **||:** The double-pipe operator is often referred to in MATLAB documentation as a short-circuit OR operator because it will terminate the evaluation of a logical expression as soon as it encounters the first "true" in a logical expression. This is particularly useful when checking to see if a certain condition is true before continuing with a special computation.

Sample: ~isnumeric(x)||x + 5 > 0

In the sample above, the overall result will be true because the first computation ~isnumeric(x) was true, so the remainder of the expression was not evaluated.

- **|:** The single-ampersand operator is often referred to in MATLAB documentation as an element-wise OR operator because it will evaluate every element in a logical expression.

Sample: ~isnumeric(x)|x + 5 > 0

In the sample above, the overall result will be an array of six true values. The reason the result is an array is because the first computation (~isnumeric(x)) was true, and since the remainder of the expression (x + 5 > 0) will also be true for all 6 characters in the string 'tigers', the result is an array of 6 true outcomes.

- **or ():** The or function is a function that behaves similarly to the OR function in Microsoft Excel. This function behaves in the same fashion as the single-ampersand element-wise operator.

Sample: or (~ isnumeric (x), x + 5 > 0)

In the sample above, the overall result will be an array of six true values since the or function behaves identically to the element-wise operator.

> The && and || operators only work if the logical values being combined are logical SCALARS. If you wish an element-wise AND or OR of two matrices, you must use either & or | or use the and/or functions.

19.2 LOGICAL VARIABLES

LEARN TO: Create and use logic variables in decisions
Define a logic matrix
Design logic within the constraints of operator priority

Logical Scalar Variables

When two individual items are compared using relational operators, the result is either a 1, representing true; or 0, representing false. In many cases, the results of such operations are used immediately by a MATLAB command, and are not actually stored in a variable.

The results of such comparisons can, however, be assigned to a variable and used later. Although the if statement will not be introduced until the next section, the following example should be simple enough to understand as an example.

● **EXAMPLE 19-2** Assume that A and B are scalars previously defined in the workspace. We wish to write a segment of MATLAB code to determine if variable A is not equal to variable B.

```
% Option 1
if A ~= B
    fprintf('A and B are not equal')
end
```

The expression A ~= B is evaluated, giving a 1 if true or a 0 if false. This result is not stored in a variable, but is immediately used by the if statement to decide whether or not to print the message. If we wanted to know what the result of the comparison was later, we would have to ask the question again, although A *or* B *might have changed in the interim so we might get a different result.*

```
% Option 2
AB=A~=B;
if AB
     fprintf('A and B are not equal')
end
```

The result of the relational question is stored in the logical variable AB, *and will have a value of 0 or 1. The icon shown beside* AB *in the workspace will be a square with a check-mark, indicating it is a logical variable.*

The program will determine if the variable AB *contains a 1 (true), and then the message will be printed; if* AB *contains a 0 (false), the message will not be printed. Note that we still have access to the result of the question later since we stored the result in* AB. *We could, for example, use this in conjunction with asking the same question later to see if the status of the relationship between* A *and* B *had changed.*

Logical Matrices

Relational comparisons can be made between a matrix and a scalar. In this case, the result is a logical matrix with the same dimensions as the matrix being compared. Each element of this logical matrix contains the result (1 or 0) of the comparison between the scalar and the corresponding element of the matrix.

● EXAMPLE 19-3

Determine the result of the following code, assuming $C = \begin{bmatrix} 1 & 0 & -1 \\ -2 & 2 & 3 \end{bmatrix}$

$$CO = C <= 0;$$

The code will examine each element in the matrix, and compare the value with zero. If the value is less than or equal to zero, the number 1 will be stored in the new CO *matrix, in the same location as the element being compared. If the value is greater than zero, the number 0 will be stored. For example, if we compare* C(1,1) – *a value of 1 – to zero, this value is greater than zero so the number 0 is stored in* CO(1,1).

The resulting matrix will be: $CO = \begin{bmatrix} 0 & 1 & 1 \\ 1 & 0 & 0 \end{bmatrix}$

Relational comparisons can also be made between two matrices, as long as they have the same dimensions. In this case, the result is a logical matrix with the same dimensions as the two matrices being compared. Each element of this logical matrix contains the result (1 or 0) of the element-wise comparisons between corresponding elements of the two matrices.

● **EXAMPLE 19-4**   Determine the result of the following code, assuming

$$C = \begin{bmatrix} 1 & 0 & -1 \\ -2 & 2 & 3 \end{bmatrix} \text{ and } D = \begin{bmatrix} 2 & -2 & -1 \\ -1 & 2 & 1 \end{bmatrix}$$

```
CD = C <= D;
```

The code will examine each element in the matrix C, *and compare the value to the same element position in matrix* D. *If the value in* C *is less than or equal the value in* D, *the number 1 will be stored in the new* CD *matrix, in the same location as the elements being compared. If the value in* C *is greater than the value in* D, *the number 0 will be stored.*

For example, if we compare the element C(1,1) *to* D(1,1), *the value of 1 is less than the value of 2 so the number 1 is stored in* CD(1,1).

The resulting matrix will be: $CD = \begin{bmatrix} 1 & 0 & 1 \\ 1 & 1 & 0 \end{bmatrix}$

Relational comparisons can be used with text strings as long as the strings have the same number of characters. Note that case matters: the lowercase letter "a" is not equal to the uppercase letter "A." Since text strings are essentially vectors containing text instead of numbers, the result of such a comparison is a logical vector containing the same number of elements as each of the two strings being compared.

Stings are compared based on the ASCII code used to represent them, so you need to know the codes assigned to the various characters, especially punctuation, to understand the results of greater than or less than comparisons. The table below shows each ASCII character and the corresponding decimal value for each letter or number. Note that there are many more characters available in the full set of ASCII values (http://www.asciitable.com/). A comprehensive list can be found in the end-pages of this text.

Character	A	B	C	D	E	F	G	H	I	J	K	L	M
Value	65	66	67	68	69	70	71	72	73	74	75	76	77

Character	N	O	P	Q	R	S	T	U	V	W	X	Y	Z
Value	78	79	80	81	82	83	84	85	86	87	88	89	90

Character	a	b	c	d	e	f	g	h	i	j	k	l	m
Value	97	98	99	100	101	102	103	104	105	106	107	108	109

Character	n	o	p	q	r	s	t	u	v	w	x	y	z
Value	110	111	112	113	114	115	116	117	118	119	120	121	122

Character	0	1	2	3	4	5	6	7	8	9
Value	48	49	50	51	52	53	54	55	56	57

You may have noticed that when variables are alphabetized in the workspace, those that begin with a capital letter come before those that begin with a lowercase letter.

If a comparison between two text strings involves greater than or less than (as opposed to just equal or not equal) the results may be surprising. For example `'a' < 'A'` is false, very likely not what you expected. On the other hand, alphabetic characters of the same case do compare as you probably expect: a is "less than" b and Y is "less than" Z. Also, non-alphanumeric characters can be problematic with greater than or less than.

● **EXAMPLE 19-5**

Determine the result of the following code, assuming

$$T = \text{'AbCd 1; 2 \# 3'}; \quad S = \text{'abCD 3: 2, 1'};$$

$$TS = T <= S;$$

The code will examine each element in the vector T, *and compare the value to the same element position in vector* S. *If the ASCII code value in* T *is less than or equal the ASCII code value in* S, *the number 1 will be stored in the new* TS *matrix, in the same location as the elements being compared. If the ASCII code value in* T *is greater than the ASCII code value in* S, *the number 0 will be stored.*

For example, if we compare the element T(1) *to* S(1), *the text "A" has an ASCII code value of 65 and the text "a" has an ASCII code value of 97. Since 65 is less than 97, the number 1 is stored in* TS(1).

The resulting matrix will be: TS = [1 1 1 0 1 1 0 1 1 0]

To determine if strings of <u>different</u> lengths are the same, you can use `strcmp` or `strcmpi`. In this case, the result is a logical scalar—true or false.

Calculations using logical variables

Logical matrices allow you to do some moderately complicated operations very easily in MATLAB. Since logical matrices contain actual numeric values (although only zeros and ones), they can be used in computations with regular numeric matrices.

● **EXAMPLE 19-6**

Assume $Q = \begin{bmatrix} 1 & -7 & 9 & -12 \\ -24 & 10 & 6 & 100 \end{bmatrix}$. Write a code segment to modify Q by dividing by 2 every element with a magnitude greater than or equal to 10, and leaving the other elements unchanged.

*We can approach this problem by creating two matrices: one containing a value of 1 for all the elements with a magnitude greater than or equal to 10 [*BigQ*], and one containing a value of 1 for all the elements less than 10 [*SmallQ*]. Then, we can recombine these two matrices for our end result.*

```
BigQ=abs (Q) >= 10;              % Find elements with magnitude ≥ 10
BigQAdjusted =0.5*BigQ.*Q;       % Divide big elements by 2
SmallQ =~BigQ.*Q;                % Remove big elements from Q
Q = BigQAdjusted+SmallQ;         % Combine the two matrices
```

$$\text{The result: } Q = \begin{bmatrix} 1 & -7 & 9 & -6 \\ -12 & 5 & 6 & 50 \end{bmatrix}$$

Note that this will work with any size matrix: for a 1000 × 2000 matrix, the code would be the same.

Priority of operators

If an arithmetic operation, such as dividing by 2 or adding 6, is performed on a logical matrix, the result is a numeric matrix.

The priority of operators must be observed carefully when mixing arithmetic, relational, and logical operators in the same expression. Particularly note that the arithmetic operators have priority over the relational operators, and the relational operators have priority over the logical operators. The one exception is **logical negation** ($\sim$ or not (A)), which has a priority equal to that of unary minus. A unary minus ($-x$) replaces the variable with the additive inverse; for example if $x = 3$, then $-x = -3$. The order of operator priorities is summarized in Table 19-1. Remember that parentheses have priority over everything.

Table 19-1 **Priority of mixed operations**

Priority	Operations
1	Transpose, Power
2	Unary Minus, Logical Negation
3	Multiplication, Division
4	Addition, Subtraction
5	Colon operator
6	Relational operators (`<`, `< =`, `>`, `>=`, `~=`, `==`)
7	`&`
8	`|`
9	`&&`
10	`||`

Functions associated with logical variables

Many of the functions used with numeric matrices can also be used with logical matrices. The table below contains a few additional functions that you might find useful. For each function, examples are given using the following variables:

```
A = [1  3  5  7];   C = [2  4  5  7];   R = A~= B;      T = B == C;
B = [2  4  6  8];   D = [2  3  5  8];   S = A + 1~= B;  U = C == D;

      Canine1='Dog';                       Canine2='Wolf';
```

Table 19-2 **Selected functions used with logical variables**

Function	Description
all	Are all elements in a given dimension of a matrix 1 (or non-zero)?
	Examples: H = all (R); % H contains 1
	I = all (T); % I contains 0
any	Are any elements in a given dimension of a matrix 1 (or non-zero)?
	Examples: J = any (S); % J contains 0
	K = any (T); % K contains 1
isequal	Determine if a group of matrices are all identical
	Examples: F = isequal (B,C); % F contains 0
	G = isequal (A,B-1); % G contains 1
islogical	Determine if a variable is a logical variable
	Examples: D = islogical (A); % D contains 0
	E = islogical (R); % E contains 1
strcmp	Case sensitive string comparison; Examples:
	CType1 = strcmp (Canine1,Canine2); % CType1 contains 0
	CType2 = strcmp (Canine1,'Dog'); % CType2 contains 1
	CType3 = strcmp (Canine1,'dog'); % CType3 contains 0
strcmpi	Case insensitive string comparison; Examples:
	CType4 = strcmpi (Canine1,Canine2); % CType4 contains 0
	CType5 = strcmpi (Canine1,'Dog'); % CType5 contains 1
	CType6 = strcmpi (Canine1,'dog'); % CType6 contains 1
xor	Exclusive OR: True if there is one 1 and one zero in corresponding elements
	Examples: L = xor (T,U); % L contains [0 1 1 0]

COMPREHENSION CHECK 19-2

$$M1 = \begin{bmatrix} 6 & -3 \\ -7 & 0 \\ 2 & 10 \end{bmatrix} \text{ and } M2 = \begin{bmatrix} 9 & -5 \\ -4 & 1 \\ 2 & 0 \end{bmatrix}$$

(a) What is placed in R1 by the statement R1 = M1 <= M2?

(b) What is placed in R2 by the statement R2 = (M2 < M1).*M2?

(c) What is placed in R3 by the statement R3 = M2 < M1.*M2?

COMPREHENSION CHECK 19-3

Assume M1 and M2 are defined as given in CC 19-2 above. Write a short section of MATLAB code that will create a matrix R4 in which each element is the larger of the corresponding elements in M1 and M2.

For the values listed above, the result should be: $R4 = \begin{bmatrix} 9 & -3 \\ -4 & 1 \\ 2 & 10 \end{bmatrix}$

19.3   CONDITIONAL STATEMENTS IN MATLAB

LEARN TO: Write an algorithm incorporating decision making in MATLAB code
Predict the number of possible outcomes given variability in a condition
Determine if two conditional statements are logically equivalent

Conditional statements are commands by which users give decision-making ability to the computer. Specifically, the user asks the computer a question framed in conditional statements, and the computer selects a path forward (it provides an answer—either numerical or as a text comment) based on the answer to the question. Sample questions are given below:

■ If the water velocity is fast enough, switch to an equation for turbulent flow!

■ If the temperature is high enough, reduce the allowable stress on this steel beam!

■ If the pressure reading rises above the red line, issue a warning!

■ If your grade is high enough on the test, state: You Passed!

In these examples, the comma indicates the separation of the condition and the action that is to be taken if the condition is true. The exclamation point marks the end of the statement. Just as in language, more complex conditional statements can be crafted with the use of "else" and similar words. In these statements, the use of a semicolon introduces a new conditional clause, known as a nested conditional statement. For example:

■ If the collected data indicate the process is in control, continue taking data; otherwise, alert the operator.

■ If the water temperature is at or less than 10 degrees Celsius, turn on the heater; or else if the water temperature is at or greater than 80 degrees Celsius, turn on the chiller; otherwise, take no action.

Single Conditional Statements

In MATLAB, a single conditional statement involves the `if` and `end` commands. If two distinct actions must occur as a result of a condition, the programmer can use the `else` command to separate the two actions. The basic structure of a single `if` statement is as follows:

```
if Logical_Expression
        Actions if true
else
        Actions if false
end
```

Note that the *Logical_Expression*, as shown in the structure of a single `if` statement, is a logical expression as described previously.

● EXAMPLE 19-7

Write a MATLAB statement to represent the following conditional statement.

If the water velocity (`v`) is less than 10 meters per second, determine the friction factor (`f`) of the piping system using laminar flow given by 64 divided by the Reynolds Number (`Re`).

English (Pseudocode)	MATLAB Code
If the water velocity is slow enough,	`if  v < 10`
use an equation for laminar flow	`f = 64/Re`
(period)	`end`

In this example, the comma indicates the separation of the condition and the action that is to be taken if the condition is true. The period marks the end of the statement.

● EXAMPLE 19-8

Write a MATLAB statement to represent the following conditional statement.

If the speed of the vehicle is greater than 65 miles per hour, display "Speeding" to the Command Window, otherwise; display "OK."

English (Pseudocode)	MATLAB Code
If the speed is greater than 65,	`if Speed > 65`
display "Speeding"	`fprintf ('Speeding')`
Otherwise,	`else`
display "OK"	`fprintf ('OK')`
(period)	`end`

In this example, the comma indicates the separation of the condition and the action that is to be taken if the condition is true. The semicolon after the word "otherwise" marks the beginning of the false action. The period marks the end of the statement.

Nested Conditional Statements

If more than two outcomes exist, the program will use an `if-elseif-else` command structure. This is similar to using the nested IF statements in Excel. Each time the word "`if`" appears, whether alone or as part of the `elseif` command, the program must ask a true/false question.

As a minimum, `if` statements can stand alone, without an `else` as seen in Example 19-7 above. As a maximum, for each outcome, the program requires one less `if` statement than outcomes. For example, if you have four desired outcomes, the program will require three IF questions (`if-elseif-elseif`) and one else statement to determine the result.

● **EXAMPLE 19-9**

Write a code segment to generate the menu shown and display the choice of the user in a sentence like: "You bought a Coke." Assume the result of clicking an option in the menu is saved in a variable called `soda` in the workspace. You can assume the user does not close the menu, but makes a valid section from the choices listed.

Recall from our discussion of the menu function, the result from a menu *selection by the user is the ordinal value of the choice. For example, if the user selects "Coke" from the menu shown, the variable* soda *would store the value 2.*

To decipher the choices into text, we can use an IF-ELSEIF-ELSE sequence:

```
soda = menu ('Select your drink','Sprite','Coke','Diet Coke','Mtn Dew');
    if soda == 1
            fprintf('You bought a Sprite\n');
    elseif soda == 2
            fprintf('You bought a Coke\n');
    elseif soda == 3
            fprintf('You bought a Diet Coke\n');
    else
            fprintf('You bought a Mtn Dew\n');
    end
```

COMPREHENSION CHECK 19-4

Write a MATLAB statement to represent the following conditional statement.

If the water temperature (stored in variable TW) is at or less than zero degrees Celsius, the phase (stored in the text variable phase) is solid; otherwise, if the water temperature is at or greater than 100 degrees Celsius, the phase is vapor; otherwise, the phase is liquid.

COMPREHENSION CHECK 19-5

Write a MATLAB function named `SumItUp` that will accept 3 input variables, and return 2 output variables. If the sum of the first two input variables is greater than 100, the function should display the inputs showing two decimal places in the following format. Assume in this formatting example that the numbers 55, 66 and 77 are the input variables:

```
The inputs are 55.00, 66.00 and 77.00.
```

Otherwise, if the sum of the first two input variables is less than or equal to 100, the function should display the formatted output using no decimal places:

```
The inputs are 25, 10 and 13.
```

The first variable the function returns should be the sum of the first and second variables. The second variable the function returns should be the sum of the second and third variables.

Equivalent Forms of Logic

Conditional statements are similar to traditional language in another way—there are many ways to express the same concept. The order, hierarchy (nesting), and choice of operators are flexible enough to allow the logic statement to be expressed in the way that makes the most sense. All of the following logic statements are equivalent for integer values of `NumTeamMembers`, but all read differently in English:

Conditional Statement	English Translation

`if NumTeamMembers>=4`
 	
  `if NumTeamMembers<=5`
 	
    `fprintf('Team size OK.')`
 	
  `end`
 	
`end`
	If the number of team members is 4 or more and if the number of team members is 5 or fewer, the team size is okay.

`if NumTeamMembers>=4&&NumTeamMembers<=5`
 	
  `fprintf('Team size OK.')`
 	
`end`
	If the number of team members is 4 or more and 5 or fewer, the team size is okay.

`if NumTeamMembers==4||NumTeamMembers==5`
 	
  `fprintf('Team size OK.')`
 	
`end`
	If the number of team members is 4 or 5 the team size is okay.

**COMPREHENSION
CHECK 19-6**

Which of the following expressions are equivalent to those shown above to determine if the status of NumTeamMembers is acceptable or needs adjusted?

(a)
```
if NumTeamMembers < 4 || NumTeamMembers ~= 5
    fprintf('Adjust team size.')
end
```

(b)
```
if NumTeamMembers >= 4 || NumTeamMembers <= 5
    fprintf('Team size OK.')
end
```

(c)
```
if NumTeamMembers ~= 4 && NumTeamMembers ~= 5
    fprintf('Adjust team size.')
end
```

(d)
```
if NumTeamMembers == 4 && NumTeamMembers == 5
    fprintf('Team size OK.')
end
```

19.4 SWITCH STATEMENTS

LEARN TO: Create a switch statement in MATLAB code
Determine when using a switch statement is appropriate
Create an "otherwise" case to execute code when logic isn't matched by the switch

A switch-case statement is another way to express if-elseif-else statements that test for equality. For certain types of questions, the switch-case statement is perhaps a little simpler to write and to understand.

The most important point about switch-case is that it ONLY tests for equality. If you need to make other types of relational tests (such as greater than), you should use if statements. Also, except in a very limited context, you cannot use logical operations (and, or, not) with switch-case statements.

The format of the switch-case structure is:

```
switch switch_expression
  case case_expression_1
      Execute code here if switch_expression==case_expression_1
  case case_expression_2
      Execute code here if switch_expression==case_expression_2
      .
      .
      .
  case case_expression_N
      Execute code here if switch_expression==case_expression_N
  otherwise
      Execute code here if switch_expression does not equal
      any of the cases
end
```

In general, the `switch-case` statement compares the value of a `switch` expression, with different `case` expressions. When it finds a `case` expression that equals the `switch` expression, it executes the code associated with that case, then goes to the end of the `switch` structure and continues. Note that only one case will be executed (the first one that is equal) each time the switch case is executed.

A common use of `switch-case` statements is processing menu selections.

● **EXAMPLE 19-10**

Write a program that allows the user to enter an angle in degrees and then select a trigonometric function from a menu to calculate. Express the result in a sentence, such as:

```
The sine of 30 degrees is 0.5000
```

One possible code:

```
Angle = input ('Enter angle in degrees: \n');
radAngle = Angle*pi/180;
trig = menu ('Select a function','sine','cosine','tangent');

switch trig
   case 1
      result = sin (radAngle);
      fprintf('The sine of %0.0f is %0.4f.\n',radAngle,result)
   case 2
      result = cos (radAngle);
      fprintf('The cosine of %0.0f is %0.4f.\n',radAngle,result)
   case 3
      result = tan (radAngle);
      fprintf('The tangent of %0.0f is %0.4f.\n',radAngle,result)
   otherwise
      fprintf('No selection made. Result set to NaN.\n')
      result = NaN;
end
```

If button number 2 (cosine) is selected, the cosine of the angle is displayed. Note that if the user closes the menu, the code between `otherwise` *and* `end` *is executed and the result is set to* `NaN` *(not a number).*

The expressions do not have to be simple variables or constants: they may also include calculations.

● **EXAMPLE 19-11**

Write a code segment to accept from the user the nominal diameter of a bolt and the actual diameter of a specific bolt. The program should then classify the bolt diameter as within less than 1%, 2%, or 5%, of the nominal value, as well as indicating if the bolt diameter is too far out of specifications when the nominal and actual diameters differ by 5% or more.

One possible code:

```
NomDiam = input ('Enter nominal diameter of bolt: \n');
BoltDiam = input ('Enter actual diameter of bolt: \n');
percent = BoltDiam/NomDiam*100-100;  % Calculate error

switch abs(fix(percent))  % round toward zero and make positive
    case 0
        fprintf('Diameter within < 1% of desired value.\n')
    case 1
        fprintf('Diameter between 1% and < 2% of desired value.\n')
    case {2,3,4}
        fprintf('Diameter between 2% and < 5% of desired value.\n')
    otherwise
        fprintf('Out of specifications (>= 5% error).\n')
end
```

*The third case bears a bit of explanation. You can place multiple expressions (in this example, simple constants) in a cell array as the case expression. If **any** of the expressions in the cell array are equal to the switch expression, then the instructions associated with that case will be executed unless, of course, a prior case was true. This is the "limited use of logical operations" mentioned earlier, since it effectively implements an "or", although the "or" is not explicitly coded.*

Text strings can also be used in switch-case structures. Note that this is case-sensitive, since it effectively implements a strcmp, not a strcmpi. If you need to test strings where case does not matter, it is probably better to use if statements in conjunction with strcmpi.

● **EXAMPLE 19-12**

Write a code segment to allow the user to enter their favorite type of pet, then the program will describe the animal as the output displayed to the user. If the user types a value that isn't one of the values specified, the code indicates that the user entry doesn't match any of the recognized animals.

One possible code:

```
pet = input ('What is your favorite pet? (Bird, Cat, or Dog)\n','s');

switch pet
    case 'Bird'
        fprintf('Your favorite pet flies through the air.\n')
    case 'Cat'
        fprintf('Your favorite pet makes a yowling noise. \n')
```

```
      case 'Dog'
         fprintf('Your favorite pet barks. \n')
      otherwise
         fprintf('Your entry does not match my database. \n')
   end
```

Note that in this example, the first letter of the response must be capitalized to have one of the first three cases selected.

COMPREHENSION CHECK 19-7

Write a MATLAB code using `switch-case` to allow the user to choose from a menu the type of water sample they wish to prepare. Based on their choice, the program should provide guidelines for how to prepare the sample. For example, if the user selects "solid," the program should state:

```
For a solid, water must be at a temperature
less than 0 degrees Celsius.
```

19.5 ERRORS AND WARNINGS

LEARN TO: Create a warning statement to display in the Command Window
Create an error expression to display in the Command Window
Design logic using `try-catch` statements to gracefully terminate the code

MATLAB contains built-in functions that allow you to create custom error and warning messages within your code, similar to those you encounter when you have a syntax error in your code or encounter a runtime error. You can use these functions, in conjunction with logical operators, to build error checking and prevention into your MATLAB code.

Error Messages

You might have noticed that when you run MATLAB code with syntax errors, the Command Window will display errors in red letters to report the error message rather than the standard black text font. In MATLAB, you can actually create your own custom error messages.

Error messages in MATLAB are shown in the Command Window in red letters:

```
Undefined function or variable 'A'.
```

If you would like to build in your own error checking in MATLAB, you can actually program custom error messages that may be more helpful than the default messages displayed by MATLAB using the error function.

● EXAMPLE 19-13

We are given the weight (in variable *w*) in newtons of an object as well as the mass (in variable *m*) in kilograms and want to determine the gravity in meters per second squared. To solve this, we will use the equation $g = w/m$, but we want to wrap that expression inside a conditional just in case the user provides a zero mass, which does not make sense in our situation, but will not cause an error in MATLAB—if you divide a number by 0 in MATLAB, the value "Inf" is calculated, which represents infinity.

```
>> w=530;
>> m=0;
>> g=w/m
g=
   Inf
```

Instead, we could write the following segment of code to force MATLAB to throw an error message:

```
if m==0
    error('Error: The mass cannot be zero!');
else
    g=w/m;
end
fprintf('The gravity is %0.1f m/s^2\n',g);
```

When you run this code given the w and m above, the message below will display in the Command Window and your code will stop executing.

```
Error: The mass cannot be zero!
```

Warning Messages

If you want to provide a warning to the user but do not want MATLAB to stop running, you can use the **warning** function. This will allow the program to continue, while giving the user information about potential issues in orange letters in the Command Window.

● EXAMPLE 19-14

Repeat Example 19-13, but this time if the user sets the mass variable to be zero, we want to display a warning message to the user and re-define the mass to be 3 kilograms to compute gravity.

```
w=530;
m=0;
if m==0
    warning('Mass=0! Using 3 kg for the mass');
    m=3;
end
g=w/m;
fprintf('The gravity is %0.1f m/s^2.\n',g);
```

*When you run this code, the warning message will display in the Command Window and your code will continue executing. Using the **warning** function, the **else** is unnecessary since the calculation will be done in either case.*

```
Warning: Mass=0! Using 3 kg for the mass
The gravity is 176.7 m/s^2.
```

Try-Catch **Statements**

To customize how MATLAB handles reporting error messages, you can use try-catch statements to handle error exceptions. An exception, in MATLAB, is a structure that contains special information such as a description of the error, as well as information concerning where the error occurred in a particular file. The try-catch statement is formatted, as follows:

```
try
        MATLAB code...
        goes here...
        .
        .
        .
catch e
        MATLAB code that executes on error occurs here.
end
```

Try-catch statements can be used over large blocks of code, even entire programs or functions, but their real value comes into play when used on smaller blocks of code to provide more meaningful feedback to the user running your program.

● **EXAMPLE 19-15**

Write a code segment to ask the user to enter a matrix. If the matrix can be muliplied by a 2 × 4 matrix, the program will exectue the operation and display "Finished!" when complete. If the multiplication is invalid, the program will produce an error message.

```
try
    i = input ('Type a matrix: \n');
    m = i * [3,3,3,3;4,4,4,4];
    fprintf('Finished!\n')
catch e
    error('Houston, we have a problem:\n\n %s', e.message)
end
```

Sample Output:

```
Type a matrix: 3
Finished!
```

In the output above, there were no errors, so the catch statements did not execute.

```
Type a matrix: [1 1 2 3 5; 2 2 1 3 4; 3 3 3 3 3]
Houston, we have a problem:
Inner matrix dimensions must agree.
```

In the output above, there was an error, so the code terminated and the code in the error handler (the catch *block) executed. Note the* fprintf *in the* try *block did NOT execute.*

In-Class Activities

ICA 19-1

Answer the following questions.

(a) For what integer values of D will the code between if and end execute?

```
if D >= -1 && 3 > D
        code
end
```

(b) For what values of F will the code between if and end execute?

```
if F >= 100 || F <= 5
        code
end
```

(c) What combinations of values for B and Q will cause a warning to be displayed?

```
if B>100 || (B<20 && Q~=0)
        fprintf('WARNING! Parameters out of bounds.\n')
end
```

ICA 19-2

Answer the following questions.

(a) For what integer values of G will the code between if and end execute?

```
if G < 2 && -5 <= G
        code
end
```

(b) For what values of R will the code between if and end execute?

```
if R < 75 || R >= 95
        code
end
```

(c) What combinations of values for W and M will cause a warning to be displayed?

```
if W<50 || (W>120 && M~=0)
        fprintf('WARNING! Parameters out of bounds.\n')
end
```

ICA 19-3

For each task listed, write a single MATLAB statement that will accomplish the stated goal.

(a) Replace each negative number in matrix M1 with zero.

(b) Given that a scalar value N is already defined, determine the sum of all elements in vector V1 that are greater than N. *HINT: Use the sum function.*

ICA 19-4

For each task listed, write a single MATLAB statement that will accomplish the stated goal.

(a) Replace each negative number in matrix M2 with −9999.

(b) Given that a scalar value N is already defined, determine the sum of all elements in matrix M3 that are less than or equal to N. *HINT: Use the sum function.*

ICA 19-5

What is stored in variable A after the following code segment is executed? If the program returns an error, indicate why.

(a)
```
A=5;
if A/2>2
    A = A*-1;
else
    A = A/2;
end
```

(c)
```
T=6; A=-1;
if T/3>2
    A = A*-1;
elseif T/3<=2
    A = A+2;
end
```

(b)
```
x=2; y=4; A=0;
if x+y<4
    A = A+2;
elseif x+y<6
    A = A+4;
end
```

(d)
```
x=2;y=0;A=10;
if x<=0&&y<=0
    A = A+2;
elseif x>=0&&y<0
    A = A/2;
elseif x>=2&&y<=0
    A = A*2;
end
```

ICA 19-6

What will be displayed by the following code in each of the cases listed below?

```
if flag==1 && alt>=30000
        fprintf('Normal operation at %0.0f feet.\n',alt)
elseif flag==0 || alt==0
        fprintf('On Ground')
elseif flag==2 && alt < 30000
        fprintf('Currently at %0.0f feet and climbing\n',alt)
elseif flag==3
        fprintf('Currently at %0.0f feet and descending\n',alt)
else
        fprintf('Status transitional')
end
```

(a) flag = 1; alt = 25000
(b) flag = 0; alt = 7500
(c) flag = 2; alt = 10000
(d) flag = 1; alt = 37000
(e) flag = 3; alt = 35000

ICA 19-7

A menu is generated using the following code:

```
Status=menu('ClassStanding','Freshman','Sophomore','Junior','Senior');
```

Write a segment of code using `if-elseif-else` that will classify the person making a menu selection as a new student (freshman) or a continuing student (sophomore, junior, or senior). The code should display one of the following messages:

```
You are a new student.
You are a continuing student.
You did not make a selection.
```

ICA 19-8

A menu is generated using the following code:

```
Status=menu('ClassStanding','Freshman','Sophomore','Junior','Senior');
```

Write a segment of code using `switch-case` that will classify the person making a menu selection as a new student (freshman) or a continuing student (sophomore, junior, or senior). The code should display one of the following messages:

```
You are a new student.
You are a continuing student.
You did not make a selection.
```

ICA 19-9

Write a program using `if-elseif-else` statements that displays a menu of traffic light colors (green, yellow, red). Depending on which button is pressed, the user should then be told to continue, slow, or stop. If the user closes the menu without making a selection, the user should be told to stop.

ICA 19-10

Write a program using `switch-case` statements that displays a menu of traffic light colors (green, yellow, red). Depending on which button is pressed, the user should then be told to continue, slow, or stop. If the user closes the menu without making a selection, the user should be told to stop.

ICA 19-11

Write a program that asks the user to enter the length of the hypotenuse, opposite, and adjacent sides of a right triangle with respect to an angle (θ). After the user has entered all three values, a menu should pop up asking if the user wants to calculate $\sin(\theta)$, $\cos(\theta)$, $\tan(\theta)$, $\cot(\theta)$, $\csc(\theta)$, or $\sec(\theta)$. The program should display a final message, such as `"For a triangle of sides h, o and a, sin(θ) = 0.3,"` where h, o, and a are replaced by the actual lengths entered by the user, displayed to one decimal place. If the user enters lengths that do not work with a right triangle, an error message should appear and the program should terminate. If the user closes the menu instead of making a valid selection, an appropriate error message should appear and the program should terminate. You may use `if` statements and/or `switch-case` statements as appropriate.

ICA 19-12

We go to a state-of-the-art amusement park. All the rides in this amusement park contain biometric sensors that measure data about potential riders while they are standing in line. Assume the sensors can detect a rider's age, height, weight, heart problems, and possible pregnancy. Help the engineers write the conditional statement for each ride at the park based on their safety specifications.

Variable Definitions:	
A	% Age of the potential rider (as an integer)
H	% Height of the potential rider (as an integer)
HC	% Heart Condition status ('yes' if the person has a heart condition, 'no' otherwise)
P	% Pregnancy status (1 if pregnant, 0 otherwise)

(a) The Spinning Beast: All riders must be 17 years or older and more than 62 inches tall and must not be pregnant or have a heart condition.

```
if _____

   fprintf ('Sorry, you cannot ride this ride');

end
```

(b) The Lame Train: All riders must be 8 years or younger and must not be taller than 40 inches.

```
if _____

   fprintf ('Sorry, you cannot ride this ride');

end
```

(c) The MATLAB House of Horror: All riders must be 17 years or older and must not have a heart condition.

```
if _____

   fprintf ('Welcome to the MATLAB House of Horror!');

end
```

(d) The Neck Snapper: All riders must be 16 years or older and more than 65 inches tall and must not be pregnant or have a heart condition.

```
if _____

   fprintf ('Welcome to The Neck Snapper!');

end
```

(e) The Bouncy Bunny: All riders must be between the ages of 3 and 6 (including those 3 and 6 years old)

```
if _____

   fprintf ('This ride is made just for you!');

end
```

ICA 19-13

A phase diagram for carbon and platinum is shown. If it is assumed the lines shown are linear, the mixture has the following characteristics. The endpoints of the division line between these two phases are labeled on the diagram.

- Below 1,700 degrees Celsius, it is a mixture of solid platinum (Pt) and graphite (G).
- Above 1,700 degrees Celsius, there are two possible phases: a Liquid (L) phase and a Liquid (L) + Graphite phase (G).

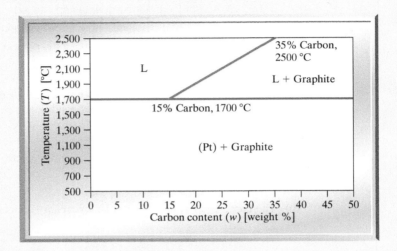

Write a program to determine the phase. The program should ask the user to enter the weight percent carbon and the temperature in degrees Celsuis. Call the phases "Pt + G," "L," and "L + G," for simplicity. If the point falls directly on the T = 1700 deg C line, include the point in the "Pt + G" phase. If the point falls directly on the L, L + G line, include the point in the "L + G" phase.

Store the phase as text in a variable. The equation of the line dividing the L and L + G phases must be found in the program using polyfit. The program should produce a formatted output statement to the command window, similar to "For X.XX weight percent carbon and a temperature of YYY degrees Celsius, the phase is PHASE," where X.XX, YYY and Phase are replaced by the actual values formatted as shown.

The partial code below is designed to implement this program. You are to fill in the missing sections of code as appropriate to complete the program.

```
Q1.                             % Appropriate housekeeping commands
w = input ('Type the Carbon content [weight %]: ');
T = input ('Type the temperature [deg C]: ');

% set parameters for L / L + G line
Carbon1 = [ Q2. ];
Temp1 = [ Q3. ];

% set parameters for L / Pt + G and L + G / Pt + G line
Carbon2 = [ Q4. ];
Temp2 = [ Q5. ];

% determine polyfit parameters for L / L+G line
PhaseLine = polyfit( Q6.              );
TPhaseLine = Q7.              );
```

```
   if  Q8.                          % Add appropriate question here
       Phase = 'Pt + G';
   elseif  Q9.                      % Is it a liquid?
       Q10.                         % Add appropriate code here
Q11.                     % First of two lines to complete if statement
Q12.                     % Second of two lines to complete if statement
   end

   fprintf Q13              % Add appropriate code
```

ICA 19-14

The graph shows a phase diagram for lead–tin solder. The most common alloy available commercially is 60% Sn (tin) and 40% Pb (lead), although eutectic solder (63% Sn and 37% Pb) is easily obtained and has some distinct advantages, primarily related to the lack of a "pasty" range, the range of temperatures in which the alloy is a mixture of solid within a liquid as it cools from liquid to solid. The gridlines have been removed from this graph to make it easier to read the phase locations.

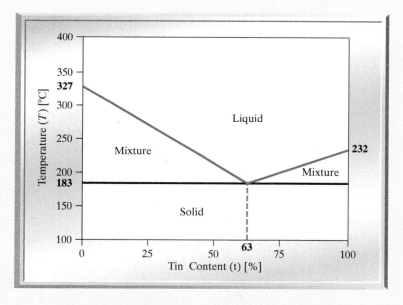

A function is to be written that will classify the phase of a eutectic Sn–Pb alloy given the percentage of tin and the temperature in units of degrees Celsius. The function should be named SnPbPhase and should accept two scalars:

- Temp, containing the temperature in °C
- PercSn, the percentage of tin

The function should return a text string named Phase containing one of the following four values:

- Liquid
- Solid
- Mixture
- Eutectic point

If a specific combination of percentage and temperature is exactly on one of the lines (other than at the intersection of the eutectic point at 63% and 183°C), the classification should be with the region below the line. The equation of the lines dividing the phases must be found in the program using `polyfit`. The program should produce a formatted output statement to the command window, similar to "`For X.XX percentage of tin and a temperature of YYY deg C, the phase is PHASE,`" where X.XX, YYY and Phase are replaced by the actual values formatted as shown.

The partial code below is designed to implement this function. You are to fill in the missing sections of code as appropriate to complete the function.

```
Q1.                    % Declaration of function and passed parameters

% set parameters for Mixture / Liquid line when Tin < 63%
Tin1=[ Q2. ];
Temp1=[ Q3. ];
LoSn = polyfit( Q4.            );
TempLoSn = Q5.            % Temperature on LoSn line at given percent Tin

% set parameters for Mixture / Liquid line when Tin > 63%
Tin2=[ Q6. ];
Temp2=[ Q7. ];
HiSn = polyfit( Q8.            );
TempHiSn = Q9.            );  % Temperature on HiSn line at given percent Tin

if Q10.                  % Add appropriate question here
   Phase = 'Eutectic Point';
elseif Q11.                  % Is it solid?
   Q12.                      % Add appropriate code here
elseif PercSn<=63 && Q13.            % Complete the question
   Phase='Liquid';
elseif Q14.              % Add appropriate question here
   Phase='Liquid';
Q15.                  % First of two lines to complete if statement
Q16.                  % Second of two lines to complete if statement
end
fprintf Q17.            % Add appropriate code
```

Upon reflection, you realize that the second and third `elseif` statements (the two that classify the material as liquid) can be written as a single `elseif` statement using a question with ONLY a SINGLE logical operator ("and" or "or"). What is the correct question to ask in a single `elseif` statement to correctly classify the material as liquid?

```
elseif Q18.            % Add appropriate question here
   Phase='Liquid';
```

1. The specific gravity of gold is 19.3. Write a MATLAB program that will ask the user to input the mass of a cube of solid gold in units of kilograms and display the length of a single side of the cube in units of inches. The output should display a sentence like the one shown below, with the length formatted to 2 decimal places. If the user types a negative number or zero for the mass of the cube, your program should display an error message and terminate.

Sample Input / Output (multiple scenarios):

```
Enter the mass of the cube [kilograms]: -3
Error: Mass must be greater than zero grams.
```

```
Enter the mass of the cube [kilograms]: 0.4
The length of one side of the cube is 1.08 inches.
```

2. An unmanned X-43 A scramjet test vehicle has achieved a maximum speed of Mach number 9.68 in a test flight over the Pacific Ocean. Mach number is defined as the speed of an object divided by the speed of sound. Assuming the speed of sound is 343 meters per second, write a MATLAB program to determine speed in units of miles per hour. Your program should ask the user to provide the speed as Mach number and return the speed in miles per hour in a formatted sentence, displayed as an integer value, as shown in the sample output below. If the user provides a negative value for the Mach number, your program should display an error message and terminate.

Sample Input / Output (multiple scenarios):

```
Enter the speed as a Mach number: -2
Error: The Mach number must not be negative.
```

```
Enter the speed as a Mach number: 0
The speed of the plane is 0 mph.
```

```
Enter the speed as a Mach number: 9.68
The speed of the plane is 7425 mph.
```

3. A rod on the surface of Jupiter's moon Callisto has a volume measured in cubic meters. Write a MATLAB program that will ask the user to type in the volume in cubic meters in order to determine the weight of the rod in units of pounds-force. The specific gravity is 4.7. Gravitational acceleration on Callisto is 1.25 meters per second squared. The input and output of the program should look similar to the output below. Be sure to report the weight as an integer value. If the user types a negative number or a number greater than 100 cubic meters for the volume of the rod, your program should display an error message using the error function indicating that the provided input is outside of the desired range and terminate.

Sample Input / Output (multiple scenarios):

```
Enter the volume of the rod [cubic meters]: -10
Error: Volume must be between 0 and 500 cubic meters
```

```
Enter the volume of the rod [cubic meters]: 501
Error: Volume must be between 0 and 500 cubic meters
```

```
Enter the volume of the rod [cubic meters]: 0.3
The weight of the rod is 397 pounds-force.
```

4. The Eco-Marathon is an annual competition sponsored by Shell Oil, in which participants build special vehicles to achieve the highest possible fuel efficiency. The Eco-Marathon is held around the world with events in the United Kingdom, Finland, France, Holland, Japan, and the United States.

    A world record was set in the Eco-Marathon by a French team in 2003 called Microjoule with a performance of 10,705 miles per gallon. The Microjoule runs on ethanol. Write a MATLAB program to determine how far the Microjoule will travel in kilometers given a user-specified amount of ethanol, provided in units of grams. Your program should ask for the mass using an input statement and display the distance in a formatted sentence similar to the output shown below. If the user provides a mass less than zero or greater than 500 grams, your program should display an error message using the error function indicating that the provided mass of ethanol is outside of the desired range of input.

    Sample Input / Output: (multiple scenarios):
    ```
    Enter mass of ethanol [grams]: -15
    Error: Mass must be between 0 and 500 grams
    ```
    ```
    Enter mass of ethanol [grams]: 1000
    Error: Mass must be between 0 and 500 grams
    ```
    ```
    Enter mass of ethanol [grams]: 100
    The distance the Microjoule traveled is 577 kilometers.
    ```

5. Assume a variable R contains a single number. Write a short piece of MATLAB code that will:

    - Generate the message: `The square root of XXXX is YYYY`, if R is nonnegative.
    - If R is negative, the code should generate the message: `R is negative. The square root of XXXX is YYYYi`.

    The value of R should be substituted for **XXXX**, and the value of the square root of the magnitude of R should be substituted for **YYYY**. Both numbers should be displayed with three decimal places.

6. Write a program that gathers two data pairs in a 2 × 2 matrix and then asks the user to input another value of x for which a value of y will be interpolated or extrapolated. Report the value of y in the correct sentence below (with numbers in the blanks).

    ```
    Given x = _____, interpolation finds that y = _____ or
    Given x = _____, extrapolation finds that y = _____.
    ```

    Sample Input/Output Matrix [0 10, 10 20] is entered and the user chooses 5:

    ```
    Given x = 5, interpolation finds that y = 15.
    ```

7. Create a program to determine whether a user-specified altitude [meters] is in the troposphere, lower stratosphere, or upper stratosphere. The program should include a check to ensure the user entered a positive value. If a non-positive value is entered, the program should inform the user of the error and terminate. If a positive value is entered, the program should calculate and report the resulting temperature in units of degrees Celsius [°C] and pressure in units of kilopascals [kPa]. Refer to the atmosphere model provided by NASA: http://www.grc.nasa.gov/WWW/K-12/airplane/atmosmet.html. **Sample Input/Output** Altitude = 500 meters.

    ```
    An altitude of 500 is in the troposphere with a temperature of
    12 degrees C and pressure of 96kPa.
    ```

8. Create a program to determine whether a given Mach number is subsonic, transonic, supersonic, or hypersonic. Assume the user will enter the speed of the object, and the program will determine the Mach number. As output, the program will display the Mach rating. The program should include a check to ensure the user entered a positive value. If a non-positive value is entered, the program should inform the user of the error and terminate.

NOTE

Due to several complicated nonlinear losses in the system that are far beyond the scope of this course, this is a case of a model in which the exponent does not come out to be an integer or simple fraction, so rounding to two significant figures is appropriate. In fact, this model is only a first approximation— a really accurate model would be considerably more complicated.

Refer to the NASA page on Mach number: http://www.grc.nasa.gov/WWW/K-12/airplane/mach.html. **Sample Input/Output** Speed = 100 m/s.

```
Subsonic, Mach number is 0.3.
```

9. Humans can see electromagnetic radiation when the wavelength is within the spectrum of visible light. Create a program to determine if a user-specified wavelength [nanometer, nm] is one of the six spectral colors listed in the chart below. Your program should ask the user to enter a wavelength, then indicate in which spectral color the given wavelength falls or state if it is not within the visible spectrum.

Color	Wavelength Interval
Red	~ 700–635 nm
Orange	~ 635–590 nm
Yellow	~ 590–560 nm
Green	~ 560–490 nm
Blue	~ 490–450 nm
Violet	~ 450–400 nm

10. For the protection of both the operator of a zero-turn radius mower and the mower itself, several safety interlocks must be implemented. These interlocks and the variables that will represent them are listed below.

Interlock Description	Variable Used	State
Brake Switch	Brake	True if brake on
Operator Seat Switch	Seat	True if operator seated
Blade Power Switch	Blades	True if blades turning
Left Guide Bar Neutral Switch	LeftNeutral	True if in neutral
Right Guide Bar Neutral Switch	RightNeutral	True if in neutral
Ignition Switch	Ignition	True if in run position
Motor Power Interlock	Motor	True if motor enabled

For the motor to be enabled (thus capable of running), all the following conditions must be true.
- The ignition switch must be set to "Run."
- If the operator is not properly seated, both guide levers must be in the locked neutral position.
- If either guide lever is not in the locked neutral position, the brake must be off.
- If the blades are powered, the operator must be properly seated.

Write a function that will accept all of the above variables except `Motor`, decide whether the motor should be enabled or not, and place true or false in `Motor` as the returned variable.

Sample Input/Output If the parameters are set to 0,0,0,0,0,1, the Motor output will be 0.

```
If the parameters are set to 0,1,0,1,1,1, the Motor output will
be 1.
```

11. Most resistors are so small that the actual value would be difficult to read if printed on the resistor. Instead, colored bands denote the value of resistance in ohms. Anyone involved in constructing electronic circuits must become familiar with the color code, and with practice, one can tell at a glance what value a specific set of colors means. For the novice, however, trying to read color codes can be a bit challenging.

You are to design a program that, when a user enters a resistance value, the program will display (as text) the color bands in the order they will appear on the resistor.

The resistance will be entered in two parts: the first two digits, and a power of 10 by which those digits will be multiplied. The user should be able to select each part from a menu. You should assume the ONLY values that can be selected by the user are the ones listed in Tables 19-4 and 19-5.

As examples, a resistance of 4,700 ohms has first digit 4 (yellow), second digit 7 (violet), and 2 zeros following (red). A resistance of 56 ohms would be 5 (green), 6 (blue), and 0 zeros (black); 1,000,000 ohms is 1 (brown), 0 (black), and 5 zeros (green). There are numerous explanations of the color code on the web if you want further information or examples.

Table 19-3 Standard resistor values

10	12	15	18	22	27	33	39	47	56	68	82

Table 19-4 Standard multipliers

1	10	100	1000	10000	100000	1000000

Table 19-5 Color codes

0	1	2	3	4	5	6	7	8	9
Black	Brown	Red	Orange	Yellow	Green	Blue	Violet	Grey	White

12. A phase diagram (from http://www.eng.ox.ac.uk/~ftgamk/engall_tu.pdf) for copper–nickel shows that three phases are possible: a solid alpha phase (a solid solution), a liquid solution, and a solid–liquid combination.

Write a program that takes as input a mass percent of nickel and a temperature in units of degress Celsius and gives as output a message indicating what phases are present. Assume the region borders are linear, and determine a method for dealing with any points that lie directly on the lines. The equation of the line dividing the phases must be found in the program using `polyfit`. The program should produce a formatted output statement to the command window, similar to "For w weight percent nickel and a temperature of T degrees Celsius, the phase is PHASE," where w, T and Phase are replaced by the actual values.

The program should also reproduce the graph as shown here with all phase division lines, and indicate the point entered by the user with a symbol.

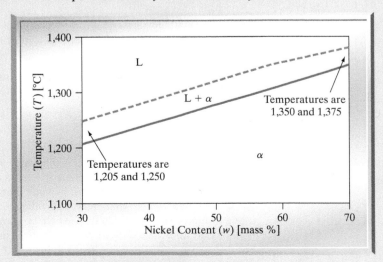

13. This generic phase diagram, based on the temperature and composition of elements A and B, is taken from http://www.soton.ac.uk/~pasr1/build.htm, where a description of how phase diagrams are constructed can also be found. The alpha and beta phases represent solid solutions of B in A and of A in B, respectively.

   The eutectic line represents the temperature below which the alloy will become completely solid if it is not in either the alpha or beta region. Below that line, the alloy is a solid mixture of alpha and beta. Above the eutectic line, the mixture is at least partially liquid, with partially solidified lumps of alpha or beta in the labeled regions.

   Assume the following:

   - The melting point of pure A is 700 degrees Celsius.
   - The melting point of pure B is 800 degrees Celsius.
   - The eutectic line is at 300 degrees Celsius, and the eutectic point occurs when the composition is 50% B.
   - The ends of the eutectic line are at 15% B and 85% B.

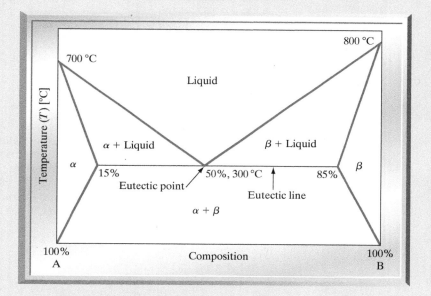

Using the simplified phase diagram, which substitutes straight lines for the curved lines typical of phase diagrams, write a MATLAB program that takes as input the mass percent of B and the temperature in units of degrees Celsius and returns the phases that may exist under those conditions. The equation of the line dividing the phases must be found in the program using `polyfit`. The program should produce a formatted output statement to the command window, similar to "For the composition of x% A, y% B and a temperature of T degrees Celsius, the phase is PHASE," where x, y, T and Phase are replaced by the actual values.

   The program should also reproduce the graph as shown here with all phase division lines, and indicate the point entered by the user with a symbol.

   Your MATLAB program should include special notes if the provided conditions are on the eutectic line or at the eutectic point.

14. Soil texture can be classified with a moist soil sample and the questions in the table below from the Soil Texture Key found at http://www.pasture4horses.com/soils/hand-texturing. php/. Each answer results in either a soil classification or directions to continue. Write a program that implements this decision tree. You may find it useful to download the key itself from the above address. You may also want to compare your results to an online implementation of the key found at the same website. Your program should include the use of menu windows to gather user responses.

Question	Yes	No
1. Does the soil feel or sound noticeably sandy?	Go to Q2	Go to Q6
2. Does the soil lack all cohesion?	SAND	Go to Q3
3. Is it difficult to roll the soil into a ball?	LOAMY SAND	Go to Q4
4. Does the soil feel smooth and silky as well as sandy?	SANDY SILT LOAM	Go to Q5
5. Does the soil mould to form a strong ball that smears without taking a polish?	SANDY CLAY LOAM	SANDY LOAM
6. Does the soil mould to form an easily deformed ball and feel smooth and silky?	SILT LOAM	Go to Q7
7. Does the soil mould to form a strong ball that smears without taking a polish?	Go to Q8	Go to Q10
8. Is the soil also sandy?	SANDY CLAY LOAM	Go to Q9
9. Is the soil also smooth and silky?	SILTY CLAY LOAM	CLAY LOAM
10. Does the soil mould like plasticine, polish, and feel very sticky when wetter?	Go to Q11	UNKNOWN SOIL
11. Is the soil also sandy?	SANDY CLAY	Go to Q12
12. Is the soil also smooth and buttery?	SILTY CLAY	CLAY

15. Your boss hands you the following segment of MATLAB code that implements a safety control system in an automobile. Recently, the engineer who wrote the code below was fired for their inability to write efficient code. The control system below takes 5 minutes for the car to execute because it was not written using nested-if statements, and worse, it does not work with multiple sensors because the former employee could not figure out how to make use of nested-if statements! Your boss has instructed you to take the former employee's code and fix it, or you might meet the same fate as the original programmer!

```
% Variable Definition:
% Input:
% Ignition: 0 if engine off, 1 if key in ignition, 2 if engine on
% Belt: 1 if buckled, 0 if unbuckled, -1 if sensor broken
% HLamp: 1 if all bulbs ok, 0 if 1 bulb out, -1 if 2 or more out
% TLamp: 1 if all bulbs ok, 0 if 1 bulb out, -1 if 2 or more out
% Light: 1 if sky is bright, 0 if sky is dark (need lamps)
% Output:
% Safety: 1 if safe, 0 if warn/caution, -1 if unsafe

function[Safety]=Vehicle(Ignition,Belt,HLamp,TLamp,Light)

if Ignition==1 || Ignition == 0
     Safety = 1;
end
if Ignition==2 && Belt == 1
     Safety = 1;
end
if Ignition==2 && Belt == 0
     Safety = 0;
end
```

```
if Ignition==2 && Belt == -1
      Safety = -1;
end
if Ignition==2 && Belt == 1 && HLamp == 1
      Safety = 1;
end
if Ignition==2 && Belt == 1 && HLamp == 0
      Safety = 0;
end
if Ignition==2 && Belt == 1 && HLamp == -1
      Safety = 0;
end
if Ignition==2 && Belt == 1 && HLamp == -1 && Light==0
      Safety = -1;
end
if Ignition==2 && Belt == 1 && TLamp == 1
      Safety = 1;
end
if Ignition==2 && Belt == 1 && TLamp == 0
      Safety = 0;
end
if Ignition==2 && Belt == 1 && TLamp == -1
      Safety = 0;
end
if Ignition==2 && Belt == 1 && TLamp == -1 && Light == 0
      Safety = -1;
end
```

16. Assume you are required to generate the menus shown below in a MATLAB program. Write a program to generate these menus and display the choice of the user in a sentence like: "You selected a car with automatic transmission." If the user clicks "Other," an input statement should allow them to type a different vehicle type (as a string). For this program, use `if-elseif` statements instead of `switch` statements.

17. Assume you are required to generate the menus shown with Review Question 19-16 in a MATLAB program. Write the program necessary to generate these menus and display the choice of the user in a sentence like "You selected a car with automatic transmission." If the user clicks "Other", an input statement should allow them to type a different vehicle type (as a string). For this program, use `switch` statements instead of `if-elseif` statements.

18. Assume you are required to generate the menus shown below in a MATLAB program. Write a program to generate these menus and display the choice of the user in a sentence like: "You selected size 8 Nike shoes." If the user clicks "Other," an input statement should allow them to type a different shoe size (as a number). For this program, use `if-elseif` statements instead of `switch` statements.

19. Assume you are required to generate the menus shown with Review Question 19-18 in a MATLAB program. Write the program necessary to generate these menus and display the choice of the user in a sentence like "You selected size 8 Nike shoes." If the user clicks "Other", an input statement should allow them to type a different shoe size (as a number). For this program, use `switch` statements instead of `if-elseif` statements.

20. The variable grade can have any real number values from 0 to 100. Ask the user to enter a grade in numerical form. Write an `if-elseif-else` statement that displays the letter grade (any format) corresponding to a numerical grade in an appropriately formatted output statement.

    A typical range of grades:

    A: $90 \le$ grade
    B: $80 \le$ grade < 90
    C: $70 \le$ grade < 80
    D: $60 \le$ grade < 70
    F: grade < 60

21. Write a MATLAB program that will allow the student to select the grade earned in a course from a menu (with the options of earning an A, B, C, D, or F) that will display the letter range for the selected grade. The output of the program displayed on the screen should be formatted as shown in the sample output. In your program, you must use a `switch` statement instead of an `if-elseif` statement. You may assume that the typical range of grades in a course is defined as listed in Review Question 19-20:

Sample Input / Output

if selected A...

If you earn a A, your earned grade is in the range: 90 <= grade.

22. *One of the fourteen NAE Grand Challenges is Engineering Better Medicines. Part of this Grand Challenge is creating individual medication plans for each patient, rather than sweeping recommendations based upon research using only one subset of the population. For example, in the past most heart attack protocols were created for white males. It has been discovered in recent years that women have different initial symptoms and respond better to a different treatment protocol than their male counterparts.*

To better tailor the medicine to the individual, you wish to write a computer program to allow the user to enter several variables, then the program will produce a suggested solution. Write the MATLAB code to . . .

(a) Ask the user to enter their name (text).

(b) Ask the user to type their weight (a number) in pounds-force.

(c) Ask the user to select their symptom from a menu, given the following choices.
  - Cold
  - Flu
  - Migraine

(d) Based upon the answer selected to the menu, set the medicine name, volume [mL] and mass [g] of the medicine tablet.

Symptom	Medicine	Volume [mL]	Mass [g]
Cold	Achoo	3.5	9
Flu	Chill	5	16
Migraine	HAche	4	11

(e) Write (a) the function call from the program and (b) a function that will accept the mass and volume of the desired medicine from the main program and return the specific gravity of the desired medicine tablet to the program. Remember: The density of water is 1000 kilograms per cubic meter.

(f) Write (a) the function call from the program and (b) a function that will accept the weight of the person, specific gravity of the medicine, and tablet volume from the main program and return the number of tablets recommended for the person to the program. To determine the number of tablets needed, the following equation should be used and then rounded up to the next whole number of tablets. Any calculations or conversions necessary should appear in the function.

$$\text{Dose} = \text{Mass of person [kg]} \left| \frac{1.25\frac{mL}{kg}}{2.5*SG} \right| \frac{1 \text{ tablet}}{\text{Volume[mL]}}$$

(g) Write an output statement that appears as follows, where N is replaced by the name of the medicine and X.XXX is replaced by the calculated specific gravity formatted to show 3 decimal places: The specific gravity of N is X.XXX.

(h) Write an output statement that appears as follows, where AAAA is the name of the user, N is the name of the medicine, YYY is the name of their symptom, and Z is the number of tablets recommended:
AAAA, your recommended dosage of N to treat a YYY: Z tablets.

NOTE: Although you may use conditional statements to solve this problem, none are needed if you set up the medicine data table as a cell array.

23. Assume two matrices, M1 and M2 have already been defined and have the same dimensions. Create a matrix Comp1 with the same dimensions as M1 and M2. Each element of Comp1 should be an integer between −3 and 3 based on the relative values of the corresponding elements of M1 and M2 according to the following rules:

- If the magnitudes (absolute values) of corresponding elements of M1 and M2 are equal, that element of Comp1 equals 0.
- If the magnitude of the element in M1 is greater than that in M2, the corresponding element in Comp1 will be positive.
- If the magnitude (absolute value) of the element in M1 is less than that in M2, the corresponding element in Comp1 will be negative.
- If the values in both M1 and M2 are positive, the magnitude of the value in Comp1 is 1.
- If the values in both M1 and M2 are negative, the magnitude of the value in Comp1 is 2.
- If the values in both M1 and M2 opposite signs (assume zero is positive), the magnitude of the value in Comp1 is 3. (NOTE: if the magnitudes of the values in M1 and M2 are equal, that element of Comp1 will contain a zero.)

Sample Input / Output

$$M1 = \begin{bmatrix} 0 & 1 & 2 \\ -2 & -1 & 0 \\ 1 & -1 & -1 \end{bmatrix} \quad M2 = \begin{bmatrix} -1 & 1 & 0 \\ -1 & 2 & 2 \\ -1 & 0 & -2 \end{bmatrix} \quad Comp1 = \begin{bmatrix} -3 & 0 & 1 \\ 2 & -3 & -1 \\ 0 & 3 & -2 \end{bmatrix}$$

NOTE: Even if you know how to use programming loops, DO NOT do so for this program. The problem should be solved using logical arrays.

CHAPTER 20
LOOPING STRUCTURES

The key to making an algorithm compact is to exploit its variables by means of a loop. A loop is a programming structure that allows a segment of code to execute a fixed number of times or until a condition is true. This chapter describes two looping structures: the `for` loop and the `while` loop.

20.1 for LOOPS

LEARN TO: Automate a segment of code using a `for` loop
Calculate the number of executions of a `for` loop
Convert an algorithm into code involving a `for` loop

You may have noticed that a number of the algorithms we have already studied have parts that are repetitive. Sometimes, we want to execute an algorithm a certain number of times:

- For every pressure sensor, record the pressure reading.
- For each employee, check the date of the employee's last safety training.

It may be useful to sample less than every possible point, as in:

- For every fifth data point, enter its value into an array for plotting.

The ability to count backwards is also useful:

- For every second counting down from 10 to 0 seconds, announce the time remaining until launch.

The syntax of a `for` loop is illustrated below:

```
for counter = start : step : finish
          % executable statements
    end
```

- *counter:* variable chosen to keep track of number of times the loop has executed
- *start:* first value of the loop
- *step:* incremental value to use to advance from start to finish
- *finish:* final value of the loop

The counter variable can be used in the loop to calculate other variables, to index an array, to set function parameters, etc.

A sample for loop is shown below. This loop will display on the screen the numbers from 1 to 5, each on a separate line.

```
for k=1:1:5
        fprintf('%0.0f\n',k)
end
```

Understanding the for Loop

Most program statements do exactly the same type of thing every time, although they may be manipulating different information. The for loop is slightly different. A for statement can be arrived at during program execution in one of two ways:

1. It can be executed immediately following a statement that was outside the loop, typically a statement immediately above it.

2. It can be executed upon returning from the end statement that marks the end of the loop after the loop has executed one or more times.

What the for statement does in these two cases is different and is crucial to understanding its operation.

1. When the for statement is arrived at from another statement *outside* the loop, it does the following:

- Places the start value into the counter variable.
- Decides whether or not to execute the instructions inside the for loop.

2. When the for statement is arrived at from its corresponding end statement below, it does the following:

- Adds the step value to the counter variable.
- Decides whether or not to execute the instructions inside the for loop.

The second step is the same in both cases and requires a bit more explanation. To determine whether or not to execute the instructions inside the loop (those between the for and its corresponding end), the for statement asks the question "Has the counter gone beyond the finish value?"

- If the answer is no, execute the statements inside the loop.
- If the answer is yes, skip over the loop and continue with the first statement (if any) immediately following the corresponding end statement.

If the loop is counting up (step > 0), then we could ask "Is the counter greater than the finish value?" If the loop is counting down (step < 0), we could use "less than" instead. Several examples are given below.

● EXAMPLE 20-1

Write the command to execute the following loop the desired amount of times.

(a) The statements in the loop will be executed four times, once each with $i = 1, 2, 3,$ and 4:

```
for i=1:1:4
        % loop statements
end
```

(b) The statements in the loop will be executed two times, once each with `time` = 1 and 3. When `time` is incremented to 5, it is "beyond" the finish value:

```
for time=1:2:4
        % loop statements
end
```

(c) The statements in the loop will be executed three times, once each with `gleep` = 4, 2, and 0:

```
for gleep=4:-2:0
        % loop statements
end
```

(d) The statements in the loop will be executed three times, once each with `raft` = 13, 7, and 1. When `raft` is decremented to −5 it is "beyond" the finish value:

```
for raft=13:-6:-4
        % loop statements
end
```

● **EXAMPLE 20-2**

Determine how many times the loop will execute and for what values of the index variable.

(a) `for time=1:2:4`
```
        % loop statements
end
```

The statements in the loop will be executed two times, once each with `time` *= 1 and 3. When* `time` *is incremented to 5, it is "beyond" the finish value:*

(b) `for raft=13:-6:-4`
```
        % loop statements
end
```

The statements in the loop will be executed three times, once each with `raft` *= 13, 7, and 1. When* `raft` *is decremented to −5, it is "beyond" the finish value.*

(c) `for k=6:1:4`
```
        % loop statements
end
```

The statements in the loop will not be executed. `k` *is "beyond" the finish value when the loop is first entered.*

(d) `S1=5;`
```
S2=7;
for wolf=S1:S2:S1^2+S2+1
        % loop statements
end
```

The statements in the loop will be executed five times, once each with `wolf` *= 5, 12, 19, 26, and 33.*

As noted earlier, it is generally a bad idea to redefine the index variable inside of the loop. Similarly, redefining any variables from which the index variable is calculated is also strongly discouraged. For example, `S1` *and* `S2` *should not be changed inside the loop.*

Arithmetic Sequences

When dealing with **arithmetic sequences**—those that require only changing the **index variable** by adding or subtracting a number from it—there are two primary ways to proceed.

1. Set up the sequence explicitly, such as k=2:2:10
2. Set the index variable to count from 1 through the desired number of iterations, and then calculate the desired values from the index values, such as k=1:1:5; k1=2k;

In some cases the direct sequence may be more intuitive, in others the calculated equivalent makes more sense.

In each of the following examples, a sequence of five numbers is given, with two solutions shown to generate that sequence. The first code segment in each example uses the for loop to count from 1 to 5, and the values desired are calculated inside the loop. The second segment of code accomplishes the same goal by manipulating the start, step, and finish values instead. Although we are using print statements inside the example loops so that you can easily type these into MATLAB and see the sequence generated, you will seldom print the index values. Most of the time, the index values will be used in a calculation of some form, not just printed to the screen.

● EXAMPLE 20-3

We desire the sequence to be 3, 6, 9, 12, 15.

```
for k=1:1:5
    fprintf('%0.0f\n',3*k)
end
```

Given that k goes through the sequence k = 1, 2, 3, 4, 5, the desired sequence could be calculated as 3k.

```
for k=3:3:15
    fprintf('%0.0f\n',k)
end
```

This illustrates the idea that multiplication and division of a sequence by a constant to generate a new sequence affects all three loop control parameters: start, step, and finish.

● EXAMPLE 20-4

We desire the sequence to be 3, 4, 5, 6, 7.

```
for k=1:1:5
    fprintf('%0.0f\n',k+2)
end
```

This can be calculated as k + 2

```
for k=3:1:7
    fprintf('%0.0f\n',k)
end
```

Adding and subtracting a constant to create a new sequence affects only the start and finish values.

● **EXAMPLE 20-5**   We desire the sequence to be 4, 6, 8, 10, 12.

Note that the standard order of operations applies, and the multiplication must be done first.

```
for k=1:1:5
    fprintf('%0.0f\n',2*k+2)
end
```

This can be calculated as $2k + 2$.

```
for k=4:2:12
    fprintf('%0.0f\n',k)
end
```

Note that all three loop parameters are affected: start *and* finish *are subject to both multiplication and addition, but* step *is only affected by multiplication.*

COMPREHENSION CHECK 20-1   Write a for loop to display every even number from 2 to 20 on the screen.

COMPREHENSION CHECK 20-2   Write a for loop to display every multiple of 5 from 5 to 50 on the screen.

COMPREHENSION CHECK 20-3   Write a for loop to display every odd number from 13 to −11 on the screen.

Using Variable Names to Clarify Loop Function

Using variables with meaningful names as loop controls makes it easier for those trying to interpret the program to keep track of what the loop is doing. The following loop keeps track of the position of an object moving at a constant speed. By defining the step distance as Speed*TimeStep, thus an increment in position, the number of steps in the loop is flexible as well. Note that these variables would need to be defined earlier in the program.

```
for Position=StartPosition:Speed*TimeStep:FinalPosition
    fprintf('%0.0f\n',Position)
end
```

Using a for Loop in Variable Recursion

An important use of loops is for **variable recursion**—passing information from one loop execution to the next. A simple form of recursion is to keep a running total. The loop below determines the total sales for all the vendors at a football game. The loop assumes that the array Sales contains the total sales for each vendor. The number of vendors is computed when the loop begins, using the `length` command, and the total sales are accumulated in `TotalSales`. Note that `TotalSales` must be initialized before the loop is entered, since it appears on the right-hand side of the equation:

```
TotalSales = 0;
for Vendor=1:1:length(Sales)
        TotalSales = TotalSales + Sales(Vendor);
end
```

This code also introduces a very important use of `for` loops: to automatically step through the values in a vector or array. Note here that the index variable `Vendor` is used sequentially to access each element of the `Sales` vector.

COMPREHENSION CHECK 20-4

Assume a vector `Vals` has already been defined. Write a `for` loop that will calculate the sum of all positive values in `Vals` and place the result in the variable `PosSum`.

Manipulating a `for` Loop Counter

Many kinds of computations can be performed in a loop. Many of the example loops above will output the value of k to the screen each time through the loop. Other sequences can be achieved by having an expression other than k in the executable part of the loop.

COMPREHENSION CHECK 20-5

Consider the following table of values. Determine the formulae to represent columns A through J. In some cases, the formulae in rows 1–10 will be similar. In other cases, the entry in the first row will be a number rather than a formula.

Create a `for` loop to display the values; use tabs in a formatted `fprintf` statement to create each column.

k	A	B	C	D	E	F	G	H	I	J
1	2	1	1	1	7.25	10	1	2	1	1.00
2	4	3	4	3	7.50	9	−1	4	2	0.50
3	6	5	9	6	7.75	8	1	8	6	0.33
4	8	7	16	10	8.00	7	−1	16	24	0.25
5	10	9	25	15	8.25	6	1	32	120	0.20
6	12	11	36	21	8.50	5	−1	64	720	0.17
7	14	13	49	28	8.75	4	1	128	5020	0.14
8	16	15	64	36	9.00	3	−1	256	40320	0.13
9	18	17	81	45	9.25	2	1	512	362880	0.11
10	20	19	100	55	9.50	1	−1	1024	3628800	0.10

Using the Counter Variable as an Array Index

The example above used the counter variable `Vendor` to access each element of the `Sales` array in sequence to add them together. If we wanted to add only the odd-numbered elements, the only change necessary would be to change the step variable to 2. If we wanted every fourth element of the array beginning with the fourth element, the `for` statement would become

```
for Vendor=4:4:length(Sales)
```

and so forth.

To access elements in a matrix, we could use a single index since MATLAB will handle this, but we would have to be very careful to make certain which row and column is being accessed. For example, if A is a 3×2 matrix, `A(4)=A(1,2)`. Since this can be quite confusing, it is usually better to use the double index notation when accessing values in a matrix. One method to accomplish this would be to use nested `for` loops, that is, a `for` loop inside another `for` loop. Let us modify the football sales example above as an example.

Assume we have a 2-D array named `Sales` where each row represents a specific vendor and each column represents a different category of item, such as drinks, hot dogs, hats, etc. Now if we want the total sales, we need to step through every element in every column (or every element in every row) and add them all up. To determine the number of vendors and items in the matrix, we use the `size` function, rather than the `length` function we used previously with the vector.

```
% Initialize the sum of all sales to 0
TotalSales = 0;
% Determine the number of vendors (rows) and items (columns)
[NumVendors, NumItems]=size(Sales)
for Vendor=1:1:NumVendors        % this will index the rows
    for Item=1:1:NumItems        % this will index the columns
        TotalSales = TotalSales + Sales(Vendor, Item);
    end
end
```

Note that the inner `for` loop (`Item` loop) goes through all items (columns) before exiting, at which point the outer `for` loop increments to the next vendor (row) and the inner loop resets to the first column and steps through all items again, but for a different vendor.

If there were four vendors (rows) and three items (columns), the order in which the entries in the `Sales` array would be added to `TotalSales` would be:

(1,1); (1,2); (1,3); (2,1); (2,2); (2,3); (3,1); (3,2); (3,3); (4,1); (4,2); (4,3);

You may recall from Chapter 16 that this problem could be solved more "simply" with a single line of code:

```
TotalSales=sum(sum(Sales));
```

There are many situations, however, where the built-in matrix operations will not accomplish the desired purpose and you MUST set up a pair of nested loops to step through the elements of the array.

COMPREHENSION CHECK 20-6

Write two nested `for` loops to determine how many positive values (including zeros) are in each column of the matrix M1, which has already been defined. The results should be stored in a row vector `PosNums` in which each element contains the number of positive values found in the corresponding column of M1.

Example: M1= [3 -6 0;-4 -8 2;8 -9 1];   PosNums=[2 0 3]

Ending `for` Loops Early

In certain situations, it might be desirable to build in logic within a `for` loop that allows for the loop to terminate when a certain situation is encountered. The `break` command instructs MATLAB to exit the loop and continue as if the entire loop sequence was finished. It is important to realize that the break command does NOT terminate the function or program—it will only exit the loop code.

● EXAMPLE 20-6

Consider the following segment of MATLAB code:

```
S = input('Type the starting point of the loop: ');
E = input('Type the ending point of the loop: ');
for i=S:1:E
    if 1/i == Inf
        fprintf('Uh oh! Division by zero!\n')
        break
    end
    fprintf('%0.1f\n',1/i)
end
fprintf('... ALL DONE!\n')
```

What is the outcome if the user enters S=1 and E=3?

When the user provides the value of 1 for the starting value and 3 for the ending value, everything runs smoothly:

```
Type the starting point of the loop: 1
Type the ending point of the loop: 3
1
0.5
0.3
... ALL DONE!
```

What is the outcome if the user enters S=-3 and E=3?

However, when the user provides the values of −3 for the starting value and 3 for the ending value, notice what happens:

```
Type the starting point of the loop: -3
Type the ending point of the loop: 3
-0.3
-0.5
-1
Uh oh! Division by zero!
... ALL DONE!
```

There are a few important concepts to note from the output of this execution of our code segment. First, the code after the `for` *loop, the output statement that displays "... ALL DONE!" is executed, so the* `break` *command will not skip any code after the* `for` *loop has terminated. Second, since the output of the number occurred after the check to see if a division by zero has occurred, the output command did not display the number zero because the* `break` *command terminated the loop, which means that no code after the* `break` *command within an iteration of a loop will execute. Last, it's important to note that the* `break` *command terminates the ENTIRE loop—not just the iteration, so the numbers 1 through 3 will not be displayed because the loop finished early.*

When a `break` command appears within a nested `for` loop, the `break` will apply to only the loop where the break occurs and will not terminate the entire nested loop.

● **EXAMPLE 20-7**   Consider the following segment of MATLAB code:

```
Si = input('Type the starting point of the inner loop: ');
Ei = input('Type the ending point of the inner loop: ');
So = input('Type the starting point of the outer loop: ');
Eo = input('Type the ending point of the outer loop: ');

for i=So:1:Eo
    for j=Si:1:Ei
      if i == j
          fprintf('Same value... skipping!\n')
          break
      end
      fprintf('%0.0f\t%0.0f\n',i,j)
    end
end
fprintf('... ALL DONE!\n')
```

What is the outcome if the user enters 3, 5, 1, 2?

When the user provides the value of 3 for the starting value and 5 for the ending value of the inner loop and 1 for the starting value and 2 for the ending value of the outer loop, everything runs smoothly since these two sets of numbers will never intersect.

```
Type the starting point of the inner loop: 3
Type the ending point of the inner loop: 5
Type the starting point of the outer loop: 1
Type the ending point of the outer loop: 2
1    3
1    4
1    5
2    3
2    4
2    5
... ALL DONE!
```

What is the outcome if the user enters 3, 5, 3, 5?

However, when the user provides the values of 3 for the starting value and 5 for the ending value of both the inner and outer loops, notice what happens:

```
Type the starting point of the inner loop: 3
Type the ending point of the inner loop: 5
```

```
Type the starting point of the outer loop: 3
Type the ending point of the outer loop: 5
Same value... skipping!
4       3
Same value... skipping!
5       3
5       4
Same value... skipping!
... ALL DONE!
```

Notice that the outer loop is unaffected by the break *command and continues looping over values 3 to 5, regardless of whether the inner loop encounters a* break *command.*

● EXAMPLE 20-8

Assume you're required to write a **MATLAB** program that will allow the user to generate a graph and plot a linear trendline of flowrate data manually provided by the user. Assume that your program will prompt the user to enter the initial time of data collection, the final time, and the interval between data samples, all in units of minutes. Your code should then iterate and prompt the user to record the corresponding flowrate sample value in units of gallons per minute at each required sample time.

```
clear
clc

AbsStart=input('What is the initial sample time [min]? ');
AbsEnd=input('What is the final sample time [min]? ');
AbsInc=input('How often should samples be taken [min]? ');

Abs = [];  % create empty vectors to hold the user input
Ord = [];
cnt = 1;  % cnt = count number of samples entered by user
for I=AbsStart:AbsInc:AbsEnd
    prompt=sprintf('Sample #%0.0f, at %0.2f min\nFlowrate (Q) [gpm]: ', cnt,I);
    Abs=[Abs I];
    x = input(prompt);
    Ord = [Ord x];
    cnt = cnt + 1;
end

% polyfit to calculate trend:
C = polyfit(Abs,Ord,1);
TrendAbs = [AbsStart:AbsInc/20:AbsEnd];
TrendOrd = C(1)*TrendAbs + C(2);

% generate plot
plot(Abs,Ord,'x',TrendAbs,TrendOrd,'-')
% other proper plot commands to show, for example, the axis labels, are
% entered here, but are not shown for space considerations
```

Sample Usage:

```
What is the initial sample time [min]?: 1
What is the final sample time [min]?: 6
```

```
How often should samples be taken [min]?: 2
Sample #1, at 1.00 min
Flowrate (Q) [gpm]: 7
Sample #3, at 3.00 min
Flowrate (Q) [gpm]: 17
Sample #5, at 5.00 min
Flowrate (Q) [gpm]: 27
```

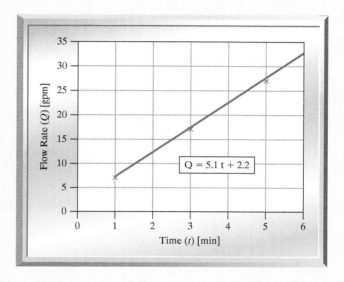

**COMPREHENSION
CHECK 20-7**

Assume a matrix M2 has already been defined. Write two nested for loops to determine how many rows of the matrix M2 contain only negative values. The results should be stored in NegRows.

Example: M2 = [3 -6 0;-4 -8 -2;8 -9 1];   NegRows=1

20.2 while **LOOPS**

LEARN TO: Automate a segment of code using a while loop
Calculate the number of executions of a while loop
Convert an algorithm into code involving a while loop

Once a for loop has started, it executes a specified number of times, regardless of what happens in the loop. At other times, we want to continue executing a loop until a particular condition is satisfied. This requires the use of a while loop, which executes until the specified condition is false. The conditional part of the while statement has the same syntax as that of the if statement.

```
                    while Logical_Expression
                              % executable statements
                    end
```

For example, while the calculation error is unacceptable, refine the calculations to improve accuracy.

```
while error >= 0.01
        % require less than 1% error
        % perform another iteration of the calculation
        % recalculate error
end
```

Converting "Until" Logic for Use in a `while` Statement

In some cases, it may make more sense to use the word *until* in phrasing a conditional loop, but MATLAB does not have such a structure. As a result, it is sometimes necessary to rephrase our conditions to fit the `while` structure.

"Until" Logic Condition	`while` Logic Translation

`until cows == home`
    `party`
`end`
	`while cows ~= home`
	    `party`
	`end`

`until homework == done`
        `TVpower = off`
`end`
	`while homework ~= done`
	        `TVpower = off`
	`end`

Initializing `while` Loop Conditions

In `for` loop constructions, the loop initializes and keeps track of the loop counter within the loop command. In a `while` loop, it is necessary to make sure that variables are properly initialized before entering encountering the loop command.

```
error=1;
while error >= 0.01
        % require less than 1% error
end
```

If `error` is not initialized, a syntax error results since the `error` term does not exist when MATLAB tries to compare it to the value 0.01. If `error` is incorrectly initialized to a value less than 0.01, the loop never executes. The initial value is chosen at random; we could have made the value any number greater than 0.01 and the program would execute correctly.

● EXAMPLE 20-9

We want to input a number from the user that is between (and including) 5 and 10, but reject all other numbers. All extraneous output should be suppressed.

```
X=0;
while X < 5 || X > 10
    X=input('Enter a number between 5 and 10');
end
```

**COMPREHENSION
CHECK** 20-8

Write a `while` loop that requires the user to input a number until a nonnegative number is entered.

● **EXAMPLE 20-10**

We have a number stored in a variable `T` that we want to repeatedly divide by 10 until `T` is smaller than 3×10^{-6}. After determining the first value of `T` that meets the condition, it should be displayed in a formatted `fprintf` statement where the value of `T` is displayed in exponential notation. All extraneous output should be suppressed.

```
T=3993;
while T > 3E-6
        T=T/10;
end
fprintf('%E\n',T);
```

● **EXAMPLE 20-11**

Given a vector of positive integers, `V`, we want to create two new vectors: vector `Even` will contain all of the even values of `V`; vector `Odd` will contain all of the odd values of `V`. To begin solving this problem, we need to seek out a MATLAB function that will help us to determine whether or not a given value is even or odd. The built-in function `rem` accepts two input arguments $(Z = rem(X,Y))$ such that `Z` is the remainder after dividing `X` by `Y`. For example, if we type `rem(3,2)`, the function would return `1` because $3/2 = 1$ with a remainder of 1.

```
V=[2, 3, 91, 87, 5, 8];
Even=[];
Odd=[]; % initially, Even and Odd are both empty vectors
fprintf('\nV =\t%0.0f', V')
while length(V)>0
        if rem(V(1),2)==0       % is first element of V even?
            Even=[Even V(1)]; % place it in Even
        else                    % is first element of V odd?
            Odd=[Odd V(1)];   % place it in Odd
        end
        V(1)=[];                % delete the first element of V
end
fprintf('\nEven =\t%0.0f', Even')
fprintf('\nOdd =\t%0.0f', Odd')
fprintf('\n')
```

The output of this code segment would be:

V	=	2	3	91	87	5	8
E	=	2	8				
O	=	3	91	87	5		

COMPREHENSION CHECK 20-9

Assume a vector V2 has already been defined and contains only values greater than 1. Write a while loop to calculate the product of the elements of V2 in sequence from the first element until the product is greater than 10^6 or all elements have been included in the product. The result should be stored in Prod.

Example: V2=[2 10 7 19];   Prod=2,660

Example: V2=[3 6 123 4 58 267 8 91 11]; Prod=137,144,016

Custom while Loop Termination

Just like the for loop, the while loop allows code to be written in such a way that the break command will terminate the loop early. Note that the behavior of the break command is the same with a while loop — it will only end the loop early and will NOT terminate a program or function. After encountering the break command, the code continues executing at the next line after the end of the loop.

Consider the following while loop, where the loop will execute while "true." This is a common approach to designing algorithms where the looping logic is indeterminate or too complicated to efficiently implement with a pure while loop or for loop structure.

```
S = 0;
while true
        A = input('Type the alpha value: ');
        if A == 5
          break
        end
        S = A + S;
        B = input('Type the beta value: ');
        if B == 7
          break
        end
        S = 2*B + S;
        end

fprintf('The final answer is: %0.0f\n',S)
```

Consider the following output sequence from the code segment shown.

```
Type the alpha value: 1
Type the beta value: 2
Type the alpha value: 4
Type the beta value: 5
Type the alpha value: 5
The final answer is: 19
```

Note the loop terminates before the alpha value of 5 can be added to the summation variable. Likewise, if the user never types the values that trigger the break commands (alpha value of 5 or beta value of 7), this code will loop "infinitely." In practice, this code will eventually terminate once the value stored in the variable is "overflown" with a value greater than the variable type can handle, but if the user continues manually typing in small numbers, this will not happen for a long time.

Recall to end an indefinite loop use CTRL+C

20.3 APPLICATION OF LOOPS: GUI

The purpose of this section is to familiarize you with creating **graphical user interfaces** (**GUIs**—often pronounced "gooey") in MATLAB and provide some insight into user-centered design to give you the tools you need to build a robust but clear interaction platform without the much "heavy" work on behalf of the program user. Designing user interfaces is different from designing algorithms to implement as programs or functions because there is an additional layer of complexity necessary to obscure some of the programming or language-specific requirements of your code. Graphical interface design is especially important when delivering a final "usable" product to a client or customer (the user) who may not necessarily have knowledge of the programming language you used to implement your solution.

Different graphical interface systems have different sets of best practices. For example, Microsoft Windows applications tend to have boxes in the upper right corner that allow users to click buttons to minimize, maximize, or close a program, whereas Mac OS X applications contain three circles in the upper left corner of windows that perform similar functions. Graphical interfaces also exist in many mobile operating systems like iOS or Android that allow handheld devices like iPhones and iPads to interact using push buttons or touch gestures to complete tasks. The remainder of this document focuses on WIMP interaction—"window, icon, menu, pointing device" like that found on programs run in Microsoft Windows (like MATLAB itself—see Fig. 20-1) or Mac OS X, but similar controls and development ideologies exist for mobile applications.

Figure 20-1 MATLAB itself is built with a GUI that allows you to click different toolbar buttons, menu items, launch new windows like the Editor Window, or type commands using the keyboard into the Command Window.

Graphical User Interface Development Environment

In MATLAB, the tool used for designing a user interface is the Graphical User Interface Development Environment (GUIDE). GUIDE can be launched in the main MATLAB window by selecting New > Graphical User Interface from the Home tab or by typing **guide** into the Command Window. The GUIDE Quick Start window (Fig. 20-2) gives you the options to either create a new GUI or open an existing GUI created with GUIDE. By default, there are a few built-in templates that give examples of how interactions are built using MATLAB commands with the GUI, but in general, most GUIs in MATLAB are built by selecting Blank GUI, the default option, and clicking the OK button.

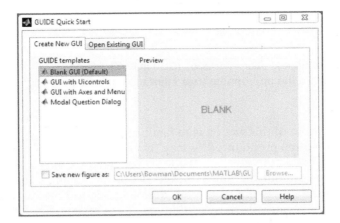

Figure 20-2 GUIDE Quick Start window.

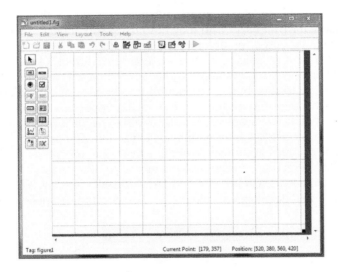

Figure 20-3 Graphical layout editor in GUIDE.

The resulting window (Fig. 20-3) is the graphical layout editor where you can arrange different user interaction controls that will allow, for example, the user of your program to click buttons, select options from check boxes or drop down menus, type values into text boxes, or an assortment of other options. This graphical layout is saved as a MATLAB Figure file with the file extension ".fig." For any GUI built in MATLAB using GUIDE, there will be both an M-File and a Figure file—both named the same and following the standard set of MATLAB file naming rules.

The graphical layout editor contains a set of buttons on the left side of the window that allows you to insert different interface controls on your GUI. To the right of the button set, the canvas of the GUI allows you to lay out exactly where the different interface controls should appear on the window of your application. Finally, the status bar at the bottom of the window contains different information depending on which user interface control is selected on the canvas. By default, the "figure" control is selected with the tag name "figure1"—this will be the main area where other controls will be placed in each window. In addition, as you move your mouse over the canvas, the "Current Point" value in the status bar updates with the current XY coordinate of your mouse within the GUI. That position will be helpful in lining up interface controls on your GUI so that it looks clean and consistent. In Table 20-1, the different user interface controls are described along with typical examples of when these controls might be used in a program window.

Table 20-1 **User interface controls in MATLAB**

Control	Name/Description	Sample Uses	Not Used For . . .
OK	**Push Button** Launches a calculation/action or opens a new dialog window.	Submit/calculate action, quit program, close window, load/open data file, cancel operation.	Setting or unsetting a parameter—use a checkbox or toggle button instead.
	Slider Slides a value between a minimum and maximum value by a step size.	Increasing or decreasing a variable value, incrementing or iterating through an expression.	Setting a value outside of the minimum or maximum value of the range—use a text box instead (or in addition to the slider).
	Radio Button Allows the user to select a single value from a mutually exclusive list of options. These are generally used inside of button group controls.	Selecting gender (male or female), water phase (solid, liquid, or gas), or other options from small groups.	Groups that have more than 5 or 6 different options (unit systems, when all SI units are included)—use a pop-up menu instead.
	Check Box Allows the user to turn on (or off) a single value. In general, check boxes are presented as a group of check boxes.	Selecting font style: bold, italic, underline. The user may want to use 1, 2, or all 3 options, or select none.	Allowing conflicting selections— a person can't be both male and female! Use a radio button instead.
EDIT	**Edit Text** Allows the user to manually type data into the program. Also called "entry fields" in some GUI environments.	Typing text (first name, last name, phone number) or numbers (zip code, weight, height, tire pressure).	Typing an element from a closed set of options—you don't want the user to type "Male"—let them select it using a radio button.
TXT	**Static Text** Allows the program to display or update text in a control that is not editable by the user. Also called "labels" or "protected fields" in some GUI environments.	Display program header labels, text entry field labels, slider values, calculated values, small error messages, or other information of interest to the program user.	Editing or typing text—use an edit text control instead.
	Pop-up Menu Allows the user to select a single option from a list instead of typing values in an edit text box.	Selecting state of birth from a list of 50 states, selecting a car manufacturer from a list, selecting the car model from a list.	Pop-up menus don't allow the user to select more than one option (e.g. Jeep and Dodge)— use a listbox control instead.
	Listbox Allows the user to select multiple options from a list instead of typing multiple values into multiple text boxes.	Select multiple beam lengths, pipe sizes, data sets for a plot, students in an engineering class, or other scenarios where you want to choose more than one option.	If you want to restrict the selection to only one option, use a pop-up menu instead.

(Continued)

Table 20-1 (Continued)

	Toggle Button Allows the user to turn on (or off) a value. Toggle buttons can be presented in groups, but can also stand alone. For exclusive selection of toggle buttons, use the toggle controls inside a button group.	Turning on or off debug output. Selecting font style: bold, italic, underline. The user may want to use 1, 2, or all 3 options, or select none. Can be used like a check box.	Can only be used in binary states (on or off)—for more than 2 states, use a control like a radio button or pop-up menu.
	Table Allows the program to display tabular data in a visually attractive and interactive (e.g. scrollable) control.	Displaying a list of spring stiffnesses for multiple springs. Displaying a matrix of values calculated by a program.	Not useful for displaying single text strings or values—use a static text control instead.
	Axes Allows the program to display a plot or other data that can be displayed on axes in MATLAB (like an image) on the program window.	Displaying a plot of data, displaying an image of a card from a deck of cards, displaying the frequency response of an audio signal.	For multiple graphs on a GUI, you might want to consider using a single axis control and a subplot to allow MATLAB to automatically handle graph alignment.
	Panel Allows the programmer to group similar user interface controls to make the window visually easier to navigate.	Grouping all of the input controls in an "input" panel, grouping all of the output controls in an "output" panel.	Does not enable exclusivity within controls like radio or toggle buttons—use a button group if you require exclusive selection of options.
	Button Group Allows the programmer to group radio and/or toggle buttons to allow the user to make a mutually exclusive (single) selection from a group of multiple controls.	Selecting gender (male or female), water phase (solid, liquid, or gas), or other options from small groups.	Groups that have more than 5 or 6 different options (unit systems, when all SI units are included)—use a pop-up menu instead.
=X	**ActiveX Control** Allows the programmer to embed a control from a different program installed on the computer.	Embedding an Adobe PDF document in a GUI, embedding a QuickTime movie player.	Cross-platform programs— many ActiveX controls are operating system specific, so a GUI built-in Windows may not run in Mac OS X or Linux versions of MATLAB.

Interacting with User Interface Controls in GUIDE

Before laying out a program interface using GUIDE, it is critical to understand a few key ideas with user interface controls—specifically, how to change or extract values or properties of controls that are set automatically by your program. To demonstrate this, if you add a push button to the canvas in GUIDE, the tag (see the bottom left of the status bar in GUIDE when the push button is selected) of the push button is

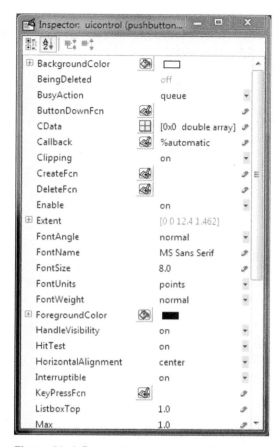

Figure 20-4 Property Inspector window for a push button control.

automatically set as "pushbutton1" by GUIDE. With this control, and all other controls, "tag" is a user interface control property that uniquely identifies that specific control on a GUI, much like how MATLAB would not allow you to have multiple variables with the same name. For each user interface control, there are a number of different properties that are automatically set by GUIDE, and understanding how those properties behave will allow for greater customization of the user interface.

The Property Inspector window allows the programmer to manually change the values in GUIDE of different user interface controls. In Fig. 20-4, the Property Inspector window shows the different properties for a push button user interface control that can be changed by typing different values if the property box contains a pencil icon or selecting different values on properties that contain a pop-up menu of different property values. For example, in this window, several properties like FontName, FontSize, FontAngle, and FontWeight will allow for customization of the font on the push button. Setting or getting the values of GUI controls can also be done in code using the get and set functions.

Interacting With User Interface Controls Programmatically: get *and* set

Before discussing the use of the get and set function to change or store property values in user interface controls, recall the use of the built-in graphing tool fplot, which we use for displaying functions in a MATLAB Figure window. In this code segment, we are plotting the sin function from $-\pi$ to π:

```
fplot('sin(x)',[-pi,pi]);
xlabel('X-Axis Text','FontSize',12,'FontWeight','bold');
ylabel('Y-Axis Text','FontSize',12,'FontWeight','bold');
grid
```

In this code segment, we are using the extra arguments in the xlabel, ylabel, functions to change properties like FontSize, FontWeight, by listing the property names and values as extra arguments in the function call. All plotting functions like fplot or plot actually create GUIs that are built in to MATLAB that have specialized functions like xlabel, ylabel, that are simply just short-cut tools that manually set the text values of the title and axis labels on plots. Since these plot windows are GUIs, the title and axis labels are actually just user interface controls like the static text labels described in Table 20-1, so these controls can actually be manually set or referenced creating a handle to the user interface control. A handle is actually just a reference that knows which control we want to modify that will allow us to access the different properties of the user interface.

To set user interface control properties using the set function, we need to pass in three arguments:

```
set(h,'PropertyName','PropertyValue');
```

where h is the variable that contains the handle reference, 'PropertyName' is the name of the property (like 'FontWeight' in the code above), and 'PropertyValue' is the value to set (like 'bold' in the code segment above).

The equivalent code to the code segment above written using set function calls:

```
fplot('sin(x)',[-pi,pi]);
xl=xlabel('X-Axis Text');
yl=ylabel('Y-Axis Text');
t=title('Title Text');
set(xl,'FontSize',12);
set(yl,'FontSize',12);
set(xl,'FontWeight','bold');
set(yl,'FontWeight','bold');
grid
```

Note that in the block of MATLAB code above, the handles to the user interface controls are created by capturing the handle references in different variables (xl, yl,) as outputs of the xlabel, ylabel, functions. Plotting functions like xlabel and ylabel were designed to be able to modify property values using extra function input arguments to reduce the number of lines of code when writing common code like creating graphs, so that is the preferred method for setting properties with those functions. The use of the set function in this fashion is only presented here as an example to help explain how this function works later when presented in the context of GUIs.

The get function works similarly to the set function by referencing user interface controls using a handle:

```
V=get(h,'PropertyName')
```

where h is the handle reference to the user interface control, 'PropertyName' is the property in the control, and V is a variable that will contain the property value for 'PropertyName'.

Consider the following segment of MATLAB code that uses the fplot function to again plot sin(x) from $-\pi$ to π and displays a title on the graph.

```
fplot('sin(x)',[-pi,pi]);
t=title('Title Text');
fs=get(t,'FontSize');
fw=get(t,'FontWeight');
fc=get(t,'Color');
st=get(t,'String');
```

In this code segment, we use the get function to read the default property values for the FontSize, FontWeight, Color, and String property values into the variables fs, fw, fc, and st. Note that fw and st are both text variables, fs is a number, and fc is a vector that contains the amount of red, green, and blue in the text font face color.

● **EXAMPLE 20-12**   In this example, the canvas (Fig. 20-5) contains a simple GUI with a few static and edit text boxes and a push button that will allow us to multiply the numbers typed into the boxes on the GUI and display them in the interface.

To begin, the controls were laid out on the GUI canvas as shown below. A list of the properties changes for the different user interface controls are documented below as well.

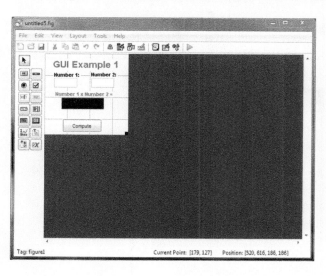

Figure 20-5 GUI for Example 20-12.

Tag: labelGUIHeader
        (static text)
String: GUI
        Example 1
ForegroundColor: blue
FontSize: 16
FontWeight: bold

Tag: labelNumber1
        (static text)
FontWeight: bold
String: Number 1:

Tag: labelNumber2
        (static text)
FontWeight: bold
String: Number 2:

Tag: label
        Multiplication
        (static text)
FontWeight: bold
String: Number 1 ×
        Number 2
ForegroundColor: red

Tag: num2 (edit text)
String: (blank)

Tag: labelResult (static text)
FontSize: 14
FontWeight: bold
ForegroundColor: white
BackgroundColor: black
String: (blank)

Tag: num1 (edit
text)
String: (blank)

Tag: button
        Compute (push
        button)
String: Compute

In addition to the changes above, the canvas was resized so that the GUI window does not contain a bunch of unnecessary unutilized space. After the GUI is properly arranged and renamed on the canvas, click the "Save and Run" button on GUIDE and the dialog shown in ▷.

Figure 20-6 will pop-up on the screen. Click Yes on the question dialog and type the name for the GUI Figure .fig file: GUIExample1.

Next, two windows will pop-up—the MATLAB Figure (Fig. 20-7) generated by GUIDE, as well as an M-File (Fig. 20-8) containing over 100 lines of MATLAB code and comments necessary to interact with the GUI. All of the functions within the M-File are actually

Figure 20-6 GUIDE save changes dialog.

Figure 20-7 MATLAB Figure generated by GUIDE in Example 20-12.

Figure 20-8 MATLAB M-File generated by GUIDE in Example 20-12.

subfunctions within the M-File, which means they can be called anywhere within this M-File, but you cannot call any of these functions from a different M-File. Subfunctions can only be written in M-Files that are implemented as a function, so the main GUI code is actually written as a function. Note that the M-File is named GUIExample1.m, which is the same file name as the MATLAB Figure we typed earlier. It is important that you do not rename this file since the Figure and M-File contain special references to "GUIExample1" throughout the code.

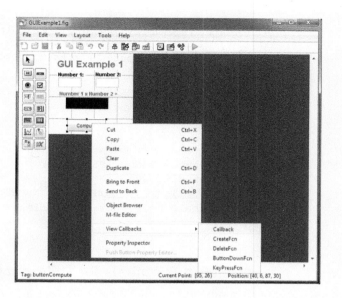

Figure 20-9 Accessing the push button callback function.

Now that the MATLAB Figure and M-File for the GUI exist, edit the M-File to insert some of the back-end code to implement the multiplication. To do this, we need to modify the callback function for the push button. Callback functions are codes that run as soon as some interaction occurs on the user interface. Examples of interaction might include clicking, double clicking, selecting an option from a menu, clicking a check box, or even events as simple as moving the mouse over a user interface control. To edit the callback function (as seen in Fig. 20-9) for the push button, right click the Compute button in GUIDE and select View Callbacks > Callback from the context menu.

At this point, the M-File Editor should pop-up and display the automatically generated code that handles the event that fires when the user clicks on the Compute button in your GUI:

```
% --- Executes on button press in buttonCompute.
function buttonCompute_Callback(hObject, eventdata, handles)
% hObject handle to buttonCompute (see GCBO)
% eventdata reserved - to be defined in a future version of
% MATLAB
% handles structure with handles and user data (see GUIDATA)
```

From here, we need to use the `get` and `set` functions to pull down the values in the edit text boxes, multiply the values together, and display the result on the GUI. To do this, the function header generated by MATLAB contains a function input called handles that is a structure variable that contains handle references to all of the user interface controls in the GUI. We can access the different user interface controls by typing `handles.tagName`, where tagName is the actual tag name embedded in different control properties. In this example, if we wanted to access the contents of the `num1` edit text box, we could type the following:

```
Num1Text=get(handles.num1,'String');
```

When we access some of the properties from user interface controls, be aware that some of the variable types might not be what you expect. In this case, the `Num1Text` variable is actually a string of text instead of a number. Before we do our computation, we must take the strings we `get` from the two edit text boxes and convert them into numbers before we can multiply them. Likewise, the `String` property in the static text field that will *contain the computed result expects the property to be set as a string, so we must convert the computed value into a string before we use the* set *function with the* String *property. The final code in the* buttonCompute *callback function should look something like:*

```
% --- Executes on button press in buttonCompute.
function buttonCompute_Callback(hObject, eventdata, handles)
% hObject handle to buttonCompute (see GCBO)
% eventdata reserved - to be defined in a future version of
% MATLAB
% handles structure with handles and user data (see GUIDATA)
Num1Text=get(handles.num1,'String');
Num2Text=get(handles.num2,'String');
M=str2double(Num1Text) * str2double(Num2Text);
set(handles.labelResult,'String',num2str(M,'%.0f'));
```

Callback and Related Functions for Different Controls

Like we saw in Example 20-12, many of the different user interface controls use callback functions or similar functions that will run when the user clicks on a control or somehow interacts with your GUI. These callback functions will only run the code within the function when the control is activated and will run again the next time the control is clicked. This idea is referred to as event-driven programming, where code will only execute when the user interacts with a control in an interface. User interaction with a control is referred to as an event, and when a callback function is executed, it is often said that the event for that control has fired.

In Table 20-2, the list of the important functions on different user interface controls is given with important properties that contain information about the text, values, or other data that might be necessary to use in the callback function. Note that there are other callback functions that may not be listed in the table that will fire on certain events like pressing a certain key on the keyboard, but those are not explicitly mentioned because they behave similarly to the standard callback functions.

Table 20-2 User interface controls

Control		Callback	Important Properties	Fires When . . .
[OK]	**Push Button**	Callback	**'String'** – text on the button	Button is pressed
[slider]	**Slider**	Callback	**'Value'** – current value of slider, number **'Min'** – minimum slider value, number **'Max'** – maximum slider value, number	Slider value changes
[radio]	**Radio Button**	Callback	**'Value'** – current value of radio, number **'Min'** – minimum radio value (not selected), number **'Max'** – maximum radio value (is selected), number	Radio button is pressed

(*Continued*)

Table 20-2 (Continued)

Control	Callback	Important Properties	Fires When . . .
Check Box	Callback	**'Value'** – current value of radio, number **'Min'** – minimum radio value (not selected), number **'Max'** – maximum radio value (is selected), number	Check box is clicked (checked or unchecked)
Edit Text	Callback	**'String'** – text in the edit text box	After editing text, user clicks outside of the textbox
Static Text	N/A	**'String'** – text in the static text box	N/A
Pop-up Menu	Callback	**'String'** – the pop-up menu contents, as a cell array of text values **'Value'** – the index into the cell array of the selected item in the pop-up menu	Selection in the pop-up menu is changed
Listbox	Callback	**'String'** – the listbox contents, as a cell array of text values **'Value'** – the index or indices into the cell array of the selected item in the pop-up menu, either a number or a vector depending on the number of selected items	Selection in the listbox is changed
Toggle Button	Callback	**'Value'** – current value of the toggle button, number **'Min'** – minimum toggle button value (not pressed), number **'Max'** – maximum toggle button value (pressed), number	The user toggles the toggle button
Table	N/A	**'Data'** – the numerical values in the table **'ColumnName'** – the names of the columns, as a cell array **'RowName'** – the names of the rows, as a cell array	N/A
Axes	N/A	The standard plot functions will work with the axes control. If the axes handle name is axes1, the plot commands need to be preceded by `axes(handles.axes1)`	N/A
Panel	N/A	The panel control is generally used for layout purposes on the GUI, but does contain some functions that will fire if the GUI is resized	N/A
Button Group	Selection-ChangeFcn	The tag name of the selected button can be extracted by calling `get(eventdata.NewValue,'Tag')`	The user changes the selected object in the button group

Built-In Dialogs and Interaction Interfaces

There are a number of other built-in dialog and interaction interfaces that can complement your GUI by allowing all interaction to appear in the user interface rather than occasionally displaying or typing values in the Command Window. These functions include:

Built-In Dialog Boxes

- dialog: Displays text in a clickable textbox as a pop-up dialog.
- msgbox: Displays text in a clickable textbox as a pop-up dialog with customizable icons and dialog title.
- errordlg: Displays text in a clickable textbox as a pop-up dialog as an error message.
- helpdlg: Displays text in a clickable textbox as a pop-up dialog as a help message.
- inputdlg: Prompts the user to type in a value into an input dialog.
- listdlg: Prompts the user to select an option from a listbox in a pop-up dialog.
- questdlg: Prompts the user to answer a question (yes/no) in a question dialog.
- warndlg: Displays text in a clickable textbox as a pop-up dialog as a warning message.
- printdlg: Displays the print dialog to allow the user to print your GUI.

Built-In Interaction Dialogs

- uigetdir: Allows the user to select a directory that contains files.
- uigetfile: Allows the user to select a file (e.g., select an Excel file to open with xlsread).
- uiputfile: Allows the user to save a file (e.g., select where and what to name an Excel file you are writing with xlswrite).
- uisetcolor: Allows the user to pick a color from a color list.
- uisetfont: Allows the user to change font properties.

For more information on any of these functions, refer to the MATLAB help and doc pages for each function.

For more examples of GUI, look at the following .zip files available in the online materials:

- SliderAndPlotExample
- UIGetFileAndPlotExample
- UITableExample

In-Class Activities

ICA 20-1

For each code segment below, determine the contents of the specified variable following execution. If an error will occur, write ERROR and explain what caused the error.

(a) What is stored in Count by the following code?

```
Count=0;
for N=10:−0.2:8.5
    Count=Count+1;
end
```

(b) What is displayed on the screen by the following code?

```
for m=3:8
    fprintf('%0.0f\n',m^2-m)
end
```

(c) What is displayed on the screen by the following code?

```
for m=3:8
    M2=m^2−m;
end
fprintf ('%0.0f\n',M2)
```

(d) What is stored in P and C?

```
S=3;
I=2;
P=1;
C=0;
for K=S:I:S^I
    P=P*K;
    C=C+1;
end
```

ICA 20-2

Write a function named `CountDown` that accepts a total time T in seconds and displays the time remaining after half of the previously displayed time has elapsed as described below. The function should also accept an integer `Steps` as also described below.

The function should immediately display the value of T, and then wait T/2 seconds, before displaying T/2. It should then wait T/4 seconds and display T/4, etc. This should continue until only $1/2^{Steps}$ of the original time remains, at which point it waits for this remaining time, displays a zero, and emits an audio tone.

It is suggested that you look up the `pause` function and the `beep` function.

Example: `CountDown(60,6)` displays the following followed by an audio tone.

60	Displayed immediately
30	Displayed 30 seconds later
15	Displayed 15 seconds later
7.5000	Displayed 7.5 seconds later
3.7500	etc.
1.8750	etc.
0.9375	etc.
0	Displayed 0.9375 seconds later accompanied by a beep

ICA 20-3

For each code segment below, determine the contents of the specified variable following execution. If an error will occur, write ERROR and explain what caused the error.

(a) What is stored in VC?

```
VC=0;
V1=[9 5 −3 6 −1 0];
for Val=1:length(V1)
   if  V1(Val) <=0
       VC=VC+1;
    end
 end
```

(b) What is stored in VS?

```
V2=[9 5 −3 6 −1 0];
for Val=2:length(V2)
     VS(Val−1)=V2(Val−1)+V2(Val);
 end
```

(c) What is stored in VE?

```
VE=0;
V1=[9 −4 −3 3 6 −1 0 5 5 −2 −2 −3];
for Val=1:length(V1)
     if V1(Val)==round(V1(Val)/2)*2
        VE=VE+1;
     end
 end
```

(d) What is stored in VC? HINT: Look up the sign function.

```
VD=0;
V1=[9 −4 −3 3 6 −1 0 5 5 −2 −2 −3];
for Val=2:length(V1)
  VD(Val)=1;
  if sign(V1(Val)) ~=sign(V1(Val−1))
    VD(Val)=−1;
  end
  if abs(V1(Val))==abs(V1(Val−1))
     VD(Val)=0;
  end
 end
```

ICA 20-4

You wish to design a program to tabulate values for the function $V = e^{-t/\tau} \cos \theta t$, a common type of voltage response in electric circuits.

(a)   The user should be asked to enter the following parameters:
- τ − time constant in seconds
- θ − frequency in radians per second
- t_0 − initial time in seconds
- t_f − final time in seconds
- *Steps* − number of divisions into which the range of time is to be divided.

(b)   The program should print a statement similar to the following:

```
Calculations of the equation e^(-t/x.xxx) cos (x.xxx t) from
x.xxx to x.xxx seconds.
```

(c)   The program should calculate the value of V [voltage] for the stated values of τ and θ over the range of time from t_0 to t_f. The results should be printed in a neatly formatted table showing both time and voltage.

ICA 20-5

Assume the vector AM contains an even number of elements. Write a short section of code that will divide the product of the even elements by the sum of the odd elements and place the result in PDS. Note that this must work correctly for any vector as long as it contains an even number of elements. Write the code using.

(a)   a for loop without using built-in functions like sum or prod

(b)   direct matrix operations, no loops.

EXAMPLE: AM =[9 3 5 0.5 10 4]
PDS = 0.25   Detailed calculation: (3*0.5*4)/(9+5+10) = 0.25

ICA 20-6

Write a function named CLASS that will accept a vector of unknown length called INT and return four variables containing the following information about the contents of the vector:

- NotInt – contains the number of values in INT that are not integers.
- NotPos – contains the number of values in INT that are zero or less.
- TooBig – contains the number of values in INT that are greater than 99. Note that NotInt has priority over NotPos and TooBig. For example, an element in INT equal to -9.43 would add one to NotInt, but NOT to NotPos.
- Ints – a 99 element vector in which each element contains the number of occurrences of the element's index value in INT. For example, if INT contains a total of fourteen 57s, Ints(57) will contain 14.

Example:
```
INT=[-3, -7.3, 0, 16, 2, 99, 11.3, 298, 176.98, 16]
   NotInt = 3
   NotPos = 2
   TooBig = 1
   Ints(2) = 1
   Ints(16) = 2
   Ints(99) = 1
```
All other elements of Ints contain a zero.

Note that the sum of all elements in the returned variables should equal the number of elements in INT.

You MAY NOT use any built in functions to count the number of occurrences of each integer between 1 and 99, nor may you use any function whose sole purpose is to determine if a value is an integer or not. You MAY use other functions, however.

ICA 20-7

For each code segment below, determine the contents of the specified variable following execution. If an error will occur, write ERROR and explain what caused the error.

(a) What is stored in A?

```
for i=1:3
   for j=1:4
       A(j,i)=i^2-j;
   end
end
```

(b) What is stored in SP?

```
M=[1 2 3;4 5 6];
[Rows,Cols]=size(M);
SP(1)=0;
for r=1:Rows
    P=1;
    for c=1:Cols
        P=P*M(r,c);
    end
    SP(r+1)=SP(r)+P;
end
```

(c) What is stored in PR?

```
M=[0 2 4 6;1 -1 2 -2; -3 0 -2 0];
[R,C]=size(M);
PR=zeros(R,C);
for row=1:1:R
   for col=1:1:C
       PR(row,col)=(PR(row,col)+M(row,col))*max(M(row,:));
   end
end
```

ICA 20-8

Write a function named GetArray that will accept two positive integers R and C representing the number of rows and columns of a matrix NA, and return the R × C matrix NA with values input by the user. For each value to be input a prompt should appear similar to the following:

```
Please input the value for row 2 and column 4:
```

with, of course, the 2 and 4 replaced by the indices of the actual element being entered.

ICA 20-9

Write a function named EvenSum that will accept a matrix of unknown size and return the sum of all elements at the intersection of even numbered rows and even numbered columns. Note that your function must work with any size matrix. Also note that if the matrix is a scalar or a vector, the function will return zero since there are no even numbered rows or columns in those cases.

EXAMPLE: For the matrix shown, A=EvenSum(Test); will place the value 13 in A. The numbers added together are shown in red.

$$Test = \begin{bmatrix} 1 & 3 & 5 & 7 & 9 \\ 0 & 1 & 2 & 3 & 4 \\ 6 & 4 & 2 & 1 & 8 \\ 3 & 5 & 2 & 4 & 0 \end{bmatrix}$$

ICA 20-10

You are assessing the price of various components from different vendors and wish to find the least expensive vendor for each component. The prices of the parts from each vendor are stored in a matrix, VendCost. Each row corresponds to a specific vendor and each column corresponds to a specific component. If a specific part is not offered by a vendor, the corresponding entry will be −1.

Write a program that will determine which vendor offers the cheapest price for each component, and place the results in a two row matrix Cheapest with the same number of columns as there are columns in VendCost. Each entry in the first row of Cheapest should be an integer corresponding to the row number of the vendor with the cheapest price for the corresponding component and the entries in row 2 should contain the lowest price for that component. You may assume that each part is available from at least one of the listed vendors. If two or more vendors offer a component at the same lowest price, you may choose either one.

You may not use the built-in min function or other similar functions to solve this problem. You may not use direct matrix operations to solve this problem; you must do it using for loops (in a meaningful way). Your solution must work for any number of vendors and any number of components.

Example:

```
VendCost =
    4.97    8.54    2.04    0.44   13.55   -1.00
    5.23    8.23    2.12    0.39   15.98    2.67
    5.24    8.22    2.09    0.51   -1.00    2.76
Cheapest =
    1       3       1       2       1       2
    4.97    8.22    2.04    0.39   13.55    2.67
```

ICA 20-11

You are studying the number of defective parts produced each week by several machines to help adjust maintenance protocols.

Assume the rows of matrix Def represent different machines and all columns except the last represent weeks. The last column contains the long-term average of the number of defects per week produced by that machine. Write a short section of MATLAB code that will generate a new matrix Comp with the same number of rows but one fewer columns as described.

The code will compare each value in the matrix, except those in the last column, to the value in the last column of the same row to compare the number of defective parts produced by each machine each week with that machine's long-term defect rate.

- If the number of errors equals that machine's average, the corresponding element in the new matrix Comp will equal 0.
- If the number of errors is greater than that machine's average, the corresponding element in the new matrix Comp will equal 1.
- If the number of errors is less than that machine's average, the corresponding element in the new matrix Comp will equal −1.

ICA 20-12

The Pascal Triangle has an amazing number of uses, from linear algebra to design of fractal antennas. Write a program following the five steps listed that will create a Pascal triangle.

1. Prompt the user to enter an integer and place it in a variable N.
2. Create an N × N matrix named Pascal filled with zeros.
3. Modify the Pascal matrix so that the first row and first column contain all ones.
4. The value of every other element of the Pascal matrix should be changed to the sum of the element to the left and the element above. You should complete row 2, then row 3, etc. until all rows have been calculated. Example for N = 5 shown.

NOTE: You MAY NOT use the pascal function built in to MATLAB.

$$
Pascal =
\begin{matrix}
1 & 1 & 1 & 1 & 1 \\
1 & 2 & 3 & 4 & 5 \\
1 & 3 & 6 & 10 & 15 \\
1 & 4 & 10 & 20 & 35 \\
1 & 5 & 15 & 35 & 70
\end{matrix}
$$

5. Reset all elements of the Pascal matrix below the minor diagonal (from lower left to upper right) to zero. Example for N = 5 shown.

$$
Pascal =
\begin{matrix}
1 & 1 & 1 & 1 & 1 \\
1 & 2 & 3 & 4 & 0 \\
1 & 3 & 6 & 0 & 0 \\
1 & 4 & 0 & 0 & 0 \\
1 & 0 & 0 & 0 & 0
\end{matrix}
$$

ICA 20-13

Write a function named ProdStats that will accept a matrix ProdData that has at least one row and at least two columns. The rows each represent a different machine in a factory, and the columns represent successive days of production. The value in each element is the number of units produced by that machine on the given day.

ProdStats should return a new matrix Trend with the same dimensions as ProdData, and a row vector TrendNum with three elements.

Each element of Trend indicates whether that day's production for that machine was less than, equal to, or greater than the previous day's production for that machine. Since the first day (first column) does not have previous data upon which to base the comparison, the first column of Trend will arbitrarily be set to all zeros. All other elements will be set to either −1 (lower production than previous day), 0 (equal production to previous day), or 1 (higher production than previous day).

The first element of TrendNum contains the total number of days that production decreased (in other words, the number of negative ones in Trend), the second element of TrendNum contains the number of days with no change in production (zeros in Trend, NOT counting the zeros on the first day), and the third element contains the number of days with higher production (ones in Trend).

Example:

$$\text{ProdData} = \begin{bmatrix} 1 & 2 & 4 & 4 & 5 & 4 \\ 7 & 8 & 9 & 0 & 1 & 5 \\ 9 & 8 & 5 & 6 & 7 & 7 \end{bmatrix}$$

$$\text{Trend} = \begin{bmatrix} 0 & 1 & 1 & 0 & 1 & -1 \\ 0 & 1 & 1 & -1 & 1 & 1 \\ 0 & -1 & -1 & 1 & 1 & 0 \end{bmatrix} \qquad \text{TrendNum} = [4 \quad 2 \quad 9]$$

ICA 20-14

For each code segment below, determine the contents of the specified variable following execution. If an error will occur, write ERROR and explain what caused the error.

(a) What is stored in Q?

```
Q=[];
N=1;
while length(Q)<4
   Q=[Q,N]*2;
   N=N*3;
end
```

(b) What is stored in IT?

```
IT=0;
for  k=3:2:7
   C=k^2;
   while C>=0
         C=C-25;
         IT=IT+1;
   end
   IT=IT*2;
end
```

(c) What is stored in R?

```
R=1;
N=1;
while R>1E-6
   R=1;
   for  K=1:N
         R=R/K;
   end
N=N+1;
end
```

ICA 20-15

Assume that a simple menu has been created by the following line of code:

```
SystemStatus=menu('System Status','ON','OFF');
```

Write a short section of code that will handle the situation if the user closes the menu instead of making a selection. If the menu is closed without a proper selection, the user should be told to try again, then the menu should be redisplayed. This should continue until the user makes a proper selection.

ICA 20-16

Write a program that will ask the user to input a single number N. If the number is nonzero, a one hundred element row vector named SEQ will be filled with the values 0.01*N, 0.02*N, . . . , 0.99*N, N. Note that this must work for both positive and negative values of N. After filling the vector, the program should ask if this is correct, or does the user want to enter a new value for N, in which case it should refill SEQ with the corrected values. This should continue until the user enters a zero, at which point the program terminates.

ICA 20-17

You are writing the code to control a chemical reaction. Sensors are used to place values into the variables Temp (temperature in degrees Celsius), Pres (pressure in atmospheres), pH (pH of solution), and Time (elapsed time in minutes since start of reaction). A function called Update reads the sensors and modifies the contents of the variables to indicate the current conditions. To use the Update function, you simply include the line

```
[Temp,Pres,pH,Time]=Update;
```

in your code as needed.

Write a program that will use the Update function once every minute to read new values from the sensors, and continue doing so as long as the pH has decreased by at least 0.02 since the last reading. (Hint: Remember the pause function – pause(n) pauses execution for n seconds.)

If at any time the pressure exceeds 5 atmospheres or the temperature exceeds 200 degrees Celsius, a message should be generated indicating which parameter is beyond the safe limits and the parameter value. In this case, the program should call the function terminate which will shut down the reaction and the program stops after printing a message to the screen such as

```
Reaction terminated after X minutes.
Final pH is x.xxx.
```

where X and x.xxx are replaced with the elapsed time and the final pH.

If at any point, the pressure exceeds 4 atmospheres or the temperature exceeds 175 degrees Celsius, an appropriate warning should be generated stating which parameter is too high and what its value is, but the reaction should continue and the program keep running.

When the pH has decreased by less than 0.02 from the previous reading, the reaction should be terminated, a message printed giving elapsed time and final pH as above, and the program should end.

You may assume that the initial pH is 8.0, the initial temperature is 30 degrees Celsius the initial pressure is 1 atmospheres, and the initial time is 0.

ICA 20-18

You are studying the effect of experience on the productivity of workers.

For a group of new workers, you record how many units each person completes per day for several weeks. You make the assumption that when the average of three consecutive days is not greater than 2% more than the maximum daily production prior to those three days, then that worker has reached maximum productivity, and you do not need to continue looking at the data for subsequent days.

The provided file, `workers.mat`, contains an array with this productivity data. Each row represents a specific worker, and the columns represent successive days. The value in each element of the matrix represents the number of units produced by a specific worker on a specific day.

Your program should analyze the data for each worker and print the following message for each worker, one per line:

```
Worker # X reached maximum productivity after Y days.
```

where X is the worker number (same as row number) and Y is the number of days where the above mentioned criterion is first reached.

If a worker has not reached maximum productivity after the trial period represented by the data, the following message should be produced instead:

```
Worker # X did not reach maximum productivity within Y days.
```

where in this case Y is the total number of days in the trial period.

Note that although this problem can be solved using `for` loops and `if` statements without a `while` statement, you are expected to use a `while` loop to stop scanning each worker's record when the day of maximum productivity has been found. (You may also use `for` loops and `if` statements as necessary, of course.)

Your code should work for any number of workers and any number of days, not just the sample data provided.

ICA 20-19

While experimenting with coding sequences, you decide to try a modification of the factorial sequence by calculating the product of consecutive odd integers instead of all consecutive integers. You call this sequence `OFact`. The first four values of the `OFact` sequence are:

OFact(1) = 1
OFact(2) = 1 * 3 = 3
OFact(3) = 1 * 3 * 5 = 15
OFact(4) = 1 * 3 * 5 * 7 = 105

Write a program that will ask the user for a maximum sequence value desired, and then print the `OFact` sequence to the command window as long as the value calculated does not exceed the maximum value entered by the user. For example, if the user specifies a maximum of 100, it would print the first three values since `OFact(4)` = 105 > 100. This should be printed in two columns: N in the first column and `OFact(N)` in the second column. All values generated should be stored in the vector `OFact` for later use.

When the program reaches the maximum value, a message should be printed that states:

```
The desired maximum was XXX.
OFact(Y) = ZZZ is the closest to this value without exceeding it.
```

where XXX is the maximum entered by the user, Y is the sequence number of the calculated value, and ZZZ is the last calculated value.

1. Write a function for finding the maximum value in a vector of data. It should receive an array as an argument and return the maximum of the values. Do not use the max built-in function.

2. A matrix named mach contains three columns of data concerning the energy output of several machines. The first column contains an ID code for a specific machine, the second column contains the total amount of energy produced by that machine in calories, and the third column contains the amount of time required by that machine to produce the energy listed in column 2 in hours.

   Write a function named MPower to accept as input the matrix mach and return a new matrix named P containing two columns and the same number of rows as mach. The first column should contain the machine ID codes, and the second column should contain the average power generated by each machine in units of watts.

3. The Fibonacci sequence is an integer sequence calculated by adding previous numbers together to calculate the next value. This is represented mathematically by saying that $F_n = F_{n-1} + F_{n-2}$ (where F_n is the nth value in the sequence, F) or:

		$0+1=$	$1+1=$	$1+2=$	$2+3=$	$3+5=$	$5+8=$	$8+13=$	$F_{n-1}+F_{n-2}=$
<u>0</u>	<u>1</u>	1	2	3	5	8	13	21	$\ldots F_n$

   Note this sequence starts with the underlined values (0, 1) and calculates the remaining values in the sequence based on the sum of the previous two values.

   Professor Bowman found this sequence to be extremely insufficient and created the Bowman sequence, which is an integer sequence calculated by adding the previous three numbers together (instead of two like in the Fibonacci sequence) to calculate the next value. This is represented mathematically by saying that $F_n = F_{n-1} + F_{n-2} + F_{n-3}$ (where F_n is the nth value in the sequence, F) or:

			$0+1+2=$	$1+2+3=$	$2+3+6=$	$6+11+20=$	$F_{n-3}+F_{n-2}+F_{n-1}=$
<u>0</u>	<u>1</u>	<u>2</u>	3	6	11	37	$\ldots F_n$

   Note this sequence starts with the underlined values (0, 1, 2) and calculates the remaining values in the sequence based on the sum of the previous three values.

   Write a MATLAB function that implements the Bowman sequence that accepts one input argument, the length of the desired Bowman sequence to generate, and returns one output variable, the Bowman sequence stored inside of an array. This function should also check to see if the number passed in to the function is a valid Bowman sequence length (think about what might constitute valid sequence lengths!). If the input is invalid, your function should display an error message and the output variable should contain only one number: −1. Otherwise if the input is valid, your function should calculate the Bowman sequence and display each value in the sequence in the Command Window.

   Sample Output:

   ```
   >> B=FUNCTIONNAME(8);
         Bowman sequence:
         0   1   2   3   6   11   20   37
   ```

4. You are working for a data analytics firm that has been asked to create a generic data collection tool that will provide basic statistics on input typed in to the screen. This data collection tool should ask the user to type the number of desired data points they need to record, the number of decimal places for all of the numbers displayed in the final output, then the program should allow them to record all of the data points into the Command Window, one by one, where the user presses the Enter key after each data point. You may assume that this program will only need to handle numeric values and will not need to worry about strings, vectors, or input of other variable types.

As soon as the user inputs all of the values, your program should generate a string representation of the vector of data, as well as provide basic statistics including the number of negative values, number of positive values, the sum of all of the values, the mean, median, and standard deviation of the data set, and the minimum and maximum values in the data set. The output should appear similar to the output shown below. Note that the vector of data does not need to be displayed with the number of decimal places specified by the user.

```
Sample Input/Output:

Type the number of data points to record: 4
Type the number of decimal places to show in output: 2
Data Point #1: 8
Data Point #2: 2
Data Point #3: 6
Data Point #4: 4

Data Set Information:

Vector = [8 2 6 4]

# Negative: 0.00
# Positive: 4.00

Minimum: 2.00
Maximum: 8.00

Sum: 20.00
Mean: 5.00
Median: 5.00
Standard Deviation: 2.58
```

5. You are part of an engineering firm on contract by the U.S. Department of Energy's Energy Efficiency and Renewable Energy task force to develop a program to help laboratory technicians measure the efficiency of their lab equipment. Your job is to write a program that measures the efficiency of hot plates.

The program will begin by suggesting four possible fluids for the technician to choose from using a menu: acetic acid, citric acid, glycerol, and olive oil. The technician is then prompted to enter the initial room temperature in units of degrees Fahrenheit, the brand name and model of the hot plate, and the theoretical power for the hot plate provided by the manufacturer.

The program will then call a function, which will determine the following:

- All fluid properties [Specific Gravity, Specific Heat] should be contained in your function, not in the main program.
- The technician will use 2 liters of fluid.
- The technician should take 2 data points, one at 2 minutes and one at 5 minutes during the heating process. The technician will then begin to heat the fluid. The program will

prompt the technician to enter each data point at the time interval. The technician will record the temperature of the fluid [degrees Fahrenheit] for the two data measurements.

- Once the final data point has been entered, the function will calculate the energy required to heat the fluid, in joules, and the power used to heat the fluid, in watts
- The function will return to the program the time interval, the temperature readings, and the power used.
- The program will then calculate the efficiency of the hot plate, in percentage.

The output of your program should look like the output displayed below; where the high-lighted blue values are example responses provided by the user (typed or by pressing a button depending on the requirements mentioned above) into your program, and the highlighted yellow values are the calculated values that will change based upon your starting properties. Note the DATA SHOWN AS RESULTS AND ON THE GRAPH ARE EXAMPLES ONLY AND MAY NOT REFLECT ACTUAL CALCULATIONS! The code should line up the output calculations. In addition, your code must display the efficiency rounded to the near-est integer and must include a percent symbol.

Finally, the program should produce a graph of the two experimental data points relat-ing time and temperature and a trendline with a formatted equation found using `polyfit`.

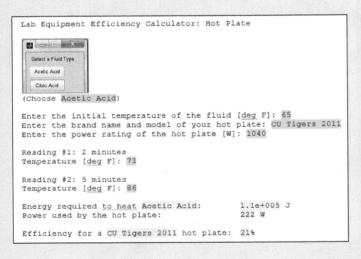

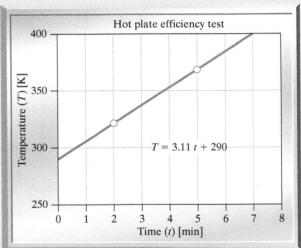

Use the following fluid properties in your program:

Fluid	Specific Gravity [—]	Boiling Point [°C]	Specific Heat [J/(g K)]
Acetic acid	1.049	118	2.18
Citric acid	1.665	153	4
Glycerol	1.261	290	2.4
Olive oil	0.915	300	1.97

6. A sample data set D is provided online in the file `Spacecraft.mat`. Use the `load` command to load this data into your workspace. A matrix D contains data on several experimental spacecraft engines. The matrix is organized in pairs of rows. Each pair of rows contains data measured during tests of the engines. For each pair of rows, the odd numbered row contains several measurements of the total energy used by the engine and the even numbered row contains the corresponding total kinetic energy imparted to the spacecraft. Recalling the equation for energy efficiency, $E_0 = \eta E_I$ we see that the efficiency of the engine is the slope of the line if the kinetic energy of the spacecraft (the output energy, E_0) is plotted versus energy input to the engine(E_I).

For each data set in matrix D:

(a) Determine the efficiency of the engine represented by each data set.

(b) For each data set with an efficiency of at least 0.8 (80%), plot the data (all data sets on the same graph) represented by red diamonds. Add a solid red trendline to each such data set, including a trendline equation.

(c) For each data set with an efficiency of at least 0.5 (50%) but less than 0.8 (80%), plot the data (all data sets on the same graph) represented by blue circles. Add a dotted blue trendline to each such data set, including a trendline equation.

(d) For each data set with an efficiency less than 0.5 (50%), plot the data (all data sets on the same graph) represented by black X's. These low-efficiency data sets will NOT have a trendline or equation added.

(e) The trendline equations should be in the form $E\#_0 = \eta E\#_I$ where # is the number of the dataset (half of the even-numbered row of the data set).

(f) The trendline equations should be positioned immediately to the right of the largest (rightmost) data point of the corresponding data set.

Note that you SHOULD NOT figure out the efficiencies and hard-code the line types, etc. Your program must do this automatically so it will work for any set of data without user intervention.

The graph should be properly labeled and formatted, but the colors and types of both the lines and data markers will not follow the standard proper plot rules since they are specified in the problem.

You may assume the largest value of E_I is 12 and the largest value of E_0 is 10.

For the sample dataset provided, your graph should be similar to the following.

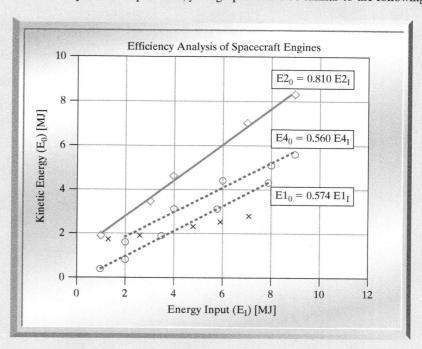

7. You will be given MATLAB file that contains salary data from a major league baseball in 2005. Use the data provided to determine:

   (a) Salary mean, median, and standard deviation for all players.
   (b) Salary mean, median, and standard deviation for the Arizona Diamondbacks.
   (c) Salary mean, median, standard deviation for all pitchers.
   (d) Salary mean, median, standard deviation for all outfielders.
   (e) Which team had the highest average salary?
   (f) Which position had the lowest average salary?
   (g) Draw a histogram and CDF in Excel for all players.
   (h) What percentage of players earned more than $1 million?

8. The following Microsoft Excel file has been provided online. The file contains energy consumption data by energy source per year in the United States, measured in petaBTUs.

Year	Fossil Fuels	Elec. Net Imports	Nuclear	Renewable
2007	101.605	0.106	8.415	6.830
2006	99.861	0.063	8.214	6.922
2005	100.503	0.084	8.160	6.444
2004	100.351	0.039	8.222	6.261
2003	98.209	0.022	7.959	6.150

   (a) Write the MATLAB code necessary to read the Microsoft Excel file and store each column of data into different variables. Create the following:

   ■ Yr: A vector of all of the years in the worksheet.
   ■ FF: A vector of all of the fossil fuels for each year in Yr.
   ■ ENI: A vector of all electric imports for each year in Yr.
   ■ Nuc: A vector of all nuclear energy consumption for each year in Yr.
   ■ Ren: A vector of all renewable energy consumption for each year in Yr.
   ■ Hdr: A cell array of all of the headers in row 1.

   You may not hard-code these variables—they should be imported from the Excel file to receive credit.

   (b) Write the MATLAB code necessary to generate the table below of nuclear energy consumption by year using formatted output in the Command Window. You may assume that you have correctly defined the vector Nuc and cell array Hdr in part (a). Note the nuclear energy consumption should be displayed to two decimal places.

Nuclear Energy Consumption by Year [petaBTU]

2007	2006	2005	2004	2003	. . . etc
8.42	8.21	8.16	8.22	7.96	

   (c) Add code to ask the user if they wish to select another type of fuel, or terminate the program. If the user wants to select again, then part (b) should repeat.

9. As early as 650 BC, mathematicians had been composing magic squares, a sequence of n numbers arranged in a square such that all rows, columns, and diagonals sum to the same constant. Used in China, India, and Arab countries for centuries, artist Albrecht Dürer's engraving Melencolia I (year: 1514) is considered the first time a magic square appears in European art. Each row, column, and diagonal of Dürer's magic square sums to 34. In addi-

tion, each quadrant, the center four squares, and the corner squares all sum to 34. An example of a "magic square" is displayed below.

16	3	2	13
5	10	11	8
9	6	7	12
4	15	14	1

Write a program to prove a series of numbers is indeed a 4 × 4 magic square. Your program should complete the following steps, in this order:

(a) Ask the user to enter their proposed magic square in a single input statement (e.g., [1 2 3 4; 5 6 7 8; 9 10 11 12; 13 14 15 16]—note this example is a 4 × 4 matrix, but NOT a magic square). You may assume the user will enter whole numbers; they will not enter either decimal values or text.

(b) Check that all values are positive; ** **for-loop or nested for-loop required in the solution.** If one or more of the values in the matrix are negative or zero, issue a statement to the command window informing the user of the mistake and exit the program. This check should work even if the user does not enter a 4 × 4 matrix; it should work regardless of the size of matrix entered.

(c) Check for an arrangement of 4 × 4. If the matrix is not a 4 × 4, issue a statement to the command window informing the user of the mistake and exit the program.

(d) Determine if the matrix is a form of a magic square. The minimum requirement to be classified as a magic square is each row and column sums to the same value. ** **for-loop or nested for-loop required in the solution.** If this criteria is not met, issue a statement to the command window informing the user they have not entered a magic square and exit the program.

(e) Determine the classification of the magic square using the following requirements:

1. If each row and column sums to the same value, the magic square is classified as "semi-magic"; the summation value is called the magic constant. ** **for-loop or nested for-loop required in the solution.**

2. If, in addition to criterion 1, each diagonal sums to the same value, the magic square is classified as "normal;" ** **for-loop or nested for-loop required in the solution. The use of built-in functions such as** diag**,** fliplr**,** rot90**,** trace **or similar built-in functions is forbidden.**

3. If, in addition to #1 and #2, the largest value in the magic square is equal to 16, the magic square is classified as "perfect;"

Format your magic square classification similar to the format shown below. You may choose to format your table differently, but each classification should contain a "yes" or "no" next to each magic square category.

The magic constant for your magic square is 24. The classification for your magic square:

Semi-magic	Normal	Perfect
yes	yes	yes

A few test cases for you to consider:

- Albrecht Dürer magic square: [16, 3, 2, 13; 5, 10, 11, 8; 9, 6, 7, 12; 4, 15, 14, 1];
- Chautisa Yantra magic square: [7, 12, 1, 14; 2, 13, 8, 11; 16, 3, 10, 5; 9, 6, 15, 4];
- Sangrada Familia church, Barcelona magic square: [1, 14, 14, 4; 11, 7, 6, 9; 8, 10, 10, 5; 13, 2, 3, 15];
- Random magic square: [80, 15, 10, 65; 25, 50, 55, 40; 45, 30, 35, 60; 20, 75, 70, 5];
- Steve Wozniak's magic square: [8, 11, 22, 1; 21, 2, 7, 12; 3, 24, 9, 6; 10, 5, 4, 23].

10. Write a program to prove a series of numbers is indeed a 4 × 4 magic square. Your program should complete the following steps, in this order:

(a) Ask the user to enter their proposed magic square in a single input statement (e.g., [1 2 3 4; 5 6 7 8; 9 10 11 12; 13 14 15 16]—note this example is a 4 × 4 matrix, but NOT a magic square). You may assume the user will enter whole numbers; they will not enter either decimal values or text.

(b) Check that all values are positive; ** **for-loop or nested `for`-loop required in the solution.** If one or more of the values in the matrix are negative or zero, issue a statement to the command window informing the user of the mistake and ask the user to enter another matrix. This check should be repeated until the user enters a matrix with positive values. This check should work even if the user does not enter a 4 × 4 matrix; it should work regardless of the size of matrix entered.

(c) Check for an arrangement of 4 × 4. If the matrix is not a 4 × 4, issue a statement to the command window informing the user of the mistake and ask the user to enter another matrix. This check should be repeated until the user enters a 4 × 4 matrix. You may assume the re-entered matrix contains only positive values; you do not need to re-check the new matrix for positive values, only for matrix dimensions.

(d) Determine if the matrix is a form of a magic square. The minimum requirement to be classified as a magic square is each row and column sums to the same value. ** **for-loop or nested `for`-loop required in the solution.** If this criteria is not met, issue a statement to the command window informing the user they have not entered a magic square and ask the user if they wish to try another magic square. This question can be posed using either a text answer entered by the user (yes, no) or by using a menu. If the user chooses to run the program again, the entire program starting with step (a) should begin again.

(e) Determine the classification of the magic square using the following requirements:

1. If each row and column sums to the same value, the magic square is classified as "semi-magic"; the summation value is called the magic constant. ** **for-loop or nested for-loop required in the solution.**

2. If, in addition to criterion 1, each diagonal sums to the same value, the magic square is classified as "normal;" ** **for-loop or nested `for`-loop required in the solution. The use of built-in functions such as `diag`, `fliplr`, `rot90`, `trace` or similar built-in functions is forbidden.**

3. If, in addition to #1 and #2, the largest value in the magic square is equal to 16, the magic square is classified as "perfect;"

Format your magic square classification similar to the format shown below. You may choose to format your table differently, but each classification should contain a "yes" or "no" next to each magic square category.

`The magic constant for your magic square is 24. The classification for your magic square:`

Semi-magic	Normal	Perfect
yes	yes	yes

After this table appears, ask the user if they wish to try another magic square. This question can be posed using either a text answer entered by the user (yes, no) or by using a menu. If the user chooses to run the program again, the entire program starting with step (a) should begin again.

A few test cases for you to consider:

- Albrecht Dürer magic square: [16, 3, 2, 13; 5, 10, 11, 8; 9, 6, 7, 12; 4, 15, 14, 1];
- Chautisa Yantra magic square: [7, 12, 1, 14; 2, 13, 8, 11; 16, 3, 10, 5; 9, 6, 15, 4];
- Sangrada Familia church, Barcelona magic square: [1, 14, 14, 4; 11, 7, 6, 9; 8, 10, 10, 5; 13, 2, 3, 15];
- Random magic square: [80, 15, 10, 65; 25, 50, 55, 40; 45, 30, 35, 60; 20, 75, 70, 5];
- Steve Wozniak's magic square: [8, 11, 22, 1; 21, 2, 7, 12; 3, 24, 9, 6; 10, 5, 4, 23].

11. A zombie picks up a calculator and starts adding odd whole numbers together, in order: $1 + 3 + 5 + \ldots$ etc. What will be the last number the zombie will add that will make the sum on his calculator greater than 10,000? Your task is to write the MATLAB code necessary to solve this problem for the zombie or he will eat your brain. The user should be asked to enter the target number (10,000), although your code should be written in such a way that if a target number other than 10,000 is entered, the correct answer for the value entered will be determined.

12. Write a function called `Balloon` that will accept a single variable named `S`. The function should replace `S` with the square of `S` and repeat this process until `S` is either greater than 10^{15} or less than 10^{-15}. The function should return a value `Q` containing the number of times `S` was squared during this process.

Examples:
- If $S = 100$, $Q = 3$ (S equals 10^{16} after the third square).
- If $S = 0.1$, $Q = 4$ (S equals 10^{-16} after the fourth square).
- If $S = 3$, $Q = 5$ (S equals 1.853×10^{15} after the fifth square).

13. You have written three functions for three different games. The names of the games (and the functions that implement them) are Dunko, Bouncer, and Munchies. Each function will accept an integer between one and three indicating the level of difficulty (1 = easy, 3 = hard), and when play is complete will return a text string, either "won" or "lost," to the program that executed the function.

Write a program that will use a menu to ask the user if he or she wants to play a game. If not, the program should terminate. If so, the program should generate another menu to allow the user to select one of the three games by name.

After selecting a game, the program should display another menu asking the user for the desired level of difficulty (Easy, Moderate, or Hard), and the game should begin by calling the appropriate function.

When the user has finished playing the selected game, a message should be displayed indicating whether the user won or lost the game. A menu should then be generated asking if the user wishes to repeat the game just played. If so, the difficulty level menu should be displayed again and the game repeated.

If the user does not wish to repeat the same game, the program should display a menu asking if the user wants to play another game. If so, the game selection menu should be generated again, followed by level selection, etc. If the user does not wish to play another game, the program should display a message saying "Thanks for playing" and terminate.

14. You are to program part of the interface for a simple ATM. When the user inserts their card and types the correct PIN (you do NOT have to write this part of the program), the system will place the users' checking account balance in a variable `CBal` and the users' savings account balance in `SBal`.

You are to write a function that will accept `SBal` and `CBal` as inputs and return two variables `NewCBal` and `NewSBal` containing the checking and savings balances after the transaction is completed. The function should do the following:

■ Display a menu titled "Main Menu" with the following three options.
- Get cash
- Get balance
- Quit

■ If "Get cash" is selected, another menu titled "Withdrawal amount" with the following four items is displayed:
- $20
- $60
- $100
- $200

■ After selecting an amount, a menu titled "From which account?" should be displayed showing the following two options:

- Checking
- Savings

■ At this point, the program should verify that the selected account contains sufficient funds for the requested withdrawal.

■ If not, a message should be displayed that says: "Sorry. You do not have sufficient funds in your SSSS account to withdraw \$XX" where SSSS is either Savings or Checking and \$XX is the selected withdrawal amount.

■ If funds are available, the program should call a function named `Disp20(x)`, where x is the number of \$20 bills to dispense. (See note about `Disp20` below.) After that, the withdrawal amount should be subtracted from the appropriate balance.

■ After processing the "Get cash" request, the program should return to the main menu.

Note About `Disp20(x)`: The purpose of this function is to dispense the requested number of \$20 bills—that is, to shove x bills out of the slot in the ATM machine. This does not really exist, since we do not have an ATM machine to work with. Thus, if you try to run your code, you will get an error ("Undefined function . . .").

In order to test your program, add the following function to your current path:

```
function[]=Disp20(x)
fprintf('%.0f $20 bills were dispensed.\n',x)
```

where x is the number of bills to be dispensed.

This allows you to know if the program reached the proper location in the code. It is fairly common in software development to use a "dummy" function in the place of a real one when the device to be controlled has not been completed or is not available in order to help verify whether the software is reaching the correct places in the code for various situations.

■ If "Get Balance" is selected, another menu titled "Which account?" should appear with the two choices:

- Checking
- Savings

and the program should then display "Your SSSS balance is \$bb.bb.," where SSSS is either Savings or Checking and \$bb.bb is the balance in the selected account.

■ After processing the "Get balance" request, the program should return to the main menu.

■ If Quit is selected, the function should return to the calling program with the updated balances in `NewCBal` and `NewSBal`. Note that the new balances will be equal to the original balances if no money was drawn from an account, but they must still be returned in the two new balance variables.

15. For this assignment, you will need the Cincinnati Reds player data file CincinnatiBaseball2010 .mat. The data in this file is a capture of the 2010 season on Baseball-Reference.com (http://www.baseball-reference.com/teams/CIN/2010.shtml).

In the MATLAB workspace provided, there are three variables of interest:

■ `PlayerData`, a 37 × 9 matrix which contains:

- Column 1: The age of the baseball player
- Column 2: Games played or pitched
- Column 3: At bats
- Column 4: Number of runs scored/allowed
- Column 5: Singles hit/allowed
- Column 6: Doubles hit/allowed
- Column 7: Triples hit/allowed
- Column 8: Home runs
- Column 9: Runs batted in

Note that each row in `PlayerData` represents a different baseball player.

- `PlayerNames`, a 37 × 1 "cell array" that contains the names of each player in the `PlayerData` matrix.
- `PlayerPositions`, a 37 × 1 "cell array" that contains the position abbreviation of each player in the `PlayerData` matrix.

(a) Create a function that will accept a single input, a cell array of player positions for an entire team—with our data set, this would be a variable like `PlayerPositions`. Your function must create a new cell array that contains only the unique positions, sorted alphabetically.

(b) Create a program that will display the average age, at bats, home runs, and runs batted in for user-selected positions. In order to allow the user to select the positions, you must use the menu function to allow the user to click positions to include in the analysis, as well as a "Done" button to allow the code to continue to display the output.

Sample Output: Assuming the user selects all positions

Position Stats for 2010 Cincinnati Reds

Pos	Ave(Age)	Ave(AB)	Ave(HR)	Ave(RBI)
1B	25	288	19	58
2B	29	626	18	59
3B	31	242	8	39
C	32	197	5	32
CF	25	514	22	77
IF	27	3	1	4
LF	29	338	11	52
MI	24	38	1	2
OF	27	123	4	11
P	27	21	0	1
RF	23	509	25	70
SS	31	347	5	34
UT	36	23	2	2

Sample Output: Assuming user presses "3B," "OF," "Done"

Position Stats for 2010 Cincinnati Reds

Pos	Ave(Age)	Ave(AB)	Ave(HR)	Ave(RBI)
3B	31	242	8	39
OF	27	123	4	11

(c) MLB.com is consistently ranked one of the top 500 websites in the United States, bringing in millions of visitors a year. However, recent surveys have shown that MLB.com is one of the slowest top 500 websites and is looking for new solutions to speed up their website. After hearing about the baseball statistics programs we have developed in our class, MLB.com has contracted us to help them create a MATLAB program to help them improve the user experience of their website. Recreate the analysis in part **(b)**, except this time export the output to a Microsoft Excel Workbook.

Sample Output: Assuming the user selects all positions

⏴	A	B	C	D	E	F
1	Position Stats for 2010 Cincinnati Reds					
2	Pos	Ave(Age)	Ave(AB)	Ave(HR)	Ave(RBI)	
3	1B	25	288	19	58	
4	2B	29	626	18	59	
5	3B	31	242	8	39	
6	C	32	197	5	32	
7	CF	25	514	22	77	
8	IF	27	3	1	4	
9	LF	29	338	11	52	
10	MI	24	38	1	2	
11	OF	27	123	4	11	
12	P	27	21	0	1	
13	RF	23	509	25	70	
14	SS	31	347	5	34	
15	UT	36	23	2	2	
16						

Sample Output: Assuming user presses "3B," "OF," "Done"

⏴	A	B	C	D	E	F
1	Position Stats for 2010 Cincinnati Reds					
2	Pos	Ave(Age)	Ave(AB)	Ave(HR)	Ave(RBI)	
3	3B	31	242	8	39	
4	OF	27	123	4	11	
5						

COMPREHENSION CHECK ANSWERS

CHAPTER 3

CC 3-1

Product	Computer	Automobile	Bookshelf
Inexpensive	Less than $300	Less than 1/5 the median annual U.S. family income	Less than $30
Small	Folds to the size of a DVD case	Two can fit in a standard parking space	Collapses to the size of a briefcase
Easy to assemble	No assembly; just turn on	All parts easily replaceable	Requires only a screwdriver
Aesthetically pleasing	Body color options available	Looks like the Batmobile©	Blends well with any décor
Lightweight	Less than one pound	Less than one ton	Less than 5% of the weight of the books it can hold
Safe	Immune to malware	Receives 5 star rating in NCAP crash tests	Stable even if top-loaded
Durable	Survives the "Frisbee® test"	200,000 mile warranty	Immune to cat claws
Environmentally friendly	Contains no heavy metals	Has an estimated MPG of at least 50	Made from recycled materials. Low VOC finish

CC 3-2

- Decrease aerodynamic drag
  - Remove unnecessary protrusions
  - Redesign body based on wind-tunnel testing
- Decrease weight
  - Use carbon-composite materials
  - Remove unnecessary material
- Increase engine efficiency
  - Use ceramic parts (e.g., valves and pistons) so engine can run hotter, thus more efficiently
  - Change to hybrid design with regenerative braking
  - Limit maximum acceleration if consistent with safety
- Manage friction
  - Improved bearings in wheels, engine, etc.
  - Redesign tires for less slippage on road surface
- Encourage fuel-efficient driving
  - Include displays for real-time and cumulative fuel usage (MPG)

CC 3-3

PAT

Hindrance: Tended to slow the team down due to difficulty understanding things.

Helpful: Always available and willing to do assigned tasks. The individuals who helped explain things to Pat probably developed a deeper understanding of the material in the process, thus this was helpful to them personally, though not to the team directly. Probably the second most useful team member.

CHRIS

Hindrance: Often absent, seldom prepared, seldom contributes, offers excuses for poor performance. Definitely the worst team member.

Helpful: Teaches the other team members about the real world, and how to deal with slackards.

TERRY

Hindrance: Not a team player, impatient, not encouraging to others, wants to dominate the team. Despite cleverness, probably the second worst team member.

Helpful: Solves problems quickly.

ROBIN

Hindrance: No obvious hindrance.

Helpful: The real leader of the group, kept things going, encouraging to weaker members. The most useful team member.

CHAPTER 5

CC 5-1

(a) Significant figures: 2   Decimal places: 4
(b) Significant figures: 3   Decimal places: 2
(c) Significant figures: 3   Decimal places: 0
(d) Significant figures: 2   Decimal places: 0
(e) Significant figures: 5   Decimal places: 0
(f) Significant figures: 5   Decimal places: 3

CC 5-2

(a) −58.9
(b) 247
(c) 2.47
(d) 0.497

CC 5-3

(a) Elevator capacity may require a conservative estimate of 180 pounds for safety limits.
(b) Serving sizes are usually measured in integer cups, so estimate at 1 cup; but to make sure the bowl is full, round up to 1.3 cups.
(c) If recording, conservative might be to round up to 33 seconds. If it doesn't matter, 30 seconds is fine.

CC 5-4

(a) Scientific notation: Engineering notation:
5.809×10^7 58.083×10^6
(b) Scientific notation: Engineering notation:
4.581×10^{-3} 4.581×10^{-3}
(c) Scientific notation: Engineering notation:
4.268×10^7 42.677×10^6

CHAPTER 6

CC 6-1

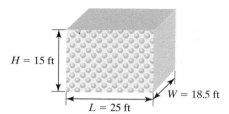

$H = 15$ ft
$W = 18.5$ ft
$L = 25$ ft

CC 6-2

Objective:

Determine the mass of the gravel in units of kilograms.

Observations:

- Assume the container is full, thus the height of the gravel is 15 feet.
- Assume the gravel is flat on the top and not mounded up.
- Neglect the space between the gravel pieces.

CC 6-3

List of variables and constants:

- ρ = density   [=] lb_m/ft^3 = 97 lb_m/ft^3—given
- V = volume of container [=] ft^3
- m = mass of gravel   [=] kg
- L = length   [=] ft   = 25 ft—given
- W = width   [=] ft   = 18.5 ft—given
- H = height   [=] ft   = 15 ft—assumed

CC 6-4

Equations:

1. Density in terms of mass and volume: $\rho = m/V$
2. Volume of a rectangle: $V = L \times W \times H$
3. Unit conversion: 1 kg = 2.205 lb_m

CC 6-5

- First, find the volume of the container; use equation (2)
  $V = L \times W \times H$
- Substituting L, W, and H:
  $V = (25\ ft)(18.5\ ft)(15\ ft) = 6937.5\ ft^3$
- Second, find the mass of gravel; use equation (1)
  $\rho = m/V$
- Substituting the density and the volume:
  $(97\ lb_m/ft^3) = m\ (6937.5\ ft^3)$ $m = 672937.5\ lb_m$
- Convert from pound-mass to kilograms:

$$\frac{672{,}937.5\,lb_m}{} \left| \frac{1\,kg}{2.205\,lb_m} \right. = 305{,}881\,kg \cong 306{,}000\,kg$$

CHAPTER 7

CC 7-1

Standard	Scientific	Engineering	With Prefix
(a) 3,100 J	3.1×10^3 J	3.1×10^3 J	3.1 kJ
(b) 26,510,000 W	2.651×10^7 W	26.51×10^6 W	26.51 MW
(c) 459,000 s	4.59×10^5 s	459×10^3 s	459 ks
(d) 0.00000032 g	3.2×10^{-7} g	320×10^{-9} g	320 ng

CC 7-2

(a) Incorrect: 5 s
(b) Incorrect: 60 mm
(c) Incorrect: 3,800 mL OR 3.8 L

CC 7-3

5.5 mi

CC 7-4

1,800 min

CC 7-5

5×10^{-9} pL

CC 7-6

2 km/min

CC 7-7

26 flushes

CC 7-8

84 ft^3

CC 7-9

14 cubits

CC 7-10

10.3 m/s

CC 7-11

Quantity	Common Units	Dimensions						
		M	L	T	Θ	N	J	I
Density	lb$_m$/ft^3	1	-3	0	0	0	0	0
Evaporation	slug/h	1	0	-1	0	0	0	0
Flowrate	gal/min	0	3	-1	0	0	0	0

CC 7-12

Quantity	Common Units	Dimensions						
		M	L	T	Θ	N	J	I
Energy	calories	1	2	-2	0	0	0	0
Power	horsepower	1	2	-3	0	0	0	0
Pressure	atmospheres	1	-1	-2	0	0	0	0
Voltage	volts	1	2	-3	0	0	0	1

CC 7-13

B. Energy

CC 7-14

M	L	T	Θ	N	J	I
1	2	-3	0	0	0	-2

CC 7-15

No; the quantity on the left hand side $\{=\}$ L/T and the quantity on the right hand side $\{=\}$ L^2/T

CC 7-16

(a) 210 Tm
(b) 0.022 light years

CC 7-17

2.72 gal

CHAPTER 8

CC 8-1

$161{,}000 \dfrac{\text{mi}}{\text{h}^2}$

CC 8-2

13.3 N

CC 8-3

2.2 N

CC 8-4

$3120 \dfrac{\text{lb}_m}{\text{ft}^3}$

CC 8-5

1.53

CC 8-6

4.85 g

CC 8-7

0.03 moles

CC 8-8

194.5 K

CC 8-9

$0.000357 \dfrac{BTU}{gK}$

CC 8-10

221 in Hg

CC 8-11

1.22 atm

CC 8-12

220 kPa

CC 8-13

2.4 L

CC 8-14

16.9 m

CC 8-15

20 K

CC 8-16

0.83 h

CC 8-17

1.04 h

CC 8-18

61.3 W

CC 8-19

0.3 V

CC 8-20

14.4 W

CC 8-21

$-1.07 \, \mu A$

CC 8-22

$\dfrac{1}{S}$

CHAPTER 9

CC 9-1

B. $MT^{-3}\Theta$

CC 9-2

D. Dimensionless

CC 9-3

$M^{-1}L^3$

CC 9-4

$\dfrac{\Delta P}{\rho v^2}$

CHAPTER 10

CC 10-1

Relative addressing; cell F23 displays 13

CC 10-2

Absolute addressing; cell H26 displays 30

CC 10-3

Mixed addressing
Cell G30 displays 30
Cell F28 displays 5

CC 10-4

Mixed addressing
Cell G30 displays 5
Cell J28 displays 30

CC 10-5

A1.	12
A2.	11
A3.	10
A4.	32
A5.	3.14159265
A6.	#NAME? (Excel doesn't understand "PI" without the function parenthesis)
A7.	110
A8.	48
A9.	1.570796
A10.	1
A11.	0.893997
A12.	0.785408
A13.	45.00055
A14.	#NAME? (Excel does not have a function named "cubrt")
Correct expression:	or =27^(1/3) =POWER(27,1/3)

CC 10-6

B

CC 10-7

The cell will be blank
32
B9

CC 10-8

A
C
B

CC 10-9

No
YES
No
YES
No

CC 10-10

** See video in online materials

CC 10-11

** See video in online materials

CC 10-12

City ascending: Fountain Inn

City descending first, Site Name descending second: Rochester Property

Contaminant ascending first, Site Name ascending second: Sangamo Weston

CHAPTER 11

CC 11-1

- No axis labels
- Is year 1 1993 or 2000 or . . .?
- Need different line types
- Missing vertical gridlines

CC 11-2

- No units or description of axis quantities (what is T?)
- Need different symbols
- No legend shown
- Need gridlines if wish to read data

CC 11-3

- Missing units on both axis
- Should be line only, no points
- No legend needed
- Poor choice of increment on abscissa (count by 27)
- Too many decimals displayed on ordinate

CC 11-4

- No variable names given
- Abscissa labels do not show enough decimals to distinguish between gridlines (0.25, 0.5, 0.75, 1 . . .)
- Poor choice of increment on ordinate (major grid count by 8, minor grid counts by 1.6)
- Need legend
- Different line types needed

CC 11-5

18 meters

32 meters

CC 11-6

- **(a)** 2. Positive and constant
- **(b)** 1. Zero
- **(c)** 5. Negative and constant
- **(d)** 3. Positive and increasing
- **(e)** 3. Positive and increasing
- **(f)** 3. Positive and increasing

CC 11-7

- **(a)** Machine 2
- **(b)** Machine 2
- **(c)** 1×10^6 feet
- **(d)** Machine 2
- **(e)** Machine 1

CC 11-8

- **(a)** Fixed: $2500; Variable: $50/year
- **(b)** Approximately $750/year
- **(c)** 2.5 years
- **(d)** 4 years

CHAPTER 12

CC 12-1

(a) atm/K   **(b)** 35.6 g   **(c)** 14.1 L

CC 12-2

63.1 lb_m/ft^3

CC 12-3

3.36×10^{-4} lb$_m$/(ft s)

CC 12-4

4.55×10^{-3} St

CC 12-5

There are 17 unique spring stiffnesses.
Each spring can be used alone. There are three unique stiffnesses: 1 N/m, 2 N/m, 3 N/m
The following parallel combinations are possible:

Parallel Combination	Effective Spring Constant
Spring 1 (1 N/m) + Spring 2 (2 N/m)	3 N/m
Spring 1 (1 N/m) + Spring 2 (2 N/m)	4 N/m
Spring 2 (2 N/m) + Spring 3 (3 N/m)	5 N/m
Spring 1 (1 N/m) + Spring 2 (2 N/m) + Spring 3 (3 N/m)	6 N/m

The following series combinations are possible:

Series Combination	Effective Spring Constant
Spring 1 (1 N/m) + Spring 2 (2 N/m)	0.67 N/m
Spring 1 (1 N/m) + Spring 3 (3 N/m)	0.75 N/m
Spring 2 (2 N/m) + Spring 3 (3 N/m)	1.2 N/m
Spring 1 (1 N/m) + Spring 2 (2 N/m) + Spring 3 (3 N/m)	0.54 N/m

Another combination is to place two in series, and connect that combination to a third in parallel.

Combination in Series...	Connected in Parallel to...	Effective Spring Constant
Spring 1 (1 N/m) + Spring 2 (2 N/m)	Spring 3 (3 N/m)	3.67 N/m
Spring 1 (1 N/m) + Spring 3 (3 N/m)	Spring 2 (2 N/m)	2.75 N/m
Spring 2 (2 N/m) + Spring 3 (3 N/m)	Spring 1 (1 N/m)	2.2 N/m

The final combination is to place two in parallel, and connect that combination to a third in series.

Combination in Parallel...	Connected in Series to...	Effective Spring Constant
Spring 1 (1 N/m) + Spring 2 (2 N/m)	Spring 3 (3 N/m)	1.5 N/m
Spring 1 (1 N/m) + Spring 3 (3 N/m)	Spring 2 (2 N/m)	1.3 N/m
Spring 2 (2 N/m) + Spring 3 (3 N/m)	Spring 1 (1 N/m)	0.83 N/m

CC 12-6

There are 12 unique combinations.

The following combinations are possible: NOTE: Units on all values are ohms [Ω].

Singles: 2, 3

2 in series: 4, 5

2 in parallel: 1, 1.2

3 in series: 7

3 in parallel: 0.75

Series combination of 2 in parallel with third: 1.72, 1.43

Parallel combination of 2 in series with third: 4, 3.2

CC 12-7

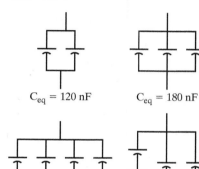

$C_{eq} = 120$ nF $C_{eq} = 180$ nF

$C_{eq} = 240$ nF

$C_{eq} = 150$ nF

CC 12-8

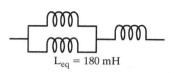

$L_{eq} = 180$ mH

CC 12-9

11.4 g

CC 12-10

117 °C

CC 12-11

$C_0 = 35$ g; $k = 1$ h^{-1}

CHAPTER 13

CC 13-1

$V = 50\,P^{-1}$

CC 13-2

$V = 30\,e^{-0.89t}$

CC 13-3

$y = -25.6\,e^{0.06\,x}$

CC 13-4

Data is exponential. The vertical offset is 5°F

$T = 5 - 20\,e^{-0.022\,t}$

CHAPTER 14

CC 14-1

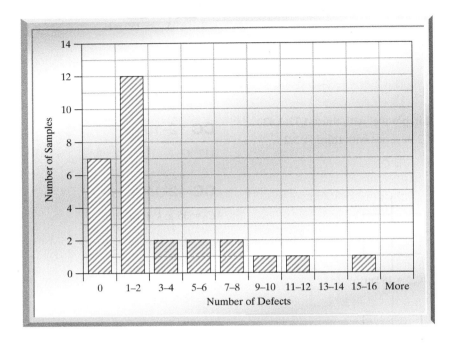

CC 14-2

Mean: 9.3 kg
Median: 9 kg
Variance: 12.9 kg^2
Standard Deviation: 3.6 kg

CC 14-3

Mean: 102.6 °C
Median: 104 °C
Variance: 295.4 °C^2
Standard Deviation: 17.2 °C

CC 14-4

(a) Population size has decreased
(b) Variance has increased
(c) Mean has increased

CC 14-5

(a) Curve (A) — Population size has decreased
(b) Curve (B) — Population size has increased
(c) Curve (E) — Mean has increased

CC 14-6

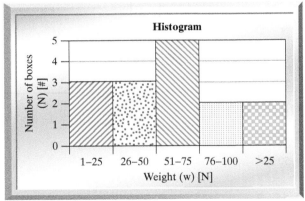

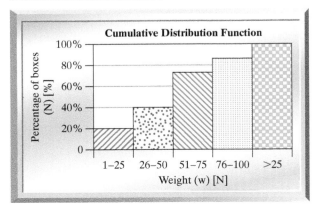

CC 14-7

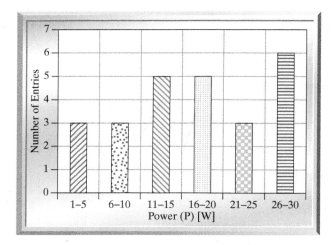

CC 14-8

Not in control

Rule 2—More than nine consecutive points below mean after 26 hr

Rule 3—Downward trend between 25 hr and 37 hr

Rule 5—Two out of three in zone A—several after 29 hr

Rule 6—Four out of five on same side of mean in zone B—start at 33 hr

Rule 8—Eight consecutive points outside of zone C—after 28 hr

CC 14-9

** See video in online materials

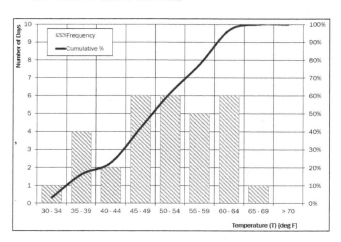

CC 14-10

** See video in online materials

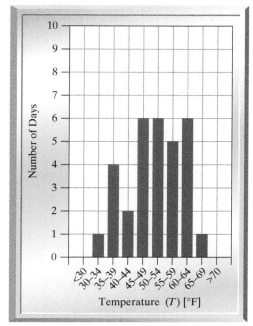

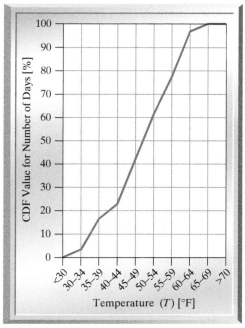

CHAPTER 15

CC 15-1

Known:

- The minimum value in the sum will be 2
- The maximum value in the sum will be 20
- Only even numbers will be included

Unknown:
- The sum of the sequence of even numbers

Assumptions:

- [None]

CC 15-2

Known:

- The minimum value in the product of powers of 5 will be 5
- The maximum value in the product of powers of 5 will be 50

Unknown:

- The product of the sequence of powers

Assumptions:

- Only include integer values

Concerning the actual operation to be performed, there are two alternate assumptions, since the wording is intentionally unclear:

1. Multiply all values between 5 and 50 that are an integer power of 5. In other words, the product of 5 and 25.
2. Multiply all integer powers of 5 with a power between 5 and 50 inclusive. In other words $5^5 * 5^6 * 5^7 * \cdots * 5^{49} * 5^{50}$.

CC 15-3

Known:

- Lowest power of 5 in product is 5
- Highest power of 5 in product is 50

Unknown:

- Product of all integer powers of 5 between the lowest and highest powers

Assumptions:

- The result will not exceed the maximum representable number in the computer. Note that by the time the sequence gets to $x = 17$, the product is approximately one googol (10100).

Algorithm:

1. Set product = 1
2. Set x = 5
3. If x is less than or equal to 50
   (a) Multiply product by 5x
   (b) Add 1 to x
   (c) Return to Step 3 and ask the question again
4. End the process

CC 15-4

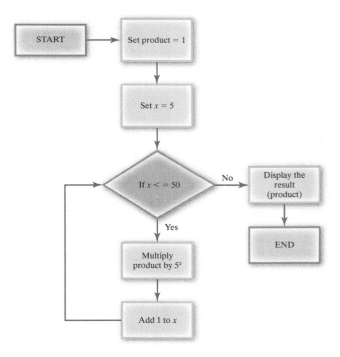

CHAPTER 16

CC 16-1

(a) Valid
(b) Valid
(c) INVALID: cannot begin with number
(d) INVALID: cannot contain special characters (@)
(e) INVALID: cannot contain special characters (-)
(f) Valid

CC 16-2

(a) 2
(b) INVALID: Y not defined; B is on the left side of the =
(c) 57
(d) 3.5
(e) INVALID: Q is not defined
(f) INVALID: Computation not allowed on left of =
(g) INVALID: Computation not allowed on left of =
(h) INVALID: Variable Name is invalid (cannot contain #)
(i) 0.4
(j) 9999
(k) INVALID: Computation not allowed on left of =
(l) 27

CC 16-3

(a) `Int = 8;`
(b) `Real2 = 35.7;`
(c) `Big2 = 47.98E56;`
(d) `Small2 = 3E - 15;`

CC 16-4

(a)
```
% Solution hardcoding coefficients
R1=(-2 + sqrt (2^2 - 4*2*1))/(2*2);
R2=(-2 - sqrt (2^2 - 4*2*1))/(2*2);

% Better solution using variables
C2=2;
C1=2;
C0=1;
R1=(-C1+sqrt(C1^2 - 4*C2*C0))/(2*C2);
R1=(-C1-sqrt(C1^2 - 4*C2*C0))/(2*C2);
```

(b)
```
% Solution using tand
Trig2=tand(75);

% Solution using tan
Trig2=tan(75*pi/180);

% Solution using degtorad function
Trig2=tan(degtorad(75));
```

CC 16-5

(a) `N4=[17;34;-94;16;0];`
(b) `Tiny=[3.4E-14,9.02E-23,1.32E-9];`
(c) `Ev=2:2:250;`
(d) `Tenths=[10:-0.1:0]';`

CC 16-6

```
Comps=(3*Vals + 5).^4-16;
```

CC 16-7

(a) `TFC=[T1,T2,T3,T4]';`
(b) `Rev=[10:2:10000,700:-7:7];`
(c) `Pow=[RV5,sqrt(RV5),RV5.^2];`

CC 16-8

(a) `Biggie(10:10:50000) = -9999;`
(b)
```
% Solution 1
   LV=LV(1:2:length(LV));

% Solution 2
   LV(2:2:length(LV))=[];
```
(c) `DS=D(1:2:length(D)) + D(2:2:length(D));`

CC 16-9

(a) `CCM1=[18 0.3;-4.1 -1;0 17];`
(b) `CCM2(2:3,3)=1E15;`
(c) `Corners=CCM3(1:2:3,1:2:3);`

CC 16-10

(a) `CC1=sqrt(QPD/2)`
(b) `CC2=17 + X1 + X2`

CC 16-11

(a) `MTS 'My hero''s hat'`
(b) `B=[blanks(17),'Dr. Willy',blanks(691)]`
(c) `% Two different solutions`
`% Two line solution`
`Avian=strrep (Avian,'wet','crepuscular');`
`Avian=strrep (Avian,'never','seldom');`
`% One line solution`
`Avian=strrep (strrep(Avian,'never',`
`'seldom'),'wet','crepuscular');`
(d) `UL=length(Ultimate);`
`UltAns = str2num(Ultimate(UL-1:UL));`

CC 16-12

(a) `Cabinet={77,'Dr.Caligari',ones(25,100)}`
(b) `Cabinet={'Diameter','Length';1.5,1:25}`

CC 16-13

(a) `CA{2,1}=CA{1,1}(7:length(CA{1,1}));`
(b) `CA{2,2}=CA{1,2}*CA{1,3};`
(c) `CA{2,3}=CA{1,2}.*CA{1,3}';`

CC 16-14

(a) `BigCell=num2cell(BigMat);`
(b) `VCellMax=cellfun(@max,VCell);`

CC 16-15

```
Resistors(1).Value=100E3;
Resistors(1).Power=1/4;
Resistors(1).Composition='Metal Film';
Resistors(1).Tolerance=0.1;

Resistors(2).Value=2.2E6;
Resistors(2).Power=1/2;
Resistors(2).Composition='Carbon'
Resistors(2).Tolerance=5;

Resistors(3).Value=15
Resistors(3).Power=50;
Resistors(3).Composition='WireWound'
Resistors(3).Tolerance=10;
```

CC 16-16

(a) `MZn=MetalData(1).SpacGrav*1000`
(b) `LtIso=min(MetalData(MNum).Isotopes)`

CC 16-17

(a) `save('TempData.mat')`
(b) `load('PressData.mat')`
(c) `save('PTData.mat','Pr1','Pr2','Tmp3')`
(d) `save('a1Var.mat','*a1'))`
(e) `load('VelData.mat','*XS*')`

CHAPTER 17

CC 17-1

c, d, e, g

CC 17-2

314.1953
`Dogs=areaCircle(10);`

CC 17-3

```
function[R]=RAC (N, A)
  R=3*sin(N^A)
end
```

CHAPTER 18

CC 18-1

```
Height=input('Please enter your height in
inches. ');

TempF=input('Please enter the temperature in
degrees Fahrenheit. ');
```

CC 18-2

```
EyeColor=input('Please enter the color of
your eyes. ','s');

Month=input('What is the current month.
','s');
```

CC 18-3

```
Month=menu('The current month is:', 'Jan',
'Feb', 'Mar', 'Apr', 'May', 'Jun', 'Jul',
'Aug', 'Sep', 'Oct', 'Nov', 'Dec');
(all on same line)
C=5
```

CC 18-4

(a) `%0.2f`
(b) `%0.3e` or `%0.3E`
(c) `0.35`
(d) `3.54e−01` or `3.54E−01`
(e) `000000.354`

CC 18-5

```
Clemson-USC Football Rivalry:

Year      USC     Clemson
2012      27        17
2011      34        13
2010      29         7
```

CHAPTER 19

CC 19-1

(a) `5 < =t && t < 10`
(b) `−30 < M && M < =20`
(c) `Y ~=100`

CC 19-2

(a) $R1 = \begin{bmatrix} 1 & 0 \\ 1 & 1 \\ 1 & 0 \end{bmatrix}$

(b) $R1 = \begin{bmatrix} 0 & -5 \\ 0 & 0 \\ 0 & 0 \end{bmatrix}$

(c) $R1 = \begin{bmatrix} 1 & 1 \\ 1 & 0 \\ 1 & 0 \end{bmatrix}$

CC 19-3

Possible Solution #1:
```
R4=(M1>M2).*M1 + (M2>M1).*M2;
```

Possible Solution #2:
```
LM=M1>M2;
R4=LM.*M1 + ~LM.*M2;
```

CC 19-4

```
if TW <=0
  phase ='solid';

elseif TW >=100
  phase ='gas';

else
  phase ='liquid';
end
```

CC 19-5

```
function[x,y]=SumItUp(a,b,c)
if a + b > 100
   fprintf('The inputs are %0.2f, %0.2f, and
   %0.2f',a,b,c)
else
   fprintf('The inputs are %0.0f, %0.0f, and
   %0.0f', a,b,c)
end
x=a + b;
y=b + c;
```

CC 19-6

Choices (a) and (c).

CC 19-7

```
Phase=menu ('Choose type of water sample',
'Solid','Liquid','Gas');
switch Phase
   case 1
        fprintf('For a solid, water must be
        at a temperature less than 0 degrees
        Celsius.')
   case 3
        fprintf('For a gas, water must be at
        a temperature more than 100 degrees
        Celsius.')
   otherwise
        fprintf('For a liquid, water must be
        at a temperature between 0 and 100
        degrees Celsius.')
end
```

CHAPTER 20

CC 20-1

```
for K=2:2:20
        disp(K)
end
```

CC 20-2

```
for K=5:5:50
        disp(K)
end
```

CC 20-3

```
for K=13:-2:-11
        disp(K)
end
```

CC 20-4

```
PosSum=0;
for E=1:length(Vals)
  if Vals(E)>0
    PosSum=PosSum+Vals(E);
  end
end
```

CC 20-5

```
D=0; % Setup for calculating D
I=1; % Setup for calculating I
% Print column headers
fprintf('k\tA\tB\tC\tD\tE\tF\tG\tH\t\tI\
tJ\n')
for k=1:10
    A=2*k;
    B=k*2-1;
    C=k^2;
    D=D+k; % Note that D was initialized to
        0 before the loop
    E=7+0.25*k;
    F=11-k;
    G=(-1)^(k+1); % There are several other
        ways to do this one
    H=2^k;
    I=I*k; % Note that I was initialized to
        1 before the loop
    J=1/k;
    % Print current row of values
    fprintf('%d\t%d\t%d\t%d\t%d\t%.2f\t%d\
        t%d\t%d\t%9.0f\t%.2f\n',...
        k,A,B,C,D,E,F,G,H,I,J)
end
```

CC 20-6

```
[M1Rows,M1Cols] = size(M1);
PosNums = zeros(1,M1Cols); %initialize
counter vector
for R = 1:M1Rows
    for C = 1:M1Cols
      if M1(R,C) >= 0
         PosNums(C) = PosNums(C)+1
      end
    end
end
```

CC 20-7

```
[M1Rows,M1Cols] = size(M1);
NegRows = M1Rows; %Assume all rows are all
negative
for R=1:M1Rows
    for C=1:M1Cols
      if M1(R,C) >= 0
         NegRows=NegRows-1; %Positive value
         found, reduce count
         break  %Go to next row
      end
    end
end
```

CC 20-8

```
% Solution 1
InVal=-1; % Initialize so loop runs first
time
while InVal<0
      InVal=input('Please enter a non-
      negative number: ');
end

% Solution 2
% This version allows the program to warn
the user they made an error.
InVal=input('Please enter a non-negative
number: '); % First attempt while InVal<0
      disp('You entered an incorrect
      value. Try again.')
      InVal=input('Please enter a non-
      negative number: '); % Next attempt
end
```

CC 20-9

```
Prod=1; % Initialize Prod
Elem=1; % Initialize pointer to vector
elements
while Prod<=1E6 && Elem<=length(V2)
      Prod=Prod*V2(Elem);
      Elem=Elem+1;  %Step to next element
end
```

INDEX